MATH FOCUS 9

MATH FOCUS 9

Senior Author and Senior Consultant
Marian Small

Authors
Kristina Farentino
Carolyn Martin
Rupi Samra-Gynane
Carol Shaw
Marian Small
Joyce Tonner
Michèle Wills

Mathematics Consultant
Chris Kirkpatrick

Assessment Consultants
Sandra Carl Townsend
Gerry Varty

NELSON EDUCATION

NELSON EDUCATION

Nelson Math Focus 9

Authors
Kristina Farentino,
Carolyn Martin,
Rupi Samra-Gynane,
Carol Shaw, Marian Small,
Joyce Tonner, Michèle Wills

Vice President, Publishing
Janice Schoening

General Manager, Mathematics, Science, and Technology
Lenore Brooks

Publisher, Mathematics
Colin Garnham

Associate Publisher, Mathematics
Sandra McTavish

Managing Editor, Mathematics
Erynn Marcus

Product Manager
Linda Krepinsky

Program Manager
Colin Bisset

Senior Project Editor
Robert Templeton, First Folio Resource Group, Inc.

Developmental Editors
Nancy Andraos
Tom Gamblin
Tony Rodrigues
First Folio Resource Group, Inc.:
David Hamilton
Susan Lishman
Wendi Morrison

Assistant Editors
Linda Watson, First Folio Resource Group, Inc.

Editorial Assistants
Caroline Winter
Ali Pervez
Kathryn Chris

Executive Director, Content and Media Production
Renate McCloy

Director, Content and Media Production
Linh Vu

Content Production Editor
Montgomery Kersell

Copy Editor
Christine Hobberlin

Proofreader
John Green

Indexer
Noeline Bridge

Production Manager
Helen Jager-Locsin

Senior Production Coordinator
Kathrine Pummell

Assessment Consultants
Sandra Carl Townsend
Gerry Varty

Design Director
Ken Phipps

Interior Design
Kyle Gell
Allan Moon

Cover Design
Eugene Lo

Cover Image
Jurgen Ziewe/Shutterstock

Asset Coordinator
Suzanne Peden

Illustrators
Steve Corrigan
Deborah Crowle
Allan Moon

Compositor
Pre-PressPMG

Photo Shoot Coordinator
Lynn McLeod

Studio Photographer
Dave Starrett

Photo/Permissions Researcher
Lynn McLeod

Printer
RR Donnelley

ISBN-13: 978-0-17-632476-6
ISBN-10: 0-17-632476-3

Printed and Bound in the United States
2 3 4 12 11 10 09

For more information contact Nelson Education Ltd., 1120 Birchmount Road, Toronto, Ontario, M1K 5G4. Or you can visit our Internet site at http://www.nelson.com.

Advisory Panel

The authors and publisher gratefully acknowledge the contributions of the following educators:

Cathy Canavan-McGrath
Program Coordinator
South Slave
Divisional Education Council
Fort Smith, Northwest Territories

Anett Chicomny
Teacher
Siksika Nation High School
Siksika Board of Education
Siksika, Alberta

Gordon Dupree
Teacher
Muskoday First Nation
Community School
Muskoday, Saskatchewan

Brandon Fletcher
Teacher Educator
Lethbridge Collegiate Institute
Lethbridge School District No. 51
Lethbridge, Alberta

Oystein Guren
Teacher
C.B. McMurdo School
Wetaskiwin, Alberta

Jeni Halowski
Teacher
Winston Churchill High School
Lethbridge School District
Lethbridge, Alberta

Denis Hlynka
Professor, Department of Curriculum, Teaching and Learning
Acting Director, Centre of Ukrainian Canadian Studies
University of Manitoba
Winnipeg, Manitoba

Chris Hunter
Mathematics Department Head
Queen Elizabeth Secondary School
Surrey, British Columbia

Elaine Jacklynn
Mathematics Curriculum Leader
Lethbridge Collegiate Institute
Lethbridge School District No. 51
Lethbridge, Alberta

Helen Jeong
Teacher
Queen Elizabeth Secondary School
Surrey, British Columbia

Colette Krause
Teacher
Christ the King
Junior/Senior High School
Leduc, Alberta

Dave McCann
Principal
Big Valley School
Clearview School Division No. 71
Big Valley, Alberta

Jacinthe Moquin
Teacher
J.H. Picard School
Edmonton Catholic Schools
Edmonton, Alberta

Kathleen Nolan
Associate Professor,
Mathematics Education
University of Regina
Regina, Saskatchewan

Michael Pruner
Mathematics Teacher
Argyle Secondary School
North Vancouver, British Columbia

Susie Robinson
District Principal for
Aboriginal Learning
Edmonton Catholic School District
Edmonton, Alberta

Doug Super
Secondary Math Teacher
Mulgrave Independent School
West Vancouver, British Columbia

Clint Surry
Teacher
Parkland Secondary School
School District No. 63 (Saanich)
Sidney, British Columbia

Gerry Varty
Director of Instruction
Wolf Creek Public Schools
Ponoka, Alberta

Kathleen Wagner
Teacher
Hugh Boyd Secondary School
Richmond, British Columbia

Favian Yee
District Coordinator
Educational Programs Branch
Delta School District
Delta, British Columbia

Literacy Consultant

Sue Quennell
Educational Consultant
Burlington, Ontario

Equity Consultant

Leith Campbell
Consultant
The Virgo Group
St. Albert, Alberta

Table of Contents

Chapter 3: Similar Polygons 96

Chapter 4: Measurement 152

Chapter 5: Linear Relations, Equations, and Inequalities 196

Chapter 6: Polynomials 272

Chapter 7: Probability 330

Chapter 8: Symmetry 362

-47.20 47.28
66.50 UNCH -65.30 66.90
87.03 -.82 -85.00
39.16 -.85 +37.53
23.18 +.17 -23.20
16.71 -.06 -16.71
35.39 -.18 -35.00
69.47 -.65 -69.25
24.41 -.73 -24.37
Sell 49.24 -.45 -48.50
Sell 42.58 -.36 -42.05
Sell 63.16 -.52 -62.78
-83.07

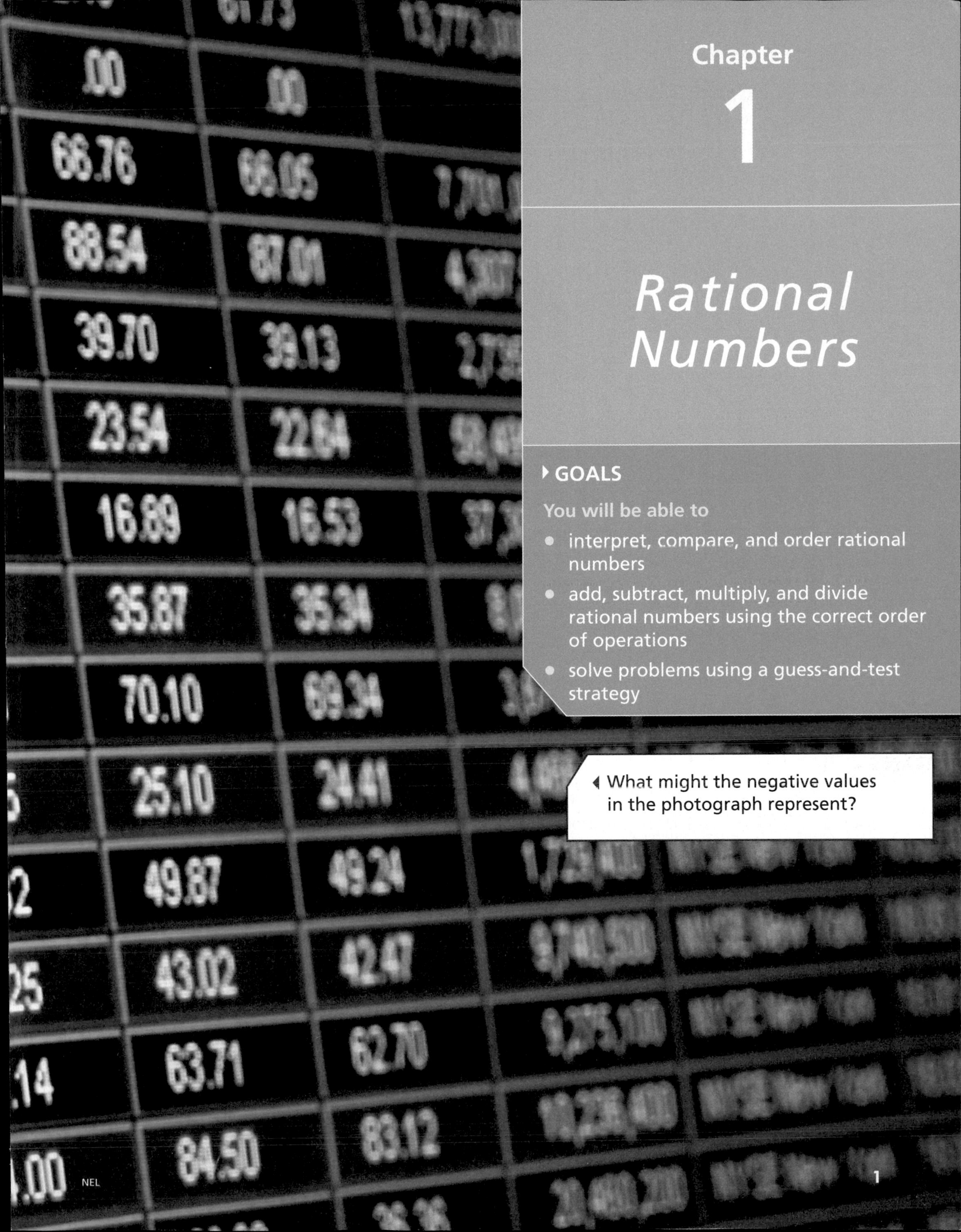

Chapter

1

Rational Numbers

GOALS

You will be able to

- interpret, compare, and order rational numbers
- add, subtract, multiply, and divide rational numbers using the correct order of operations
- solve problems using a guess-and-test strategy

What might the negative values in the photograph represent?

CHAPTER 1 Getting Started

Fraction Patterns

David and Jia-Wen are exploring a sequence of fractions.

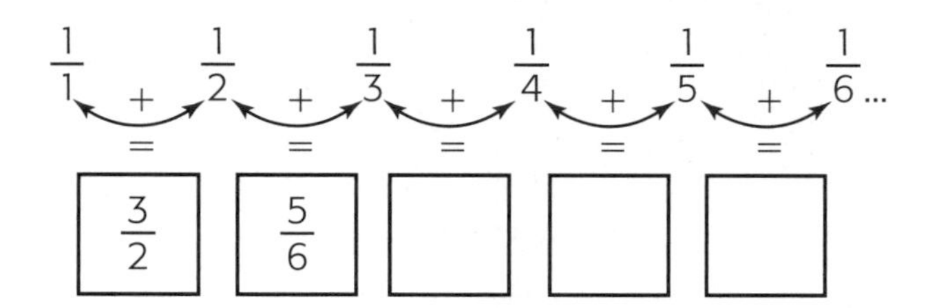

? How can you use patterns to predict the 20th sum, difference, product, and quotient using this sequence of fractions?

A. Describe the pattern in David and Jia-Wen's original sequence of fractions.

B. Add consecutive terms (pairs of neighbouring fractions) until five sums have been calculated. For example, $\frac{1}{1} + \frac{1}{2} = \frac{3}{2}$, $\frac{1}{2} + \frac{1}{3} = \frac{5}{6}$, and so on.

C. Describe the pattern and use it to predict the 20th sum.

D. Subtract consecutive terms of David and Jia-Wen's original sequence instead of adding them, until five differences have been calculated.

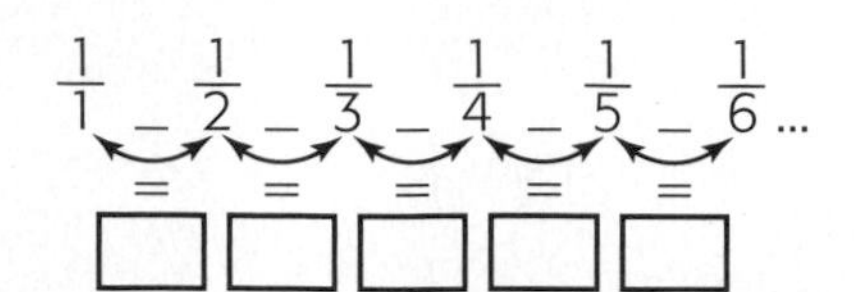

E. Describe the subtraction pattern and use it to predict the 20th difference.

F. Repeat parts D and E using multiplication.

G. Repeat parts D and E using division.

H. Explain why the values in the pattern decrease for addition, subtraction, and multiplication.

I. Why might it have been harder to predict what the division pattern would be?

J. Which patterns do you think were the easiest to predict? Why?

WHAT DO You Think?

Decide whether you agree or disagree with each statement. Be ready to explain your decision.

1. You can add $\frac{1}{2}$ and $\frac{4}{5}$ only by using a common denominator.

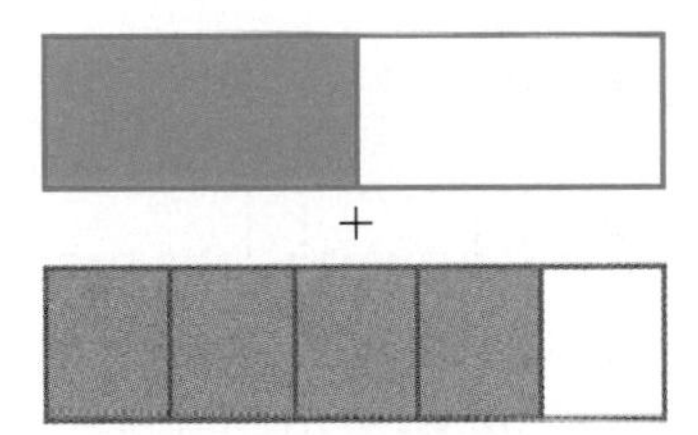

2. When you divide two negative numbers, the quotient must be greater than $+1$.

$$-8 \div (-4) = ■$$

3. To subtract one negative number from another, just subtract their opposites and then take the opposite of the difference.

4. The only number between $\frac{1}{2}$ and $\frac{1}{4}$ is $\frac{1}{3}$.

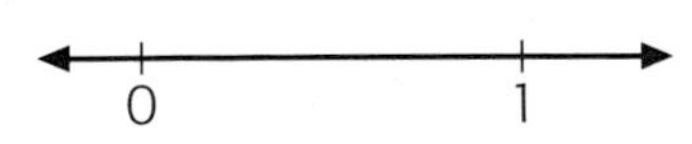

1.1 Interpreting Rational Numbers

GOAL

Relate rational numbers to fractions and integers.

LEARN ABOUT the Math

Rachel looked at the thermometer outside. The temperature was between −18 °C and −19 °C.

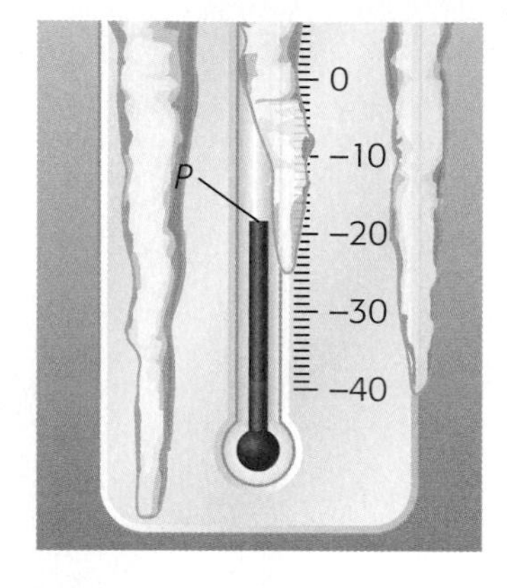

? What might the temperature be?

A. What is the value of the **rational number** located at *P*? Explain.

B. What other form of that number could you use to describe *P*?

C. What is the value of the rational number located at *R*? Explain.

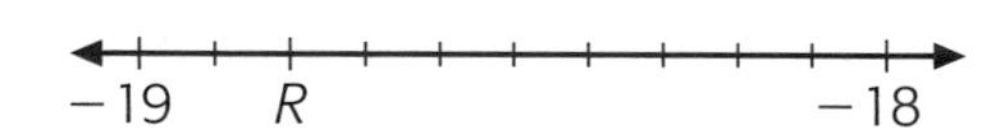

D. Why are the values at *P* and *R* both possible solutions to Rachel's problem?

E. List three other possible solutions to the problem. Write one in decimal form, one as the **opposite** of an improper fraction, and one as the opposite of a mixed number.

rational number

a number that can be expressed as the quotient of two integers, where the divisor is not 0; it can be written in fraction, mixed-number, or decimal form or as an integer; e.g., 3.25, −5.8, $\frac{2}{3}$, −2, $-1\frac{1}{4}$

opposites

two numbers with opposite signs that are the same distance from 0; e.g., +2 and −2 or +0.5 and −0.5

Reflecting

F. How could thinking about the opposites of −18 and −19 help you solve Rachel's problem?

G. How do you know that between any two rationals there are always many other rationals?

H. How do you know that any integer or fraction is also a rational number?

Communication *Tip*

Sometimes rational numbers are called rationals. Rational numbers like −0.6 and $\frac{5}{8}$ are read as "negative six tenths" and "positive five eighths" or just "five eighths."

WORK WITH the Math

EXAMPLE 1 | Recognizing equivalent rational numbers

Which of the following represent the same rational number?

$$\frac{-3}{2}, \frac{3}{-2}, \frac{-6}{-4}, -\frac{6}{4}, -1\frac{1}{2}, -1.5$$

Thomas's Solution

$\frac{-3}{2}, \frac{3}{-2}, \frac{-6}{-4}, -\frac{6}{4}, -1\frac{1}{2}, -1.5$

$A \quad B \quad C \quad D \quad E \quad F$

I will label the numbers to make sure that I use them all.

−1.5

−2 −1

$-1\frac{1}{2}$

The number halfway between -1 and -2 should be $-1\frac{1}{2}$, but it's also -1.5 since $\frac{1}{2} = 0.5$.

$-1\frac{1}{2} = -1.5$ so $E = F$

$-\frac{6}{4} = \frac{3}{2}$

$-\frac{3}{2} = -1\frac{1}{2}$

$-1\frac{1}{2} = -\frac{6}{4}$ so $E = D$

Since $\frac{6}{4} = \frac{3}{2}$, then $-\frac{6}{4} = -\frac{3}{2}$.

Since $\frac{3}{2} = 1\frac{1}{2}$, then $-\frac{3}{2} = -1\frac{1}{2}$.

C is different from D, E, and F.

I know that $\frac{-6}{-4} = (-6) \div (-4)$. When you divide two negatives, the result is positive, so this cannot be the same as -1.5.

$\frac{-3}{2} = (-3) \div 2$

$= -1.5$

$A = F$

The only ones left to think about are $\frac{-3}{2}$ and $\frac{3}{-2}$.
If there is a loss of \$3 that 2 people share, each loses \$1.50, so it makes sense that $\frac{-3}{2} = -1.5$.

$\frac{3}{-2} = 3 \div (-2)$

$= -1.5$

$B = F$

To figure out the quotient, I think about what number to multiply (-2) by to get $+3$. It has to be negative to get a positive product. It has to be -1.5 since $1.5 \times 2 = 3$.

Since $A = B = D = E = F$, the equivalent rational numbers are $\frac{-3}{2}, \frac{3}{-2}, -\frac{6}{4}, -1\frac{1}{2}$, and -1.5.

All five of these numbers are located at the same place on a number line.

EXAMPLE 2 | Locating a rational number between two other rational numbers

List five different rational numbers between $-\frac{1}{5}$ and $-\frac{1}{3}$.

Larissa's Solution

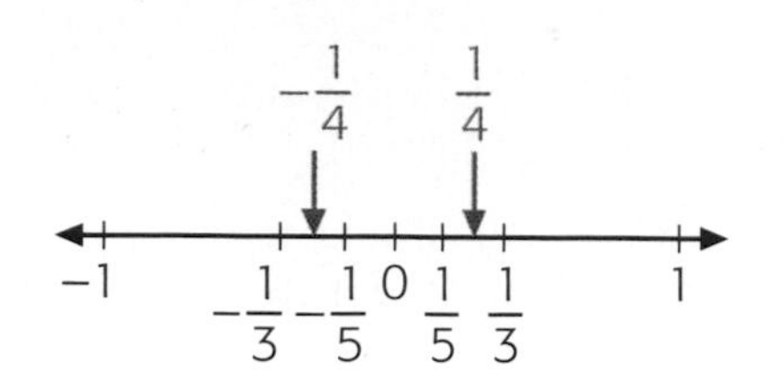

It helps to place $-\frac{1}{5}$ and $-\frac{1}{3}$ on a number line first. I did this by placing their opposites on the number line, and then reflecting across zero.
Opposites must be the same distance from 0. Since $\frac{1}{4}$ is between $\frac{1}{3}$ and $\frac{1}{5}$, I know that $-\frac{1}{4}$ must be between $-\frac{1}{5}$ and $-\frac{1}{3}$.

$-\frac{1}{3} = -0.3333...$

$-\frac{1}{5} = -0.2$

I changed the fractions to decimals to get other in-between rational numbers.

Since 0.3 and 0.28 are between 0.2 and 0.333..., then -0.3 and -0.28 must be between $-\frac{1}{5}$ and $-\frac{1}{3}$.

$-\frac{1}{5} = -\frac{6}{30}$ and $-\frac{1}{3} = -\frac{10}{30}$,

I used equivalent fractions.

so $-\frac{7}{30}$ and $-\frac{8}{30}$ are between them.

Five rational numbers between $-\frac{1}{5}$ and $-\frac{1}{3}$ are

$-\frac{1}{4}$, -0.3, -0.28, $-\frac{7}{30}$, and $-\frac{8}{30}$.

EXAMPLE 3 | Using a rational number to describe a situation

Name three situations that you might describe using the rational number -3.4.

Sam's Solution

-3.4 could be a temperature between -3 °C and -4 °C.

-3.4 m could be the number of metres below sea level that a scuba diver is.

-3.4 could be the number of seconds before the launch of a spacecraft, if you call the launch of the spacecraft time 0.

I know that you can have negative temperatures, negative distances, and negative times (times before an event), so I'll use those ideas.

In Summary

Key Idea

- Rational numbers include integers, fractions, their decimal equivalents, and their opposites.

Need to Know

- Rational numbers can be positive, negative, or zero.
- Every integer is a rational number because it can be written as the quotient of two integers.

  For example, some ways -5 can be written are $\frac{-5}{1}$, $\frac{5}{-1}$, and $\frac{-10}{2}$.
- Just as with fractions, there are many ways to write the same rational number.

  For example, $-2.5 = \frac{-5}{2} = -\frac{5}{2} = \frac{5}{-2} = -2.50 = -\frac{10}{4}$.
- Every rational number (except 0) has an opposite. For example, $-2\frac{3}{4}$ and $2\frac{3}{4}$ are opposites, since they are both the same distance from 0 on a number line.

Checking

1. Write the following rational numbers as quotients of two integers.

a) -0.5 b) $-2\frac{1}{4}$ c) $-5\frac{6}{7}$ d) 7.2

2. Write the following rational numbers in decimal form.

a) $-\frac{1}{4}$ b) $-2\frac{3}{8}$ c) $-7\frac{5}{6}$ d) $4\frac{3}{10}$

3. List three rational numbers between each pair.

a) $-\frac{2}{3}$ and $-\frac{4}{5}$ b) $-\frac{1}{2}$ and $\frac{1}{4}$ c) 0.6 and $1\frac{1}{8}$

Reading Strategy

Visualizing

Use number lines to visualize your answers to question 3.

Practising

4. Multiple choice. Which values describe the positions of X and Y?

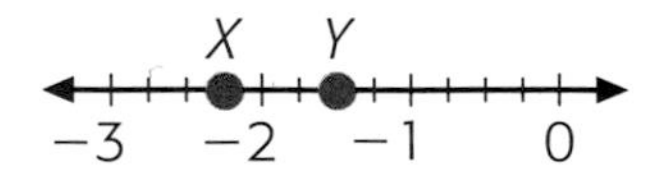

A. -2.2 and -1.5 **C.** $-2\frac{3}{4}$ and $-1\frac{1}{2}$

B. -2.1 and -1.2 **D.** $\frac{-9}{4}$ and $\frac{3}{-2}$

5. Multiple choice. Which of these rational numbers are equivalent?

X: -4.2 Y: -2.4 Z: $-\frac{42}{10}$ W: $\frac{24}{10}$

A. X, Z, and W **B.** X and Z **C.** X and W **D.** X and Y

6. Identify the values represented by B, D, K, M, and T as quotients of two integers.

T M K D B

−4 −2 0 2

7. Write each as the quotient of two rational numbers.
   a) 5.1   b) $-4\frac{1}{5}$ c) -3.02 d) $9\frac{2}{3}$

8. Write each in decimal form.
   a) $5\frac{2}{5}$ b) $-7\frac{2}{4}$ c) $-\frac{19}{3}$ d) $\frac{-13}{-5}$

9. Draw a number line. Mark integers from -10 to 2 on it. Estimate and mark the location of each of these on your number line.
   a) $-\frac{5}{2}$ c) -7.2 e) $-3\frac{2}{3}$ g) -0.78
   b) $1\frac{2}{3}$ d) -6.9 f) $\frac{2}{3}$ h) -8.4

10. a) Describe a real-life situation that involves the number -1.2.
    b) Describe a real-life situation that involves the number $-\frac{2}{3}$.

11. Explain why $-\frac{3}{4} = \frac{-3}{4} = \frac{3}{-4}$.

12. a) Name three fractions between $\frac{2}{8}$ and $\frac{3}{8}$.
    b) How would your answers in part a) help you name three rational numbers between $-\frac{2}{8}$ and $-\frac{3}{8}$?
    c) Are your answers in part a) rational numbers? Explain.

13. Agree or disagree with each. Explain why.
    a) The opposite of every mixed number can be written as a rational number in decimal form.
    b) If one number is greater than another, so is its opposite.

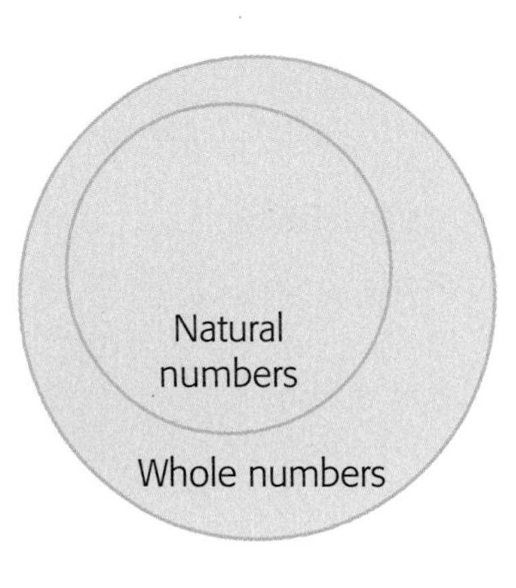

14. The natural numbers are the numbers 1, 2, 3, 4,...
    The whole numbers are the numbers 0, 1, 2, 3,...
    Extend this Venn diagram to show the relationship between these sets of numbers: integers, whole numbers, natural numbers, and rational numbers.

Closing

15. If you were describing rational numbers to someone without just repeating the definition, what is the most important thing you could say to help them quickly understand what rational numbers are?

Extending

16. a) Explain why $\frac{5}{9}$ can be written as the repeating decimal 0.555... (or $0.\overline{5}$).
    b) How would you write $-\frac{5}{9}$ as a decimal?
    c) How would you write $-\frac{5}{90}$ as a repeating decimal?
    d) How are your answers to parts b) and c) related?

17. Design an appropriate symbol for the term rational number. Explain why your symbol is appropriate.

Curious MATH

How Many Rational Numbers Are There?

You might think there are twice as many rational numbers between 0 and -2 as between 0 and -1. There are actually the same number. To show that this is true, you need to show that you can match each rational between 0 and -2 with exactly one rational number between 0 and -1 and vice versa.

Write each rational number between 0 and -2 on the bottom number line as $-\frac{a}{b}$. Match it with $-\frac{a}{2b}$ on the top number line.

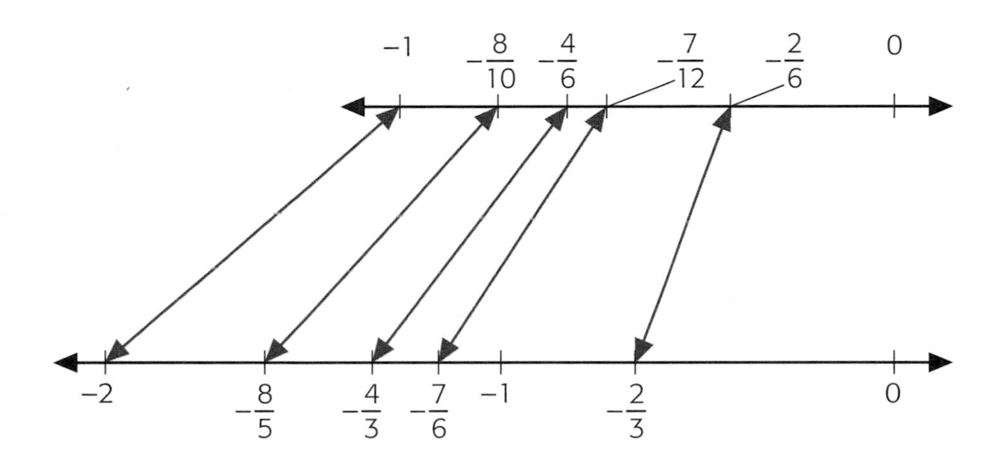

1. Choose other rational numbers between 0 and -2. Use the matching rule $-\frac{a}{2b}$ matches $-\frac{a}{b}$ to show that each number you chose matches one number between 0 and -1.
2. List different rational numbers between 0 and -1. Show that each matches one number between 0 and -2.
3. How do you know that if $-\frac{a}{b}$ is between 0 and -2, then $-\frac{a}{2b}$ is between 0 and -1?
4. Why does it make sense that if there is a one-to-one match between two sets of numbers, then the sets are the same size?
5. How many rational numbers are there between 0 and -1 or between 0 and -2?

1.2 Comparing and Ordering Rational Numbers

GOAL

Order a set of rational numbers.

LEARN ABOUT the Math

Larissa described going east from her house as moving in a positive direction and going west as moving in a negative direction.

On five different days, she described how far she was from home:

-3.7 km $\quad -5.2$ km $\quad -5.3$ km $\quad 5.1$ km $\quad -1.4$ km

? On which day was Larissa farthest from home?

A. Draw a number line from -10 to 10. Estimate and mark the position of each of Larissa's locations on the number line if her home is at 0.

B. List the location numbers from least to greatest.

C. Which position was farthest from home?

Reflecting

D. How does your answer to part C show that just because a number is farthest from 0 in a list of numbers, it might not be the greatest?

E. How could you have looked at the location numbers and ordered them without marking them on the number line?

WORK WITH the Math

EXAMPLE 1 Ordering rationals in fraction and decimal form

Order these numbers from least to greatest.

$-3.4 \quad -5\frac{1}{2} \quad 12.1 \quad 15\frac{2}{3} \quad -5\frac{3}{4} \quad \frac{8}{3}$

David's Solution

The three greatest numbers are the positives.

$\frac{8}{3} = 2\frac{2}{3} < 12.1 < 15\frac{2}{3}$

First I wrote $\frac{8}{3}$ as a mixed number. It's between 2 and 3, so it's less than 12.1 and $15\frac{2}{3}$.

Since these are the only positives, I know they are the greatest.

$-3.4 > -5\frac{1}{2}$ and $-5\frac{3}{4}$

I know that $-3.4 > -4$ and that the other two negatives are less than -4, so -3.4 is the greatest negative.

$-5\frac{3}{4}$

$-6 \quad -5\frac{1}{2} \quad -5$

I divided the part of the number line between -5 and -6 into 4 equal sections to place the last two numbers. $-5\frac{3}{4}$ is farther to the left, so it's least.

The order of the numbers from least to greatest is

$-5\frac{3}{4} \quad -5\frac{1}{2} \quad -3.4 \quad \frac{8}{3} \quad 12.1 \quad 15\frac{2}{3}$

Larissa's Solution

$-5\frac{1}{2} = -5.5$

$-5\frac{3}{4} = -5.75$

$\frac{8}{3} = 1\frac{2}{3} \doteq 1.67$

I know that $15\frac{2}{3}$ is the greatest. I decided to write the other numbers in fractional form as decimals, since I find decimals easier to work with.

The five numbers that are less than $15\frac{2}{3}$ are

-3.4, -5.5, 12.1, -5.75, and 1.67.

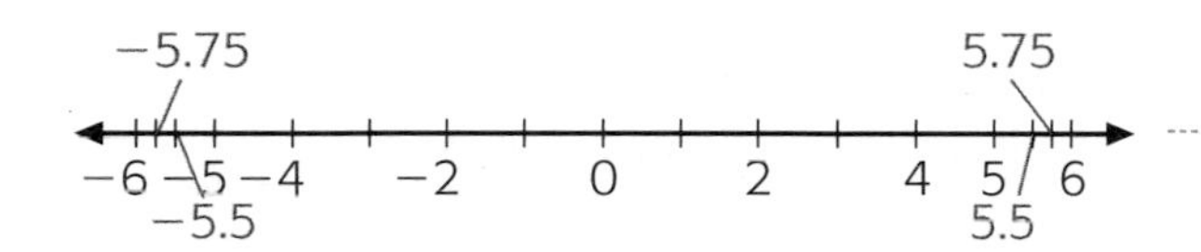

I know that -3.4 is greater than the other negative values and that 1.67 and 12.1 are greater than all the other decimals.

I know that $-5.75 < -5.5$ since the opposite of 5.5 is closer to 0 than the opposite of 5.75.

I thought of the numbers on a number line.

The order of all the numbers except $15\frac{2}{3}$, as decimals, is -5.75, -5.5, -3.4, 1.67, 12.1.

The order of the numbers from least to greatest is

$-5\frac{3}{4} \quad -5\frac{1}{2} \quad -3.4 \quad \frac{8}{3} \quad 12.1 \quad 15\frac{2}{3}$

EXAMPLE 2 | Comparing rationals that describe situations

Order these rational numbers from least to greatest.

$-4\frac{1}{2}$, $8\frac{1}{4}$, $-2\frac{1}{4}$, $-\frac{5}{8}$, $-2\frac{3}{4}$, $-\frac{5}{10}$, and $5\frac{3}{4}$

Rachel's Solution

$5\frac{3}{4} < 6$ and $8\frac{1}{4} > 6$, so $8\frac{1}{4}$ is greater than $5\frac{3}{4}$.

I know that $5 < 8$, but $\frac{3}{4} > \frac{1}{4}$. To be sure which was least, I compared both numbers to a benchmark of 6.

These are the two greatest values.

I know that negative values are less than positive ones, so the five negative values are less than $5\frac{3}{4}$ and $8\frac{1}{4}$.

$-4\frac{1}{2} < -4$

I compared three of the negatives to a benchmark of -4; one was to the left and two were to the right of -4.

$-2\frac{1}{4} > -3$, which is greater than -4.

$-2\frac{3}{4} > -3$, which is greater than -4.

So, $-4\frac{1}{2} < -2\frac{1}{4}$ and $-4\frac{1}{2} < -2\frac{3}{4}$.

$\frac{1}{4} < \frac{3}{4}$, since $1 < 3$.

When the denominators of two fractions are the same, you can compare numerators.

So, $-\frac{3}{4} < -\frac{1}{4}$

If a positive fraction is closer to 0 than another, its opposite is also closer to 0, and so it is greater.

$-2\frac{3}{4} < -2\frac{1}{4}$

$-2\frac{3}{4}$ and $-2\frac{1}{4}$ are each exactly 2 to the left of $-\frac{3}{4}$ and $-\frac{1}{4}$, so $-2\frac{3}{4}$ is farther to the left of 0 than $-2\frac{1}{4}$.

$-\frac{5}{8}$ and $-\frac{5}{10}$ are both greater than $-2\frac{3}{4}$, $-2\frac{1}{4}$, and $-4\frac{1}{2}$.

$-\frac{5}{8}$ and $-\frac{5}{10}$ are both between 0 and -1, so they are greater than -1.

$\frac{5}{8} > \frac{5}{10}$, so $-\frac{5}{8} < -\frac{5}{10}$.

$\frac{5}{10}$ and $\frac{5}{8}$ have the same numerator, but 10 is a greater denominator. $\frac{5}{8}$ is farther to the right of zero than $\frac{5}{10}$, so $-\frac{5}{8}$ is farther to the left of zero than $-\frac{5}{10}$.

From least to greatest, the rational numbers are

$-4\frac{1}{2}$, $-2\frac{3}{4}$, $-2\frac{1}{4}$, $-\frac{5}{8}$, $-\frac{5}{10}$, $5\frac{3}{4}$, and $8\frac{1}{4}$.

I realized I could have just compared the integer parts for the rational numbers with different integer parts: $-4 < -2 < 0 < 5 < 8$.

In Summary

Key Ideas

- Rationals can be compared in the same ways as integers and fractions.
- Negatives are always less than positives. A negative farther from 0 is always less than a negative closer to 0.

Need to Know

- To compare rationals in fraction form, it helps to use mixed number representations, equivalent fractions with common denominators or common numerators, or benchmarks. For example,

$$-3\frac{1}{2} > -4\frac{1}{3} \text{ since } -3 > -4$$

$$-\frac{3}{5} > -\frac{7}{8} \text{ since } -\frac{24}{40} > -\frac{35}{40} \text{ or since } -\frac{21}{35} > -\frac{21}{24}$$

$$-\frac{2}{3} < -\frac{1}{5} \text{ since } -\frac{2}{3} < -\frac{1}{2} \text{ and } -\frac{1}{5} > -\frac{1}{2}$$

- You can also express all the rational numbers as decimals and compare them in decimal form.

Checking

1. List three rationals between $-5\frac{2}{3}$ and $-4\frac{2}{3}$.

2. Explain why $-3\frac{3}{4} < -3\frac{1}{8}$.

3. You and your friends are standing at a point called 0. You use positive numbers to describe going east and negative numbers to describe going west. One friend moves to +3.2. Another moves to −2.3. A third moves to −0.9. Which of your friends moved the least distance? In what direction?

Practising

4. Use >, <, or = to make each statement true. Explain how you know parts b) and d) are true.

a) 0 ■ -0.5

b) -4.3 ■ -3.4

c) $-1\frac{2}{5}$ ■ $1\frac{2}{5}$

d) $-4\frac{1}{2}$ ■ $-\frac{9}{2}$

e) 5.6 ■ $5\frac{3}{5}$

f) $-2\frac{3}{10}$ ■ $2.\overline{3}$

5. Replace the ■ with a value to make each statement true.

a) $-2.3 < -■.4$

b) $-1.■ < -■.8$

c) $-0.■ < 0.■$

d) $1.9 < ■.4$

e) $-1.■ > -1.■$

f) $■.8 > 4.■$

6. Order each from least to greatest.

a) $-12.2, -14\frac{1}{2}, 3\frac{1}{4}, -4\frac{2}{3}$

b) $-8.4, -10.2, -10.3, 8.8, 8\frac{2}{3}$

c) $\frac{3}{8}, -\frac{3}{8}, \frac{3}{15}, \frac{-3}{15}$

d) $14.2, -2.9, -2\frac{3}{4}, 10.1$

7. Draw X and Y on a number line to make both statements true.
X is between -2 and -3 but greater than -2.8.
Y is greater than X but less than -2.2.

8. **Multiple choice.** Which number sentence describes how P compares to Q?

P Q
−6 −5 −4

A. $-5.6 < -4.8$

B. $-5.3 < -4.4$

C. $-5.6 > -4.8$

D. $-5.3 > -4.4$

9. **Multiple choice.** Which correctly orders $+8.1, -4.3, -4\frac{1}{3}, +0.9$, and $-\frac{24}{5}$ from least to greatest?

A. $-4.3, -4\frac{1}{3}, -\frac{24}{5}, 0.9, 8.1$

B. $-4\frac{1}{3}, -4.3, -\frac{24}{5}, 0.9, 8.1$

C. $-\frac{24}{5}, -4\frac{1}{3}, -4.3, 0.9, 8.1$

D. $-\frac{24}{5}, -4\frac{1}{3}, -4.3, 8.1, 0.9$

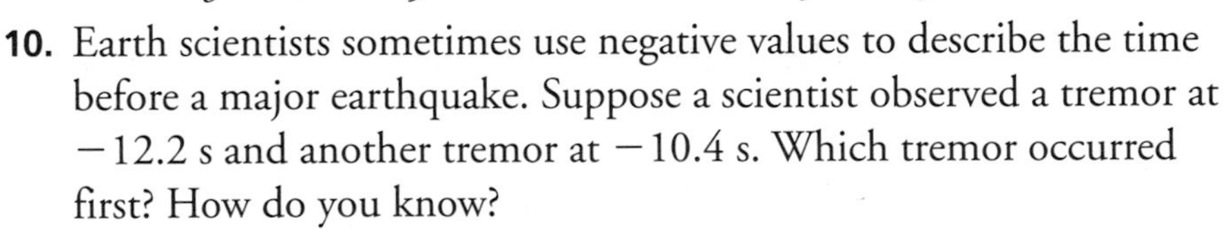

10. Earth scientists sometimes use negative values to describe the time before a major earthquake. Suppose a scientist observed a tremor at -12.2 s and another tremor at -10.4 s. Which tremor occurred first? How do you know?

11. Why would you probably use a different strategy to compare -4.3 and $-4\frac{1}{3}$ than to compare $+8.1$ and -4.3?

12. a) Describe three different strategies you might use to order these rational numbers.

$$-\frac{11}{2},\quad -7.5,\quad -\frac{7}{5},\quad -1\frac{1}{2},\quad -2\frac{1}{2},\quad \frac{5}{8},\quad \frac{1}{100}$$

b) Use your strategies to order the numbers from least to greatest.

13. Point Q, -1.25, is between point P at -1.2 and point R at -1.3.

R Q P

−1.5 −1.3 −1.2 −1

−1.25

a) Copy the number line. Draw a point S between P and Q. Label it with a value.

b) Draw a point T between P and S. Label it with a value.

c) Repeat two more times, each time drawing a new point between P and the last point and labelling it with a value.

d) How can you be sure there is always another rational number between two given ones? Use an example to explain.

e) What does this tell you about how many rational numbers there must be?

14. If a and b are positive numbers and $a < b$, how do $-a$ and $-b$ compare? Explain why.

15. Rational numbers can be written in either decimal form or fraction form. Which form do you find easier to use when ordering rational numbers? Use examples to justify your decision.

Closing

16. Agree or disagree with the following statement and explain your reasons. "If you can order integers and you can order fractions, you have all the skills needed to order rational numbers."

Extending

17. Order these from least to greatest: $-0.242\ 424...$, $-\frac{1}{4}$, $-\frac{24}{100}$, $-\frac{24}{98}$

18. The same digit is substituted into each blank. The order from least to greatest is

$$-■\frac{3}{5}, -7\frac{1}{■}, -4\frac{■}{11}, -4\frac{2}{■}.$$

What could the digit be? Explain.

19. Let x represent a value that could be anywhere between -2.4 and -3.8. Let y represent a value that could be anywhere between -4 and -3.5. About what fraction of the time will it be true that $x < y$?

1.3 Adding and Subtracting Rational Numbers

YOU WILL NEED

- a calculator with fraction capability

GOAL

Solve problems that involve adding and subtracting rational numbers.

LEARN ABOUT the Math

Jia-Wen's father started working for a new company and was given shares in the company. Jia-Wen paid attention to how those share prices were changing.

Changes in share prices are sometimes reported using rational numbers. A positive number describes an increase in price and a negative number describes a decrease.

The dollar value of a single share in Jia-Wen's father's company changed as follows:

Week 1: -0.68 Week 2: -0.25 Week 3: $+1.34$

? By how much did the increase in week 3 make up for the losses in weeks 1 and 2?

EXAMPLE 1 | Adding and subtracting rationals

Jia-Wen's Solution: Representing sums and differences with a number line

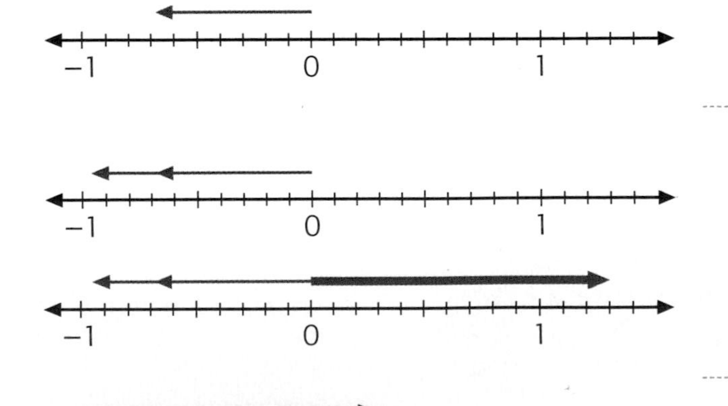

I used a number line to estimate the total change. I modelled each loss by going to the left. Then, I added the second loss to the first one.

I drew an arrow 1.3 units long and moved it to begin at the end of the second loss.

I can tell the gain was greater than the combined loss since the positive arrow is longer than the two negative ones together.

$0.68 + 0.25 = 0.93$
So, the combined loss is
$-0.68 + (-0.25) = -0.93$

To see exactly how much more, I compared the total loss to the gain.

The positive gain is 1.34. The difference is
$1.34 - 0.93 = 0.41$
The gain is 0.41 more than the loss.

I compared the length of the gain arrow to the combined lengths of the loss arrows.

Rachel's Solution: Using reasoning to add and subtract

$$\begin{aligned}(-0.68) + (-0.25) &= -(0.68 + 0.25)\\ &= -(0.93)\\ &= -0.93\end{aligned}$$

I figured that if I am adding two negative numbers, the sum would be negative, just as with integers.

$$\begin{aligned}-0.93 + 1.34 &= 1.34 - 0.93\\ &= 0.41\end{aligned}$$

To add the gain of 1.34, I could subtract 0.93 from 1.34.

The final increase overcame the total loss by 0.41.

Sam's Solution: Using the zero principle

$$(-0.68) + (-0.25) + 1.34 = x$$

I decided I was adding the two negative numbers and one positive number. I decided to use the zero principle.

$$[-0.68 + 0.68] + [-0.25 + 0.25] + 1.34$$
$$= x + 0.68 + 0.25$$

I added the same amounts to both sides of the equation so that I could use the zero principle. I added $0.68 + 0.25$.

$$\begin{aligned}0 + 0 + 1.34 &= x + 0.93\\ 1.34 &= x + 0.93\\ 1.34 - 0.93 &= x\\ 0.41 &= x\end{aligned}$$

I know that a number plus its opposite is 0.

Reflecting

A. How were the three solutions alike?

B. Why might one person think of the problem as an addition and another person think of it as a subtraction?

C. How is adding rationals like adding integers?

WORK WITH the Math

EXAMPLE 2 | **Estimating the sum and difference of rational numbers**

A temperature changed over the course of 3 h as follows:

Hour 1: +2.3 °C
Hour 2: −4.5 °C
Hour 3: −2.7 °C

About how much higher or lower than the original temperature was the final temperature?

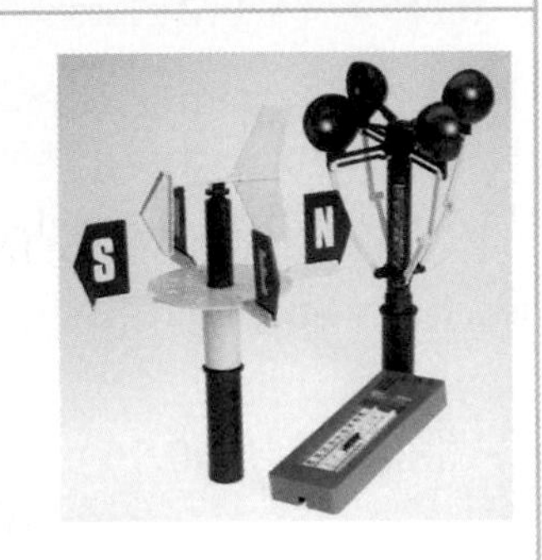

Thomas's Solution

−2.7 is almost the opposite of 2.3, so those two temperatures add to a value close to 0 °C.

> I noticed that the temperatures in hour 1 and hour 3 were close to opposites.

The final temperature was about 4 °C or 5 °C below the original temperature.

> I realized I just needed to use the decrease in hour 2 to estimate the total decrease.

EXAMPLE 3 | **Adding rationals in fraction form**

Calculate $3\frac{1}{4} + \frac{-7}{3}$.

Larissa's Solution

$3\frac{1}{4} + \frac{-7}{3}$ is about $3 + (-2) = 1$.

> I estimated first. $3\frac{1}{4}$ is a little more than 3 and $\frac{-7}{3} = -2\frac{1}{3}$ is about −2. I used $3 + (-2)$ to estimate.

$$3\frac{1}{4} = \frac{13}{4} = \frac{39}{12}$$
$$\frac{-7}{3} = -\frac{7}{3} = -\frac{28}{12}$$

> I wrote $3\frac{1}{4}$ as $\frac{13}{4}$. Then, I wrote each rational using equivalent fractions with the same denominator, 12.

$$3\frac{1}{4} + \frac{-7}{3} = \frac{39}{12} + \left(-\frac{28}{12}\right) = \frac{11}{12}$$

> I added the rationals by adding the numerators.

$\frac{11}{12}$ is close to 1, so my answer is reasonable.

> I compared my result to my estimate to check.

EXAMPLE 4 | Subtracting rationals in fraction form

Calculate $1\frac{1}{3} - \frac{2}{-5}$.

David's Solution: Using a number line to visualize

$1\frac{1}{3} - \frac{2}{-5}$ is the distance from $\frac{2}{-5} = -\frac{2}{5}$ to $1\frac{1}{3} = \frac{4}{3}$ on a number line.

I know that to calculate a difference, I can think about the distance from the second value to the first one.

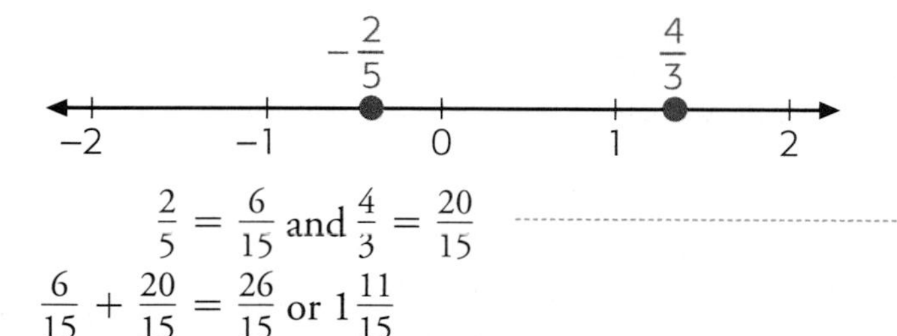

$\frac{2}{5} = \frac{6}{15}$ and $\frac{4}{3} = \frac{20}{15}$

$\frac{6}{15} + \frac{20}{15} = \frac{26}{15}$ or $1\frac{11}{15}$

I added $\frac{2}{5}$ to get from $-\frac{2}{5}$ to 0 and $\frac{4}{3}$ to get from 0 to $\frac{4}{3}$.

Thomas's Solution: Using a calculator

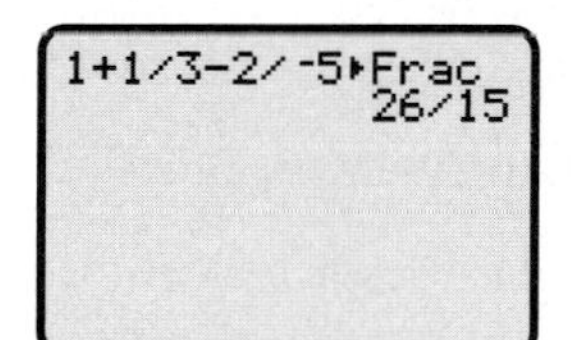

To subtract a negative, I used the – key for the subtraction and the (−) key to change the value of 5 to a negative.

$\frac{26}{15} = 1\frac{11}{15}$

In Summary

Key Ideas

- Adding and subtracting rational numbers in the form of decimals combines the rules for adding and subtracting positive decimals with the rules for adding and subtracting integers.

  For example, $-4.3 + 5.25 = 5.25 - 4.3 = 0.95$.
- Adding and subtracting rational numbers in the form of fractions combines the rules for adding and subtracting positive fractions with the rules for adding and subtracting integers.

  For example, $5\frac{3}{4} - \left(-2\frac{1}{3}\right) = 5\frac{3}{4} + 2\frac{1}{3}$.

Need to Know

- It is useful to estimate sums and differences to verify calculations of sums and differences.
- You can visualize a number line and use a combination of locations and distances to estimate and calculate sums and differences of rationals.

Checking

1. Evaluate.
   a) $-4.2 + (-3.8)$
   b) $\frac{7}{8} + \left(-\frac{2}{3}\right)$
   c) $2\frac{1}{5} + \left(-\frac{1}{2}\right)$
   d) $2.5 - 5.6$
   e) $-\frac{4}{3} - \left(-\frac{3}{4}\right)$
   f) $-3\frac{4}{5} - 1\frac{2}{3}$

2. You lose \$1.20 on each share you own and then gain back \$0.65. Write the total loss on each share as a rational number.

Practising

3. Estimate the sums or differences. Explain your thinking.
   a) $3.64 - 72.9$
   b) $-12.2 - (-18.9)$
   c) $-9.37 - 5.93$
   d) $0.47 - (-21.6)$
   e) $3.42 - (-5.6) + 11.3$
   f) $-5.1 + (-5.82) + 5.01$

4. Calculate exact answers for question 3.

5. **Multiple choice.** Which sum or difference is about $+16$?
   A. $-2.3 - 18.4$
   B. $14.1 + (-2.1)$
   C. $-4.1 - (-19.8)$
   D. $23.98 + (-8.9)$

6. **Multiple choice.** Yaroslav takes $\frac{3}{4}$ h to cut his family's front lawn and $1\frac{1}{3}$ h to cut the back lawn. How much longer does it take Yaroslav to cut the back lawn than the front?
   A. $1\frac{1}{2}$ h
   B. $1\frac{1}{3}$ h
   C. 35 min
   D. 45 min

7. Consider these numbers: -4.2, -8.94, -5.362, $+9.4$, $+1.205$
   Which two numbers have
   a) a sum of 5.2?
   b) a difference of 6.567?
   c) a sum of 4.038?
   d) a difference of -3.578?

8. Determine the missing digits for each. Use a calculator to help you.
   a) $-3.5\blacksquare 2 + \blacksquare.42\blacksquare = 1.846$
   b) $-1\blacksquare.382 - (4.17\blacksquare) + 8.\blacksquare 3 = -7.\blacksquare 27$
   c) $-2.45\blacksquare - (-5.\blacksquare 63) = \blacksquare.705$
   d) $-5.1\blacksquare - (-\blacksquare.8) - 7.\blacksquare = -9.21$

9. a) How could using the zero principle help you add $3.4 + (-8.9)$?
   b) Why would the zero principle not help you add $-3.4 + (-8.9)$? What other strategy could you use instead?

10. Calculate. Show your work.
    a) $-\frac{3}{8} + 1\frac{3}{4}$
    b) $-5\frac{1}{2} + 2\frac{2}{3}$
    c) $\frac{6}{5} - \frac{3}{2}$
    d) $1\frac{3}{4} + \left(-3\frac{2}{5}\right)$
    e) $-3\frac{2}{3} - 4\frac{1}{5}$
    f) $\frac{5}{-8} - \left(-\frac{11}{3}\right)$

11. The daily changes in price for a share during a week were $-\$2.78$, $-\$5.45$, $\$0.38$, $\$1.38$, and $\$2.12$. The price of the share was $\$58.22$ at the start of the week. What was the price at the end of the week?

12. How do you know that $-2.3 - \left(-3\frac{1}{4}\right)$ is

a) greater than $-2.3 + \left(-3\frac{1}{4}\right)$? **b)** about 1?

13. Determine the value that makes each equation true.

a) $-1\frac{3}{4} + \blacksquare = 1$ **b)** $-1\frac{3}{4} - \blacksquare = 1$

14. James finished the Manitoba Marathon in a time of 3:57:53.3 (hours: minutes: seconds). The winner of the marathon finished in a time of 2:25:55.6. Determine how much longer James took to complete the marathon than the winner did.

15. Evaluate each expression for the given values.

a) $x - y$ when $x = -4.1$ and $y = -3.2$

b) $x + y + z$ when $x = 2.5$, $y = -7.8$, and $z = -4.1$

c) $x - y$ when $x = -2\frac{1}{2}$ and $y = -3\frac{3}{4}$

d) $x + y$ when $x = -1\frac{1}{2}$ and $y = 2\frac{1}{4}$

16. To recreate the work of the voyageurs during the fur trade, a relay race was held on the Red River near St-Boniface, MB. Participants canoed to specific points to find a message like those at right, which led them to a fur cache. What rational number operations would you use to determine each of the following?

a) the distance of the last leg **b)** the total distance paddled

Message 1: 1.5 km south
Message 2: 0.68 km north
Message 3: 2.3 km south
Message 4: north to the starting point

17. List two rational numbers a and b that are not integers and that would make each statement true.

a) $a + b$ is negative, but $a - b$ is positive.

b) $a + b$ is positive, but $a - b$ is negative.

c) $a + b$ and $a - b$ are both negative.

18. Describe a real-world problem where you might calculate $-3.2 - (-4.5)$. Solve your problem.

Closing

19. Describe a strategy for calculating the sum and a strategy for calculating the difference of -3.4 and $+5.005$.

Extending

20. The sum of two rational numbers is $\frac{23}{40}$. Their difference is $-1\frac{3}{40}$. What are the numbers?

21. The sum of two rationals is 17.4 less than the difference. What could the rationals be?

EXAMPLE 2 | Solving a problem involving rational numbers

a) Use the numbers 1 and -5 in the blanks so that $\frac{●}{◆} \times 2\frac{3}{4}$ has the least possible value.

b) Use the numbers 1 and 2 in the blanks so that $\frac{-●}{5} \div ■\frac{3}{4}$ has the greatest possible value.

Jia-Wen's Solution

a) The missing number is either

$$\frac{1}{-5} = -\frac{1}{5}$$

or $\frac{-5}{1} = -\frac{5}{1}$

The product had to be negative since the fraction involved a positive and negative value.

$\frac{1}{5} < \frac{5}{1}$, so $-\frac{1}{5} > -\frac{5}{1}$

$$-\frac{5}{1} \times 2\frac{3}{4} < -\frac{1}{5} \times 2\frac{3}{4}$$

If you multiply a negative number by a positive number, the answer is less if the negative number is less.

$$\begin{aligned}\frac{-5}{1} \times 2\frac{3}{4} &= -5 \times \frac{11}{4}\\ &= -\frac{55}{4}\end{aligned}$$

I checked by multiplying. I was right, since $-\frac{55}{4}$ is almost -14 and $-\frac{11}{20}$ is not even -1.

$$\begin{aligned}\frac{1}{-5} \times 2\frac{3}{4} &= -\frac{1}{5} \times \frac{11}{4}\\ &= -\frac{11}{20}\end{aligned}$$

$-\frac{5}{1} \times 2\frac{3}{4}$ gives the least product.

b)

$$\begin{aligned}\frac{-1}{5} \div 2\frac{3}{4} &= -\frac{1}{5} \div \frac{11}{4}\\ &= -\frac{1}{5} \times \frac{4}{11}\\ &= -\frac{4}{55}\end{aligned}$$

$$\begin{aligned}\frac{-2}{5} \div 1\frac{3}{4} &= -\frac{2}{5} \div \frac{7}{4}\\ &= -\frac{2}{5} \times \frac{4}{7}\\ &= -\frac{8}{35}\end{aligned}$$

The only possibilities are $-\frac{1}{5} \div 2\frac{3}{4}$ or $-\frac{2}{5} \div 1\frac{3}{4}$. To divide, I converted the mixed number and multiplied by the reciprocal. $-\frac{4}{55}$ is about $-\frac{1}{12}$. $-\frac{8}{35}$ is about $-\frac{1}{4}$, which is less.

$-\frac{2}{5} \div 1\frac{3}{4}$ gives the greatest quotient.

In Summary

Key Ideas

- Multiplying and dividing rational numbers in decimal form combines the rules for multiplying and dividing positive decimals with the rules for multiplying and dividing integers. For example,

$$(-3.2) \div 1.2 = -(3.2 \div 1.2)$$

- Multiplying and dividing rational numbers in the form of fractions combines the rules for multiplying and dividing positive fractions with the rules for multiplying and dividing integers. For example,

$$5\tfrac{3}{4} \times \left(-2\tfrac{1}{3}\right) = -\left(\tfrac{23}{4} \times \tfrac{7}{3}\right)$$

Need to Know

- You can divide rational numbers in the form of fractions by using a common denominator and dividing the numerators. For example,

$$-\frac{12}{25} \div \frac{3}{5} = -\frac{12}{25} \div \frac{15}{25}$$

- You can also divide by multiplying by the reciprocal. For example,

$$-\frac{12}{25} \div \frac{3}{5} = -\frac{12}{25} \times \frac{5}{3}$$

Checking

1. Evaluate.

a) $(-2)(9.5)$

b) $\frac{-4}{7} \times \frac{6}{-5}$

c) $(-8) \div (0.5)$

d) $\frac{2}{5} \div \left(-\frac{5}{8}\right)$

2. How much less is $\frac{-3}{4} \div \frac{5}{6}$ than $\frac{-3}{4} \times \frac{5}{6}$?

3. A water tank lost $\frac{1}{3}$ of its volume of water one day and then $\frac{1}{2}$ of what was left the next day. What rational number describes the volume of water after the second day as compared to the original volume?

Practising

4. Calculate.

a) $-\frac{2}{3} \times \frac{5}{8}$

b) $-\frac{2}{3} \times \frac{-5}{8}$

c) $\frac{2}{3} \times \frac{-8}{5}$

d) $-\frac{5}{8} \div \frac{2}{3}$

e) $\frac{-2}{3} \div \left(-\frac{5}{8}\right)$

f) $\frac{2}{3} \div \frac{5}{8}$

5. **Multiple choice.** Which expression is about $-\frac{1}{2}$?

A. $-\frac{2}{3} \times \frac{1}{8}$ **B.** $\frac{8}{9} \div \left(-\frac{1}{2}\right)$ **C.** $\frac{4}{5} \div \left(1\frac{1}{2}\right)$ **D.** $-\frac{2}{3} \div \frac{5}{4}$

6. **Multiple choice.** Without evaluating, determine which expressions have the same product as $\left(\frac{3}{4}\right)\left(\frac{5}{8}\right)$.

W: $\left(\frac{-3}{-4}\right)\left(\frac{5}{8}\right)$ X: $-\left(\frac{3}{4}\right)\left(-\frac{5}{8}\right)$ Y: $\left(-\frac{3}{8}\right)\left(-\frac{5}{4}\right)$ Z: $\left(\frac{-3}{4}\right)\left(\frac{5}{-8}\right)$

A. X and Y
B. X and Z
C. X, Y, and Z
D. all of these expressions

7. Use the numbers −1, −3, and 8 in the blanks so that $\frac{■}{■} \times ■\frac{2}{3}$ has
   a) the least possible value
   b) the greatest possible value

8. Consider the numbers −4.2, −1.3, −8.4, and 7.3.
   a) Which two have a product of 35.28?
   b) Which two have a quotient of about −1.75?

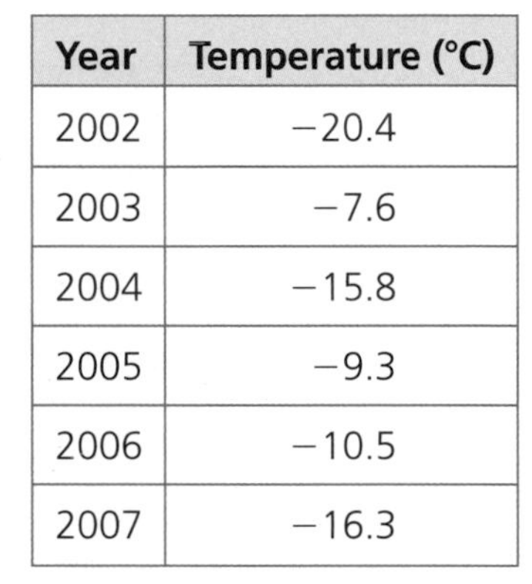

Year	Temperature (°C)
2002	−20.4
2003	−7.6
2004	−15.8
2005	−9.3
2006	−10.5
2007	−16.3

Source: Environment Canada

9. The temperatures at Fort Nelson, BC, at 5:00 a.m. on December 25 from 2002 to 2007 are shown in the table. Determine the mean temperature at 5:00 a.m. on December 25 for these years.

10. Calculate. Show your work.
   a) $\left(\frac{5}{-12}\right)\left(\frac{-8}{15}\right)$
   b) $\left(3\frac{6}{7}\right)\left(-8\frac{1}{3}\right)$
   c) $\frac{15}{16} \div \left(-1\frac{1}{24}\right)$
   d) $-4\frac{2}{3} \div \frac{7}{12}$
   e) $(-3.2) \div (-8.4)$
   f) $7.2 \div (-0.6)$

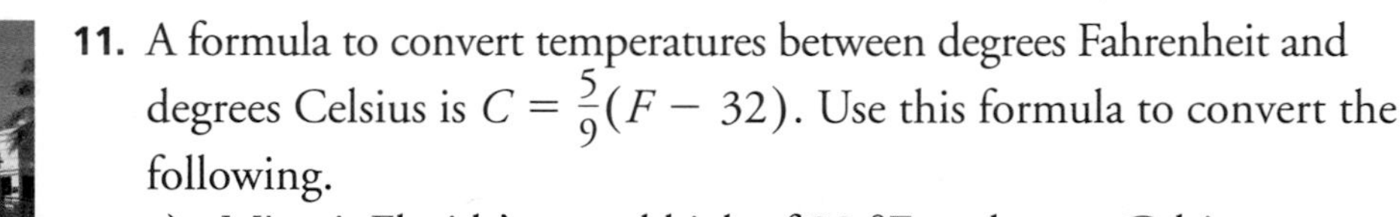

11. A formula to convert temperatures between degrees Fahrenheit and degrees Celsius is $C = \frac{5}{9}(F - 32)$. Use this formula to convert the following.
   a) Miami, Florida's record high of 98 °F to degrees Celsius
   b) Anchorage, Alaska's record low of −37 °F to degrees Celsius
   c) 0 °C to degrees Fahrenheit

12. Two tanks hold the same amount of water. Tank 1 loses $\frac{2}{3}$ of its volume. Tank 2 gains $\frac{1}{4}$ of its volume. What is the final ratio of water volume, comparing tank 1 to tank 2?

13. An investment loses $\frac{1}{2}$ of its value and then loses another $\frac{2}{3}$ of the new value.
   a) What fraction of its original value is the final value?
   b) Can you multiply $-\frac{1}{2} \times \left(-\frac{2}{3}\right)$ to calculate the answer to part a)? Explain.

14. A pail of water has been sitting for a while, and $\frac{1}{8}$ of the water has evaporated.

a) What could $\frac{3}{4} \times \left(-\frac{1}{8}\right)$ describe about this situation?

b) What could $-\frac{1}{8} \div \left(-\frac{1}{4}\right)$ describe about this situation?

15. The product of two rationals is $-\frac{12}{25}$. What might their quotient be?

16. The product of $-\frac{3}{4}$ and two other rationals is $\frac{1}{4}$. The quotient of the two other rationals is $-\frac{3}{4}$.

$$-\frac{3}{4} \times \frac{\bullet}{\blacklozenge} \times \frac{\blacktriangle}{\blacksquare} = \frac{1}{4}$$

$$\frac{\bullet}{\blacklozenge} \div \frac{\blacktriangle}{\blacksquare} = -\frac{3}{4}$$

a) How do you know that one unknown rational is positive and one is negative?

b) What could the unknown rationals be?

17. Evaluate each expression for the given values. Use a calculator.

a) $x - 2y$ when $x = -9.78$ and $y = 3.2$

b) $(x + y)(x - y)$ when $x = 2.5$ and $y = -7.8$

c) $x(x + y)$ when $x = -2\frac{1}{2}$ and $y = 3\frac{3}{4}$

d) $\frac{x}{y} + \frac{y}{x}$ when $x = -1\frac{1}{2}$ and $y = 2\frac{1}{4}$

Closing

18. Create a brief "instruction manual" to help someone with the rules for multiplying and dividing rational numbers.

Extending

19. Calculate each product.

a) $-9 \times 0.2222...$ **b)** $-99 \times 0.232\,323...$

20. The product of a positive and a negative rational number is 2 greater than their sum. What could they be?

21. The width of a rectangle is $\frac{1}{4}$ of the length. If you increase the width by 12 m and double the length, you obtain a perimeter of 60 m. Determine the dimensions of the original rectangle.

CHAPTER 1

Mid-Chapter Review

FREQUENTLY ASKED Questions

Study *Aid*

- See Lesson 1.1, Example 2.
- Try Mid-Chapter Review questions 1 and 2.

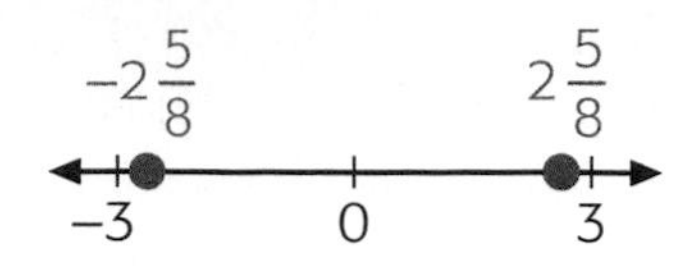

Q: How do you place a negative rational on a number line?

A: You place the negative rational as far to the left of 0 as its opposite is to the right. For example, place $-2\frac{5}{8}$ to the left of 0, the same distance that $2\frac{5}{8}$ is to the right of 0. Notice that $-2\frac{5}{8}$ is the same as $-2 + \left(-\frac{5}{8}\right)$, which is not equal to $-2 + \frac{5}{8}$.

Study *Aid*

- See Lesson 1.2, Example 1.
- Try Mid-Chapter Review questions 4, 5, and 7.

Q: How can you determine whether one rational number is greater than another?

A: Numbers can be compared on a number line. If a number is farther to the right, it is greater. Therefore, any negative rational is less than any positive one.

It helps to look first at the integer part of a rational to decide where to place it. Sometimes writing all the numbers in the same form, either as decimals or as fractions with a common positive numerator or denominator, makes comparison easier.

For example, $-3\frac{1}{2} < -1\frac{2}{3}$ since $-3 < -1$.

$-2\frac{1}{2} < -2\frac{2}{5}$ since $-2.5 < -2.4$ or since $-2\frac{5}{10} < -2\frac{4}{10}$.

Study *Aid*

- See Lesson 1.3, Examples 1, 3, and 4.
- Try Mid-Chapter Review questions 9 and 10.

Q: How can you add and subtract rational numbers to solve problems?

You add in situations where you combine. For example, suppose the level of water in a full pail goes down to the $\frac{1}{4}$ mark and then $\frac{5}{8}$ of another identical pail is added back in.

$$\begin{aligned} -\frac{3}{4} + \frac{5}{8} &= -\frac{6}{8} + \frac{5}{8} \\ &= -\frac{1}{8} \end{aligned}$$

The new level is $\frac{1}{8}$ of a pail lower than the original level.

You subtract in situations where you have a loss or reduction. For example, suppose the level of water in a pail goes down by $\frac{1}{4}$ of the pail's capacity, and then the remaining water is poured into a new identical pail to the $\frac{3}{8}$ mark.

$$-\frac{1}{4}-\frac{3}{8}=-\frac{2}{8}-\frac{3}{8}$$
$$=-\frac{5}{8}$$

The new level is $\frac{5}{8}$ of a pail lower than the original level.

Q: How can you multiply and divide rational numbers to solve problems?

A: You multiply and divide rationals by combining the rules you know for multiplying and dividing integers with those for multiplying and dividing positive fractions or decimals.

For example, suppose one investment loses $\frac{3}{4}$ of its value. Then, it loses $\frac{5}{8}$ of that new value. What fraction of the value of the original investment is the final value?

$\frac{1}{4}\times\frac{3}{8}=\frac{3}{32}$ is the final value. That's because you end up with $\frac{1}{4}$ of the value after the first loss and then $\frac{3}{8}$ of that after the second loss.

For example, suppose you have two investments of equal value. The first investment loses $\frac{3}{4}$ of its value; the second loses $\frac{5}{8}$ of its value. How much more is the loss per dollar on the first investment than on the second one?

$$-\frac{3}{4}\div\left(-\frac{5}{8}\right)=\frac{6}{8}\div\frac{5}{8}$$
$$=\frac{6}{5}$$

For each dollar lost on the second investment, you lose $\frac{6}{5}$ of a dollar, or $1.20, on the first investment.

Study ***Aid***

- See Lesson 1.4, Example 2.
- Try Mid-Chapter Review questions 12, 13, and 14.

Practice

Lesson 1.1

1. What rational numbers describe the points A, B, and C?

A B C

-5 0 2

2. Locate each rational on a number line from -10 to $+10$.
   a) -2.6 **b)** $\frac{-18}{4}$ **c)** $\frac{23}{-3}$ **d)** $-8\frac{1}{3}$
3. On a February day, the daytime high temperature in Saddle Lake First Nations Reserve, AB, was -4.5 °C. The temperature in Portage la Prairie, MB, on the same day was -12.8 °C. Which place was colder? Explain.

Lesson 1.2

4. Use $>$, $<$, or $=$ to make true statements. Explain how you know each statement is true.
   a) $-\frac{2}{3} \blacksquare -\frac{5}{6}$ b) $\frac{2}{3} \blacksquare \frac{5}{8}$ c) $-2\frac{1}{4} \blacksquare -\frac{9}{4}$ d) $\frac{2}{-5} \blacksquare -\frac{3}{10}$

5. Write these rational numbers in order from least to greatest.
   a) $-\frac{3}{5}, \frac{1}{-3}, -1\frac{1}{3}$
   b) $\frac{-2}{5}, -2\frac{1}{5}, \frac{4}{5}$
   c) $0.7, -0.3, -0.\overline{3}$
   d) $0, -1.5, -2$

6. List four rational numbers between $-\frac{3}{8}$ and $-\frac{1}{2}$.

7. A rational number of the form $\frac{\blacksquare}{6}$ is between $-\frac{3}{4}$ and $-\frac{1}{2}$. What is the numerator of the rational number?

Lesson 1.3

8. Calculate.
   a) $2\frac{1}{4} - 5\frac{1}{3}$
   b) $\frac{3}{5} + \left(-\frac{8}{9}\right)$
   c) $-7.2 - (-4.8)$
   d) $-\frac{5}{8} + \left(-\frac{1}{3}\right)$
   e) $-3.5 + (-7.7)$
   f) $-7\frac{1}{14} + \left(-\frac{1}{4}\right)$

9. Kristen walked 5.7 km east and then 9.1 km west. How far east or west was Kristen from her original position?

10. The difference of two rational numbers is $\frac{3}{5}$. The sum is $\frac{1}{3}$. What are the rational numbers?

Lesson 1.4

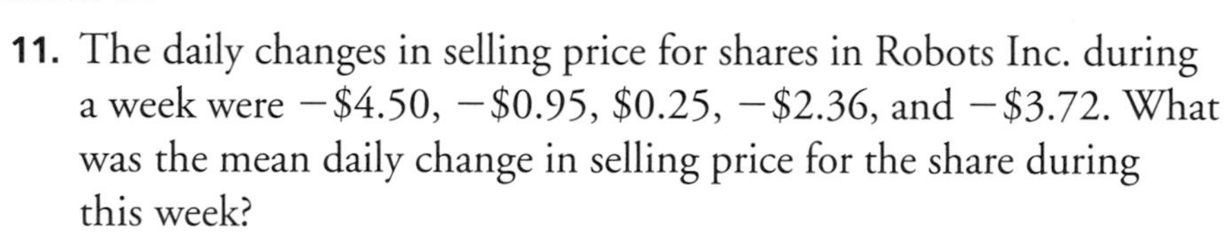

11. The daily changes in selling price for shares in Robots Inc. during a week were $-\$4.50$, $-\$0.95$, $\$0.25$, $-\$2.36$, and $-\$3.72$. What was the mean daily change in selling price for the share during this week?

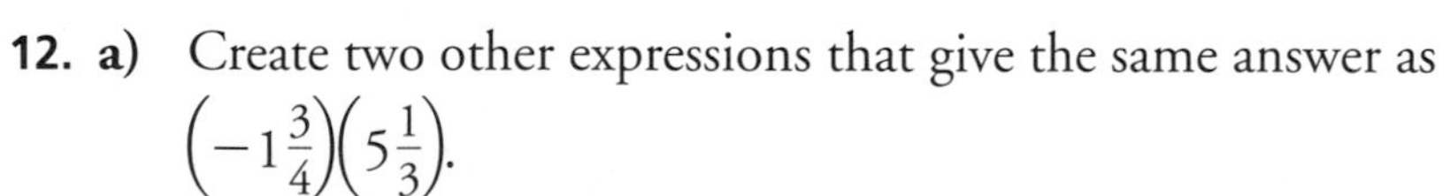

12. a) Create two other expressions that give the same answer as $\left(-1\frac{3}{4}\right)\left(5\frac{1}{3}\right)$.
    b) Describe a situation that $\left(-1\frac{3}{4}\right)\left(5\frac{1}{3}\right)$ might represent.

13. Noah had 1.5 times as much savings as Kelly had debt. Then, Kelly doubled her debt. What rational number division describes Noah's money as compared to Kelly's?

14. Create and solve your own problem involving multiplying or dividing rational numbers.

1.5 Order of Operations with Rational Numbers

GOAL

Extend the order of operations rules to rational numbers.

YOU WILL NEED

- a calculator with fraction capability

LEARN ABOUT the Math

Sam is solving a puzzle where he has to put in operations signs, $\times$, $-$, $\div$, and $+$, to make this statement true.

$$\frac{1}{2} \blacksquare (-2) \blacksquare \left(-\frac{3}{2}\right) \blacksquare \frac{1}{2} \blacksquare 5 = -16$$

? Which signs should Sam use?

A. How do you know that the sign before the 5 cannot be a $+$ sign?

B. Why is it more likely that you multiply by the 5 than divide by it?

C. How does knowing that the value is -16 help you know that the sign between -2 and $-\frac{3}{2}$ cannot be a $\times$ or $\div$ sign?

D. Where does each sign go?

Reflecting

E. Why would you not need to know the order of operations rules if the $+$ sign were last?

F. Why do you need to know the order of operations rules if the $+$ sign is not last?

Communication *Tip*

The convention for order of operations is BDMAS:
B: First calculate anything inside brackets.
DM: Divide and multiply from left to right.
AS: Add and subtract from left to right.

WORK WITH the Math

EXAMPLE 1 Using the order of operations to evaluate a rational-number expression

Evaluate $-2\frac{1}{2} + x \div y$ on a calculator when $x = 5\frac{1}{3}$ and $y = -1\frac{7}{9}$. Does your calculator follow the rules for order of operations?

Larissa's Solution

$$-2\frac{1}{2} + x \div y \rightarrow \frac{-5}{2} + \frac{16}{3} \div \left(\frac{-16}{9}\right)$$

I substituted the given values for the variables.

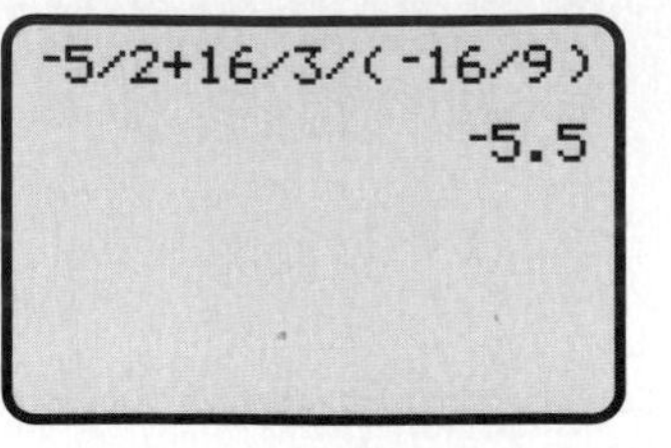

The answer on my calculator was -5.5, which is $-5\frac{1}{2}$.

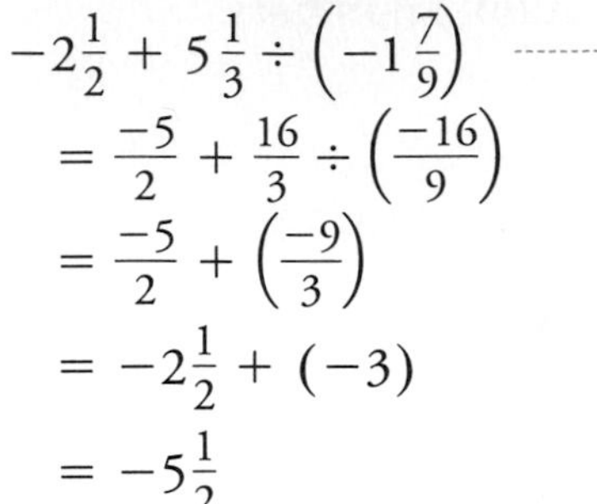

$$\begin{aligned}
&-2\tfrac{1}{2} + 5\tfrac{1}{3} \div \left(-1\tfrac{7}{9}\right)\\
&= \frac{-5}{2} + \frac{16}{3} \div \left(\frac{-16}{9}\right)\\
&= \frac{-5}{2} + \left(\frac{-9}{3}\right)\\
&= -2\tfrac{1}{2} + (-3)\\
&= -5\tfrac{1}{2}
\end{aligned}$$

I calculated by hand to see if the calculator used the order of operations. I followed the order of operations the same way I would if the numbers were all integers or all fractions.

The calculator did follow the rules for order of operations.

EXAMPLE 2 | Solving a problem using the order of operations

Thomas had been texting daily temperatures to Sam.

Temperatures	−0.2	+5.8	−5.1	+9.1

Thomas then told Sam how to calculate the mean.
He texted, "Add the numbers and divide by 4." Sam wrote:

$$\begin{aligned}
-0.2 + 5.8 + (-5.1) + 9.1 \div 4 &= -0.2 + 5.8 + (-5.1) + 2.275\\
&= 2.775
\end{aligned}$$

2.775 is the average temperature.

What is wrong with Sam's calculation? What is the actual average?

Thomas's Solution

Sam's error was that he divided only the 9.1 by 4.

Sam should have used brackets around $-0.2 + 5.8 + (-5.1) + 9.1$ before dividing by 4.

Correction:

$[-0.2 + 5.8 + (-5.1) + 9.1] \div 4$

First I did the addition since the values are in brackets.

$$\begin{aligned}
&= [-5.3 + 14.9] \div 4\\
&= 9.6 \div 4\\
&= 2.4
\end{aligned}$$

I added the positives and the negatives separately.

The actual average is 2.4.

In Summary

Key Idea

- The rules for order of operations with rationals are the same as with integers:
  - Do what is in brackets first.
  - Multiply and divide from left to right.
  - Add and subtract from left to right.

Checking

1. Which operation would you perform first in each situation?
   a) $2.4 - [3.5 + (-2.9)] \times (-5)$
   b) $(-5.2 - 1.4) \div (-3) \times (2.1)$

2. Share values went up and down over the course of a week as shown at right. What was the mean daily change?

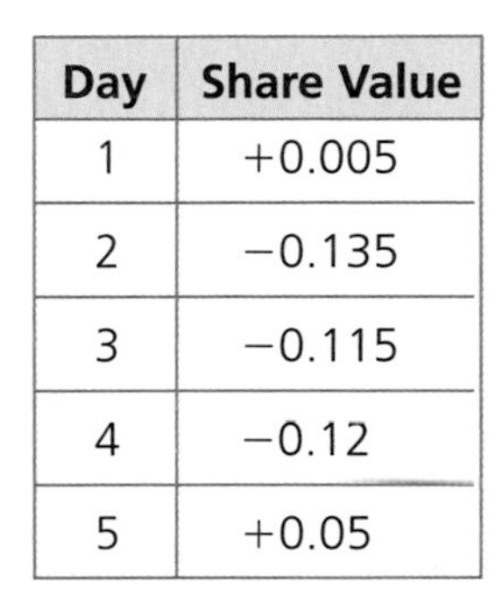

Day	Share Value
1	+0.005
2	−0.135
3	−0.115
4	−0.12
5	+0.05

Practising

3. Which operation would you perform last in each situation?
   a) $3.7[3.5 + (-2.9)] \div [2.5 + (-1.8)]$
   b) $8 \div (-1.3) + (-6.8 - 3.4)$
   c) $\frac{2}{3} \times \frac{5}{4} - \frac{3}{4} \times \frac{9}{5}$

4. Temperatures went up and down over the course of five days as follows:
   -4.2 °C, -1.4 °C, $+1.9$ °C, $+3.7$ °C, -1.8 °C
   What was the mean daily change?

5. **Multiple choice.** What is the value of
   $[2.4 - 5.7] \times [-5.1 - (-1.8)] + 0.2$?
   A. 11.09 **B.** 17.23 **C.** 17.83 **D.** 16.23

6. **Multiple choice.** What is the value of
   $-0.7 - 0.3 \div (-0.15) \times 0.2 + 2$?
   A. 0.4 **B.** 1.7 **C.** −0.46 **D.** −1.609 090 9...

7. Mika calculated $\left(-\frac{3}{4}\right) + \left(-\frac{2}{3}\right) \div \frac{1}{3}$ as $-4\frac{1}{4}$. Is Mika correct? Explain.

8. Evaluate.
   a) $-3\frac{2}{3}x \div y$ when $x = 2\frac{1}{2}$ and $y = -3\frac{3}{4}$
   b) $2x - \frac{5}{3}y$ when $x = -1\frac{3}{4}$ and $y = -\frac{7}{10}$

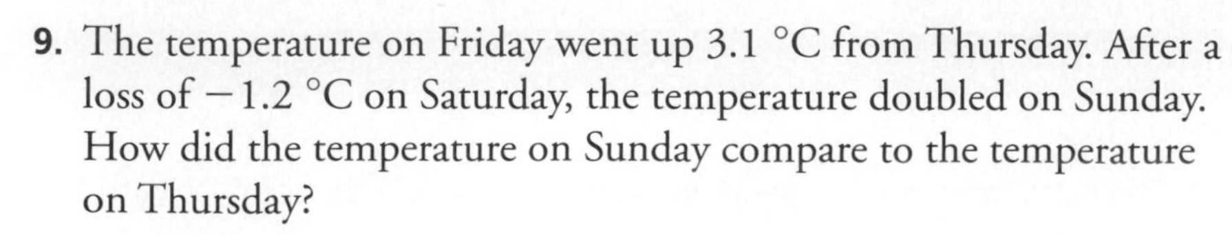

9. The temperature on Friday went up 3.1 °C from Thursday. After a loss of −1.2 °C on Saturday, the temperature doubled on Sunday. How did the temperature on Sunday compare to the temperature on Thursday?

10. For which calculations would you not need to know the order of operations rules?

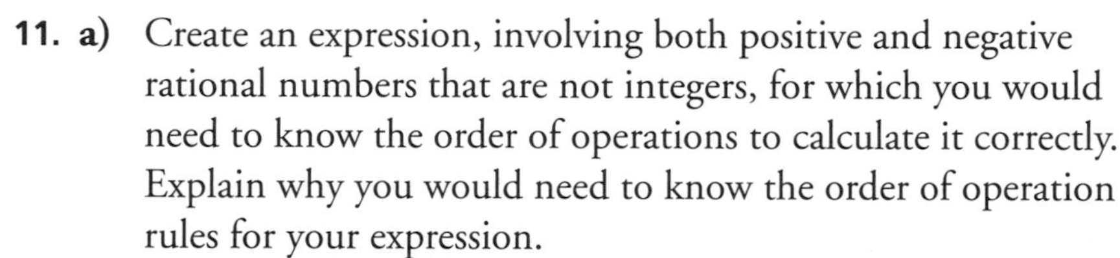

a) $\left(-\frac{2}{3}\right) - \frac{5}{8} - \left(-\frac{4}{5}\right)$

b) $\left(-\frac{2}{3}\right) \times \frac{5}{8} - \left(-\frac{4}{5}\right)$

c) $\left(-\frac{2}{3}\right) - \frac{5}{8} - \left(-\frac{4}{5}\right) \times 2$

d) $\left(-\frac{2}{3}\right) \div \frac{5}{8} \times \left(-\frac{4}{5}\right)$

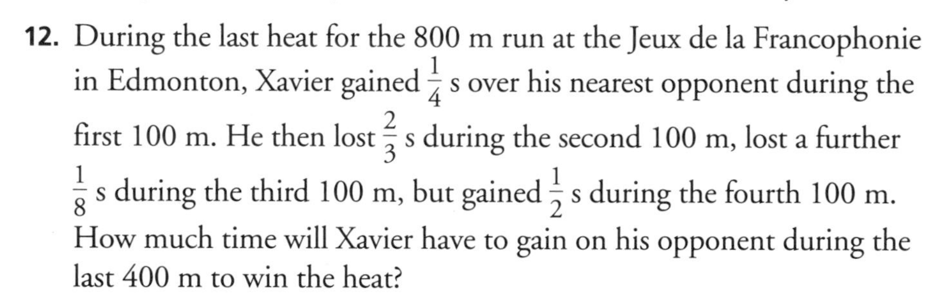

11. a) Create an expression, involving both positive and negative rational numbers that are not integers, for which you would need to know the order of operations to calculate it correctly. Explain why you would need to know the order of operation rules for your expression.

b) Check to see if your calculator follows those rules for order of operations when you enter rational numbers. How do you know?

12. During the last heat for the 800 m run at the Jeux de la Francophonie in Edmonton, Xavier gained $\frac{1}{4}$ s over his nearest opponent during the first 100 m. He then lost $\frac{2}{3}$ s during the second 100 m, lost a further $\frac{1}{8}$ s during the third 100 m, but gained $\frac{1}{2}$ s during the fourth 100 m. How much time will Xavier have to gain on his opponent during the last 400 m to win the heat?

Closing

13. Why is it essential that the rules for order of operations for rational numbers be the same as the order of operations for integers?

Extending

14. Create an expression involving rational numbers where you perform an addition before you perform any multiplications or divisions. Calculate the value of that expression.

15. Where would you add brackets in each expression to make it true?

a) $3\frac{1}{2} + 4 \div 0.75 + (-8.1) = 1.9$

b) $-1.2 + -3 \div 1.5 + 1.5 - \frac{1}{5} \times 13 = -4$

16. You subtract a rational number from $-\frac{2}{3}$, double the answer, and then divide by $-\frac{1}{4}$. The result is 8. What was the rational number?

1.6 Calculating with Rational Numbers

GOAL

Use number sense to compare the results of adding, subtracting, multiplying, and dividing rationals.

EXPLORE the Math

Jia-Wen noticed that, for $-\frac{2}{3}$ and $\frac{4}{5}$,

$$\left(-\frac{2}{3}\right) - \frac{4}{5} < \left(-\frac{2}{3}\right) \div \frac{4}{5} < \left(-\frac{2}{3}\right) \times \frac{4}{5} < \left(-\frac{2}{3}\right) + \frac{4}{5}$$

The order from least to greatest is $-\quad\div\quad\times\quad+$

But for $-\frac{2}{3}$ and $\frac{1}{3}$,

$$\left(-\frac{2}{3}\right) \div \frac{1}{3} < \left(-\frac{2}{3}\right) - \frac{1}{3} < \left(-\frac{2}{3}\right) + \frac{1}{3} < \left(-\frac{2}{3}\right) \times \frac{1}{3}$$

The order from least to greatest is $\div\quad-\quad+\quad\times$

? How can you choose pairs of rational numbers to get four different possible orderings as the result of adding, subtracting, multiplying, and dividing them?

1.7 Solve Problems Using Guess and Test

GOAL

Solve problems involving rational numbers using a guess-and-test strategy.

LEARN ABOUT the Math

Eight students rated their video game enjoyment on a scale from −10 to 10.

- The mean score was 1.625.
- Three scores were negative and added to −7.
- Two positive scores were double two other ones.
- There were no negative doubles.

? What were the eight scores?

EXAMPLE 1 | Using guess and test to determine data values

Thomas's Solution

1. Understand the Problem
I know the numbers all have to be between −10 and 10.
I know there have to be eight numbers.
I know the mean of the eight numbers is 1.625.
I know that three numbers are negative and that they add to −7.
I know that exactly two numbers are the double of two other ones and they are positive.

2. Make a Plan
I will figure out the total of all the numbers, and then the total of the positive numbers.
I will figure out what the five positive numbers add to. Then, I will make sure that they add to the correct total but also make sure that two numbers are double the other two.

3. Carry Out the Plan
Since the mean is based on eight numbers,

Total of all eight numbers $= 8 \times 1.625 = 13$

Total of negatives $= -7$
Total of positives $+ (-7) = 13$
Total of positives $= 20$

First, I tried 8 and 4 and 6 and 3 as the doubles:
$8 + 4 + 6 + 3 +$ another positive $= 20$
This is not possible since $8 + 4 + 6 + 3$ is already 21.

Then, I tried 6 and 3 and 2 and 1 as the doubles:

$20 - (6 + 3 + 2 + 1) = 20 - 12 = 8$

These values worked because 8 is not the double of any other positive. The positives are 6, 3, 2, 1, and 8.
The negatives had to add to -7. I tried -1, -2, and -4, but -4 is double -2 and there can be no negative doubles.
Next, I tried -1, -1 and -5.

My solution is that the scores are 3, 6, 1, 2, 8, -5, -1, and -1.

4. Look Back
I checked by adding and dividing by 8 to make sure that the mean was correct.
$[3 + 6 + 1 + 2 + 8 + (-5) + (-1) + (-1)] \div 8 = 1.625$

Reflecting

A. How did Thomas use logical reasoning in solving the problem?

B. How did using guess and test help Thomas to solve the problem?

C. Could Thomas have found a different solution? Explain.

WORK WITH the Math

EXAMPLE 2 | Using guess and test to solve a measurement problem

The number of kilometres in the perimeter of this park is about 6 less than the number of square kilometres in its area. What is the width?

■.125 km
10.875 km

Sam's Solution

1. Understand the Problem
I have to determine the width so that the number of units in the perimeter is about 6 less than the number of units in the area.

2. Make a Plan
I will use estimates for the width and then determine the perimeter and the area.

3. Carry Out the Plan
First, I estimated the length as 11 km.
I tried a width of 5 km.

The perimeter is about $2 \times 16 = 32$ km.
The area is about $5 \times 11 = 55$ km^2.
$55 - 32 = 23$
So, the difference is too much.

I tried a width of 3 km.
The perimeter is about $2 \times 14 = 28$ km.
The area is about $3 \times 11 = 33$ km^2.
$33 - 28 = 5$
The difference is not quite enough, but it is close.

The diagram said the width was actually ■.125 km and the length was actually 10.875 km. Since I was so close, I used 3.125 km.
Perimeter $= 2 \times 14.000 = 28.000$ km
Area $= 3.125 \times 10.875 = 33.984$ km^2 (rounded to the nearest thousandth)

The difference is 5.984, rounded to the nearest thousandth. This is very close to 6. Therefore, the width is 3.125 km.

4. Look Back
I checked the perimeter and area for widths of 2.125 km and 4.125 km. For 2.125 km, perimeter $= 24$ km and area $\doteq 23$ km^2. For 4.125 km, perimeter $= 32$ km and area $\doteq 45$ km^2. So, the missing digit could only be 3.

In Summary

Key Idea

- You can use guess and test in combination with other strategies to help you solve problems. Once you guess, you can use the results of your guess to improve your next guess.

Checking

1. You subtract a rational number from its triple. The result is $-\frac{5}{8}$. What is the rational number?

Practising

2. The mean of five numbers is -5. The sum of the positive numbers in the set is 37 greater than the sum of the negative numbers in the set. What could the numbers be?

3. The number of kilometres in the perimeter of this park is 8 greater than the number of square kilometres in its area. What is the width? Use a calculator to help.

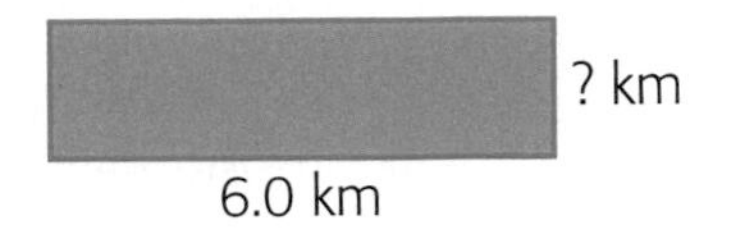

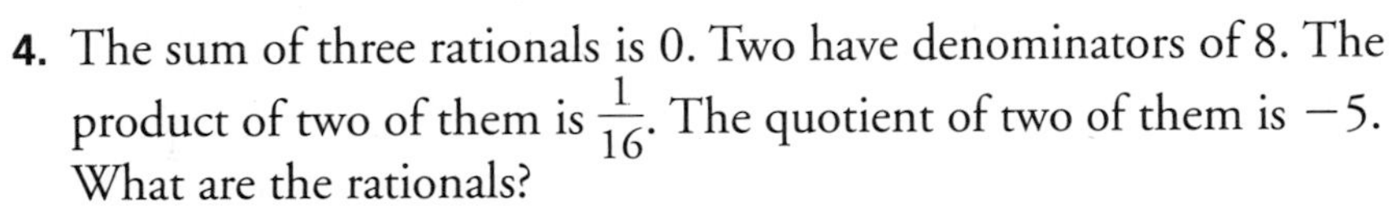

4. The sum of three rationals is 0. Two have denominators of 8. The product of two of them is $\frac{1}{16}$. The quotient of two of them is -5. What are the rationals?

5. The product of two opposites is -1.8225. What are the numbers? Use a calculator to help you guess and test.

6. The sum of five numbers is $-\frac{1}{4}$. The numbers include two pairs of opposites. The quotient of two values is 2. The quotient of two different values is $-\frac{3}{4}$. What are the values?

7. A share price increased in value one day, doubled that increase the next day, and then decreased \$0.12 in value the following day. If the total change was \$0.33, by how much did the share go up the first day?

8. A rational number with a denominator of 9 is divided by $\left(-\frac{2}{3}\right)$. The result is multiplied by $\frac{4}{5}$ and then $-\frac{5}{6}$ is added. The final value is $\frac{1}{10}$. What was the original rational?

9. Two rational numbers are added. The sum is $\frac{1}{4}$ more than the product. What are the rational numbers?

Closing

10. Why is guess and test a good strategy to use for questions like question 3? Why might you also work backward?

Extending

11. Create a problem involving rational numbers that would be reasonable to solve with a guess-and-test strategy. Then, solve it using that strategy.

Math GAME

Compare Six

Number of players: 2 to 4

YOU WILL NEED

- Rational Number Cards

How to play

1. Choose two rational number cards.
2. Decide whether and in what order to add, subtract, multiply, or divide the numbers to get the greatest value possible.
3. The player with the greatest value wins a point. In the event of a tie, no points are scored.
4. The first player to reach 6 points wins.

Sample Turn

Thomas's Draw

I've drawn $\frac{1}{4}$ and $-\frac{2}{3}$.

If I add, multiply, or divide, the answer is negative. I'll subtract $-\frac{2}{3}$ from $\frac{1}{4}$.

$$\begin{aligned}\frac{1}{4} - \left(-\frac{2}{3}\right) &= \frac{3}{12} + \frac{8}{12} \\ &= \frac{11}{12}\end{aligned}$$

Larissa's Draw

I've drawn $\frac{3}{5}$ and $-\frac{2}{5}$. If I multiply or divide, the answer is negative. If I add, it's only $\frac{1}{5}$, but if I subtract, I get 1; I win the point!

CHAPTER 1

Chapter Self-Test

1. **Multiple choice.** Which value is equivalent to $\frac{-4}{-5}$?

   A. $\frac{-4}{5}$ **B.** $-\frac{4}{5}$ **C.** $\frac{4}{-5}$ **D.** $\frac{4}{5}$

2. **Multiple choice.** Which set of numbers is arranged in order from least to greatest? Explain.

   A. $-\frac{11}{5}, \frac{-11}{-5}, -2\frac{2}{5}$ **C.** $-2\frac{2}{5}, -\frac{11}{5}, \frac{-11}{-5}$

   B. $\frac{-11}{-5}, -\frac{11}{5}, -2\frac{2}{5}$ **D.** $-2\frac{2}{5}, \frac{-11}{-5}, -\frac{11}{5}$

3. Which value is farther from zero: $-4\frac{1}{3}$ or 4.3? Explain.

4. List three rationals between $-3\frac{1}{4}$ and $-\frac{27}{8}$.

5. Calculate. Show your work.

   a) $\frac{-4}{7} - \left(-2\frac{1}{2}\right)$ d) $\left(-\frac{4}{5}\right)\left(\frac{8}{3}\right)\left(-\frac{5}{6}\right)$

   b) $-2\frac{2}{3} \div \frac{3}{4}$ e) $3.2(-4.1) \div (2 + 3.4) \times 3$

   c) $-3\frac{1}{5} + \left(\frac{-4}{3}\right) + 4.5$ f) $5\frac{1}{3} - \left(2 \times 4\frac{1}{2}\right) + \frac{8}{3} \div 2$

6. The high temperatures, in degrees Celsius, for a city during a five-day period increased or decreased as follows:

   $$+4.2°, +1.7°, -11.7°, -2.3°, +5.2°$$

   a) What was the total increase or decrease from the start of the period until the end?

   b) What was the average daily change in temperature?

7. The height of the water level in a tank dropped by $\frac{1}{4}$. Katia used $\frac{3}{5}$ of what was left. What rational number describes the final height as a fraction of the original height?

8. The following are true about two rational numbers.
   - The product is greater than the quotient.
   - The sum is less than the difference.

   List three things that you know about the numbers and explain how you know those things.

WHAT DO You Think Now?

Revisit What Do You Think? on page 3. How have your answers and explanations changed?

Chapter Review

FREQUENTLY ASKED Questions

Study | *Aid*

- See Lesson 1.5, Examples 1 and 2.
- Try Chapter Review questions 17, 18, and 19.

Q: How do you apply the order of operations when working with rational numbers?

A: You use the same rules as you would use if working with integers or positive fractions or decimals. In order,

- computations in brackets
- multiplication and division from left to right
- addition and subtraction from left to right

For example,

$$\begin{aligned} &-3\left[\frac{1}{3} - \left(-\frac{2}{3}\right)\right] - 5 \div (-2) \\ &= -3(1) - 5 \div (-2) \\ &= -3 - (-2.5) \\ &= -0.5 \end{aligned}$$

Study | *Aid*

- Try Chapter Review question 20.

Q: How can you predict whether the sum, difference, product, or quotient of two rational numbers will be greatest?

A: You have to consider whether the numbers are positive or negative. You also have to consider whether they are between -1 and 1 or not.

For example,

- If you add or subtract a negative, the difference will be greater than the sum.

$$5 - \left(-\frac{1}{2}\right) > 5 + \left(-\frac{1}{2}\right) \text{ since } 5\frac{1}{2} > 4\frac{1}{2}.$$

- If you multiply or divide a negative by a negative fraction between 0 and -1, the product will be less than the quotient.

$$-3\left(-\frac{1}{2}\right) < (-3) \div \left(-\frac{1}{2}\right) \text{ since } \frac{3}{2} < 6.$$

- If you multiply or divide a negative by a negative less than -1, the product will be greater than the quotient.

$$(-3)(-2) > (-3) \div (-2) \text{ since } 6 > \frac{3}{2}.$$

Practice

Lesson 1.1

1. Locate each value on a number line.

   a) -2.6 b) $-\frac{24}{5}$

2. Which rational is between -10 and -9: $\frac{-29}{3}$ or $\frac{-31}{3}$? How do you know?

3. Write each as a quotient of integers.

   a) -4.2 b) $1\frac{4}{5}$ c) $-\frac{3}{8}$

4. Describe a situation that the number $-1\frac{2}{3}$ might represent.

5. What is wrong with this Venn diagram?

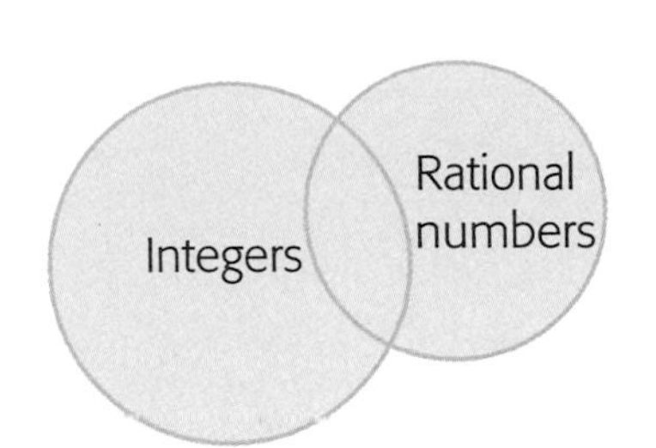

Lesson 1.2

6. Order from least to greatest.

   a) $-5.1, 0.3, \frac{-8}{3}, 1.2, -\frac{1}{5}$ b) $\frac{3}{5}, -\frac{2}{3}, \frac{-8}{9}, \frac{4}{7}, -\frac{1}{4}$

7. List three rational numbers between each pair of rationals.

   a) $-4\frac{1}{3}$ and $-4\frac{3}{4}$ b) -5.01 and -5.006 c) $-\frac{4}{5}$ and $-\frac{2}{3}$

8. Explain why $-\frac{1}{2} > -\frac{8}{2}$ even though $1 < 8$.

Lesson 1.3

9. Ann started gym $\frac{2}{3}$ h before lunch. Her art class began an hour and a half after lunch. Lunch lasted $\frac{3}{4}$ h. Use a rational expression to tell how many hours before art class her gym class started.

10. Estimate. Show your reasoning.

a) $-3\frac{1}{2} - \left(-8\frac{3}{4}\right)$ **c)** $-3.7 + (-17.1)$

b) $\frac{8}{3} + \left(-\frac{17}{5}\right)$ **d)** $\frac{2}{3} + \left(-\frac{16}{5}\right)$

11. Calculate the sums and differences in question 10. Show your work.

12. A share price increased by \$0.05 one day, decreased by \$0.02 the next day, and decreased again by \$0.01 the following day. What was the total change?

13. The sum of two rational numbers is $-\frac{1}{2}$. The difference is $-\frac{11}{10}$. What are the two rational numbers?

Lesson 1.4

14. Calculate. Show your work.

a) $-\frac{5}{2}\left(-\frac{4}{5}\right)$ **c)** $\left(1\frac{2}{3}\right)\left(-\frac{4}{9}\right)$ **e)** $\left(-\frac{6}{5}\right) \div \left(-\frac{2}{3}\right)$

b) $\frac{2}{3}\left(-\frac{6}{5}\right)\left(-\frac{5}{3}\right)$ **d)** $\frac{2}{7} \div \left(-\frac{9}{14}\right)$ **f)** $(-3) \div \left(-1\frac{2}{3}\right)$

15. One share lost \$0.25. Another share lost \$0.03. What is the ratio of the losses? Write the ratio as a rational number.

16. The quotient of two rationals is -1.5. The product is $-\frac{3}{32}$.

a) What are the rationals?

b) How do you know there has to be another possible answer?

Lesson 1.5

17. Calculate. Show your work.

a) $\frac{2}{5} \div \left(\frac{-3}{5} + \frac{1}{10}\right)$ **c)** $\left(\frac{1}{8} + \frac{-2}{3}\right) \times \frac{12}{13}$

b) $-\frac{5}{6} + \left(-\frac{2}{3}\right) \div \frac{3}{4}$ **d)** $-1\frac{1}{2} + \frac{-1}{-2} - \left(-\frac{3}{5}\right)$

18. Aaron calculated $-6.2 \div (3.1 + 1.9) \times (-2)$ as -9.8. Is this correct? Explain.

19. Use a calculator to determine how much less $\left(-4 + \frac{3}{5}\right) \div \frac{2}{3}$ is than $\left(-4 + \frac{3}{5}\right) \times \frac{2}{3}$.

Lesson 1.6

20. Determine two rational numbers a and b so that
$a \times b > a \div b > a - b > a + b$.

Lesson 1.7

21. The sum of three numbers is 1. One number is (-2) times another. The quotient of another pair of the numbers is 4. What are the numbers? Explain.

Chapter Task

Creating a Game

To review for a test, Jia-Wen and her friends are creating a game for players who know rational numbers. They decide to use a card game where you keep cards that match. They want a game with at least 24 cards.

? What cards can you create for a game like Jia-Wen's?

A. Why might these cards match?

A number between $-\frac{4}{5}$ and $-\frac{3}{4}$	-0.78

B. What card might match this card? Explain why it matches.

These numbers are in order: $-2\frac{1}{3}$, $-\frac{5}{3}$, ■, -1.2

C. What pair of cards might you make to review equivalence of rational numbers? Explain why your pair works.

D. What pair of cards might you make to review creating situations involving rational numbers?

E. What pairs of cards might you use to compare the results of adding and subtracting two rationals?

F. What pairs of cards might you use to compare the results of multiplying and dividing two rationals?

G. What pairs of cards might you use to review order of operations involving calculations with rationals?

H. Create the cards and rules for a game like Jia-Wen's.

Task | ***Checklist***

- ✔ Did you check to make sure that you considered different ideas about rational numbers?
- ✔ Did you use some "creative" matches?
- ✔ Did you explain your rules clearly?
- ✔ Did you explain why your matches make sense?

Chapter

2

Powers, Exponents, and Square Roots

GOALS

You will be able to

- represent repeated multiplication using powers
- simplify expressions involving powers
- solve problems involving powers
- communicate about calculations involving powers
- calculate and estimate square roots of positive rational numbers

How many small cubes are in each large cube?

CHAPTER 2

Getting Started

YOU WILL NEED
- centimetre cubes

Product Display

Nicole works part time at an electronics store. She is setting up a display of video game consoles. Each console is in a cube-shaped box with a side length of 60 cm. The display must be in the shape of a cube.

? What could be the volume of the display?

A. Arrange some centimetre cubes to make a larger cube.

B. Suppose each cube represents one box in the display. What are the dimensions of your display?

C. How can you calculate the floor area of your display?

D. How can you calculate the volume of your display?

E. What is the volume of your display?

F. Repeat parts A to E using two other arrangements of centimetre cubes.

WHAT DO You Think?

Decide whether you agree or disagree with each statement. Explain your decision.

1. A square can have an area of 8.41 cm^2.
2. A cube can have a side length, area of a face, and volume with the same numerical value.

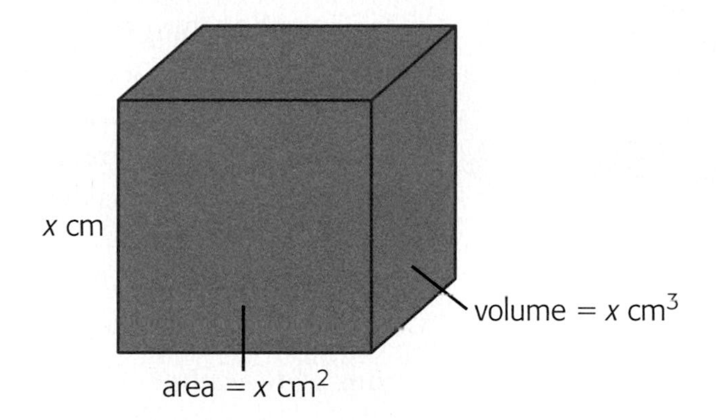

3. There is one method you can use to factor a number.

4. When you square a number, the result is just as likely to be less than the original number as it is greater.

2.1 Modelling Squares and Cubes

YOU WILL NEED

- a calculator
- centimetre cubes
- centimetre grid paper

power

a numerical expression that shows repeated multiplication; e.g., the power 2^3 is a shorter way of writing $2 \times 2 \times 2$. It is read as "two to the third" or "two cubed"—2 is the **base** and 3 is the **exponent**. We say 2 has the exponent 3.

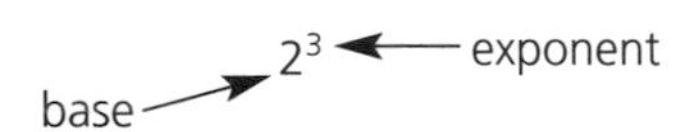

GOAL

Represent perfect squares and perfect cubes using models.

INVESTIGATE the Math

Yvonne is making a gift for her sister's Naming Ceremony. It will be a cube with a square photo on each face. The sides of the photos will be natural number centimetre lengths. She wants the cube to be as large as possible, but she is mailing it and it cannot be more than 5000 cm^3 in volume.

? What should be the dimensions of the cube?

A. Complete the second and third rows in the table expressing each side length, face area, and volume as a **power**.

Side Length of Cube, s (cm)	Side Length as a Power, s^1	Area of Face of Cube, $s \times s$ (cm^2)	Area of Face as a Power, s^2	Volume of Cube, $s \times s \times s$ (cm^3)	Volume of Cube as a Power, s^3
2	2^1	$2 \times 2 = 4$	2^2	$2 \times 2 \times 2 = 8$	2^3
4				$4 \times 4 \times 4 = 64$	4^3
8		$8 \times 8 = 64$			

B. Continue to complete rows for other side lengths as necessary.

C. What should be the side length of Yvonne's cube? Explain how you know.

base

the number used as a factor in a power

exponent

the number used to express the number of factors in a power

Reflecting

D. You can represent the value 64 with two different models, s^2 and s^3. How is the model of the form s^2 different from the model of the form s^3?

E. How do you know that 225 can represent the area of one of the square faces of a cube with natural number centimetre lengths, but not the volume?

F. How do you know that 343 can represent the volume of a cube like Yvonne's, but not the area of one face?

WORK WITH the Math

EXAMPLE 1 | Modelling square powers

A square wall tile has an area of 100 cm^2. Represent the area of this tile as a geometric model and as a power.

Bay's Solution

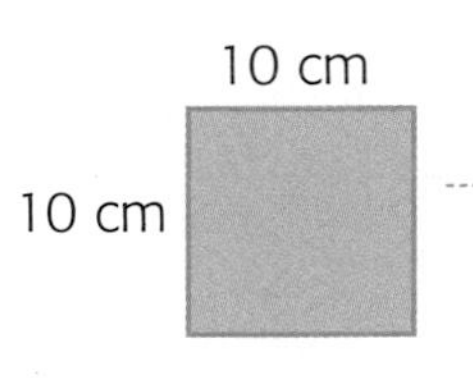

The tile is square, so the geometric model must be square too. Since $100 = 10 \times 10$, each side of the square must be 10 cm.

$100 = 10^2$

100 is a **perfect square**, so I wrote it as a power using a base of 10 and an exponent of 2.

perfect square
the product of a natural number multiplied by itself; e.g., 49 is a perfect square because $7 \times 7 = 49$.

EXAMPLE 2 | Modelling cube powers

A softball comes in a cube-shaped box with a volume of 1728 cm^3. Represent the volume of this box as a geometric model and as a power.

Amanda's Solution

The box is a cube.

Each side of the box must have the same length and the base must be a square. I knew the cube would be more than 10 cm on a side, because 1728 is more than $10^3 = 1000$.

$12 \times 12 \times 12 = 1728$

I tried 12. Since the volume is even, I knew the side length must also be even.

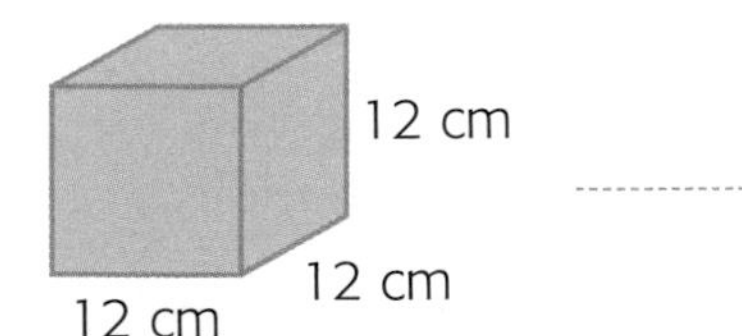

The geometric model is a cube that looks like this.

$1728 = 12^3$

1728 is a **perfect cube**, so I wrote it as a power using a base of 12 and an exponent of 3.

perfect cube
the product of a natural number multiplied by itself twice; e.g., 343 is a perfect cube because $7 \times 7 \times 7 = 343$.

In Summary

Key Idea

- You can represent some powers using a geometric model. For example, you can represent a perfect square as the area of a square with natural-number-length sides and a perfect cube as the volume of a cube with natural-number-length sides.

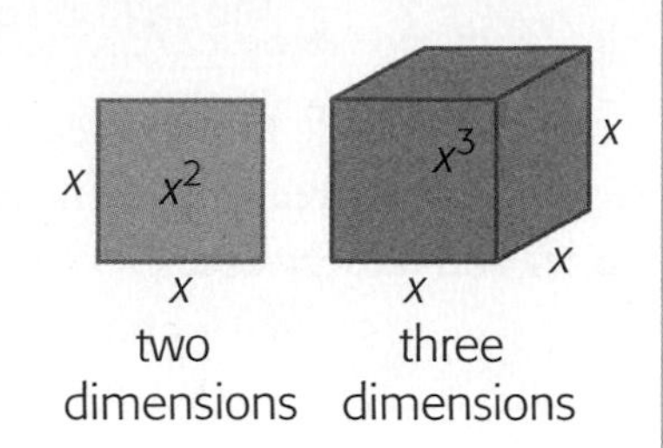

Need to Know

- A perfect square can be written as a power: $n^2 = n \times n$.
- A perfect cube can be written as a power: $n^3 = n \times n \times n$.

Checking

1. Represent each geometric model as a power.

a) 

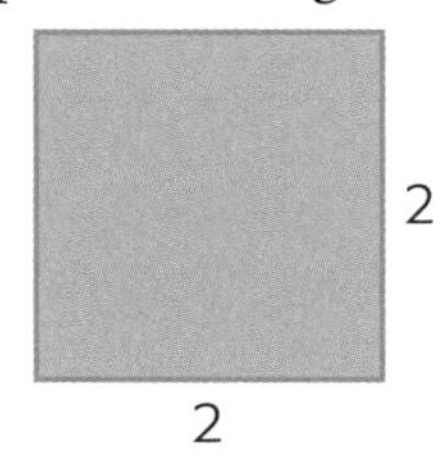

b)

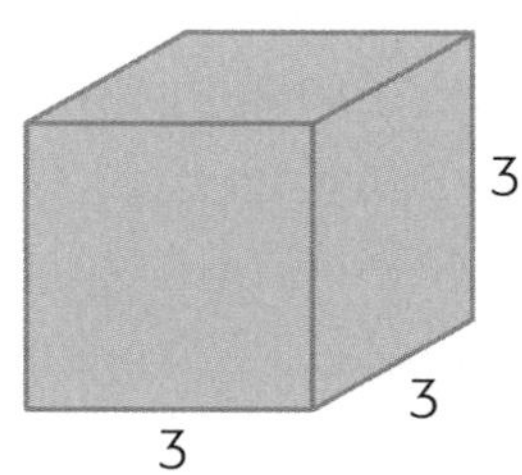

2. a) Write $6 \times 6 \times 6$ as a power. **b)** Write 11×11 as a power.

3. a) Determine the side length of a square with an area of 81 m^2.
b) Determine the side length of a cube with a volume of 8 cm^3.

Practising

4. Determine the value of ■.

a) $4 \times 4 = ■^2$ **c)** $■^2 = 100$ **e)** $7^2 = ■$
b) $3 \times 3 \times 3 = ■^3$ **d)** $■^3 = 27$ **f)** $5^3 = ■$

5. A square floor mat has a side length of 5 m. Write the area of the mat as a power.

6. The side length of a cube is 12 cm. Determine the following:
a) the area of one face **b)** the **surface area** **c)** the volume

7. Joga is making palak paneer. He used a large cube of cheese that had a volume of 3375 cm^3.
a) Sketch a model of the cheese. Label the side lengths.
b) Joga sliced the cheese into 3 cm cubes. How many cubes did he have?

8. How many more perfect squares than perfect cubes are there between 1 and 1000?

9. **Multiple choice.** A square floor mat has a side length of 22 m. What is the area of the mat as a power?
   A. 222 m^2 **B.** 22^3 m^3 **C.** 22^2 m^2 **D.** 2^{22} m^2

10. **Multiple choice.** Determine the area of one face of a cube with a side length of 14 cm.
    A. 196 cm^2 **B.** 196 cm^3 **C.** 14 cm^2 **D.** 2744 cm^3

11. **Multiple choice.** Determine the volume of a cube with a side length of 14 cm.
    A. 196 cm^2 **B.** 196 cm^3 **C.** 14 cm^2 **D.** 2744 cm^3

12. Sketch geometric models for 4^2 and 4^3. How are the models alike and different?

13. Austin says that he can draw a geometric model for any power of 2. Do you agree or disagree with him? Justify your decision.

14. Two perfect squares have a difference of 169.
    a) How far apart are the square roots?
    b) How far apart are the cubes of the values in part a)?

15. Which numbers have the same values as their square and their cube?

16. Nasri is creating a mosaic using tiles for art class. He has a frame that is 60 cm by 60 cm and divided into four sections. The frame's border is 2 cm wide. He has many tiles with these dimensions: 1 cm by 1 cm, 2 cm by 2 cm, 3 cm by 3 cm, 5 cm by 5 cm, and 10 cm by 10 cm. Sketch some designs for Nasri's mosaic. Use graph paper to help you.

Closing

17. How could you prove to someone that there are more perfect squares than perfect cubes in the numbers between 100 and 200?

Extending

18. Nicole and her friend Hélène are preparing *sucre à la crème*. They use plates that are 20 cm by 30 cm and cut the treats into 2 cm cubes. They will sell 10 cubes for $1.00. They hope to raise about $50. How many plates will Nicole and Hélène need?

19. Sean and Damien bought Patrick an MP3 player for his birthday. They have a sheet of wrapping paper that is 30 cm by 60 cm. Can they wrap the box without cutting the paper? Sketch how you know.

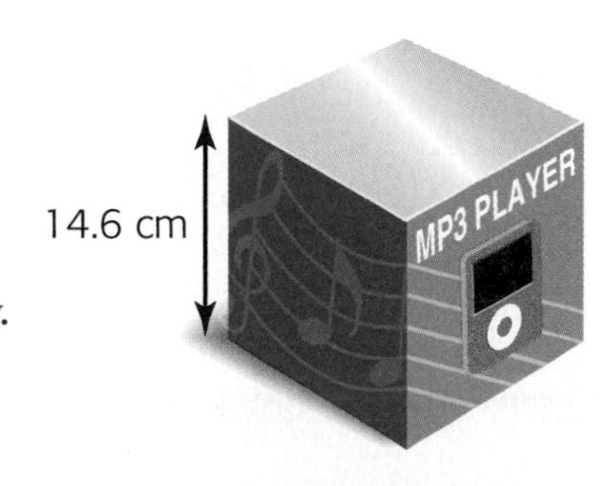

20. You have seen that 64 is a perfect square and a perfect cube. Determine two other numbers with this property.

2.2 Expressing a Number as a Power

GOAL

Use powers to represent repeated multiplication.

YOU WILL NEED

- a calculator

LEARN ABOUT the Math

Yvonne uses square sticky notes to leave messages for her mom. She decides to make a cube-shaped holder for the notes in woodworking class. She wants the holder to hold eight packs of notes. Each sticky-note pack is a cube and each sticky note is 8 cm wide.

? What should the capacity of the container be?

EXAMPLE 1 | Representing volume using a power

Yvonne's Solution

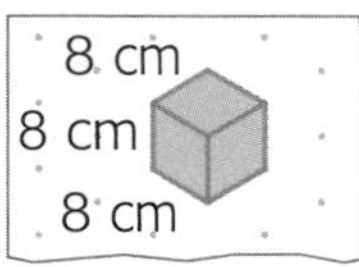

Each sticky-note pack is a perfect cube; each pack has dimensions 8 cm by 8 cm by 8 cm.

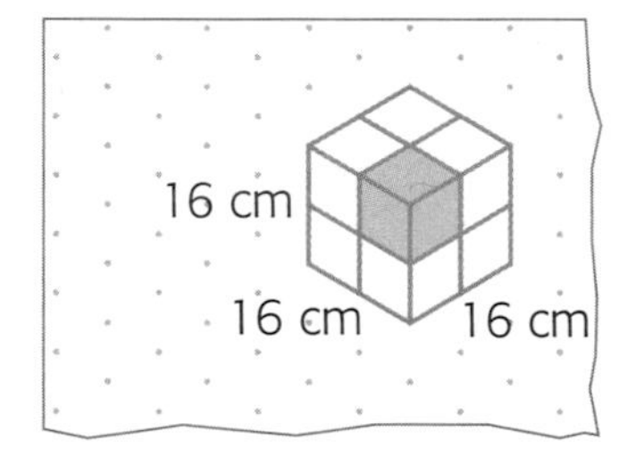

I want the holder to be in the shape of a cube and I want it to hold eight packs. I must make the large cube two packs wide, two packs high, and two packs long. The larger cube is 16 cm by 16 cm by 16 cm.

The capacity is
$16 \times 16 \times 16 = 4096$ cm^3.
The capacity of the container is 16^3 cm^3.

I described the capacity of my holder with a power. The side length is the base of the power and the number of dimensions is the exponent.

Reflecting

A. How can Yvonne use the fact that $4^3 = 64$ to calculate 16^3?

B. Why can you use powers to describe $4 \times 4 \times 4$, but not to describe $2 \times 3 \times 4$?

WORK WITH the Math

EXAMPLE 2 | Evaluating a power

Evaluate $\left(-\frac{1}{2}\right)^2$ and $-\left(\frac{1}{2}\right)^2$.

Derek's Solution

$$\left(-\frac{1}{2}\right)^2 = \left(-\frac{1}{2}\right) \times \left(-\frac{1}{2}\right)$$

I wrote the power as a repeated multiplication. I had to repeat everything inside the brackets.

$$-\left(\frac{1}{2}\right)^2 = \frac{1}{4}$$

I multiplied from left to right.

$$-\left(\frac{1}{2}\right)^2 = (-1)\left(\frac{1}{2}\right)^2$$
$$= (-1) \times \left(\frac{1}{2}\right) \times \left(\frac{1}{2}\right)$$
$$= \left(-\frac{1}{2}\right) \times \left(\frac{1}{2}\right)$$
$$-\left(\frac{1}{2}\right)^2 = -\frac{1}{4}$$

I wrote the power as a repeated multiplication. I didn't repeat the minus sign with each $\frac{1}{2}$, because it wasn't in brackets.

I multiplied from left to right.

The two powers represent different numbers.

Communication *Tip*

A base without an exponent is understood to have an exponent of 1; so, $5 = 5^1$.

EXAMPLE 3 | Evaluating a power by using a pattern

Evaluate 3^0, 5^0, $(-1)^0$, and 0^0.

Nicole's Solution

$3^3 = 3 \times 3 \times 3 = 27$
$3^2 \quad = 3 \times 3 = 9 \quad (27 \div 3)$
$3^1 \quad = 3 \quad (9 \div 3)$
$3^0 \quad = 1 \quad (3 \div 3)$
I expect that $3^0 = 3^1 \div 3 = 1$.

I used a pattern. I started with an exponent of 3. I decreased the exponent by 1. I noticed that when the exponent decreases by 1, the value of the power is divided by 3.

$5^3 = 5 \times 5 \times 5 = 125$
$5^2 \quad = 5 \times 5 = 25 \quad (125 \div 5)$
$5^1 \quad = 5 \quad (25 \div 5)$
$5^0 \quad = 1 \quad (5 \div 5)$

I did the same with 5^0. The result was the same.

$$(-1)^3 = (-1)(-1)(-1) = -1$$
$$(-1)^2 = (-1)(-1) = 1 \quad (-1 \div -1)$$
$$(-1)^1 = -1 \quad (1 \div -1)$$
$$(-1)^0 = 1 \quad (-1 \div -1)$$

I got the same result with $(-1)^0$, although in this case, the value of the power just flipped between -1 and 1.

$$0^3 = 0 \times 0 \times 0 = 0$$
$$0^2 = 0 \times 0 = ? \quad (0 \div 0)$$

0^0 is undefined.

I tried the same pattern with 0^0 but it didn't work this time. I can't write these expressions as the previous value divided by 0, because division by 0 is undefined, not 0. I can't use the pattern to determine the value of 0^0.

In Summary

Key Idea

- Powers are used to represent repeated multiplication. The base represents the number being multiplied and the exponent, when it is a whole number, tells how many times the base appears. For example, $7^6 = 7 \times 7 \times 7 \times 7 \times 7 \times 7$ and $\left(\frac{6}{7}\right)^3 = \left(\frac{6}{7}\right)\left(\frac{6}{7}\right)\left(\frac{6}{7}\right)$

Need to Know

- Any power with a nonzero base and an exponent of 0 is equal to 1; that is, $x^0 = 1, x \neq 0$.
- If there are no brackets in a power, the exponent applies only to its positive base: $-3^4 = (-1)(3 \times 3 \times 3 \times 3) = -81$. -3^4 is the opposite of 3^4, just as -3 is the opposite of 3.
- A power has a negative base when the base is negative and is enclosed in brackets. For example, $(-3)^4 = (-3)(-3)(-3)(-3) = 81$.

Checking

1. Represent each repeated multiplication as a power.

a) $5 \times 5 \times 5 \times 5 \times 5 \times 5$

b) $(3.2 \times 3.2) \times (3.2 \times 3.2)$

c) $(-4)(-4)(-4)$

d) $-(7)(7)(7)(7)(7)$

e) $\left(\frac{5}{7}\right)\left(\frac{5}{7}\right)\left(\frac{5}{7}\right)$

f) $\left(\frac{3}{4}\right)\left(\frac{3}{4}\right)\left(\frac{3}{4}\right)\left(\frac{3}{4}\right)\left(\frac{3}{4}\right)$

Practising

2. Represent each repeated multiplication as a power.

a) $4 \times 4 \times 4 \times 4 \times 4 \times 4$

b) $(6 \times 6) \times (6 \times 6)$

c) $(-5.4)(-5.4)(-5.4)$

d) $-(8)(8)(8)(8)(8)$

e) $\left(\frac{8}{9}\right)\left(\frac{8}{9}\right)\left(\frac{8}{9}\right)\left(\frac{8}{9}\right)$

f) $\left(\frac{2}{3}\right)\left(\frac{2}{3}\right)\left(\frac{2}{3}\right)\left(\frac{2}{3}\right)$

3. Represent each power using repeated multiplication.
a) 2^4 **b)** $(-2)^4$ **c)** -2^4 **d)** $-(-2)^4$

4. Evaluate each power.
a) -7^3 **c)** $(-3)^4$ **e)** -12.4^2
b) $(-7)^3$ **d)** -3^4 **f)** $(-12)^2$

5. Complete the table.

	Power	Base	Exponent	Repeated Multiplication	Value in Standard Form
a)	9^4				6561
b)		5		$(5)(5)(5)$	
c)		-2	5		
d)				$-(6)(6)(6)$	
e)	-4^6				

6. Multiple choice. Which power does not represent 256?
A. 2^8 **B.** 4^4 **C.** 8^3 **D.** 16^2

7. Multiple choice. Which statement is true?
A. $3.1^3 = 3.1 \times 3.1 \times 3.1$ **C.** $-3^3 = (3)(3)(3)$
B. $(-1)^6 = -1$ **D.** $-6^2 = 36$

8. Multiple choice. Evaluate $(-5)^4$.
A. -625 **B.** 25 **C.** 625 **D.** -54

9. Shelby says that for any power with a positive integer base, when the base and exponent are switched, the greater power is always the one with the greater base. Do you agree or disagree? Justify your decision.

10. If a power has a negative integer base, can you predict whether the power has a positive or negative value? Explain.

11. Arrange in order from least to greatest.

$$-2^4, (-2)^4, -(-2^2), (-1)^{100}, (-1)^{31}$$

12. Ihor read that, in Japan, some farmers grow watermelons inside cubes so the melons grow in the shape of a cube. He bought a sheet of special plastic that is 45.0 cm by 70.0 cm.
a) Determine the area of the sheet of plastic.
b) The surface area of a cube is $6s^2$, where s is the length of one side. Determine the dimensions of the side length of the largest plastic cube Ihor can build.

13. a) Calculate 2^4, 3^4, 4^4, and 5^4.

b) Calculate 2^5, 3^5, 4^5, and 5^5.

c) The fourth power of one number is 13 greater than the fifth power of another. What are the numbers?

d) How could you have predicted that the bases in part c) would be fairly small?

14. a) Complete the pattern: $1^1 = 1$, $1^2 = 1 \times 1 = ■$, $1^3 = ■$, $1^4 = ■$, $1^5 = ■$

b) Use the pattern to evaluate 1^x, where x is any whole number.

15. a) Order the following from least to greatest: 6^4, 6^3, 6^2, 6^0, 6^1.

b) Would the order change if you replaced 6 with 5, -5, or 0?

16. Order the following from least to greatest: 2^3, 3^2, 3^4, 4^3, 3^5, 5^3.

17. Represent each repeated multiplication as a power.

a) $s \times s \times s \times s$

b) $(-y)(-y)$

c) $(t \times t) \times (t \times t)$

d) $-(p)(p)(p)$

18. Marilyn has 49 pennies, 32 nickels, 9 dimes, 25 quarters, 8 loonies, and 16 toonies in a jar.

a) Write a power to represent the number of each type of coin.

b) Write an equation using the powers in part a) to represent the total number of coins.

Closing

19. Derek says $4^5 > 5^4$, since a power with a higher exponent is always greater. Do you agree? Explain.

Extending

20. a) Evaluate $(-2)^3(-2)^4$, $(-2)^2(-2)^6$, and $(-2)(-2)^5$.

b) Express each answer in part a) as a power with a base of (-2).

c) Look for a pattern. How could you get the power in part b) just by looking at the question in part a)?

21. Sue wanted to invite all 128 families of the Grade 9 class at her school to the Math Olympics, an evening of math games and contests. She didn't have time to call every family herself, so she decided to call two families and ask each person she called to call two more families, and so on.

a) Determine how many rounds of calls will be needed.

b) Represent the number of families as a power.

Math GAME

Super Powers

Number of players: 2 to 4

YOU WILL NEED

- a deck of 40 cards (no face cards)
- a calculator

How to Play

1. On each turn, draw two cards from the deck.
2. Form a power with your cards, using one number as the base and one number as the exponent.
3. Calculate the value of your power. Use a calculator to check your answer.

The value of the cards: 1 2 3 4 5 6 7 8 9 10

4. The player with the greater power on each turn wins one point.
5. Play until one player has 10 points.

Shelby's Draw

I drew these two cards.

I could have chosen 9^3 as a power but I chose 3^9 instead because it was greater.
$3^9 = 3 \times 3 \times 3 \times 3 \times 3 \times 3 \times 3 \times 3 \times 3 = 19\ 683$

Yvonne's Draw

I drew these two cards.

I chose 6^7.
$6^7 = 6 \times 6 \times 6 \times 6 \times 6 \times 6 \times 6$
$= 279\ 936$
My power is greater, so I get the point.

2.3 Expressing a Number in Many Ways

YOU WILL NEED

- a calculator

GOAL

Represent a number in many ways using powers.

EXPLORE the Math

Amanda and Yvonne are playing a game. They have five numbers and they want to see who can write a number the most ways using the sums, differences, products, or quotients of powers. The only rule is that they cannot use powers with an exponent of 0 or 1.

Amanda predicts you can write a greater number in more ways than a lesser number. Yvonne doesn't agree.

$$54 = 5^2 + 5^2 + 2^2$$
$$54 = 9^2 - 3^3$$
$$54 = 6^3 \div 2^2$$
$$54 = 5^2 \times 3^2 - 3^3 - 12^2$$

? How could you decide whether Amanda is right or wrong?

2.4 Multiplying and Dividing Powers

GOAL

Simplify products and quotients of powers with the same base.

YOU WILL NEED

- a calculator

INVESTIGATE the Math

Derek wants to determine the value of this expression: $(5^4)(5^4) \div (5^2)^3$. He wonders if he can write it so that it will be easier to calculate the value.

? How can Derek simplify this expression?

A. Rewrite Derek's expression as a fraction, with powers in both the numerator and denominator.

B. Write the numerator using repeated multiplication.

C. Express the numerator as a single power. How does this new power relate to the original powers in the numerator?

D. Write the denominator using repeated multiplication.

E. Express the denominator as a single power. How does this new power relate to the original powers in the denominator?

F. Write the quotient as a single power. How does this new power relate to the other two?

G. How could Derek have simplified his original expression?

Reflecting

H. Why does it make sense that sometimes you add, sometimes you subtract, and sometimes you multiply exponents to simplify expressions involving powers?

I. In each case, write a rule you can use to simplify
- the product of two powers with the same base
- the quotient of one power and another with the same base
- a power raised to an exponent

J. Why do the bases need to be the same for some of the exponent rules you wrote in part I to work?

WORK WITH the Math

EXAMPLE 1 Simplifying numerical expressions using exponent laws

Simplify. **a)** $(3^2)(3^4)$ **b)** $6^5 \div 6^3$ **c)** $(4^2)^5$

Bay's Solution

a) $(3^2)(3^4) = 3^{2+4}$
$= 3^6$

The powers are to be multiplied, and their bases are the same.
I added the exponents.

b) $6^5 \div 6^3 = 6^{5-3}$
$= 6^2$

The powers are to be divided, and their bases are the same.
I subtracted the exponents.

c) $(4^2)^5 = 4^{2\times5}$
$= 4^{10}$

The power is to be raised to an exponent.
I multiplied the exponents.

EXAMPLE 2 Simplifying algebraic expressions using exponent laws

Simplify. **a)** $(x^6)(x^5)$ **b)** $x^7 \div x^2$ **c)** $(x^5)^4$

Derek's Solution

a) $(x^6)(x^5) = x^{6+5}$
$= x^{11}$

The powers are to be multiplied, and their bases are the same.
I added the exponents.

b) $x^7 \div x^2 = x^{7-2}$
$= x^5$

The powers are to be divided, and the bases are the same.
I subtracted the exponents.

c) $(x^5)^4 = x^{5\times4}$
$= x^{20}$

The power is to be raised to an exponent.
I multiplied the exponents.

EXAMPLE 3 Simplifying using several exponent laws

Simplify. **a)** $(-2)^7(-2)^3 \div [(-2)^2]^3$ **b)** $\frac{(y^3)^5}{(y)(y^4)}$

Shelby's Solution

$(-2)^7(-2)^3 \div [(-2)^2]^3 = (-2)^{7+3} \div [(-2)^2]^3$
$= (-2)^{10} \div [(-2)^2]^3$

I added the exponents of the powers that were multiplied.

$$= (-2)^{10} \div (-2)^{2\times 3}$$
$$= (-2)^{10} \div (-2)^{6}$$

I multiplied the exponents of the power in the divisor.

$$= (-2)^{10-6}$$
$$= (-2)^{4}$$

I subtracted the exponent of the divisor.

$$(-2)^7(-2)^3 \div [(-2)^2]^3 = (-2)^4 \text{ or } 16$$

b) $$\frac{(y^3)^5}{(y)(y^4)} = \frac{y^{3\times 5}}{y^{1+4}}$$

I multiplied the exponents of the power in the numerator and added the exponents of the powers in the denominator.

$$= \frac{y^{15}}{y^{5}}$$

$$= y^{15-5}$$
$$= y^{10}$$

I subtracted the exponent of the divisor.

EXAMPLE 4 Representing a power as an equivalent power

Austin and Shelby want to spread the news about school picture day. Austin will call two people and ask each one to call two more people, and so on. Shelby will call four people and ask each one to call four more people, and so on. Shelby says, with her plan, the same number of people would be called on the fourth round of calls as on the eighth round of calls with Austin's plan. Is Shelby right?

Austin's Solution: Representing 2^8 as a power with a base of 4

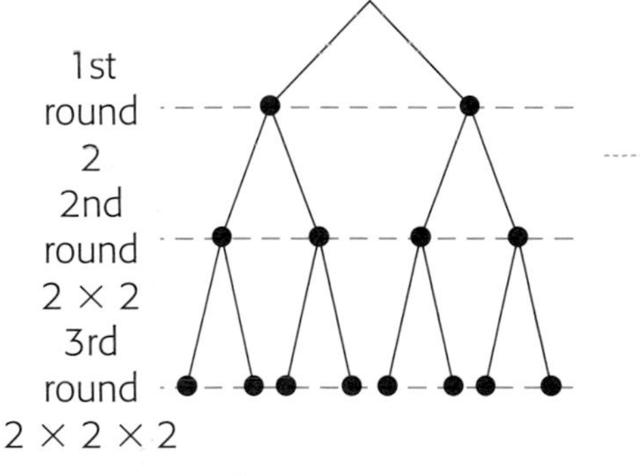

I drew a diagram of my plan. The number of people called doubles with each round. So, 2^1 people will be called in round 1, 2^2 people in round 2, and 2^3 people in round 3.

In round 8, 2^8 people will be called using my plan.

To represent the number of calls in round 8 as a power, I think the base should be 2 and the exponent should be the number of the round.

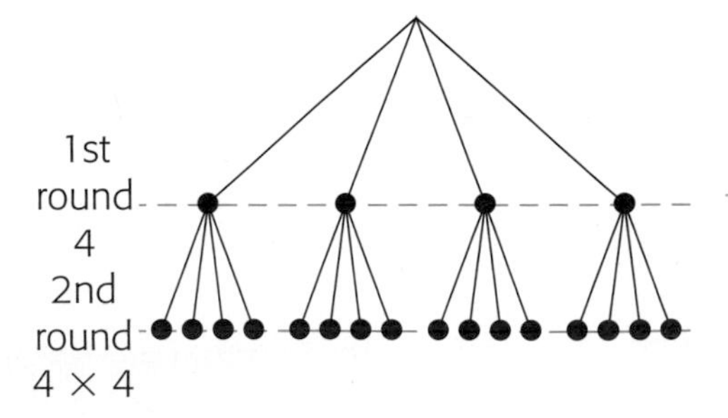

I drew a diagram of the first two rounds of Shelby's plan. The number of people called is multiplied by 4 with each round. So, 4^1 people will be called in round 1, 4^2 people in round 2, and so on.

In round 4, 4^4 people will be called using Shelby's plan.

$$2^8 = (2 \times 2) \times (2 \times 2) \times (2 \times 2) \times (2 \times 2)$$
$$= (2^2)(2^2)(2^2)(2^2)$$
$$= (2^2)^4$$
$$= 4^4$$

Shelby is right.

To compare the number of people called under my plan to Shelby's plan, I paired the 2s and wrote each pair as 2^2, which is equal to 4. I knew I had four 4s multiplied together. After round 8, 4^4 people would be called under my plan.

In Summary

Key Ideas

- **Exponent law for products**
  To simplify the product of two powers with the same base, keep the base the same and add the exponents.

  $(a^m)(a^n) = a^{m+n}$; for example, $(2^2)(2^3) = 2^{2+3} = 2^5$.

- **Exponent law for quotients**
  To simplify the quotient of two powers with the same base, keep the base the same and subtract the exponents.

  $(a^m) \div (a^n) = a^{m-n} (a \neq 0)$; for example, $(2^5) \div (2^3) = 2^{5-3} = 2^2$.

- **Exponent law for a power of a power**
  To raise a power to an exponent, keep the base the same and multiply the exponents. $(a^m)^n = a^{mn}$; for example, $(4^2)^3 = 4^{2 \times 3} = 4^6$.

Need to Know

- The exponent laws only work when the powers have the same base; for example, you can't multiply $(3^2)(5^2)$ using the exponent law for powers.

Checking

1. Simplify.

a) $(9^2)(9^7)$

b) $7^2 \times 7^5 \times 7$

c) $\frac{2^6}{2^5}$

d) $\frac{(5^4)^2}{5^8}$

e) $\frac{(11^8)^5}{11^9}$

f) $(8^8)(8^3) \div (8^2)^2(8^2)$

2. Express each number as a power with a different base.

a) 16 **b)** 4^3 **c)** 9^4

3. Simplify.

a) $(x^4)(x^6)$ **b)** $a^8 \div a^6$ **c)** $(m^3)^4$

Practising

4. Express each as a power with a single exponent.

a) $(10^6)(10^7)$
b) $(3^4)^2(3^3)$
c) $\frac{12^5}{12^2}$
d) $(2^3)^3 \div 2^4$
e) $(6^3)^5 \div (6^2)^4$
f) $\frac{(5^7)(5^5)}{(5^4)^2(5^2)}$

5. Evaluate.

a) $(-2)^3(-2)^2$
b) $(-1)^4(-1)^7$
c) $\frac{(-11)^7}{(-11)^5}$
d) $\frac{[(-8)^2]^3}{(-8)^5}$
e) $\frac{[(-3^{10})]^2}{[(-3)^8]^2}$
f) $\frac{(-6)^9(-6)^9}{[(-6)^3]^3(-6)^3}$

6. Determine the exponent that makes each statement true.

a) $2^6 = 4^{\blacksquare}$
b) $6^6 = 216^{\blacksquare}$
c) $625^2 = 25^{\blacksquare}$
d) $27^4 = 3^{\blacksquare}$

7. Multiple choice. Which is not equivalent to $(3^3)(3^4)$?

A. 3^{12}
B. 2187
C. 3^7
D. $(3^3)(3^2)(3^2)$

8. Multiple choice. For which exponent is $2^4 = 4^{\blacksquare}$ true?

A. 1
B. 2
C. 3
D. 4

9. Multiple choice. For which exponent is $4^3 = 2^{\blacksquare}$ true?

A. 3
B. 4
C. 5
D. 6

10. Use a numerical example to illustrate each exponent law.

a) $(a^m)(a^n) = a^{m+n}$
b) $a^m \div a^n = a^{m-n}\ (a \neq 0)$
c) $(a^m)^n = a^{mn}$

11. Oksana solved the following question:

$$\begin{aligned}\frac{2^3 \times 2^8}{(2^3)(2^3)^2} &= \frac{2^{24}}{(2^3)(2^6)}\\ &= \frac{2^{24}}{2^9}\\ &= 2^{15}\\ &= 32\,768\end{aligned}$$

When she checked the answer with her calculator she got 4. Identify the mistake Oksana made.

12. Express each as a power with a single exponent.

a) $(x^3)(x^2)$
b) $\frac{y^7}{y^2}$
c) $(s^2)^3(s^5)$
d) $\frac{(p^5)^3}{p^{11}}$

13. Determine if each solution is correct or incorrect. If a solution is incorrect, correct the error and solve.

a) $\dfrac{(3^2)^3(3^4)}{3^7}$
$= \dfrac{(3^6)(3^4)}{3^7}$
$= \dfrac{3^{10}}{3^7}$
$= 3^3$
$= 27$

b) $\dfrac{4^8 \times 4^2}{(4^4)(4^2)^3}$
$= \dfrac{4^{10}}{(4^4)(4^5)}$
$= \dfrac{4^{10}}{4^9}$
$= 4^1$
$= 4$

c) $\dfrac{[(-7)^5]^3(-7)^5}{[(-7)^3]^3(-7)^7}$
$= \dfrac{(-7)^{15}(-7)^5}{(-7)^9(-7)^7}$
$= \dfrac{(-7)^{20}}{(-7)^{15}}$
$= (-7)^5$
$= -16\ 807$

14. a) Simplify $\frac{3^5}{3^5}$ by first writing the powers as products.

b) Simplify $\frac{3^5}{3^5}$ using the exponent law for quotients.

c) Evaluate $\frac{3^5}{3^5}$.

d) How does knowing the exponent laws for quotients help explain why $a^0 = 1$?

e) Discuss whether a^0 would have a similar meaning for any value of a (except 0).

15. How do you know that $10^n \neq 8^n$ if the two powers are whole numbers?

16. Write each power in a simplified form.

a) 4^6 as a power of 2

b) 27^5 as a power of 3

c) 9^6 as a power of (-3)

d) $(-125)^8$ as a power of (-5)

17. Simplify.

a) $(x^4)(x^2)^2$

b) $\dfrac{(m^5)^2}{m^8}$

c) $[(y)(y^2)]^3$

d) $(a^2)^2$

e) $(a^2)(a^2)(a^2)$

f) $\dfrac{(b)(b^5)(b^4)}{b^5}$

Closing

18. Explain why $3^5 \times 3^4 = 3^9$, but $3^5 \times 4^3 \neq 12^8$.

Extending

19. a) Is there a whole number for which $3^{20} = 4^n$? Explain why or why not.

b) Can you write $5^4 \times 125^3$ as a single power? Explain why or why not.

c) Can you write $5^x + 5^y$ as a power of 5? Explain why or why not.

Mid-Chapter Review

FREQUENTLY ASKED Questions

Q: How can you model perfect squares and perfect cubes?

A: You can use drawings or concrete materials to model perfect squares or perfect cubes. A perfect square has two equal natural number factors: the length and width of a square. A perfect cube has three equal natural number factors: the length, width, and height.

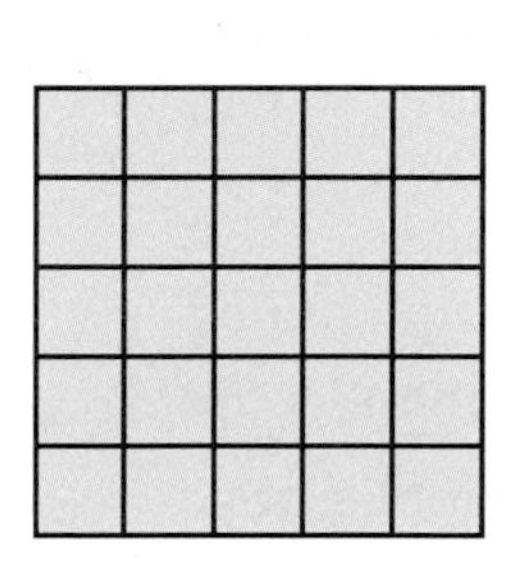

$$25 = 5 \times 5$$
$$= 5^2$$

perfect square

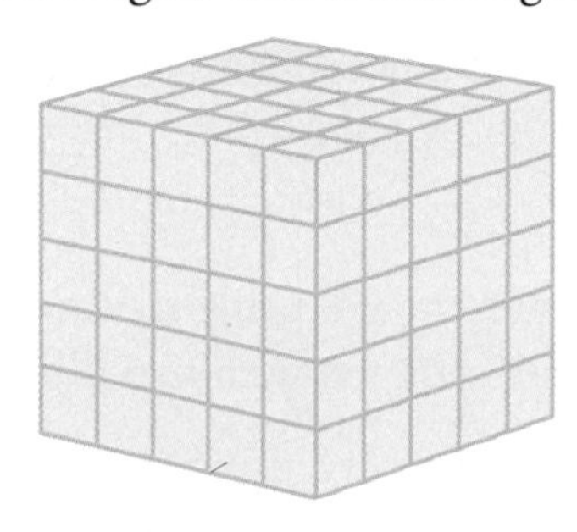

$$125 = 5 \times 5 \times 5$$
$$= 5^3$$

perfect cube

Study Aid

- See Lesson 2.1, Examples 1 and 2.
- Try Mid-Chapter Review questions 1, 2, and 3.

Q: How can you use powers to represent numbers?

A: You can use powers to represent repeated multiplication. For example, you can represent $5 \times 5 \times 5 \times 5 \times 5 \times 5$ by the power 5^6. The exponent, 6, tells how many times the base, 5, appears in the power. You can use powers to represent perfect squares or perfect cubes. For example, the perfect square 36 can be represented by the power 6^2. The perfect cube 27 can be represented by the power 3^3.

Study Aid

- See Lesson 2.2, Examples 1, 2, and 3.
- Try Mid-Chapter Review questions 4, 5, 6, and 7.

Q: How can you use the exponent laws to simplify expressions?

A: You can use the exponent laws to simplify numerical and algebraic expressions.

	Exponent Law for Products	**Exponent Law for Quotients**	**Exponent Law for Power of a Power**
Statement of Exponent Law	$(a^m)(a^n) = a^{m+n}$	$a^m \div a^n = a^{m-n}$ $(a \neq 0)$	$(a^m)^n = a^{mn}$
Example	$(2^2)(2^3) = 2^{2+3} = 2^5$	$3^4 \div 3^2 = 3^{4-2} = 3^2$	$(4^2)^3 = 4^{2\times3} = 4^6$

Study Aid

- See Lesson 2.4, Examples 1, 2, and 3.
- Try Mid-Chapter Review questions 8, 9, 10, and 11.

Practice

Lesson 2.1

1. Sketch a model to represent the following. Label each side length.

a) 21^2
b) 8^2
c) 15^3
d) $11 \times 11 \times 11$

2. Calculate each dimension.

a) the side length of a square with an area of 196 cm^2
b) the dimensions of a cube with side face of 16 cm^2

16 cm^2

3. List two perfect squares between 0 and 1000 that are also perfect cubes. Show your work.

Lesson 2.2

4. a) Represent -8 using repeated multiplication.
b) Represent -8 with two different powers.

5. a) Represent 216 using repeated multiplication.
b) Represent 216 as a power. Show your work.

Reading Strategy

Evaluating

Share your answers to questions 6 and 7 with a partner. Do you agree? Defend your responses.

6. Evaluate each power without a calculator. Show your work.

a) 1^3
b) $(-5)^3$
c) -3^4
d) $-(-2)^3$
e) 8^0
f) $\left(\frac{-2}{3}\right)^4$

7. Put the answers to question 6 in increasing order.

Lesson 2.4

8. Express each as a power with a single exponent.

a) $(10^4)(10^7)$
b) $(3^4)^2(3^4)$
c) $\frac{(-9)^4}{(-9)^2}$
d) $\frac{(2^3)^3}{2^4}$
e) $\frac{(5^3)^5}{(5^2)^4}$
f) $\frac{(-6)^7(-6)^5}{[(-6)^4]^2(-6)^2}$

9. Express 1024 as a combination of powers using addition, subtraction, multiplication, and division. Identify as many possibilities as you can.

10. To win a prize in a contest, Rafi had to answer the following skill-testing question.

Express as a power of 2: $(8)(64) \div 16^2 = \blacksquare$

What should his answer be?

11. Simplify.

a) $(b^4)(b^2)(b)$
b) $n^{10} \div n^7$
c) $(d^3)^9$
d) $\frac{(a^4)(a^5)}{(a^2)^3}$

Curious MATH

Google This!

In 1920, mathematician Edward Kasner asked his nine-year-old nephew Milton Sirotta what name he should give to the number 10^{100}. "A googol," came the boy's reply, and the name stuck. How large do you think a googol is?

1. What does 10^{100} mean?
2. If you were to write 10^{100} out in long hand, how many zeros would there be after the 1?
3. The number 10^{googol} is called a googolplex. Describe what the number 10^{googol} would look like.
4. Express 10^{googol} in another way.
5. How long does it take you to write all the digits of one million (10^6)? What about one billion (10^9)? Suppose you could keep writing zeros without taking a break. About how long would it take you to write out the whole number equivalent of a googol? What about a googolplex?
6. Suggest three numbers greater than a googolplex. Explain how much longer each number would take to write out.
7. Why might the founders of Google have chosen this name for their search engine?

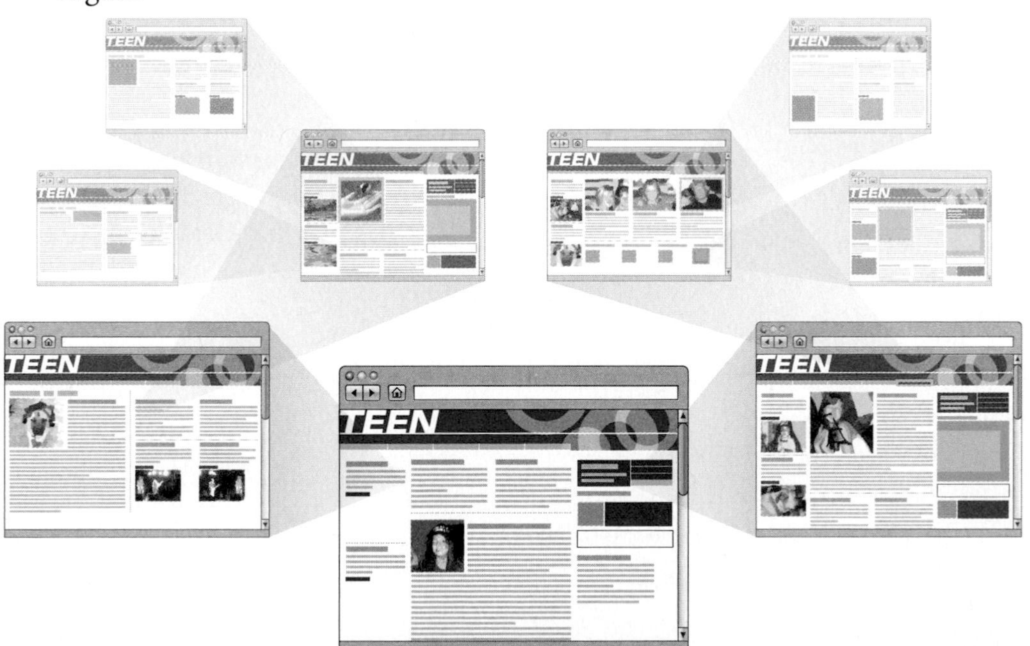

2.5 Combining Powers

YOU WILL NEED

- a calculator

GOAL

Simplify products and quotients of powers with the same exponent.

Yvonne's cube

20 cm

LEARN ABOUT the Math

Nicole and Yvonne made origami paper cubes for a math project.

? How will the volume and surface area of Yvonne's cube compare to those for Nicole's cube?

EXAMPLE 1 | Comparing the surface area and volume of cubes

Nicole's Solution

$$\begin{aligned}\text{Surface area} &= 6 \text{ faces} \times \text{area of one face} \\ &= 6 \times 4^2 \\ &= 6 \times 4 \times 4 \ \ (\text{or } 6 \times 16) \\ &= 96 \text{ cm}^2\end{aligned}$$

I calculated the surface area and volume of my cube.

$$\begin{aligned}\text{Volume} &= \text{length} \times \text{width} \times \text{height} \\ &= 4^3 \\ &= 64 \text{ cm}^3\end{aligned}$$

$$\begin{aligned}\text{Surface area} &= 6 \times (4 \times 5)^2 \\ &= 6 \times (4 \times 5) \times (4 \times 5) \\ &= 6 \times (4 \times 4) \times (5 \times 5) \\ &= 6 \times 4^2 \times 5^2 \\ &= 6 \times 16 \times 25 \\ &= 2400 \text{ cm}^2\end{aligned}$$

I calculated the surface area and volume of Yvonne's cube. I wrote the side length of 20 as 4×5 to make it easier to compare to my cube.

$$\begin{aligned}\text{Volume} &= (4 \times 5)^3 \\ &= (4 \times 5) \times (4 \times 5) \times (4 \times 5) \\ &= (4 \times 4 \times 4) \times (5 \times 5 \times 5) \\ &= 4^3 \times 5^3 \\ &= 64 \times 125 \\ &= 8000 \text{ cm}^3\end{aligned}$$

$$\frac{2400}{96} = \frac{25}{1}$$

The surface area of Yvonne's cube is 25 times greater than that of my cube.

I wrote the ratio of the surface area of Yvonne's cube to the surface area of my cube, and then simplified.

$$\frac{8000}{64} = \frac{125}{1}$$

The volume of Yvonne's cube is 125 times greater than mine.

I wrote the ratio of the volume of Yvonne's cube to the volume of my cube, and then simplified.

Reflecting

A. How could Nicole have predicted she could calculate the surface area of Yvonne's cube by multiplying her own cube's surface area by 25?

B. How could Nicole have predicted that she could calculate the volume of Yvonne's cube by multiplying her own cube's volume by 125?

C. How do Nicole's calculations show why $(4 \times 5)^2 = 4^2 \times 5^2$ and $(4 \times 5)^3 = 4^3 \times 5^3$?

WORK WITH the Math

EXAMPLE 2 | Simplifying the base of a power

Yvonne calculated the volume of a cube with a side length of 7 cm as 343 cm^3. How can she use that calculation to figure out the volume of a cube with a side length of 14 cm?

Yvonne's Solution

$343 = 7^3$

The volume of the new cube is 14^3.

I knew that $14 = 2 \times 7$, so I could use the exponent law or I could write $(2 \times 7)^3 = (2 \times 7) \times (2 \times 7) \times (2 \times 7)$

That's the same as $2 \times 2 \times 2 \times 7 \times 7 \times 7$.

I realized that I could just multiply the old volume of 7^3 by 2^3.

That's an easy multiplication.

$$14 = 2 \times 7$$
$$14^3 = (2 \times 7)^3$$
$$= 2^3 \times 7^3$$
$$= 8 \times 7^3$$

The volume of a cube with a side length of 14 cm is $8 \times 343 = 2744$ cm^3.

EXAMPLE 3 | Evaluating powers with different bases

Evaluate $2^5 \times 5^4$.

Shelby's Solution

$$\begin{aligned} 2^5 \times 5^4 &= 2 \times 2 \times 2 \times 2 \times 2 \\ &\quad \times 5 \times 5 \times 5 \times 5 \end{aligned}$$

I wrote the expression using repeated multiplication.

$$\begin{aligned} &= 2 \times (2 \times 5) \times (2 \times 5) \\ &\quad \times (2 \times 5) \times (2 \times 5) \end{aligned}$$

I rearranged the 2s and 5s because $2 \times 5 = 10$, and that's easier to multiply by than 2s or 5s.

$$= 2 \times 10 \times 10 \times 10 \times 10$$

I multiplied the 2s by the 5s.

$$\begin{aligned} &= 2 \times 10^4 \\ &= 2 \times 10\ 000 \\ &= 20\ 000 \end{aligned}$$

I simplified using powers.

EXAMPLE 4 | Simplifying expressions involving powers

Simplify $(2^3 \times 4^2)^3$.

Austin's Solution

$$(2^3 \times 4^2)^3 = (2^3 \times 2^4)^3$$

I noticed that 4^2 can be expressed as a power with a base of 2, where $4^2 = (2^2)^2$ or 2^4.

$$\begin{aligned} &= (2^{3+4})^3 \\ &= (2^7)^3 \end{aligned}$$

I simplified using the product law.

$$= 2^{21}$$

I could simplify even further using the power of a power law.

EXAMPLE 5 | Simplifying powers in fraction form

Simplify $\left(\frac{-3^2}{4^3}\right)^3$.

Derek's Solution

$$\left(\frac{-3^2}{4^3}\right)^3 = \frac{(-3^2)}{(4^3)} \times \frac{(-3^2)}{(4^3)} \times \frac{(-3^2)}{(4^3)}$$
$$= \frac{-3^2 \times -3^2 \times -3^2}{4^3 \times 4^3 \times 4^3}$$
$$= \frac{(-3^2)^3}{(4^3)^3}$$

I figured out what the expression meant by using repeated multiplication and the rules for multiplying fractions.

I realized that I could have just applied the power to the numerator and denominator separately.

$$= \frac{-3^{2\times3}}{4^{3\times3}}$$
$$= \frac{-3^6}{4^9}$$

I simplified using the exponent law for a power of a power.

In Summary

Key Idea

- An exponent can be applied to each term in a product or quotient involving powers.
  That is, $(ab)^m = a^m b^m$ and $\left(\frac{a}{b}\right)^m = \frac{a^m}{b^m}$ $(b \neq 0)$.
  For example, $(3 \times 7)^2 = 3^2 \times 7^2$ and $\left(\frac{3}{7}\right)^2 = \frac{3^2}{7^2}$.

Need to Know

- Sometimes an expression is easier to evaluate if you simplify it first; for example, $2^5 \times 5^5$ is easier to evaluate when it is simplified to $(2 \times 5)^5 = 10^5$ and $2^3 \times 8^2$ is easier to evaluate if you rewrite it as a single power of 8: $2^3 \times 8^2 = 8^1 \times 8^2 = 8^3$.

Checking

1. Express as a product or quotient of two powers.

a) $(2 \times 3)^4$ **b)** $\left(\frac{2}{3}\right)^5$ **c)** $(3^2 \times 5^4)^3$ **d)** $\left(\frac{3^3}{7^2}\right)^2$

2. Write each expression as a power with a single base. Show your work.

a) 2×4 **b)** $(3^2 \times 9)^3$ **c)** $(4^2 \times 16^2)^4$ **d)** $\left(\frac{5^2}{5}\right)^4$

Practising

3. Write each expression as a power with a single base. Show your work.

a) $(3 \times 7)^2$ **b)** $(4 \times 6)^3$ **c)** $(9 \div 3)^2$ **d)** $(24 \div 3)^3$

4. Simplify. Express as a single power where possible.

a) $(8^3 \times 5^2)^4$

b) $(4^3 \times 3^2)^2(4^5 \times 3^2)^3$

c) $[(2^4)(3^3)]^2(2^2 \times 3^3)^3$

d) $\left(\frac{4^6}{4^4}\right)^3$

e) $\left(\frac{2^4}{7^2}\right)^3$

f) $\frac{(2^5 \times 5^2)^2}{(2^4 \times 5)^2}$

5. Evaluate.

a) $(2^3 \times 3^2)^2$

b) $(3^2 \times 1^2)^2(3^2 \times 1^2)^3$

c) $\left(\frac{5^5}{5^3}\right)^3$

d) $\frac{(2^6 \times 4^3)^2}{(2^3 \times 4^2)^2}$

6. Multiple choice. Simplify $(2^2 \times 4^2)^3$.

A. 2^{18} **B.** 2^{24} **C.** 4^{18} **D.** 2^9

7. Multiple choice. Simplify $(1.8^3 \times 1.8^2)^2$.

A. 1.8^7 **B.** 1.8^{12} **C.** 1.8^6 **D.** 1.8^{10}

8. Multiple choice. Simplify $\left(\frac{5^6}{5^2}\right)^4$.

A. 5^{16} **B.** 5^{12} **C.** 5^{24} **D.** 5^5

9. Kalyna can only enter one-digit numbers on her calculator. The exponent key and the display are working fine. Explain how she can evaluate each power using her calculator.

a) 25^4 **b)** 16^2

10. Simplify $4^3 \times 250^3$, to make it easier to evaluate. Show your work.

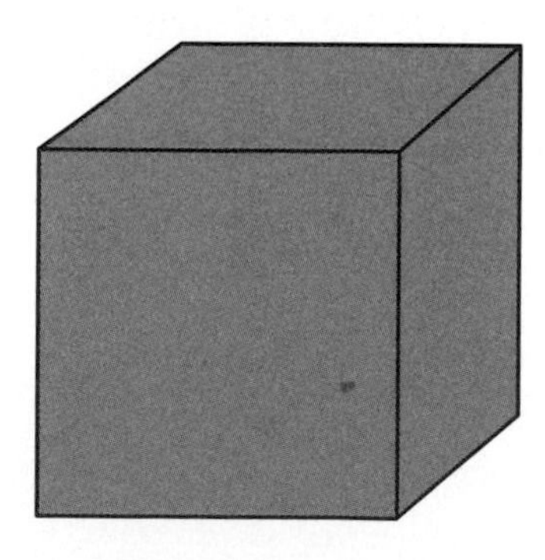

11. The side length of a cube is 3^5 units.

a) Determine the surface area of the cube without using powers.
b) Determine the surface area using powers.
c) Did you prefer the method you used in part a) or part b)? Explain why.
d) Determine the volume without using powers.
e) Determine the volume using powers.
f) Did you prefer the method you used in part d) or part e)? Explain why.

12. Navtej wants to paint her room and is on a budget. She found a 4 L can of paint, in a colour that she liked, on the mistints shelf at the hardware store. She knows that 500 mL covers 6 m^2. She wants to use two coats of paint. Represent the area that she is able to paint using a power. Recall that 1 L = 1000 mL.

13. Hye-Won is making ornamental paper lanterns for her Chinese New Year party. Her first lantern is a cube.

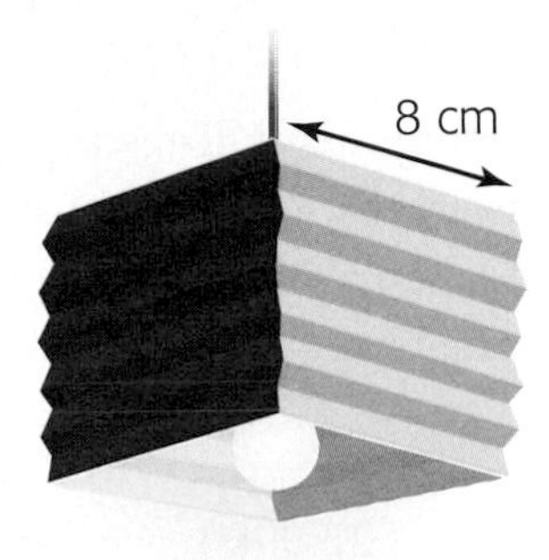

volume = 512 cm^3

a) Express the volume of the lantern as a power.

b) Another lantern has a volume of 2^{15} cm^3. How many times as high is that cube than the first lantern?

14. Describe two different ways to evaluate $\frac{6^3}{2^3}$. Which would you use? Why?

15. Suppose you are asked to evaluate $2^8 \times 25^4$ and $10^5 \times 8^3$. Which expression might you simplify first? Which one might you not simplify? Explain.

Reading Strategy

Evaluating

Find someone who used a different way from you in questions 14 and 15. Justify your choices to each other.

Closing

16. Explain how can you simplify $40^3 \times 5^5$ to calculate it using mental math.

Extending

17. a) Can you express $(0.81)^3$ as an equivalent power with a single base of 0.9, $(0.81)^3 = 0.9^{■}$? Explain how you know.

b) Can you express $(0.9)^3$ as an equivalent power with a base of 0.81, $(0.9)^3 = (0.81)^{■}$? Explain how you know.

c) When can you express a power with a base of 0.9 as an equivalent power with the base of 0.81?

18. Express each amount as a power with a single base. Show your work.

a) $(0.25^4 \times 0.5^2)^3$ **b)** $(1.2^3 \times 1.44)^2$ **c)** $\left(\frac{0.16^3}{0.4^3}\right)^3$

2.6 Communicate about Calculations with Powers

YOU WILL NEED

- a calculator

GOAL

Clearly explain the steps for calculating with powers.

WIN A TRIP FOR 2 TO BANFF
Entry Form
Name: ____________
e-mail: ____________
Phone no: ____________
Answer the following skill-testing question:
$4 + 5^3 - 3^2 + 8 \times (27 \div 9)^2$

INVESTIGATE the Math

Bay and Austin were answering this skill-testing question. Bay's answer was 1152 and Austin's answer was 192. Austin started to show Bay why his answer was correct, but then his cell phone rang and he was distracted. Here is his explanation.

Use order of operations.

$4 + 5^3 - 3^2 + 8 \times (27 \div 9)^2$	brackets first
$= 4 + 5^3 - 3^2 + 8 \times (3)^2$	then exponents
$= 4 + 125 - 9 + 8 \times 9$	divide/multiply
$= 4 +$	

? **Why is this question a good test of mathematical skill?**

A. Use the Communication Checklist to help you improve and complete Austin's explanation.

B. Why is this question a good test of mathematical skill?

Communication *Checklist*

- ✔ Did you include all the steps?
- ✔ Did you explain why you did each step?
- ✔ Did you explain how you did each step?
- ✔ Did you justify your conclusion?

Reflecting

C. Why is it important for an explanation to be complete and clear?

WORK WITH the Math

EXAMPLE 1 | Communicating about powers and exponents

Does $6^2 + 6^5 = 6^7$? Explain.

Austin's Solution

$6^2 + 6^5$ means $(6 \times 6) + (6 \times 6 \times 6 \times 6 \times 6)$. — I thought about what $6^2 + 6^5$ means and what 6^7 means.

6^7 means $6 \times 6 \times 6 \times 6 \times 6 \times 6 \times 6$.

I think $6^2 + 6^5$ and 6^7 are not equal, because 6^7 is 36 times greater than 6^5, not 36 more.

I calculated to make sure. Since powers represent repeated multiplication, I did that before adding.
My answer makes sense, because 36 + 7776 cannot be the same as 36 × 7776.

Check

$$\begin{aligned} 6^2 + 6^5 &= 36 + 6^5 \\ &= 36 + 7776 \\ &= 7812 \\ 6^7 &= 279\,936 \end{aligned}$$

$7812 \neq 279\,936$, so $6^2 + 6^5 \neq 6^7$.

EXAMPLE 2 | Simplifying using order of operations

Calculate $5^2 + [16 \times (2^2 - 6)]$.

Nicole's Solution

$5^2 + [16 \times (2^2 - 6)]$

I used order of operations.
I underlined the operations as I did them.

$$\begin{aligned} &\underline{5^2} + [16 \times (\underline{2^2} - 6)] \\ &= 25 + [16 \times \underline{(4 - 6)}] \\ &= 25 + [\underline{16 \times (-2)}] \end{aligned}$$

I need to evaluate the expression inside the innermost brackets first. It contains an exponent and so does the first term. I evaluated these powers. I then evaluated the expression in the round brackets by subtracting. This left an expression inside the square brackets which I evaluated by multiplying.

$$\begin{aligned} &= 25 + (-32) \\ &= -7 \end{aligned}$$

I added the remaining numbers.

Communication | ***Tip***

You can use the memory aid **BEDMAS** to remember the rules for order of operations.
Perform the operations in **B**rackets first.
Calculate **E**xponents and square roots next.
Divide and **M**ultiply from left to right.
Add and **S**ubtract from left to right.

$6^2 \times 6^5 = 6^7$

EXAMPLE 3 | Simplifying fractions using order of operations

Calculate $\frac{(4^2 + 3^2) \div 5 + 5}{(4^2 - 3^2) + 3}$.

Derek's Solution

$$\frac{(4^2 + 3^2) \div 5 + 5}{(4^2 - 3^2) + 3} = \frac{(16 + 9) \div 5 + 5}{(16 - 9) + 3}$$

$$= \frac{25 \div 5 + 5}{7 + 3}$$

$$= \frac{5 + 5}{10}$$

I used order of operations to evaluate each expression in the numerator and denominator.

Numerator: I evaluated the expression in the brackets by evaluating the powers then adding. I divided the result by five and then added five to this.

Denominator: I evaluated the expression in the brackets by evaluating the powers then subtracting. I then added three to this.

$$= \frac{10}{10}$$

$$= 1$$

I divided the numerator by the denominator.

In Summary

Key Idea

- When everyone follows the same order of operations, everyone gets the same answer to a question.

Need to Know

- Use BEDMAS (Brackets, Exponents, Division, Multiplication, Addition, Subtraction) to remember the order of operations.
  - Evaluate the contents in brackets first, starting with the innermost brackets.
  - Evaluate powers.
  - Multiply and divide from left to right.
  - Add and subtract from left to right.

Checking

1. Show the steps to evaluate each expression.

a) $4(3)^2$ **b)** $9^2 + 9 \div 3^2$ **c)** $12 + (-6)^2 \div 3$

Practising

2. a) Evaluate $3^2 \times 4 + 2^2 - 10$.

b) Evaluate $3^2 + 4 \times 2^2 - 10$.

c) Would you use the expression in part a) or part b) for a skill-testing question? Explain why.

3. Evaluate. Explain your strategy.
   a) $3^2 + 3^5$ b) $12^2 + 4^2$ c) $8^4 - 8^2$ d) $7^3 - 2^7$

4. Evaluate.
   a) $4^3 + 3^2 \times 4 \div 2$
   b) $5^2 - 5 \div 5 + 2 - 1$
   c) $\dfrac{(5^2 - 3) \times 2 \div 11 + 3}{3^2 - (2^2 \times 5)}$

5. a) Evaluate $12^2 + 5^2 - 64 \div 4^2$ with a calculator.
   b) Does your calculator follow the order of operations? How do you know?

6. Give an example of a product of two powers that is the same as their sum. Explain how you came up with your example.

7. Explain why 2 is the only base for which $a^2 - a^1 = a^2 \div a^1$.

8. Is it possible for a power with a base of 5 to be equal to a power with a base of 10? Explain.

9. Which is greater: 2^{30} or 3^{20}? How can you answer this without a calculator?

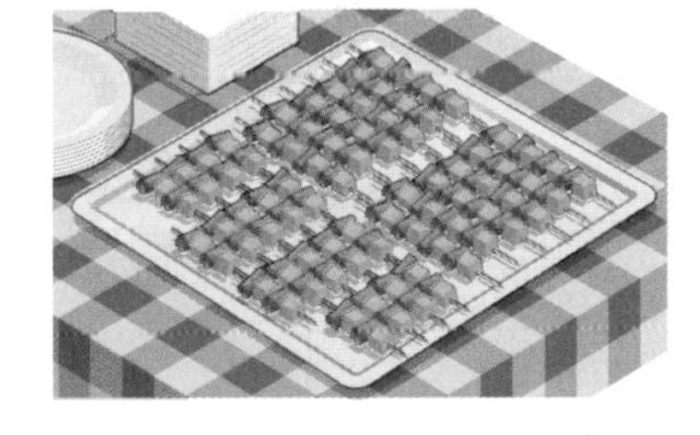

10. Larry is preparing meat and cheese skewers for a party. He has 18 small skewers and 12 large skewers. Each small skewer needs 2 cubes of cheese. Each large skewer needs twice as many cubes of cheese.
    a) Which expression best describes how many cubes of cheese Larry needs? Explain why.
       A. $18 \times 2^2 + 12 \times 2$ B. $(18 \times 2) + (12 \times 2^2)$

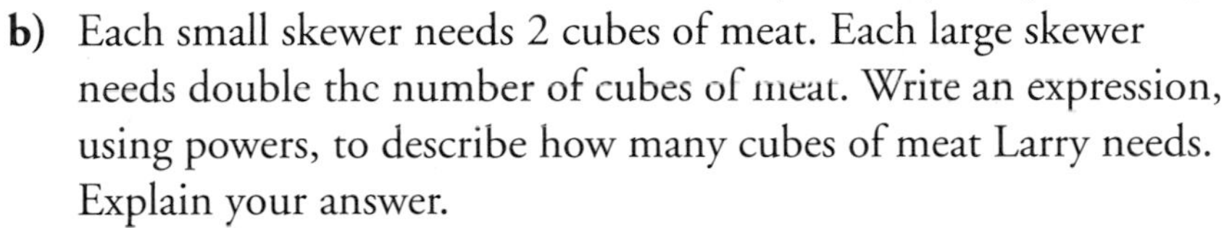

    b) Each small skewer needs 2 cubes of meat. Each large skewer needs double the number of cubes of meat. Write an expression, using powers, to describe how many cubes of meat Larry needs. Explain your answer.
    c) How many cubes of meat does Larry need?

Closing

11. Why is it important to use the order of operations when you use mathematics to communicate?

Extending

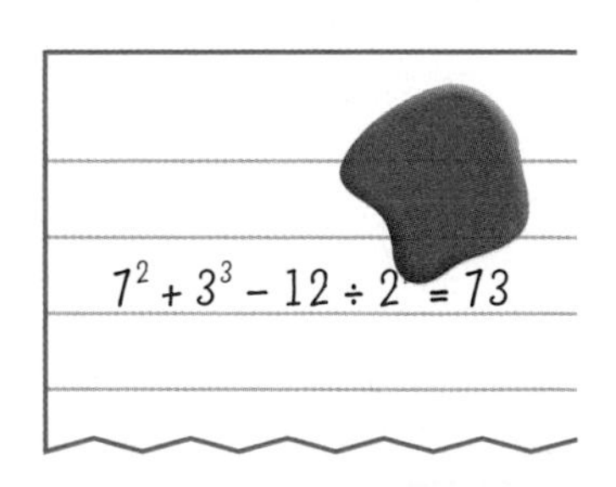

12. Ruby copied the solution to a math problem from the board during class. When she got home to review the problem, she spilled her juice on her homework and couldn't make out one of the exponents in the question and part of the solution.

    a) Explain how Ruby can determine the missing exponent.
    b) Rewrite the original question and show all the steps to solve it.

13. To evaluate an expression involving a power, do you have to calculate the power before multiplying and dividing? Explain using examples.

2.7 Calculating Square Roots

YOU WILL NEED

- a calculator

GOAL

Calculate the square roots of fractions and decimals.

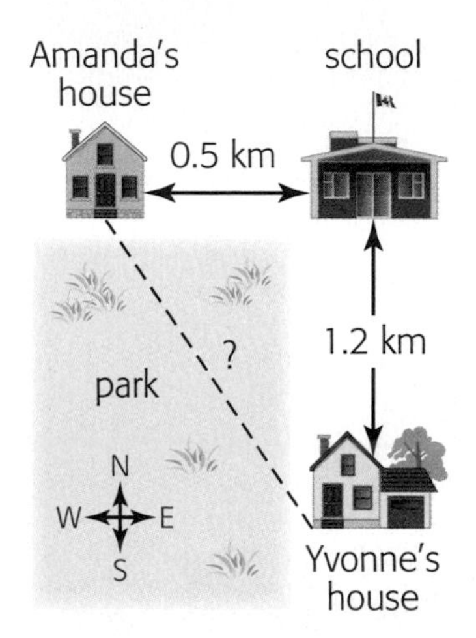

LEARN ABOUT the Math

Amanda walks 0.5 km east to go to school. On Thursdays, she goes to Yvonne's house after school to play video games. Yvonne's house is 1.2 km south of the school. Amanda cuts through the park to get home.

? How far does Amanda walk to get home from Yvonne's house?

Technology | *Tip*

Different calculators calculate square roots in different ways. With some, you press [√] first and then enter the number. With others, you enter the number first and then press [√]. There are other ways too.

EXAMPLE 1 Applying the Pythagorean theorem

Amanda's Solution

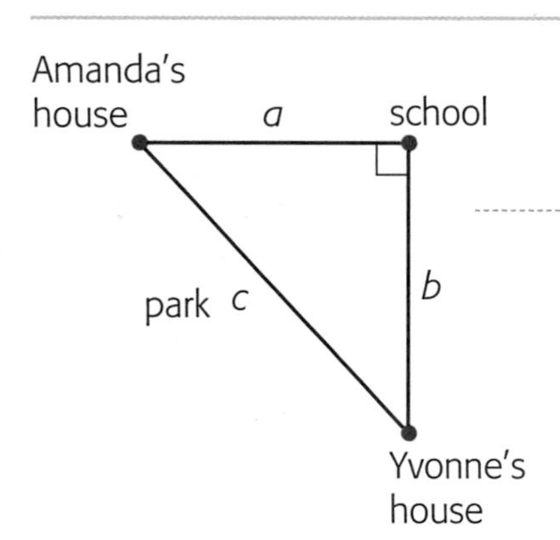

The triangle is a right triangle. The distance across the park is the hypotenuse, so it must be greater than 1.2 km.

$c^2 = a^2 + b^2$

$c^2 = (0.5)^2 + (1.2)^2$

$c^2 = 0.25 + 1.44$

$c^2 = 1.69$

I used the Pythagorean theorem to write a relationship between the sides in the right triangle. I solved for c^2.

$c = \sqrt{1.69}$

I calculated the square root on my calculator.

[√] [1] [.] [6] [9] [=] 1.3

$c = 1.3$ km

[1] [.] [3] [^] [2] [=] 1.69

I checked my answer by squaring. The square root is an exact value since squaring it results in the number I started with.

It's 1.3 km between our houses.

My answer seems reasonable because the distance across the park is greater than 1.2 km.

Yvonne's Solution: Using Fractions

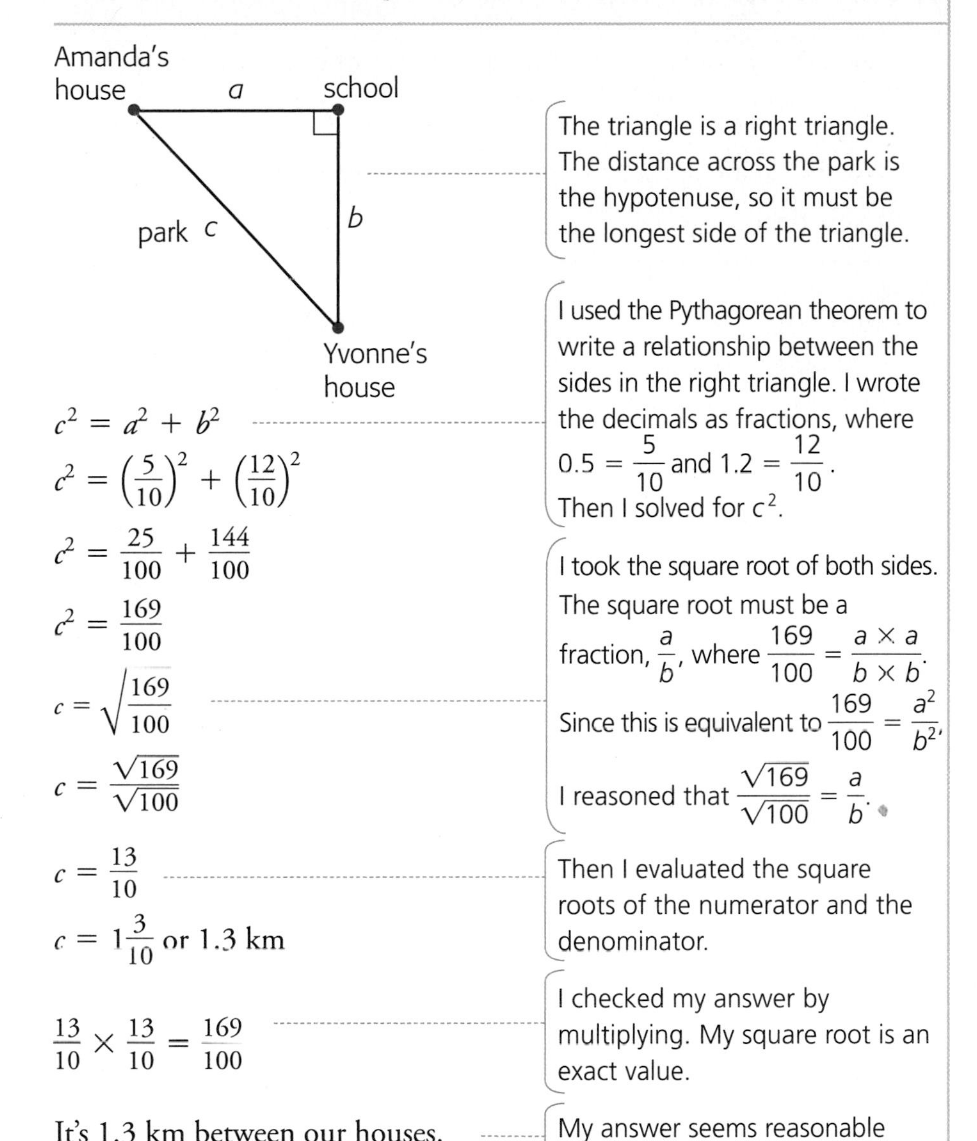

Reflecting

A. How are Amanda's and Yvonne's methods similar? How are they different?

B. Do you prefer Amanda's method or Yvonne's method? Explain why.

C. Explain how Yvonne determined the square root of the fraction in her solution.

WORK WITH the Math

EXAMPLE 2 | Determining the square root of decimals greater than and less than 1

When is the square root of a number greater than the number?

Bay's Solution

1 1

$\sqrt{1} = 1$

I know that the side length of a square with an area of 1 square unit is 1 unit. I'll try squares with greater and lesser areas.

1.21 1.1

$\sqrt{1.21} = 1.1$

I calculated the side length of a square with an area greater than 1. The square root is less than the number.

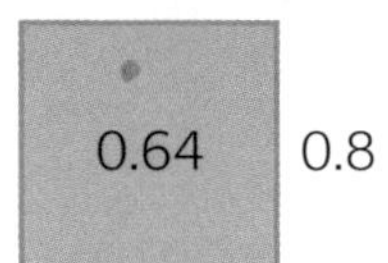

$\sqrt{0.64} = 0.8$

I calculated the side length of a square with an area of less than 1 square unit. The square root is greater than the number.

The square root of a number is greater than the number when the number is between 0 and 1.

I think this is going to happen for all squares whose sides have length greater than 0 but less than 1.

EXAMPLE 3 | **Determining the square root of a fraction using a quotient**

Austin is building a patio using square concrete patio slabs; 25 of the slabs cover 9 m^2. What are the dimensions of the top of each slab?

Austin's Solution

The top of each slab has an area of $\frac{9}{25}$.

I divided to determine the area of one top.

The length of each side is $\sqrt{\frac{9}{25}}$.

Since the top is a square, I know the length and width must be equal. I can calculate the length of each side by determining the square root of its area.

$\sqrt{\frac{9}{25}} = \frac{\sqrt{9}}{\sqrt{25}}$

The square root of a quotient is the same as the quotient of the square roots.

$= \frac{3}{5}$

I calculated the square root of the numerator and the denominator.

$= 0.6$

I wrote the fraction as a decimal.

The top of the slab has dimensions of 0.6 m by 0.6 m.

EXAMPLE 4 | Using order of operations with a square root

Calculate $2^4 \times \sqrt{36} + 4^2 \div 2 + 1$.

Amanda's Solution

$2^4 \times \sqrt{36} + 4^2 \div 2 + 1$
$= 16 \times 6 + 16 \div 2 + 1$
$= 96 + 8 + 1$
$= 105$

I treated the square root like a power. I evaluated the powers first. Then, I divided and multiplied. Lastly, I added.

In Summary

Key Idea

- If a positive number is less than 1, then its square root will be greater than the original number. If a positive number is greater than 1, then its square root will be less than the original number.

Need to Know

- The square root of a quotient equals the quotient of the square roots. $\sqrt{\frac{a}{b}} = \frac{\sqrt{a}}{\sqrt{b}}$
- If the numerator and denominator of a fraction are both perfect squares, then the square root of the fraction is an exact value.
- If a decimal can be written as an equivalent fraction whose numerator and denominator are perfect squares, then the square root of the decimal is an exact value.

Checking

1. Enter the missing numbers.

   a) $\sqrt{49} = \sqrt{\blacksquare \times \blacksquare}$
   b) $\sqrt{\blacksquare} = 11$
   c) $\sqrt{\frac{4}{9}} = \frac{\blacksquare}{3}$
   d) $\sqrt{\frac{\blacksquare}{81}} = \frac{7}{9}$
   e) $\frac{\sqrt{144}}{\sqrt{225}} = \frac{\blacksquare}{\blacksquare}$
   f) $\frac{\sqrt{\blacksquare}}{\sqrt{\blacksquare}} = \frac{10}{13}$

2. A square field has an area of 1.44 km^2. Calculate its length and width without a calculator. Show your work.

Practising

3. Enter the missing numbers.

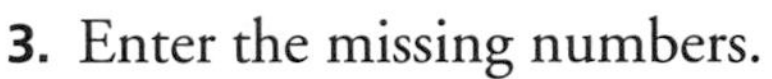

   a) $\sqrt{3.61} = \blacksquare$ b) $\sqrt{\blacksquare} = 0.07$ c) $\sqrt{\frac{100}{289}} = \blacksquare$ d) $\frac{\sqrt{\blacksquare}}{\sqrt{\blacksquare}} = \frac{4}{6}$

4. Calculate.

   a) $\sqrt{\frac{9}{1}}$
   b) $\sqrt{\frac{81}{9}}$
   c) $\sqrt{\frac{729}{81}}$

5. Based on your answers to question 4, how can you predict the answer to $\sqrt{\frac{64}{16}}$?

6. Evaluate.

   a) $7^2 + \sqrt{4} \times 4^2 - 2$ b) $(\sqrt{81} + \sqrt{64})^2 \div 17 + 6$

7. **Multiple choice.** Evaluate $\sqrt{\frac{121}{256}}$.

   A. $\frac{11}{16}$
   B. $\frac{121}{256}$
   C. $\frac{14\,641}{65\,536}$
   D. $\frac{16}{11}$

8. Determine each square root to one decimal place.

   a) $\sqrt{2.56}$
   b) $\sqrt{1.96}$
   c) $\sqrt{1.69}$
   d) $\sqrt{1.44}$
   e) $\sqrt{0.8100}$
   f) $\sqrt{0.4900}$
   g) $\sqrt{0.36}$
   h) $\sqrt{0.25}$

9. Label the square and square root from each part of question 8 on a number line. The first one is done for you.

   $\sqrt{2.56}$

   0 0.2 0.4 0.6 0.8 1.0 1.2 1.4 1.6 1.8 2.0

10. The square root of 1 is 1. That is, $\sqrt{1} = \sqrt{1 \times 1} = 1$. Is any other positive rational number equal to its square root? How do you know?

11. The square root of a number is 16.5. What is the number?

12. You know that $\sqrt{576} = 24$. What decimal square roots could you calculate easily using that information? Explain.

13. Bittu has a new TV with an 84 cm screen. He wants to put it above his fireplace in a space 150 cm wide and 75 cm high. Will the TV fit into the space?

14. a) Complete each statement.

A. $\sqrt{\frac{1}{4}} = \sqrt{0.■} = \frac{1}{2}$ **B.** $\sqrt{0.04} = \frac{1}{■}$ **C.** $\sqrt{0.■} = \frac{1}{■}$

b) Explain how you know your answers are reasonable.

15. Verify each statement and correct those that are incorrect.

a) $\sqrt{6.4} = 3.2$
b) $\sqrt{0.9} = 0.03$
c) $\sqrt{256} = 16$
d) $\sqrt{0.25} = 0.5$

16. Calculate.

a) $\sqrt{0.09}$ **b)** $\sqrt{0.0009}$ **c)** $\sqrt{0.000\,009}$ **d)** $\sqrt{0.000\,000\,09}$

17. What pattern do you notice in the answers in the previous question?

18. What is the area of the yellow region?

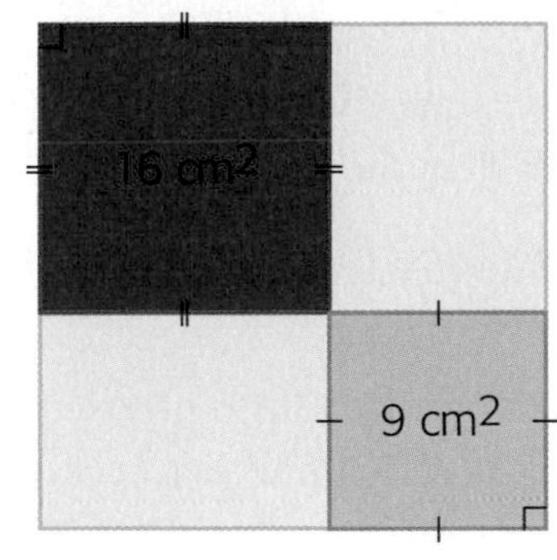

Closing

19. Which of these have a square root that is an exact value: 0.49, 4.9, 0.0049? Explain.

Extending

20. Could $\sqrt{\frac{■}{9}}$ be a fraction with a denominator of 2? Explain.

21. The area of a circle with radius r is πr^2, where $\pi \doteq 3.14$. What is the radius of a circle of area 50.24 cm^2?

22. The area of the square is 12.25 cm^2. Estimate the radius of the circle.

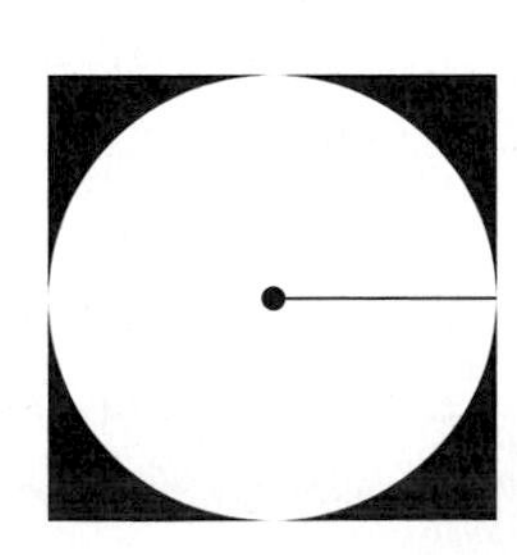

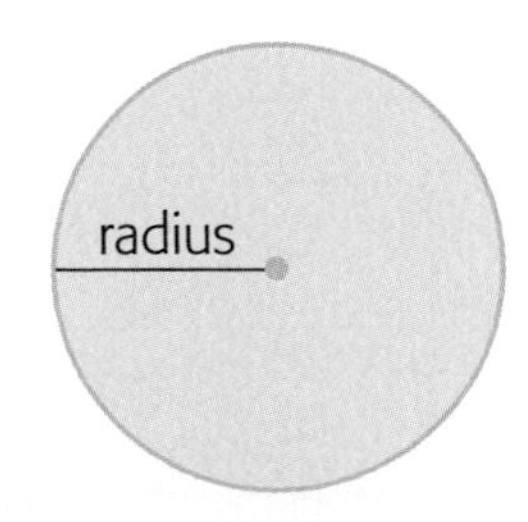

2.8 Estimating Square Roots

YOU WILL NEED

- a calculator

GOAL

Use perfect square benchmarks to estimate square roots of other fractions and decimals.

INVESTIGATE the Math

Bay is preparing for the Egg Drop Experiment in science class. Bay will try to drop the egg 23.7 m, without breaking it. He needs to determine how long an egg will take to hit the ground. He will estimate the drop time for the egg using the formula $time = 0.45\sqrt{height}$, where time is measured in seconds and height in metres.

? How long will it take an egg to hit the ground?

A. Substitute the known value into the formula.

B. What is the greatest perfect square less than the height? What is the least perfect square greater than the height?

C. Which of the two numbers you found in part B is the given height closer to?

D. Estimate the square root of the height to one decimal place using the numbers from part B as benchmarks. Check your answer by multiplying and estimate again if you need to.

E. Determine $\sqrt{23.7}$ m to two decimal places using a calculator.

F. Write 23.7 as an improper fraction. Is the square root of 23.7 an exact value? Explain how you know.

G. How long will this egg take to hit the ground, to one decimal place?

Reflecting

H. Why is it helpful to estimate the square root of a number that is not a perfect square?

WORK WITH the Math

EXAMPLE 1 | Estimating a square root to verify a calculation

Shelby knew that square root problems involve two identical numbers, so she said $\sqrt{110} = 55$. Is her answer reasonable?

Shelby's Solution

$\sqrt{110} = 55$
100............110............121

I decided to estimate. I know 110 isn't a perfect square, so I thought of square numbers that are less than 110 and greater than 110.

$\sqrt{100} = 10$ $\sqrt{121} = 11$

I compared the square roots of these numbers to my estimate.

$\sqrt{110}$ is between 10 and 11, so my estimate of $\sqrt{110} = 55$ is not reasonable.

Yvonne's Solution

$\sqrt{110} = 55?$
$55^2 = 3025$
Obviously, $3025 \neq 110$, so the square root of 110 is not 55. The answer is not reasonable.

I squared the answer on my calculator.

EXAMPLE 2 | Estimating a square root by reasoning

Estimate $\sqrt{0.84}$.

Nicole's Solution

0.84 is $\frac{84}{100}$
That is close to $\frac{81}{100}$, and its square root is $\frac{9}{10}$, or 0.9.

I thought of the decimal in hundredths and looked for a square root that I knew that was close to it.

I estimated 0.92 as the square root.

Since $0.84 > 0.81$, I chose a number a little greater than 0.9.

$0.92 \times 0.92 = 0.8464$

I checked my estimate by squaring it.

$\sqrt{0.84}$ is about 0.92

My estimate is not an exact value.

EXAMPLE 3 | Reasoning about square roots of decimals

Is either of these square roots an exact value: $\sqrt{0.49}$, $\sqrt{4.9}$? Evaluate each.

Bay's Solution

$$\sqrt{0.49} = \sqrt{\frac{49}{100}} = \frac{\sqrt{49}}{\sqrt{100}} = \frac{7}{10} \text{ or } 0.7$$

I can write 0.49 as a fraction where the numerator and denominator are perfect squares, so $\sqrt{0.49}$ is an exact value.

$0.7 \times 0.7 = 0.49$

I checked by multiplying.

$$\sqrt{4.9} = \sqrt{\frac{49}{10}} = \frac{\sqrt{49}}{\sqrt{10}}$$

or

$$\sqrt{4.9} = \sqrt{\frac{490}{100}} = \frac{\sqrt{490}}{\sqrt{100}}$$

I cannot write 4.9 as a fraction where the numerator and denominator are perfect squares.
In my first try, the numerator is a perfect square, but the denominator is not.
In my second try, the denominator is a perfect square, but the numerator is not, so $\sqrt{4.9}$ is not an exact value.

$4 < 4.9 < 9$ so the square root of 4.9 is a decimal between 2 and 3.

I chose perfect square benchmarks of 4 and 9 to estimate $\sqrt{4.9}$.

$\sqrt{4.9} \doteq 2.2$

Because 4.9 is much closer to 4 than to 9, I estimated a decimal value close to 2.

$2.2 \times 2.2 = 4.84$

[√] [4] [.] [9] [=] 2.2135943

I checked by multiplying.
Then I compared my estimate to the value determined using a calculator.
My estimate was reasonable.

EXAMPLE 4 | Identifying a square root between two numbers

The area of a square is between $\frac{3}{10}$ units^2 and $\frac{7}{10}$ units^2. What might the side length of the square be?

Derek's Solution: Using a number line

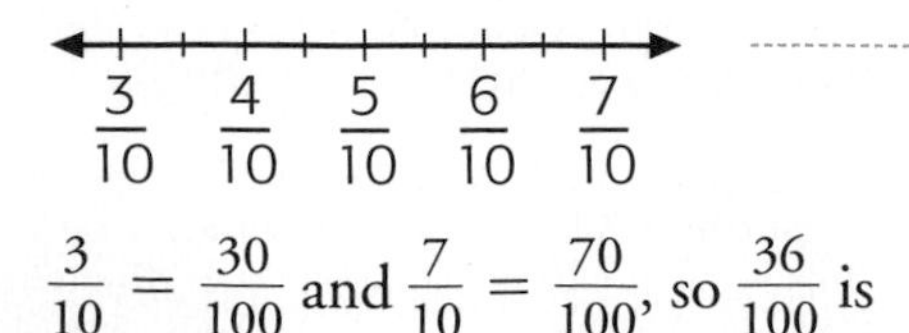

$\frac{3}{10} = \frac{30}{100}$ and $\frac{7}{10} = \frac{70}{100}$, so $\frac{36}{100}$ is

I needed a value between $\frac{3}{10}$ and $\frac{7}{10}$.
I looked for a number whose square root would be easy to calculate.

between $\frac{3}{10}$ and $\frac{7}{10}$.

$\sqrt{\frac{36}{100}} = \frac{6}{10}$ — I took the square root.

The side length of the square might be $\frac{6}{10}$ units.

Austin's Solution: Using reasoning

$\frac{3}{10} = 3 \div 10 = 0.3$ — I wrote $\frac{3}{10}$ and $\frac{7}{10}$ as decimals.

$\frac{7}{10} = 7 \div 10 = 0.7$

$0.3 < 0.5 < 0.7$ — I chose a number between 0.3 and 0.7 and determined the square root with my calculator. Then I used a nearby estimate.

[√] [0] [.] [5] [=] [.7071067]

The side length of the square might be $\frac{7}{10}$ units.

In Summary

Key Idea

- You can use perfect squares as benchmarks to estimate the square root of numbers that are not perfect squares. For example, to estimate $\sqrt{259}$, think that 16^2 is 256 and 17^2 is 289, so $\sqrt{259}$ must be closer to 16 than 17, or about 16.1.

Need to Know

- You can check the square root of a number by multiplying the square root by itself, or squaring it.
- Decimals that cannot be written as equivalent fractions with numerators and denominators that are both perfect squares have square roots that are not exact values.

Checking

1. List the two closest whole numbers between which each square root lies.
   a) $\sqrt{8.5}$ b) $\sqrt{52.4}$ c) $\sqrt{149.7}$ d) $\sqrt{\frac{5}{9}}$
2. Estimate each square root in question 1 to two decimal places using your calculator.
3. How do you know your answers to question 2 are reasonable?

Practising

4. Calculate the side length of a square with an area of $6.4\ cm^2$.

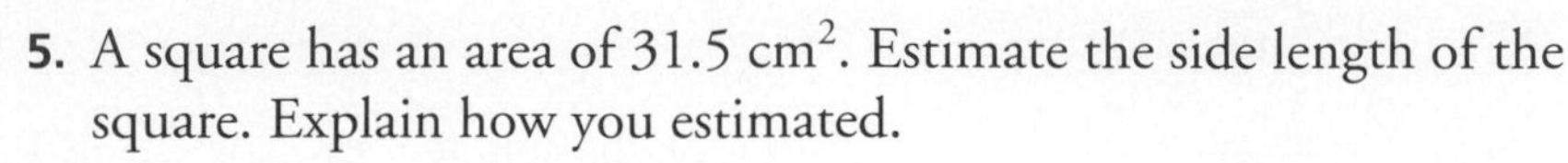

5. A square has an area of 31.5 cm^2. Estimate the side length of the square. Explain how you estimated.
6. The areas of some squares are shown. Estimate the length of the sides of each square. Then, determine the lengths using a calculator.
   a) 1.44 $units^2$ **c)** 0.01 $units^2$ **e)** $\frac{16}{144}$ $units^2$
   b) 75.6 $units^2$ **d)** $\frac{1}{4}$ $units^2$ **f)** $\frac{36}{25}$ $units^2$
7. **Multiple choice.** Between which two whole numbers does $\sqrt{26.7}$ lie?
   A. 25 and 30 **B.** 10 and 20 **C.** 5 and 6 **D.** none of these
8. **Multiple choice.** Calculate the side length of a square with an area of 6.4 cm^2.
   A. 1.6 cm **B.** 40.96 cm **C.** 2.5 cm **D.** 0.8 cm
9. Pearl is going to paint her bedroom wall pink. The wall is 2.5 m by 2.5 m. She has bought a can of paint that will cover 20 m^2.
   a) Estimate to determine if she has enough paint for two coats. Show your work.
   b) What is the side length of the largest square she can paint with two coats? Answer to the nearest metre.
10. A square-based shed has a floor area of 50.6 m^2. Which estimate is closer to the length of the front of the shed: 7.2 m or 7.7 m? Explain how you can answer this without using a calculator.

11. **a)** How do you know that $\sqrt{0.7} > 0.8$?
    b) Will the square root of a decimal always be greater than the square root of the decimal that is 0.1 greater? Explain.
12. Explain how you know that $\sqrt{6.4}$ cannot be 0.8 or 0.08.
13. A baseball diamond is a square with a side length of about 27 m. Joe throws the ball from second base to home plate. Estimate how far Joe threw the ball.

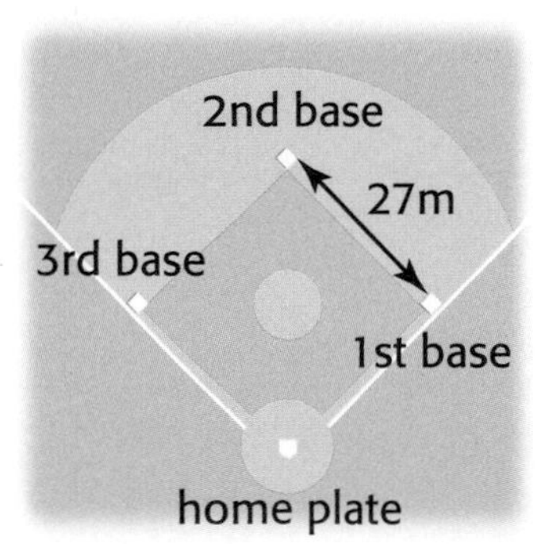

Closing

14. It's sometimes easier to calculate the square root of a decimal hundredth than a decimal tenth without a calculator, for example, 1.44 than 14.4. Is the same true for estimating?

Extending

15. Hedy estimated $\sqrt{2358}$ as 50. Explain how you could give a closer estimate.
16. The area of the rectangle is 156 cm^2. Divide the rectangle into squares to determine the approximate length of each side. Describe why you chose the strategy you used.

$A = 156$ cm^2

Chapter Self-Test

1. Sketch and label a representation for each of the following.
   a) 18^3 b) 1.2^2 c) a cube with a volume of 729 cm^3

2. Krista has a set of stacking cubes. The numerical value of the volume of the largest cube is 40 times greater than the numerical value of the area of one face of the smallest cube. The smallest cube has a volume of 125 cm^3.
   a) Determine the side length and surface area of the smallest cube. Show your work.
   b) Determine the side length and volume of the largest cube.

3. Represent each item as a power and evaluate it.
   a) $2 \times 2 \times 2 \times 2 \times 2$ b) $(-7)(-7)(-7)(-7)(-7)(-7)$

4. In Darrell's DVD collection, there are 10 action movies, 18 comedies, 4 cartoons, and 32 mysteries.
   a) Write an expression using powers to represent the number of DVDs in each category.
   b) Write an expression using the product of two different powers for the total number of DVDs.

5. Simplify as a single power and evaluate.
   a) $(-4)^3(-4)^5$
   b) $(2^7)(2^2)^3$
   c) $(1^7)^5 \div (1)^5$
   d) $(14^3)^5 \div 14^{15}$
   e) $-(2^4 \times 6^2)^3$
   f) $\dfrac{(2^5 \times 3^2)^2}{(2^4 \times 3)^2}$

6. Simplify
   a) $(x^5)(x^8) \div x^7$ b) $(a^4)^2$ c) $(c^3)^3 \div (c^2)^2$

7. Solve $3 \times 4 + (6 + 2)^2 \div 2$ using order of operations. Show each step.

8. Enter the missing numbers. Round to two decimal places if necessary.
   a) $\sqrt{56} = ■$
   b) $\sqrt{■} = 2.3$
   c) $\sqrt{\dfrac{81}{144}} = \dfrac{■}{■}$
   d) $\dfrac{\sqrt{■}}{\sqrt{■}} = \dfrac{6}{7}$
   e) $\sqrt{\dfrac{20}{5}} = ■$
   f) $\sqrt{0.36} = ■$

9. A square garden has an area of 76 m^2.
   a) Between which two whole numbers is the side length? Explain how you determined these numbers without a calculator.
   b) Determine the side length to two decimal places.

WHAT DO You Think Now?

Revisit What Do You Think? on page 49. Have your answers and explanations changed?

Chapter Review

FREQUENTLY ASKED Questions

Study | *Aid*

- See Lesson 2.5, Examples 1, 2, 3, 4, and 5.
- Try Chapter Review question 12.

Q: How can you simplify a power involving products and quotients?

A: In a product, the exponent applies to each factor. $(ab)^m = a^m b^m$
For example, $(2 \times 3)^5 = 2^5 \times 3^5$.
In a quotient the exponent applies to both the numerator and denominator. $\left(\frac{a}{b}\right)^m = \frac{a^m}{b^m}$.
For example, $\left(\frac{3}{5}\right)^2 = \frac{3^2}{5^2}$.

Study | *Aid*

- See Lesson 2.6, Examples 1, 2, and 3 and Lesson 2.7, Example 4.
- Try Chapter Review questions 13 and 14.

Q: How can you evaluate an expression involving many operations?

A: Use BEDMAS (Brackets, Exponents, Division, Multiplication, Addition, Subtraction) to help you remember the order to perform the operations. For example,

$4 + 6[2^3 + (6 - 4)] \div 2$	Evaluate what is in the **B**rackets. Start with the innermost brackets, if there is more than one set.
$= 4 + 6[2^3 + 2] \div 2$	Evaluate powers next, using the **E**xponents.
$= 4 + 6[8 + 2] \div 2$	
$= 4 + 6(10) \div 2$	**D**ivide and **M**ultiply from left to right.
$= 4 + 60 \div 2$	
$= 4 + 30$	**A**dd and **S**ubtract from left to right.
$= 34$	

Study | *Aid*

- See Lesson 2.7, Examples 1, 2, and 3, and Lesson 2.8, Examples 1, 2, 3, and 4.
- Try Chapter Review questions 15, 16, 17, 18, and 19.

Q: How can you calculate or estimate a square root?

A1: You can use the square root key on your calculator ($\sqrt{\ }$). For example, [√] [2] [7] [.] [4] [=] [5.234500931]
You can check your answer by multiplying the square root by itself to see if you get the original number.

A2: You can use perfect squares as benchmarks to estimate the square root of numbers that are not perfect squares. For example, $\sqrt{27.4}$ is between $\sqrt{25}$ and $\sqrt{36}$, and is much closer to $\sqrt{25}$. It is likely about 5.2.

Practice

Lesson 2.1

1. Sketch a model to represent the following. Label each side length.
   a) a square field with an area of 225 m^2
   b) 10^2
   c) a cube with a side length of three units

2. a) Calculate the side length of a square with an area of 196 mm^2.
   b) Calculate the side length of a cube with a volume of 125 cm^3.

3. Nita is planting 49 carrot seeds to grow in her garden. She wants to plant them in a square plot. She needs to plant them 3 cm apart, and 3 cm apart from the edge of the plot.
   a) Sketch the square garden with the seeds.
   b) Determine the dimensions of the garden.
   c) Determine the area of the garden.

Lesson 2.2

4. Complete the table.

	Power	Base	Exponent	Repeated Multiplication	Value
a)	$(-3)^4$				
b)				$-(6)(6)(6)$	
c)		-4			256

5. Evaluate without using a calculator. Show your work.
   a) 6^2 b) -2.3^3 c) $-(-1)^3$

6. Susan needs to wrap two gift boxes in the shape of cubes. She has a sheet of wrapping paper 140 cm by 30 cm. One box is 7 cm by 7 cm by 7 cm. Each side of the other box has an area of 529 cm^2. Does she have enough wrapping paper to wrap both boxes? Show your work.

Lesson 2.4

7. Simplify.
   a) $(5^5)^5(5^2)$ b) $\frac{(12^2)^3}{12^2}$ c) $(19^7)(19) \div (19^2)^2(19^2)$

8. Evaluate.
   a) $(6^2)(6^3)^2$ b) $\frac{(4^5)^2}{4^6}$ c) $\frac{(-3^2)(-3^7)}{(-3^2)^3(-3^3)}$

9. Simplify.
   a) $[(x^5)(x^2)]^2$ b) $a^9 \div a^5 \div a$ c) $(v^4)^6 \div (v^3)^5$

10. Use repeated multiplication to explain why each statement is true.

a) $\frac{8^5}{8^3} = 8^2$ b) $6^2 \times 6^5 = 6^7$

11. Express 32^2 with a base of 2.

Lesson 2.5

12. Express as a power with a single base. Show your work.

a) $(6^3 \times 36^4)^2$ b) $\left(\frac{7^6}{7^3}\right)^4$

Lesson 2.6

13. Simplify without using a calculator. Show all your work.

a) $16^2 - 8^2 \div 2^2$ b) $6^2 + 2 \times 3^2 - 8$

14. Which question would you ask to see if someone understands order of operations? Explain why.

A. $9^4 \times 3^2 + 4^3$ **B.** $9^4 + 3^2 \times 4^3$

Lesson 2.7

15. Evaluate.

a) $\sqrt{289}$

b) $\sqrt{39.69}$

c) $\sqrt{\frac{16}{36}}$

d) $\frac{\sqrt{121}}{\sqrt{144}}$

e) $\frac{\sqrt{25}}{5}$

f) $\sqrt{70.8964}$

16. Verify each statement. Show your work.

a) $\sqrt{4.9} = 0.7$ b) $\sqrt{4.8} = 2.4$ c) $\sqrt{0.0036} = 0.06$

Lesson 2.8

17. A square arena has an area of 200 m^2.

a) Without using a calculator, state the two whole numbers between which its side length is located.

b) Which whole number from part a) is a better estimate, and why?

c) Determine the length of its side to two decimal places.

18. A square garden has an area of 40 m^2. Which is a better estimate for the length of the garden: 6.3 m or 6.9 m? Explain how you can answer this without using a calculator.

19. Katie and her brother Nick started a window washing business to earn money in the summer. In one job, they had to wash windows that were 4.8 m off the ground. There was a hedge of large bushes beside the house so they needed to set the base of the ladder 3.2 m away from the house. About how long did the ladder need to be?

Chapter Task

Testing Skills

YOU WILL NEED

- a calculator

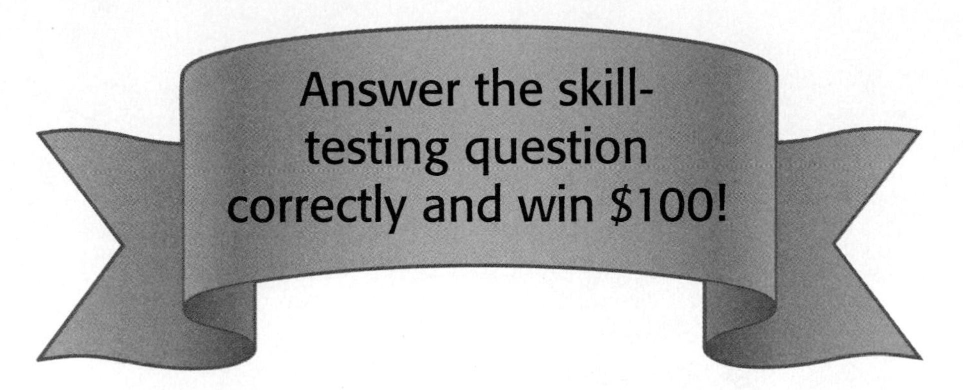

A Mathletics Council is holding a contest to promote math awareness. The winners of the contest will share the $100 prize equally. To win, a contestant needs to answer a skill-testing math question correctly. You have been asked to create the question. Your question must meet the following criteria.

- The answer to the question must be 100.
- There must be at least four numbers in the question.
- The operations must include a power and a square root.
- To answer the question correctly, order of operations (BEDMAS) must be used. If you just solve the question from left to right, you will not get 100 as your answer.
- It must be tricky, because you want only a few people to win.
- You must provide the correct solution to your question.
- You must also provide examples of some mistakes that people might make.

? What is the best skill-testing question you can create?

Task | ***Checklist***

✔ Did you show all the steps in your solution(s)?

✔ Did you verify your solutions?

Chapter 3

Similar Polygons

GOALS

You will be able to

- use the concept of similarity to compare polygons
- draw and interpret scale diagrams of 2-D shapes
- solve problems using properties of similar polygons or scale diagrams
- communicate about the concept of similarity

Which polygons in the blanket have the same shape?

Getting Started

YOU WILL NEED

- Rectangles
- a ruler

Sorting Swatches

The art teacher has asked you to sort some rectangular pieces of fabric for a project.

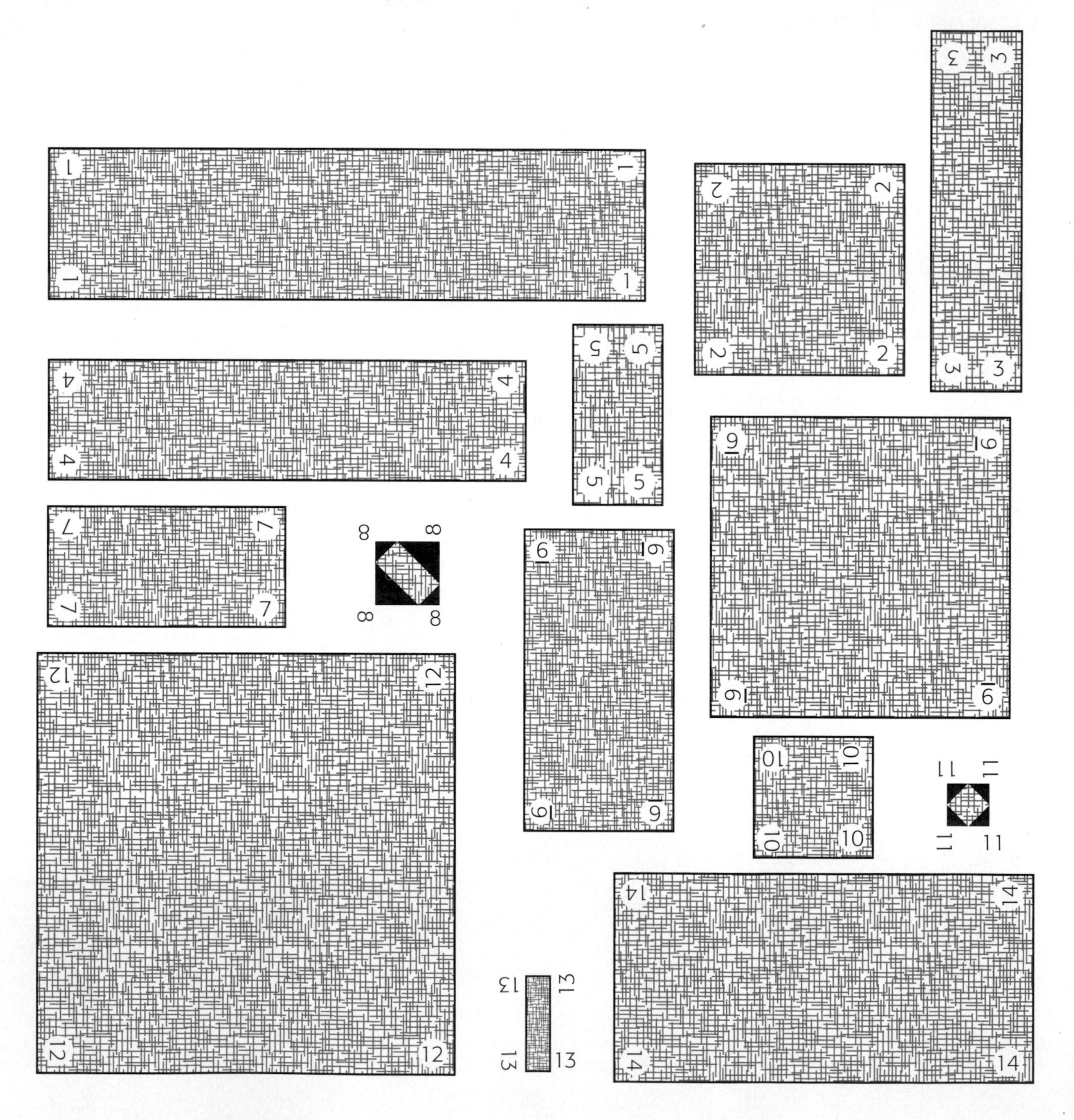

How can you select a sorting rule for the rectangles?

A. Organize the rectangles into groups that you think have the same shape but differ in size.

B. Create a separate table like the one shown for each group of rectangles from part A.

Group__

Rectangle	Length	Width	Area	Perimeter
1				

C. Measure the side lengths of each rectangle and record them in your tables. Record the longer measurement as the length.

D. Calculate the area and perimeter of each rectangle and record them in your tables.

E. Look for patterns in your tables.

F. How can you use the patterns you found to make a sorting rule for the rectangles?

WHAT DO You Think?

Decide whether you agree or disagree with each statement. Explain your thinking.

1. If you extend the length and width of a rectangle by the same amount, you get a rectangle that has the same shape as the original, but the size is different.
2. Two rectangles are different sizes, but both are long and thin. The ratio of length to width for each rectangle must be the same.
3. Two different parallelograms each have a 30° angle. They will have the same shape but may be different sizes.
4. A large hexagon and a small hexagon each have four equal sides. They will be the same shape, but will be different sizes.

3.1 Enlargements and Reductions

YOU WILL NEED

- a ruler

GOAL

Recognize whether or not one shape is an enlargement or reduction of another.

EXPLORE the Math

Rachel made several enlargements and reductions of a photo for her display on Winter Olympic sports. She knows that the snowboarder will differ in size, but his body should not be distorted. Some of the photos don't look right.

Original photo

A.

B.

C.

D.

E.

? **How can Rachel tell which images are true enlargements or reductions?**

3.2 Determining Similarity

GOAL

Develop strategies to determine if two shapes are similar.

YOU WILL NEED

- a ruler
- a protractor

LEARN ABOUT the Math

Jia-Wen and Sam are sorting isosceles triangles to solve a puzzle in a magazine.

Sam thinks that triangle *GHI* is the answer.

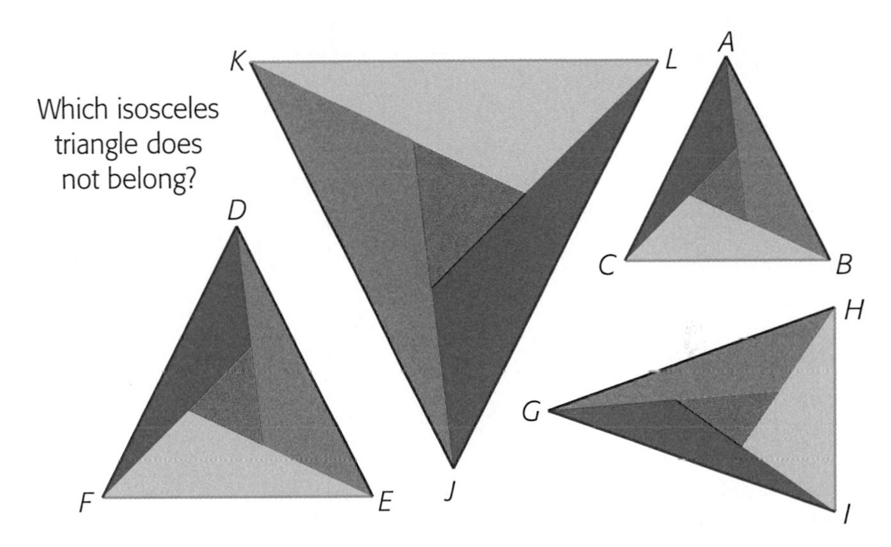

? How can you verify that Sam is correct?

EXAMPLE 1 | Sorting shapes by properties

Sam's Solution: Comparing angles

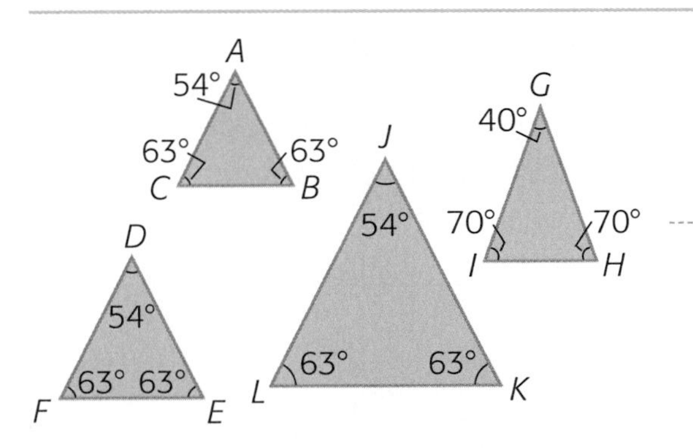

I noticed that the **corresponding angles** in the triangles with the same shape seem to be equal. I decided to measure the angles to see how they compared. I sketched the triangles to record the measurements.

$\triangle$ *GHI* does not belong. Its angles are 40°, 70°, and 70° and do not equal the corresponding angles in the other triangles.
All the other triangles have angles that are 54°, 63°, and 63°.

corresponding angles
angles that match when two shapes are arranged to look the same; e.g., in Sam's triangles, $\angle ACB$ and $\angle DFE$ are corresponding angles.

Jia-Wen's Solution: Comparing sides

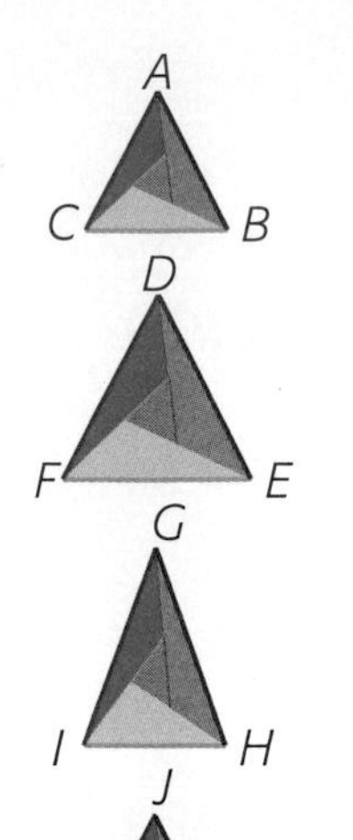

Triangle	Base (cm)	Side 1 (cm)	Side 2 (cm)
ABC	2.7	3	3
DEF	3.6	4	4
GHI	2.7	4	4
JKL	5.4	6	6

I measured the sides of each triangle and wrote the measurements in a table so that I could look for patterns.

For $\triangle JKL$ and $\triangle ABC$

Base: $LK : CB$
$5.4 : 2.7$
$2 : 1$

I noticed that the shape for $\triangle ABC$ and the shape for $\triangle JKL$ look the same. The measurements for $\triangle JKL$ are double the measurements for $\triangle ABC$.

Side 1: $JK : AB$
$6 : 3$
$2 : 1$

Side 2: $JL : AC$
$6 : 3$
$2 : 1$

This means the ratio of the bases is the same as the ratio of the sides.

The ratios of the lengths of **corresponding sides** are the same.

For $\triangle DEF$ and $\triangle ABC$

Base: $FE : CB$
$3.6 : 2.7$
$4 : 3$

I decided to compare the sides in other pairs of triangles that look like they have the same shape.

Side 1: $DE : AB$
$4 : 3$

Since $\triangle ABC$, $\triangle DEF$, and $\triangle JKL$ all have the same ratios of corresponding sides, they are all **similar polygons**.

Side 2: $DF : AC$
$4 : 3$

The ratios of corresponding sides are the same.

$\triangle ABC \sim \triangle DEF \sim \triangle JKL$

corresponding sides

sides that match if two shapes are arranged to look the same; e.g., in the parallelograms below, *AB* and *EF* are corresponding sides.

similar polygons

two or more polygons that are identical or where each polygon looks like an enlargement or reduction of the other. In similar polygons, the ratios of all corresponding linear measures are the same, and all corresponding angles are equal; e.g., in the similar polygons below, $\angle D$ and $\angle H$ are corresponding angles and *AD* and *EH* are corresponding sides.

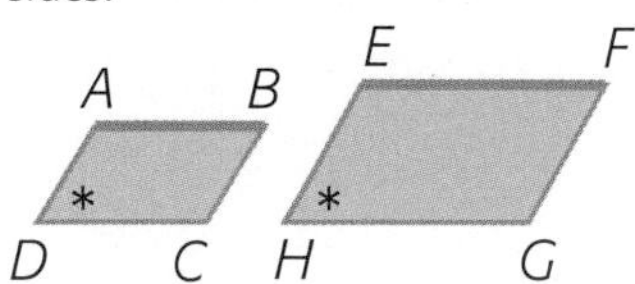

For $\triangle JKL$ and $\triangle GHI$

Bases: $KL : HI$

$5.4 : 2.7$

$2 : 1$

Side 1: $JK : GH$

$6 : 4$

$3 : 2$

Then, I compared ^ *GHI* to each of the other triangles to see if the ratios of corresponding sides were different.

The ratios of corresponding sides are different. $\triangle JKL$ and $\triangle GHI$ are not similar.

$\triangle DEF$ and $\triangle GHI$ are not similar. They have the same side lengths but different base lengths, so I know the ratios of corresponding sides are different.

$\triangle ABC$ and $\triangle GHI$ are not similar. They have the same base lengths but different side lengths, so I know that the ratios of corresponding sides are different.

$\triangle GHI$ does not belong because when you compare it to the other triangles, the corresponding sides form different ratios.

Communication | *Tip*

The symbol ~ is used to show that two shapes are similar. For these two similar trapezoids, you can write *JKLM* ~ *NOPQ*. Notice that the first, second, third, and fourth letters in each trapezoid's name represent corresponding angles.

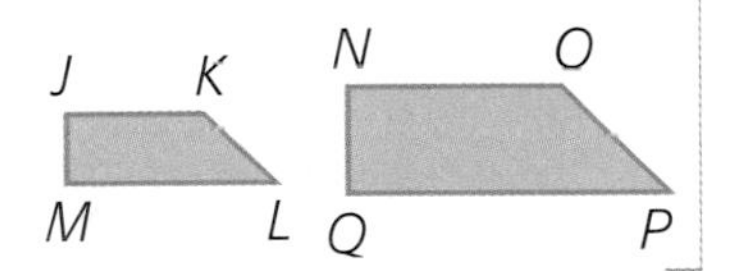

Reflecting

A. If two triangles have two pairs of corresponding sides in the same ratio, can you conclude that they are similar?

B. If all of the corresponding angles of a triangle are equal, the triangles are similar. How many pairs of corresponding angles do you need to show are equal before you can conclude that two triangles are similar?

C. Should you look for proportional sides or equal angles to test whether four-sided figures are similar? Explain.

Reading Strategy

Activating Knowledge

What do you already know about polygons that will help you to answer these questions?

WORK WITH the Math

EXAMPLE 2 | Comparing ratios within shapes

Are these rectangles similar? If so, by how much is *ABCD* enlarged to get *EFGH*?

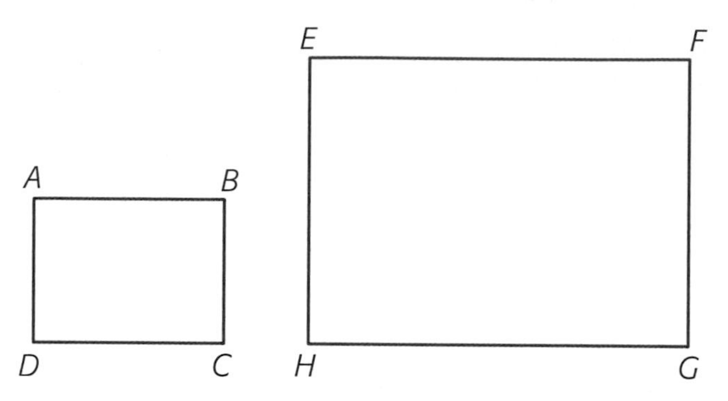

David's Solution

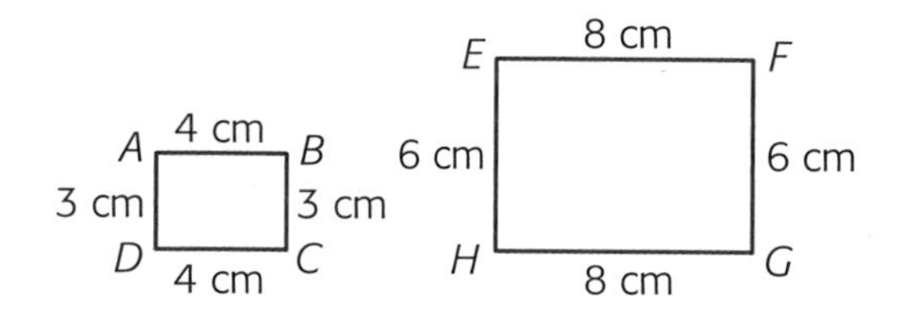

All rectangles have equal angles, so measuring the angles wouldn't help me decide. I measured and recorded the lengths and widths.

Ratios of lengths of corresponding sides:
$AB:EF \quad 4:8 = 1:2$
$AD:EH \quad 3:6 = 1:2$
The ratios are the same.
$ABCD \sim EFGH$
EFGH is twice as large as *ABCD*.

I didn't have to check *BC*:*FG* or *CD*:*GH* because in rectangles opposite sides are equal, so I knew the ratios would be the same.

Length : Width
$AB:AD \quad 4:3$

$EF:EH \quad 8:6 = 4:3$

While I was working on the solution, I noticed that the ratio of the length to width in each rectangle was 4:3.

I think I can compare the ratios of all corresponding sides between rectangles or I can compare the ratio of lengths and widths within rectangles to determine similarity.

EXAMPLE 3 | Checking for similarity

The student council sent in design *ABCDEF* and asked for a reduction of it to be put onto T-shirts. When the T-shirts arrived, the design looked like *GHIJKL*. How can they convince the company that an error has been made?

Larissa's Solution

$AB : GH$ 2 : 1
$BC : HI$ 2 : 1
$CD : IJ$ 2 : 1
$DE : JK$ 2 : 1
$EF : KL$ 3 : 2.5, or 1.2 : 1
$FA : LG$ 2 : 1

I decided to write a letter to the company explaining why the designs are not the same shape.
I chose to measure, and then compare, the pairs of corresponding sides.

The two hexagons are not similar. Their corresponding angles must also not be equal.

$\angle AFE = 92°$ $\angle GLK = 69°$

To confirm my conjecture, I measured $\angle AFE$ and $\angle GLK$.

One pair of corresponding angles are not the same. My conjecture is correct.

When something should be true for all cases, I only have to show one case where it fails. Just showing that the angles were different would have been enough.

In Summary

Key Ideas

- Polygons are similar if the ratios of all pairs of corresponding sides are the same and all pairs of corresponding angles are equal. $\angle A = \angle D$, $\angle B = \angle E$, and $\angle C = \angle F$.
- The ratios of sides within one shape are the same as the ratio of the corresponding sides within a similar shape. $AB : BC = DE : EF$

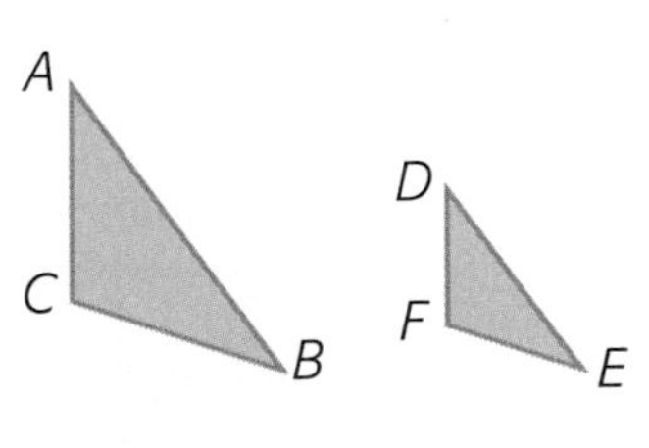

(continued)

Need to Know

- To show that two polygons are similar, you must compare the ratios of the side lengths and check that corresponding angles are equal.

same angles, but not similar

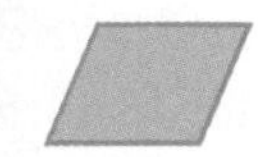

corresponding sides in same ratio, but not similar

Checking

1. Is each pair of shapes similar? Explain how you know.
   a) A and E
   b) B and D
   c) A and B
   d) D and E
   e) A and C
   f) C and E

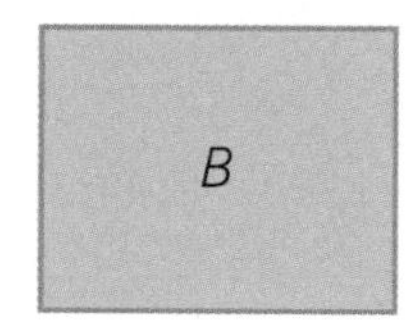

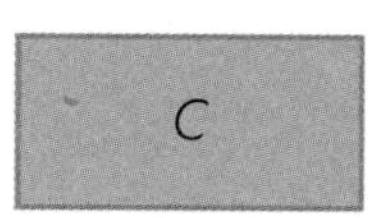

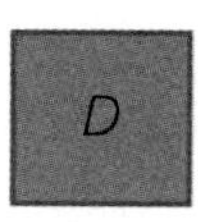

2. Three rectangles have these dimensions: 6 cm by 2 cm, 12 cm by 4 cm, and 18 cm by 6 cm. Are they similar? Explain your thinking.

Practising

3. Which shapes are similar?

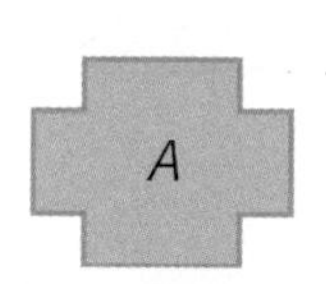

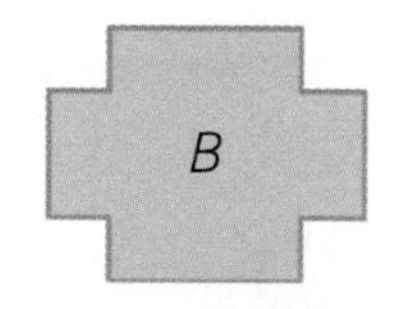

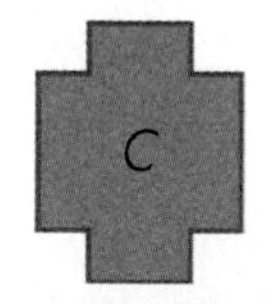

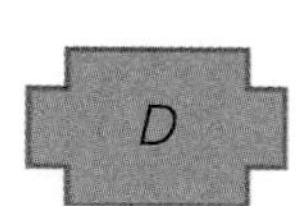

4. Is each pair of shapes similar? Justify your answer.
   a)

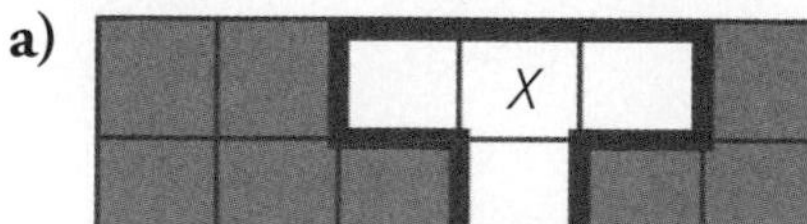

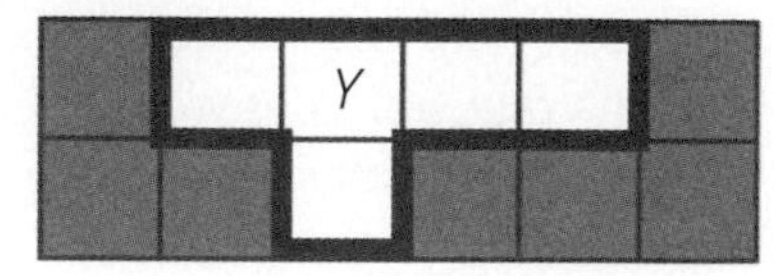

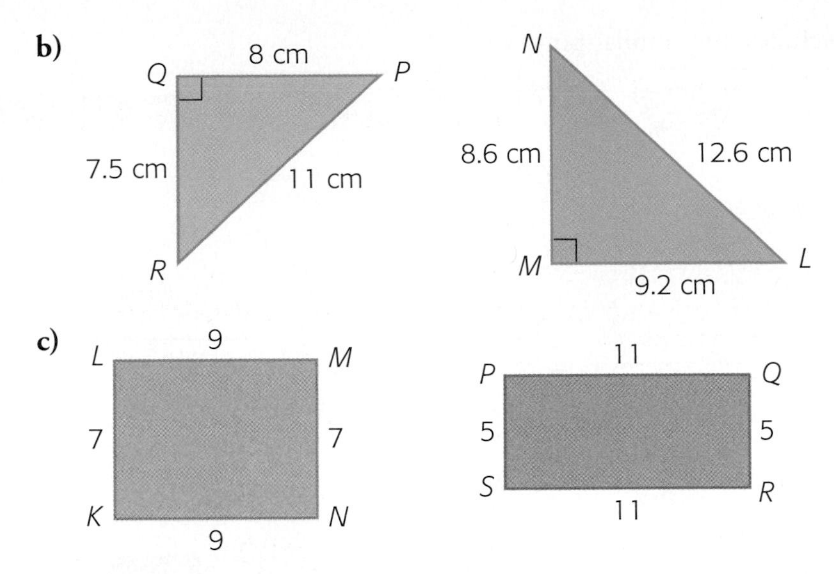

5. Select the similar shape for each.

	Shape	A	B	C	D
a)					
b)					
c)					

6. The triangles at right are similar. How can you prove it?

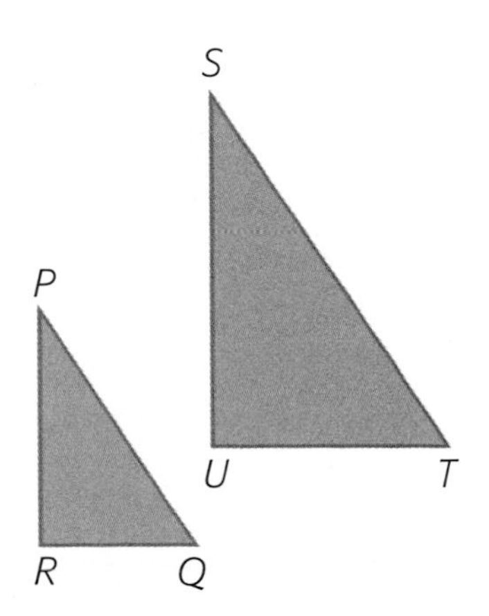

7. Which shapes are similar? Justify your decisions.

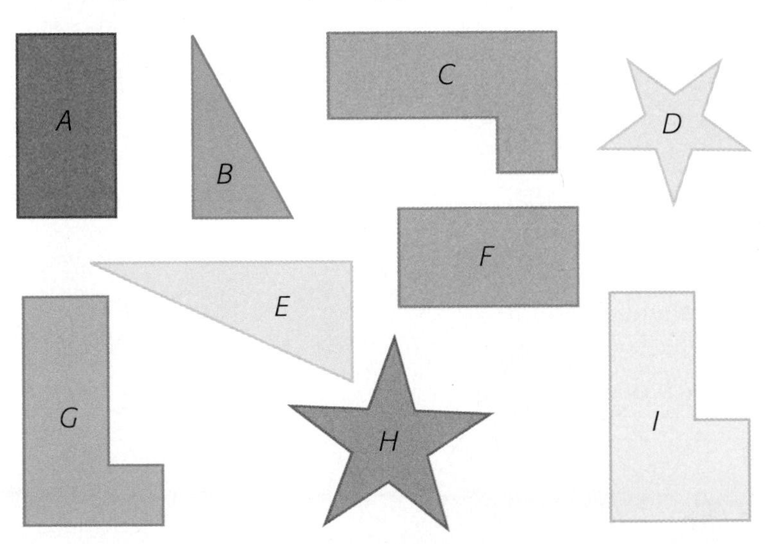

8. Multiple choice. Which set includes only similar polygons?

A.

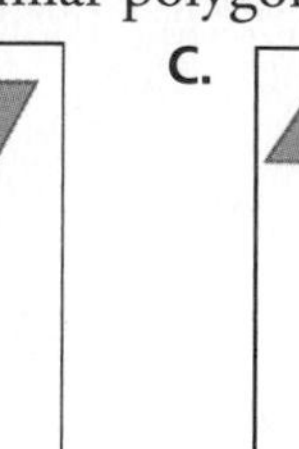

C.

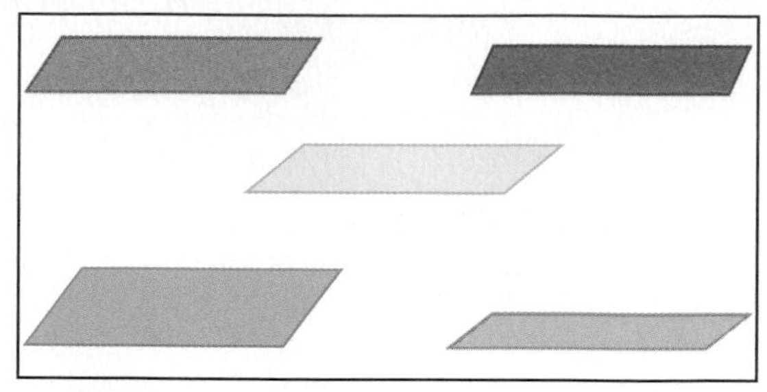

B.

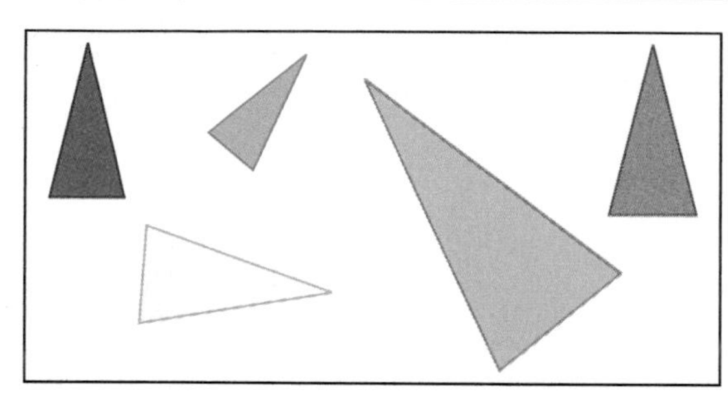

D.

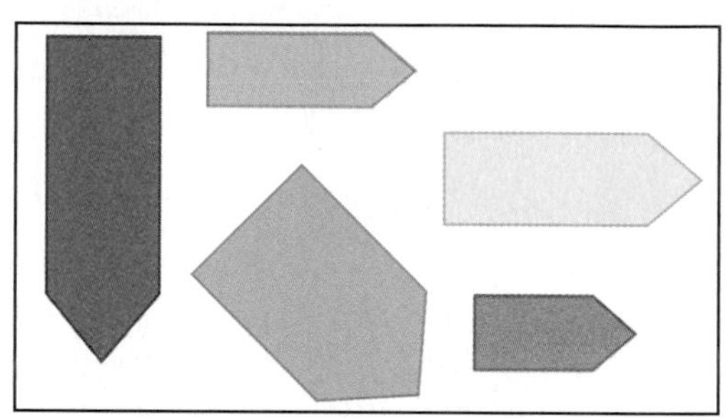

9. Multiple choice. Which ratio represents the relationship between the corresponding sides of these similar trapezoids?

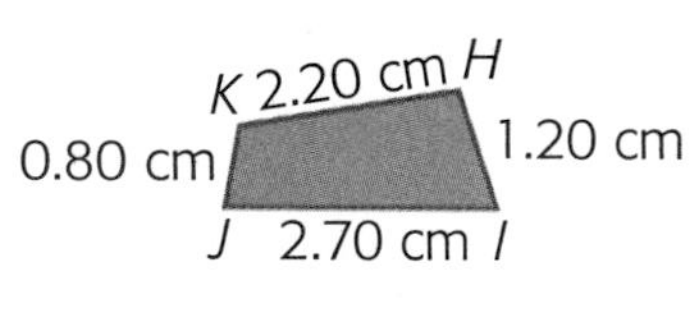

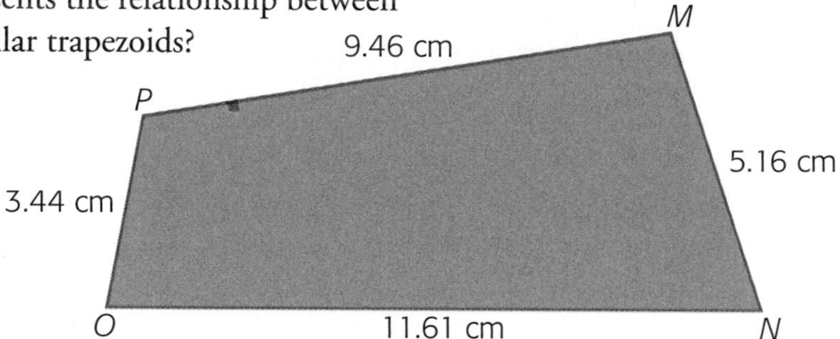

A. 1:2.1 **B.** 1:4.3 **C.** 2:3 **D.** 1:3.4

10. Measure the dimensions of the parallelograms and calculate the ratio of the lengths of adjacent sides AB and AD and EF and EH. What conclusion can you make?

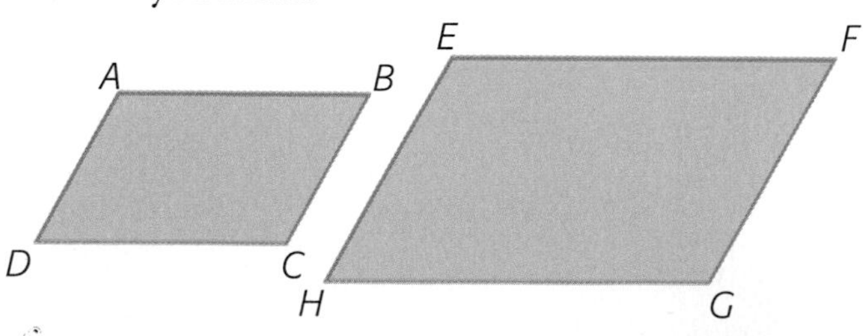

11. Measure the sides of the similar shapes and determine

a) the ratio of corresponding sides

b) the ratio of base to height within each shape

12. These sets of polygons are similar. What is the length of side AB?

a)

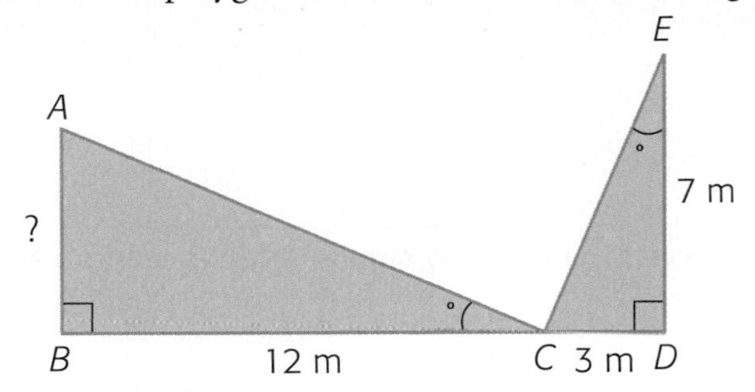

b)

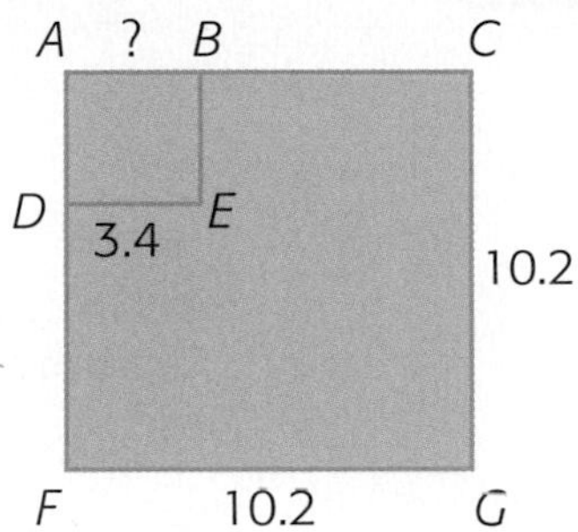

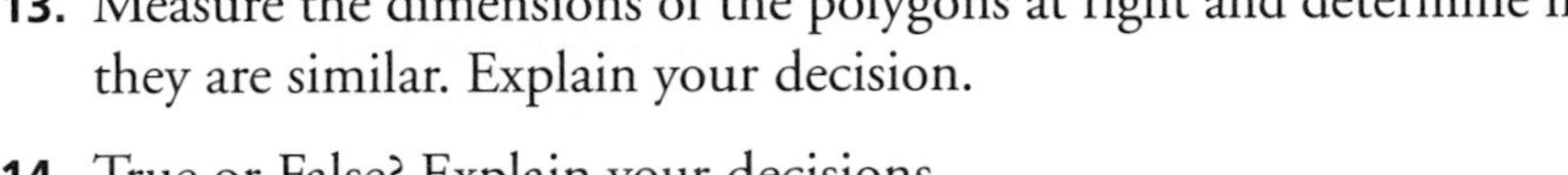

13. Measure the dimensions of the polygons at right and determine if they are similar. Explain your decision.

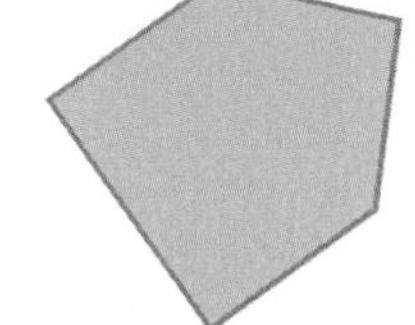

14. True or False? Explain your decisions.

a) All congruent shapes are similar.
b) All similar shapes are congruent.
c) All rectangles are similar.
d) All squares are similar.
e) All equilateral triangles are similar.
f) All isosceles triangles are similar.

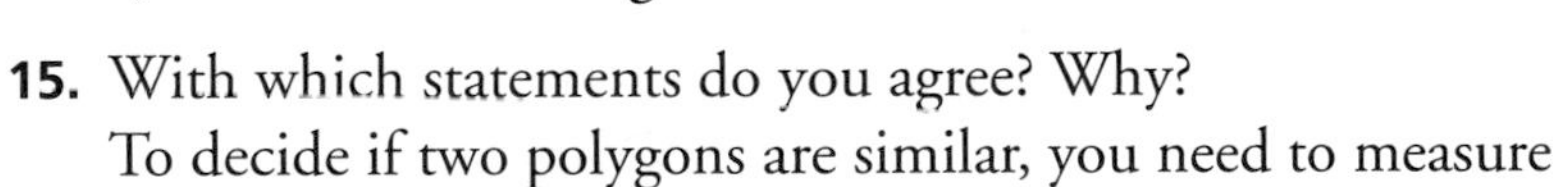

15. With which statements do you agree? Why?
To decide if two polygons are similar, you need to measure

A. just two sides of each polygon
B. all the sides of each polygon
C. all the angles of each polygon
D. all the sides and all the angles

Closing

16. $\triangle ABC$ has angles of 45°, 45°, and 90°. $\triangle DEF$ has angles of 60°, 60°, and 60°. Are the triangles similar? Explain.

Extending

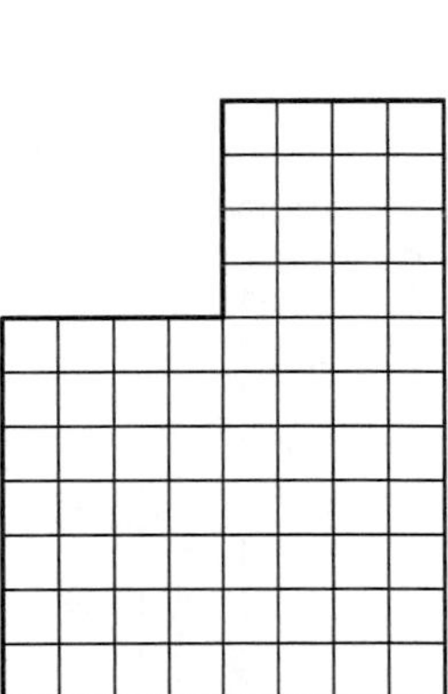

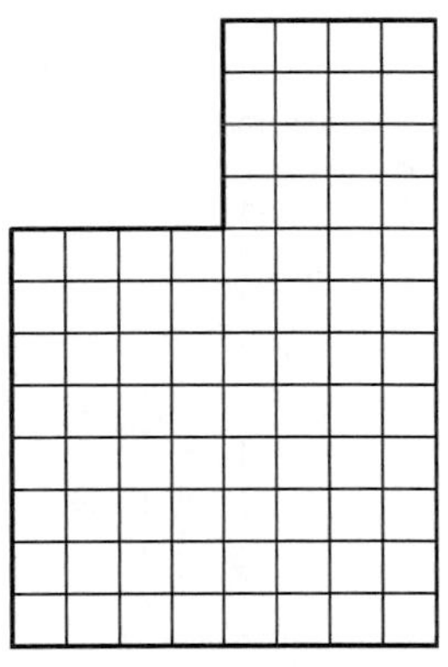

17. a) Draw the shape at right on grid paper.
b) Sketch four shapes inside that are similar to the original shape.

18. Suppose that $\triangle PQR \sim \triangle LMN$ and $\angle P = 90°$.

a) What angle in $\triangle LMN$ equals 90°? How do you know?
b) $MN = 13$ cm, $LN = 12$ cm, $LM = 5$ cm, and $PQ = 15$ cm. How long are PR and QR?

19. How would you convince someone that $\triangle ABC$ is similar to $\triangle DBE$?

3.3 Scale Factors

YOU WILL NEED

- a ruler
- a protractor
- a calculator

GOAL

Describe the relationship between similar shapes using a scale factor.

LEARN ABOUT the Math

Thomas went to the architect's talk on career day. He had a chance to look at the blueprints that builders use to construct buildings.

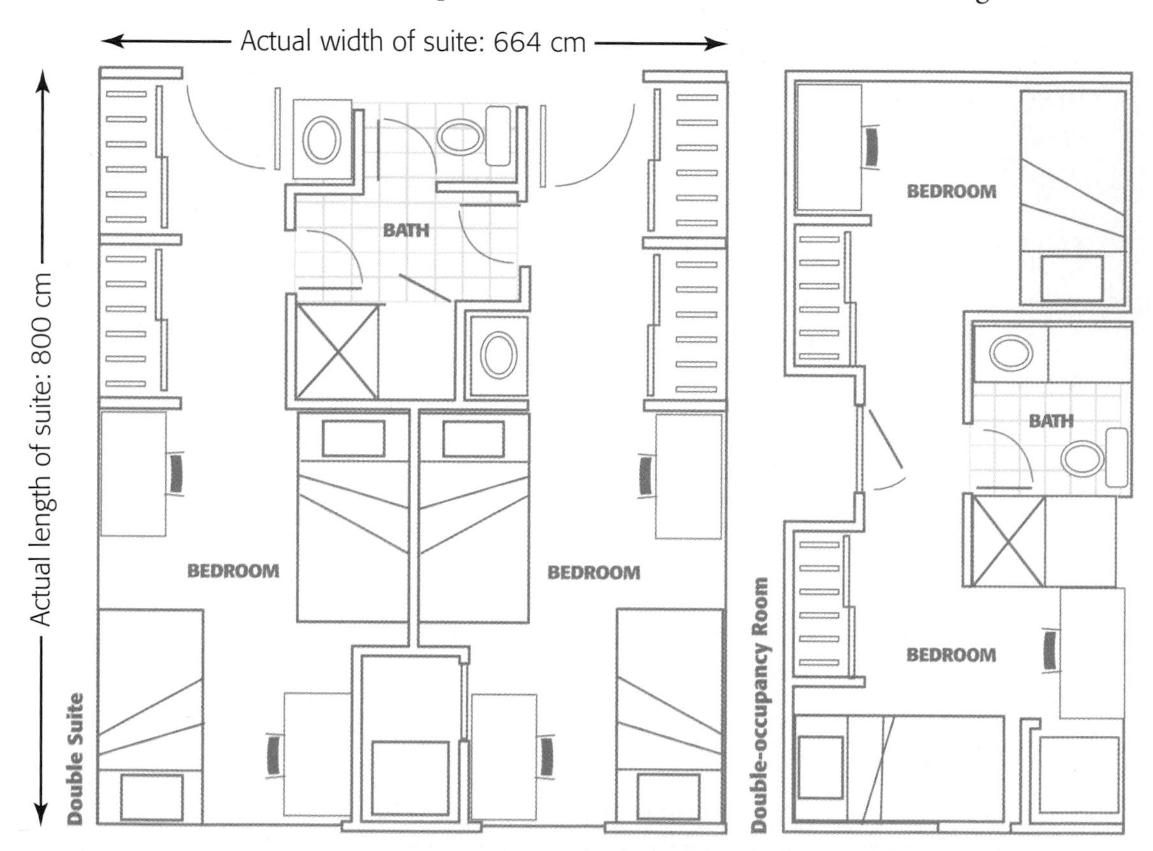

? If a measurement is missing on the blueprint, how can the actual measurement be determined?

A. Complete the table to compare the dimensions of the blueprint with the floor plan of the actual building. What do you notice?

	Blueprint	Floor Plan	Ratio
Length of double suite	10 cm	800 cm	
Width of double suite	8.3 cm		

B. Why is it important that the blueprint be similar to the actual floor plan?

C. What is the **scale factor** of the blueprint and the building?

D. Explain how the scale factor relates the length of the double suite on the blueprint to that of the building.

E. Use the scale factor to determine the width of the double-occupancy room in the building.

scale factor

the factor one dimension of a polygon is multiplied by to calculate the corresponding dimension of a similar polygon

Reflecting

F. If you know two shapes are similar, how can you calculate the scale factor?

G. If a measurement is missing on diagrams of similar shapes, how can you use the scale factor to calculate the missing measurement?

Communication | *Tip*

The scale factor can be expressed as a ratio, a percent, or as a whole number, fraction, or decimal. For example, if lengths are doubled, the scale ratio can be described as 2:1, 200%, or 2.

WORK WITH the Math

EXAMPLE 1 | Using scale factors to determine similarity

Determine which of these shapes are similar. For the shapes that are similar, determine the scale factor.

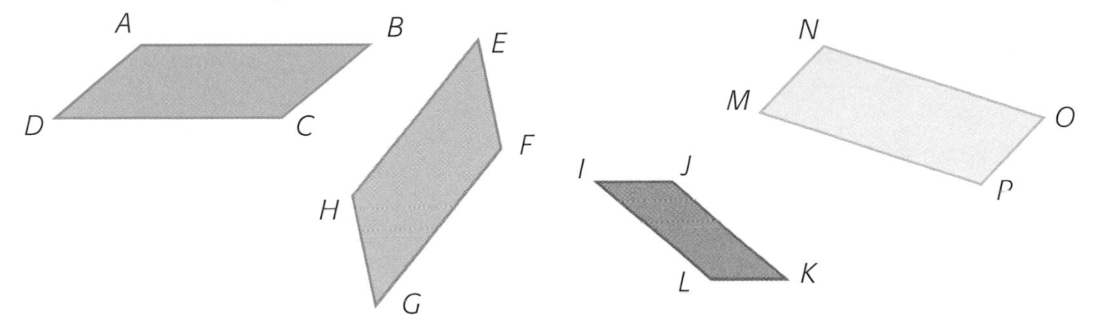

Rachel's Solution

$\angle DAB = 140°$ $\angle EFG = 130°$ $\angle IJK = 140°$ $\angle MNO = 115°$
$\angle ABC = 40°$ $\angle FGH = 50°$ $\angle JKL = 40°$ $\angle NOP = 65°$
$\angle DCB = 140°$ $\angle GHE = 130°$ $\angle KLI = 140°$ $\angle OPM = 115°$
$\angle CDA = 40°$ $\angle HEF = 50°$ $\angle LIJ = 40°$ $\angle PMN = 65°$

I measured all of the angles. The only two parallelograms with all of the corresponding angles the same are *ABCD* and *IJKL*. They could be similar.

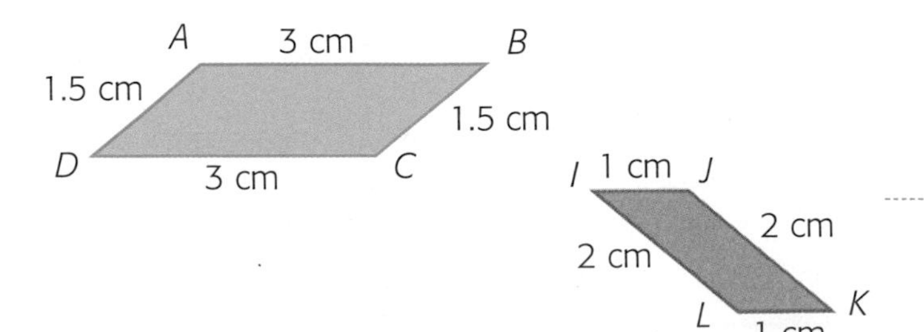

I measured the side lengths for *ABCD* and *IJKL*.

$AB:JK = 3:2$ or $1.5:1$ $AD:JI = 1.5:1$
$DC:IL = 3:2$ or $1.5:1$ $BC:KL = 1.5:1$

I determined the ratios of the corresponding sides.

parallelogram $IJKL \sim$ parallelogram $ABCD$.
The scale factor for the enlargement of $IJKL$ to $ABCD$ is $3:2$ or 1.5 or 150%.
The scale factor for the reduction of $ABCD$ to $IJKL$ is $2:3$ or $\frac{2}{3}$ or about 67%.

I could also write the scale factor for the enlargement as $\frac{3}{2}$ or $1.5:1$.

EXAMPLE 2 Scale factors greater than 1

Thomas is planning a trip from Regina to Edmonton for a hockey tournament. He wants to know how long the trip will take.

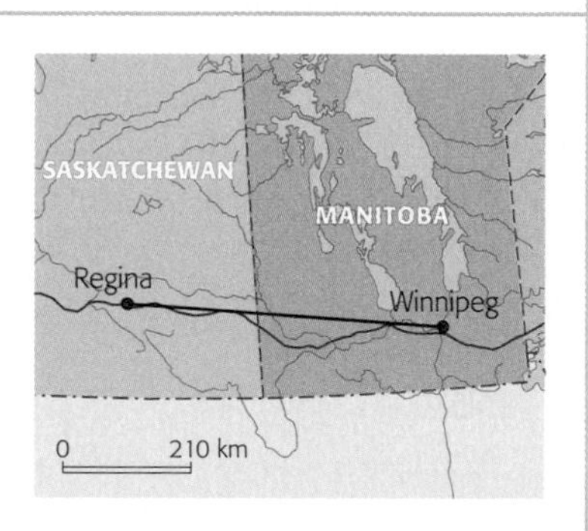

Thomas's Solution

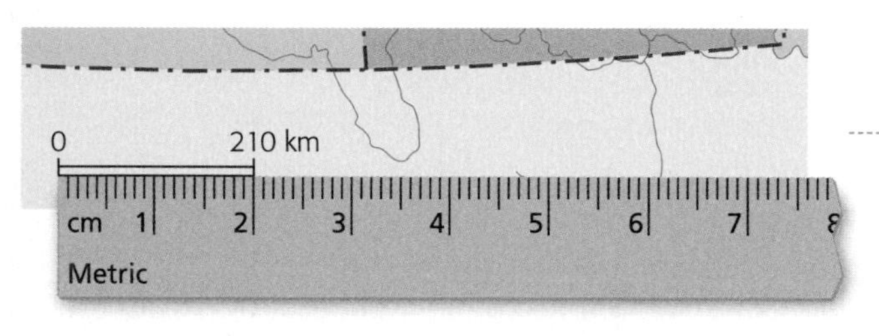

The highway from Regina to Winnipeg is not straight, but it is close, so I can use a ruler on the map to estimate the distance from Regina to Winnipeg.

The scale says 210 km is represented by 2 cm on the map. To figure out what to multiply by, the measurements have to be in the same units. I know that 210 km is 21 000 000 cm, so the scale factor is 21 000 000 : 2, or 10 500 000.

I used the relationship between units to calculate the scale factor.
I expect the scale factor to be greater than 1, since the actual distance is an enlargement of the map.

Regina to Winnipeg: 5.5 cm

I measured the distance from Regina to Winnipeg on the map.

$5.1 \times 10\,500\,000 = 53\,550\,000$ cm
$53\,550\,000 \div 100 = 535\,500$ m
$535\,500 \div 1000 = 535$ km

I multiplied by the scale factor to calculate the real distance.

535 km is close to 500 km and I will travel at about 100 km/h. I estimate the trip will take about 5 hours.

I rounded the distance and estimated my travelling speed to estimate how long the trip will take.

EXAMPLE 3 | Scale factor less than 1

Art students are making bags in their textile course. Their assignment is to make new bags that are 60% of the size of the pattern shown, but maintain the original shape. What will be the reduced measurements?

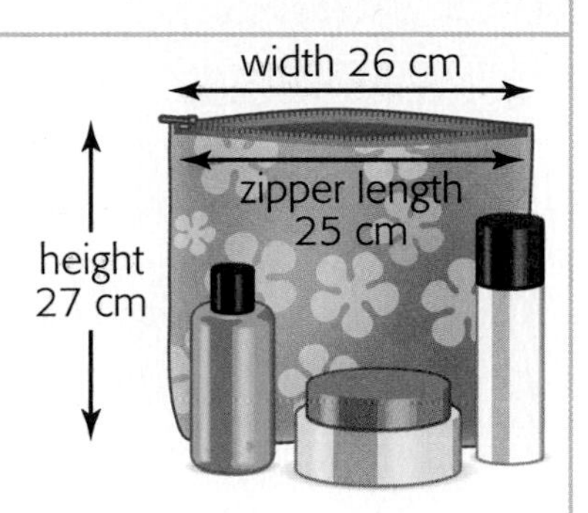

David's Solution: Using decimals

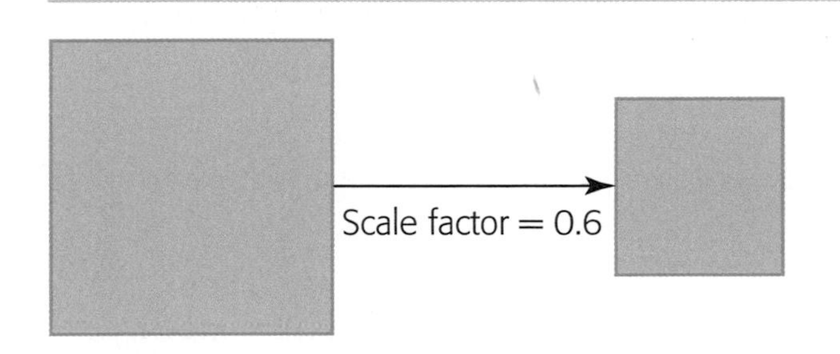

The new dimensions will be similar to the original dimensions. I expect the scale factor to be between 0 and 1, since the new bag is a reduction of the pattern. The scale factor is 0.6, since the new bag is 60% as wide.

$27 \times 0.6 = 16.2$
$26 \times 0.6 = 15.6$
$25 \times 0.6 = 15$

I multiplied each measurement by the scale factor 0.6 to calculate the new measurement.

The reduced dimensions will be 16.2 cm by 15.6 cm. The zipper will be 15 cm long.

Larissa's Solution: Using equivalent ratios

The scale factor is 6 : 10

The length and width of the new bag will be 60% as long as the old size. As a ratio, that's 60 : 100 or 6 : 10.

For the 27 cm side:

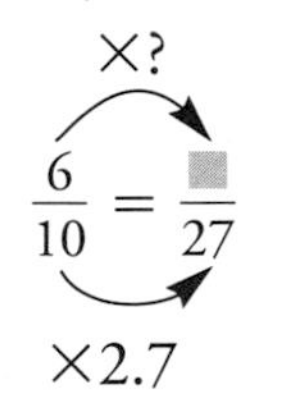

$$\frac{6}{10} = \frac{\blacksquare}{27}$$

The ratio of the new measurements to the old measurements will be equivalent to $\frac{6}{10}$.

$10 \times 2.7 = 27$
$6 \times 2.7 = 16.2$

For the 26 cm side:

$$\frac{6}{10} = \frac{\blacksquare}{26}$$

$10 \times 2.6 = 26$
$6 \times 2.6 = 15.6$

For the 25 cm zipper:

$$\frac{6}{10} = \frac{\blacksquare}{25}$$

$10 \times 2.5 = 25$
$6 \times 2.5 = 15$

The reduced bag will be 16.2 cm by 15.6 cm. The bag will need a zipper 15 cm long.

In Summary

Key Ideas

- The ratio of a side length of a shape and the corresponding side length of a similar shape is the **scale factor**.
- You can multiply any length of a shape by the scale factor to calculate the corresponding length of a similar shape.

Need to Know

- When the scale factor is a number between 0 and 1, the new shape is a reduction of the original shape.
- When the scale factor is a number greater than 1, the new shape is an enlargement of the original shape.

Checking

1. $\triangle ABC \sim \triangle DEF$.

a) Write a statement using a scale factor that expresses one shape as an enlargement of the other.

b) Write a statement using a scale factor that expresses one shape as a reduction of the other.

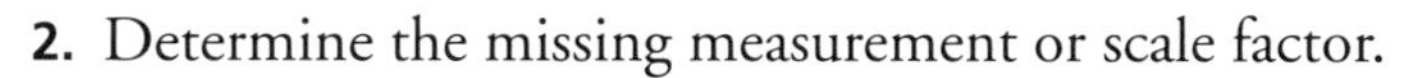

2. Determine the missing measurement or scale factor.

	Scale Factor	Side Length	Corresponding Side Length
a)	4	6 cm	
b)	0.6		30 m
c)	25%	160 km	
d)		18 m	6 m

Practising

3. Complete the ratios for these similar triangles.

a) $\frac{AC}{DF} = \frac{?}{DE}$

b) $\frac{CB}{?} = \frac{AB}{DE}$

c) $\frac{8}{6} = \frac{16}{?}$

4. Kaycee saw two different ads about condominiums that are going to be built. Each ad shows the plan of the balcony in different sizes. What is the scale factor between the diagrams?

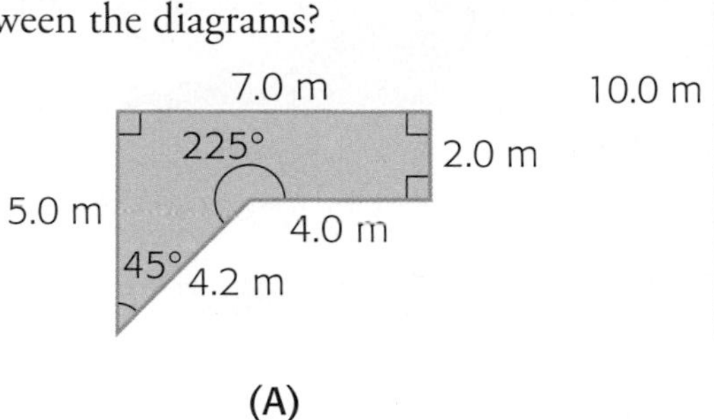

(A)

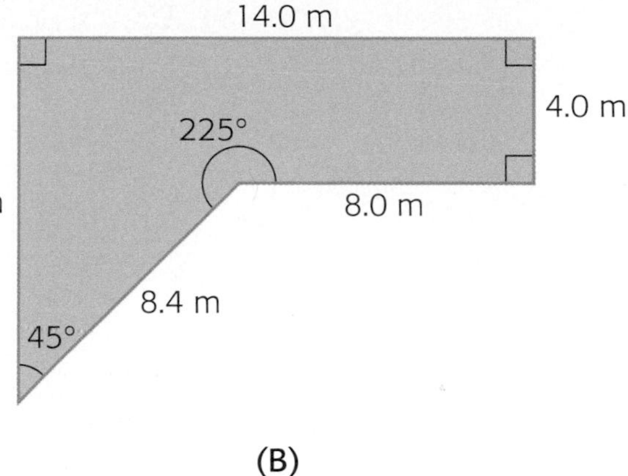

(B)

5. **a)** Explain why these polygons are similar.
   b) Calculate the scale factor.

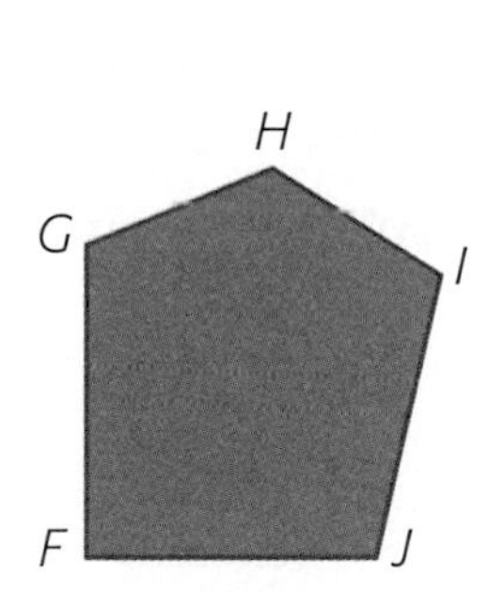

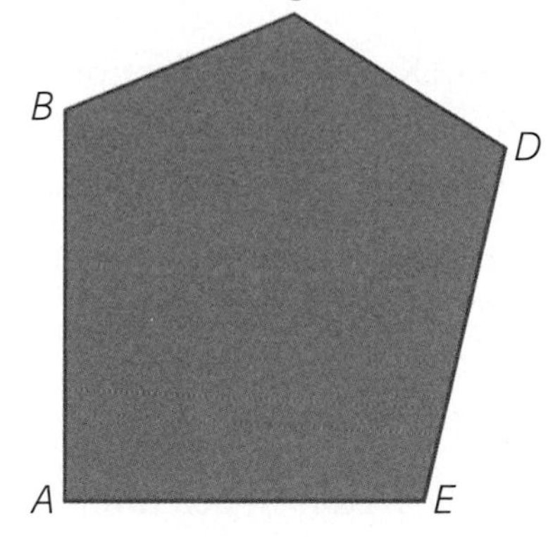

6. **Multiple choice.** To calculate the scale factor that reduced pentagon *ABCDE*
   A. divide the length of *FG* by the length of *AB*
   B. multiply the length of *DC* by the length of *IH*
   C. multiply the length of *JI* by the length of *BC*
   D. divide the length of *AE* by the length of *FJ*

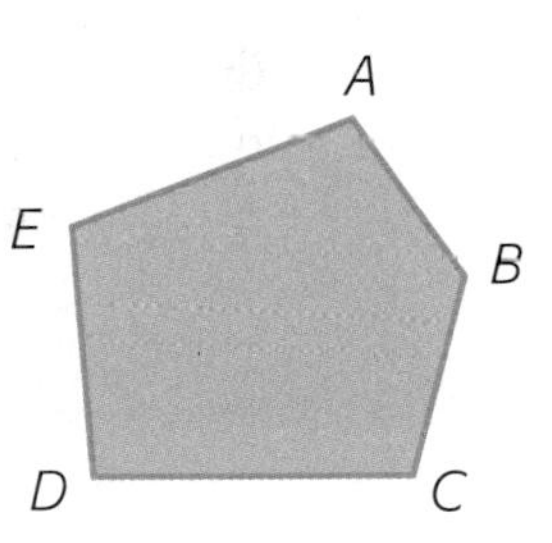

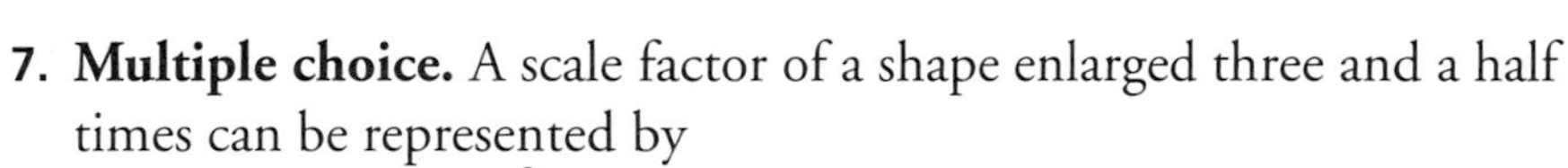

7. **Multiple choice.** A scale factor of a shape enlarged three and a half times can be represented by
   A. 0.35 **B.** $\frac{3}{5}$ **C.** 350% **D.** 35

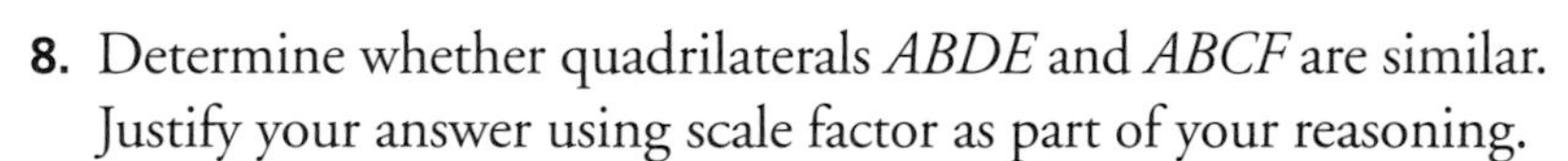

8. Determine whether quadrilaterals *ABDE* and *ABCF* are similar. Justify your answer using scale factor as part of your reasoning.

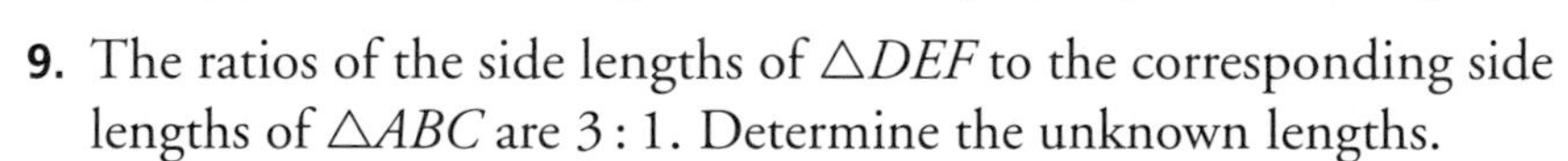

9. The ratios of the side lengths of $\triangle DEF$ to the corresponding side lengths of $\triangle ABC$ are 3 : 1. Determine the unknown lengths.

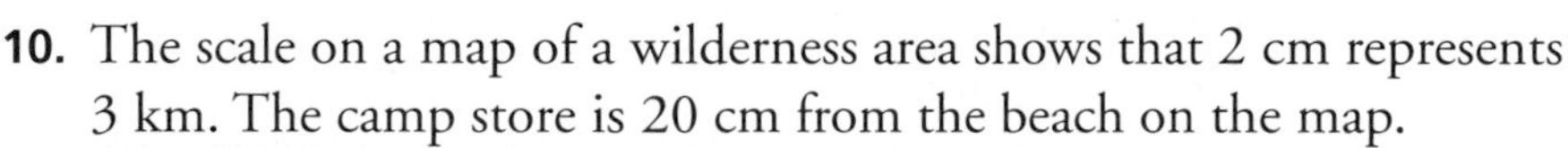

10. The scale on a map of a wilderness area shows that 2 cm represents 3 km. The camp store is 20 cm from the beach on the map.
   a) What is the scale factor between the map and the wilderness area?
   b) How far apart are the camp store and the beach?

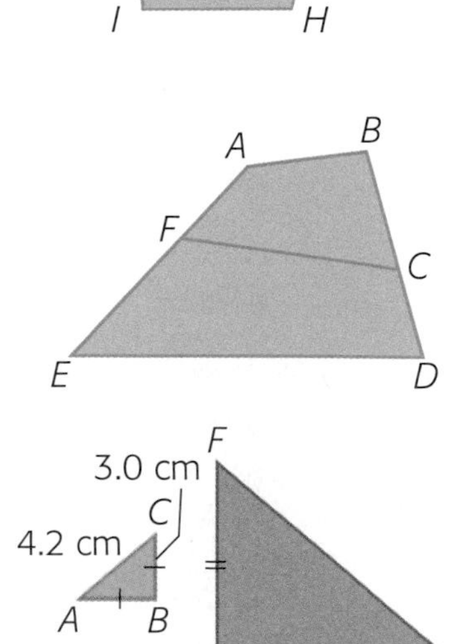

11. Use a scale factor to determine the missing side lengths for each pair of similar shapes.

a)

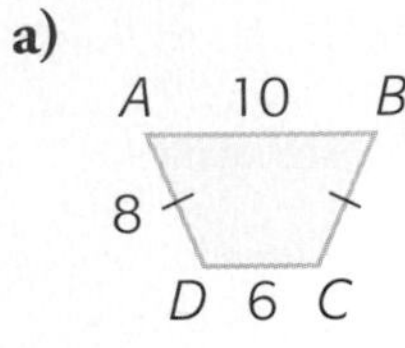

b)

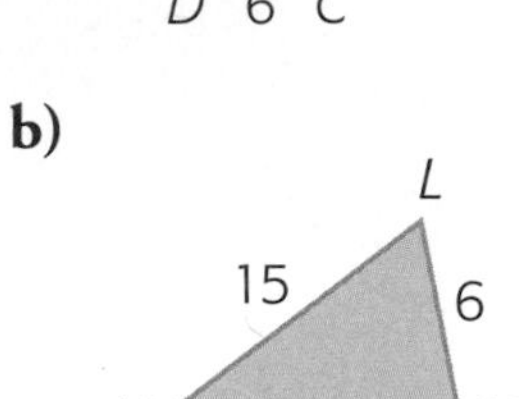

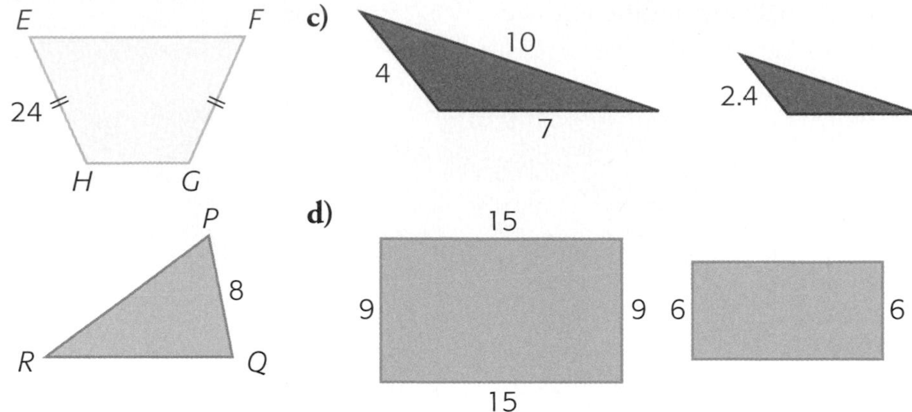

12. An IMAX screen is eight stories high and measures 21.5 m by 15.6 m. A similar screen is 2.15 m long. What is the scale factor between the similar screen and the IMAX screen?

13. A software program offers these preset paper sizes for printing:
A4 (210 mm by 297 mm)
A5 (148 mm by 210 mm)
B5 (182 mm by 257 mm).

Use scale factors to determine if the paper sizes are similar.

14. **a)** Find an example of a diagram online that includes a scale factor. Calculate the actual measurements.
b) Use another scale factor to draw a new diagram.

Closing

15. **a)** Draw a scale diagram of a place in your community or your home.
b) What scale factor did you use?
c) How did you decide which scale to use?

Extending

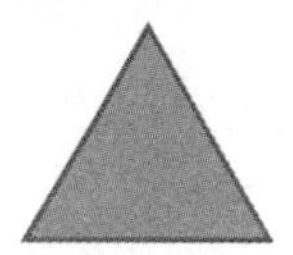
Figure 1

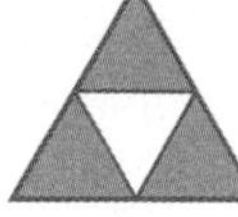
Figure 2

Figure 3

Figure 4

16. Fractal patterns demonstrate similarity. The triangles in each figure of the fractal pattern to the left are similar.
a) What is the scale factor between the triangle in Figure 1 and each triangle in Figure 2?
b) What is the scale factor between the triangles in Figure 2 and the triangles in Figure 3?
c) What visual pattern do you notice as the figure number increases?

17. Design a pictograph or symbol for scale factor that you could use in maps. Explain how it represents the idea of scale.

Curious MATH

Similarity in the Human Body

YOU WILL NEED
- a measuring tape
- a calculator
- a ruler

Yao De-Fen, the tallest living woman, stands 233.3 cm tall.

Leonid Stadnik, the tallest living man, stands 257 cm tall.

1. Work with a partner. Measure your heights and your arm spans.
2. Draw a rectangle using your height and arm span as the length and width.
3. Create a ratio to represent the ratio of the length (height) and the width (arm span) of the rectangle.
4. Apply what you know about ratios to calculate what De-Fen's or Leonid's arm span might be.
5. Do you think your calculation represents De-Fen's or Leonid's arm span accurately? Explain.

Math GAME

Similar Sketches

The goal of this game is to be the last player to draw a polygon on the game board.
Number of players: 2–4

YOU WILL NEED
- Game Board
- a ruler
- a die

How to Play

1. Spin a pencil on the desk. The player closest to the writing end goes first.
2. On your turn, roll the die, and then draw a polygon on the game board grid using the number you rolled as one of the side lengths.
   The next player must then draw a similar polygon that differs in size and does not overlap the first polygon.
3. Players take turns, being sure to not overlap any polygons that have already been drawn.
4. The last player to be able to fit a polygon on the grid wins the game.

Larissa's turn

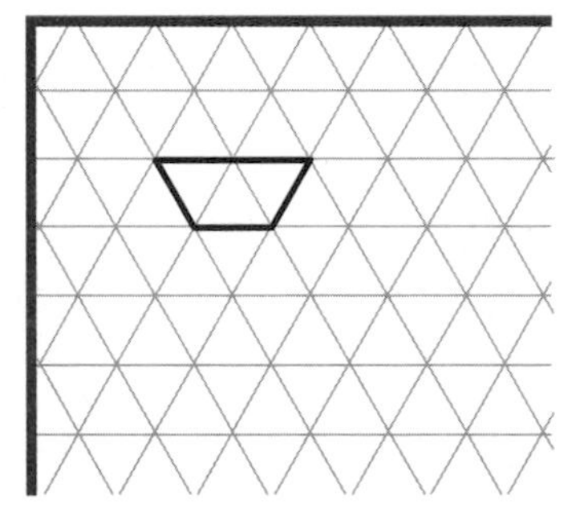

I rolled a 1.
I decided to draw a trapezoid with a 1 unit side length.

Jia-Wen's similar shape

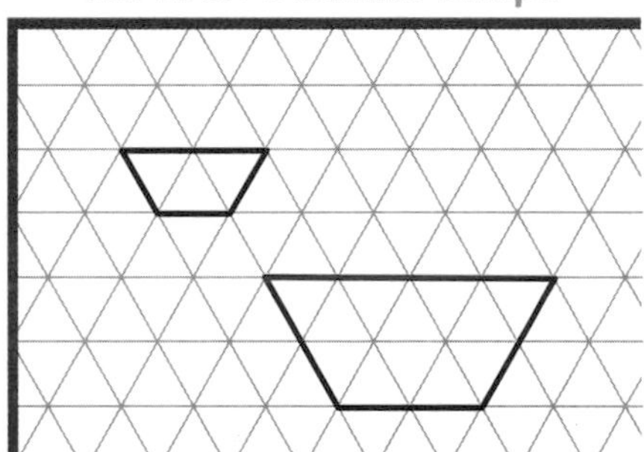

I drew a larger trapezoid similar to Larissa's.
I used a scale factor of 2.
Now it's my turn to roll the die.

Mid-Chapter Review

FREQUENTLY ASKED Questions

Q: What strategies can you use to determine if two polygons are similar?

A: You can measure the side lengths to see if all pairs of corresponding sides are enlarged or reduced by the same scale factor. If they are, the ratios of all corresponding sides will be equal. Measure the corresponding angles to confirm that they are equal. If the corresponding angles are equal and the ratios of corresponding sides are equal, then the shapes are similar.

Study *Aid*

- See Lesson 3.2, Examples 1, 2, and 3.
- Try Mid-Chapter Review questions 1, 2, 3, and 6.

Q: How can you calculate the missing dimension in a pair of similar shapes?

A1: You can calculate the scale factor using corresponding side lengths that are given. Then, use the scale factor to calculate the missing dimension in another pair of corresponding sides.

For example, the ratio of lengths of corresponding sides in *ABCD* and *EFGH* is 1 : 2. The scale factor for the enlargement is 2.

The side that is x metres long must be twice as long as the corresponding side, so $x = 6$ m.

You can also represent the scale factor as a reduction of the larger shape to a smaller shape. In that case the scale factor is $\frac{1}{2}$.

Study *Aid*

- See Lesson 3.3, Examples 1, 2, and 3.
- Try Mid-Chapter Review questions 4 and 5.

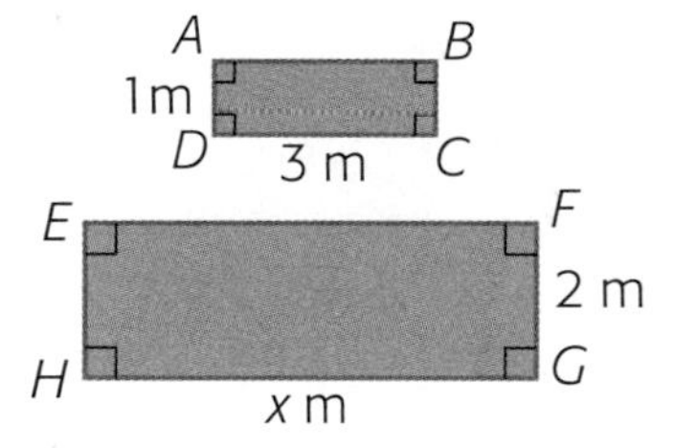

A2: You can calculate the ratio of two side lengths in one of the shapes, and then set it equal to the ratio of the corresponding sides in the other shape and solve.

$$1:3 = 2:x$$
$$x = 6$$

A3: You can calculate the ratios of two side lengths within each shape as fractions.

$$\frac{1}{3} = \frac{2}{x}$$
$$x = 6$$

Practice

Lesson 3.1

1. Which images look like they are the same shape but are a different size?

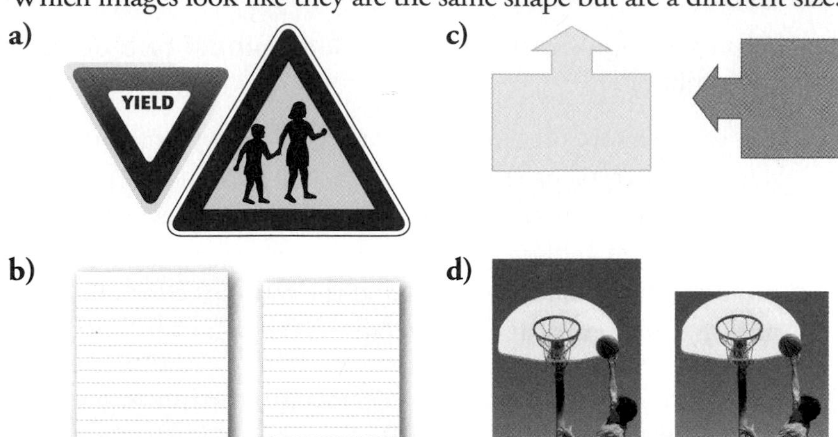

Lesson 3.2

2. List the corresponding sides and angles in these similar polygons.

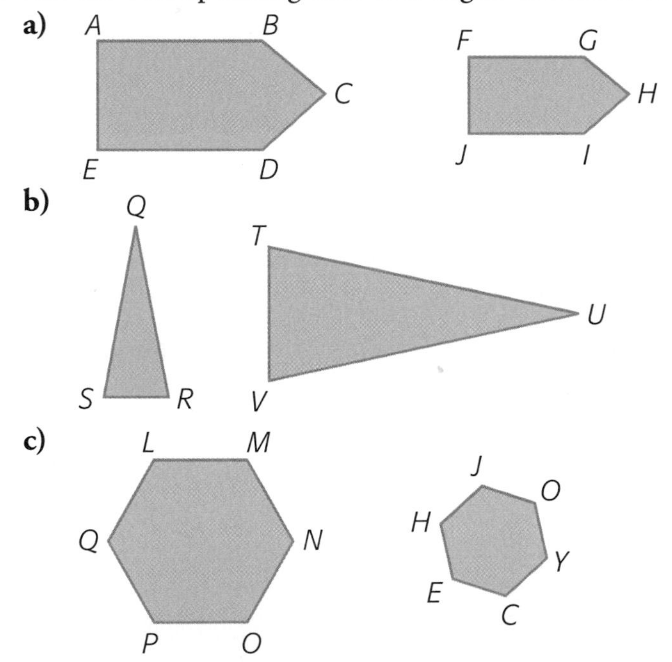

3. Describe the relationships between similar polygons.

4. Calculate the length of *EF*.

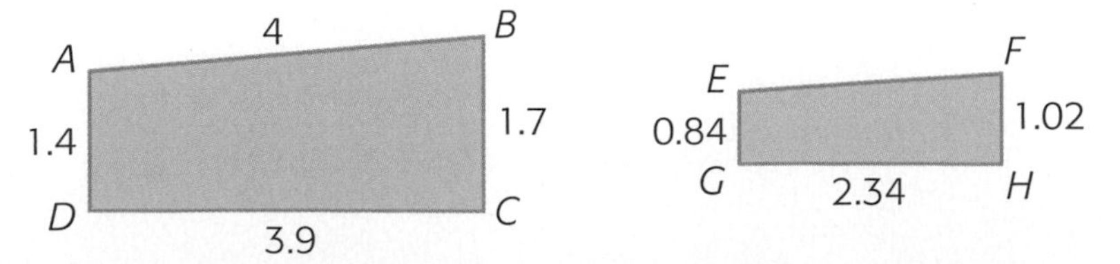

Lesson 3.3

5. a) Arianna is enlarging a banner for the sports banquet at her school. How long should the larger banner be?

b) Steve is cutting glass for his project. He is reducing the pattern to fit a smaller frame. How long will the top of the glass be?

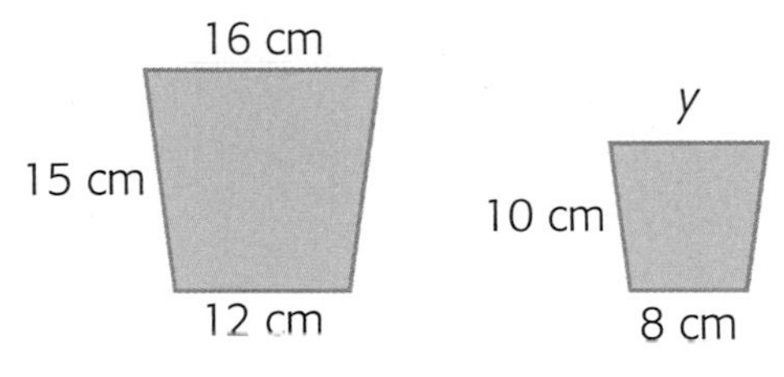

c) A sign shop is creating a sign for the Penta Group from a pattern emailed by the company. What scale factor is the sign shop using?

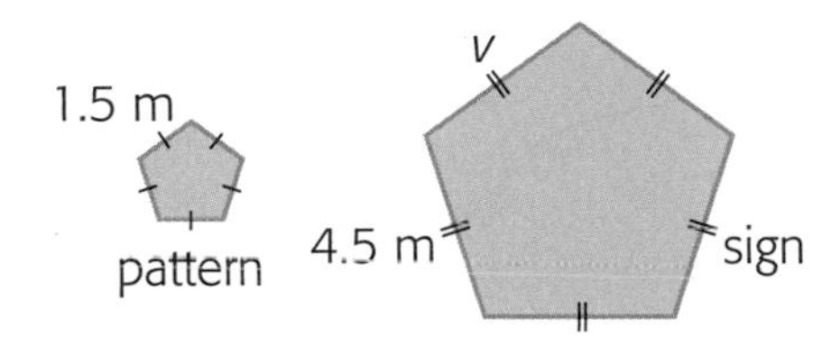

6. Is each pair of shapes similar? If so, determine the scale factor. If not, explain why not.

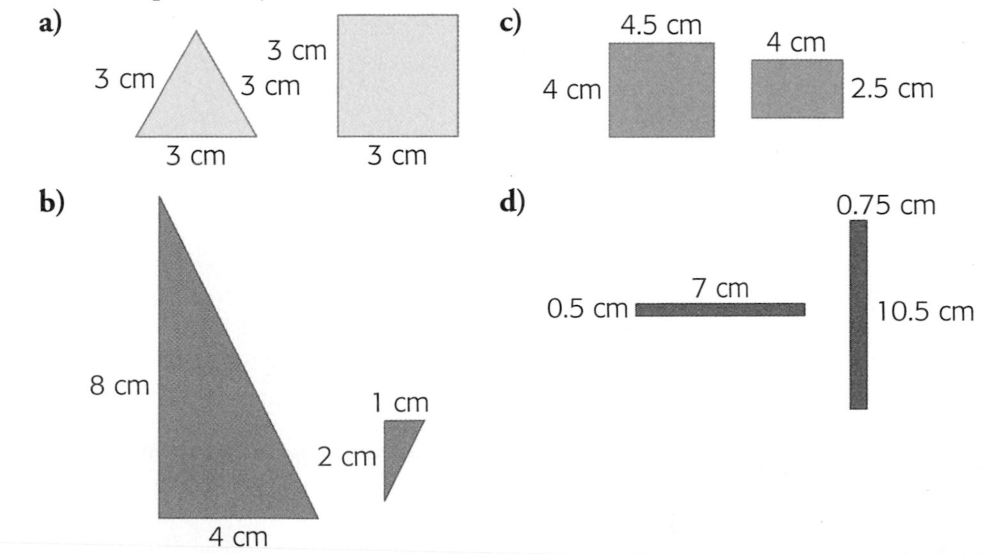

3.4 Drawing a Similar Polygon

YOU WILL NEED

- a ruler
- a protractor

GOAL

Use a scale factor to draw a similar shape.

LEARN ABOUT the Math

David found old patterns for kites online. He wants to draw enlargements.

? How can David enlarge a kite design?

EXAMPLE 1 | Enlarge using protractor and ruler

David's Solution

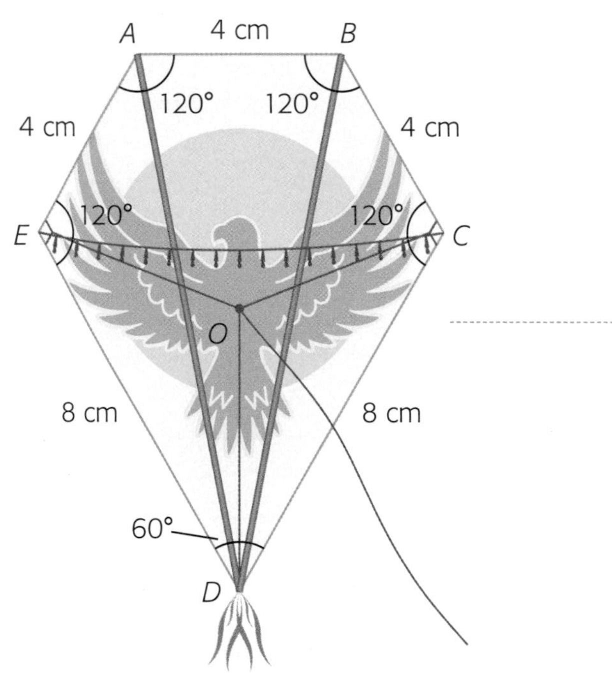

My kite will be similar to the design I saw on the Internet. The side lengths of my kite will be in proportion to the side lengths of the diagram. The angles will be the same.

I printed a copy of the design. I measured the sides and angles of the pentagon and recorded them on the printout.

$$4:20 = 1:5$$

$AB \quad 4 \times 5 = 20$ cm

I decided to make the kite 20 cm across the top (AB). Since the original drawing was 4 cm across, I will use a scale factor of 5 to enlarge the kite.

$BC \quad 4 \times 5 = 20$ cm

$CD \quad 8 \times 5 = 40$ cm

$DE \quad 8 \times 5 = 40$ cm

$EA \quad 4 \times 5 = 20$ cm

I used the scale factor to calculate the rest of the new side lengths for the enlarged kite.

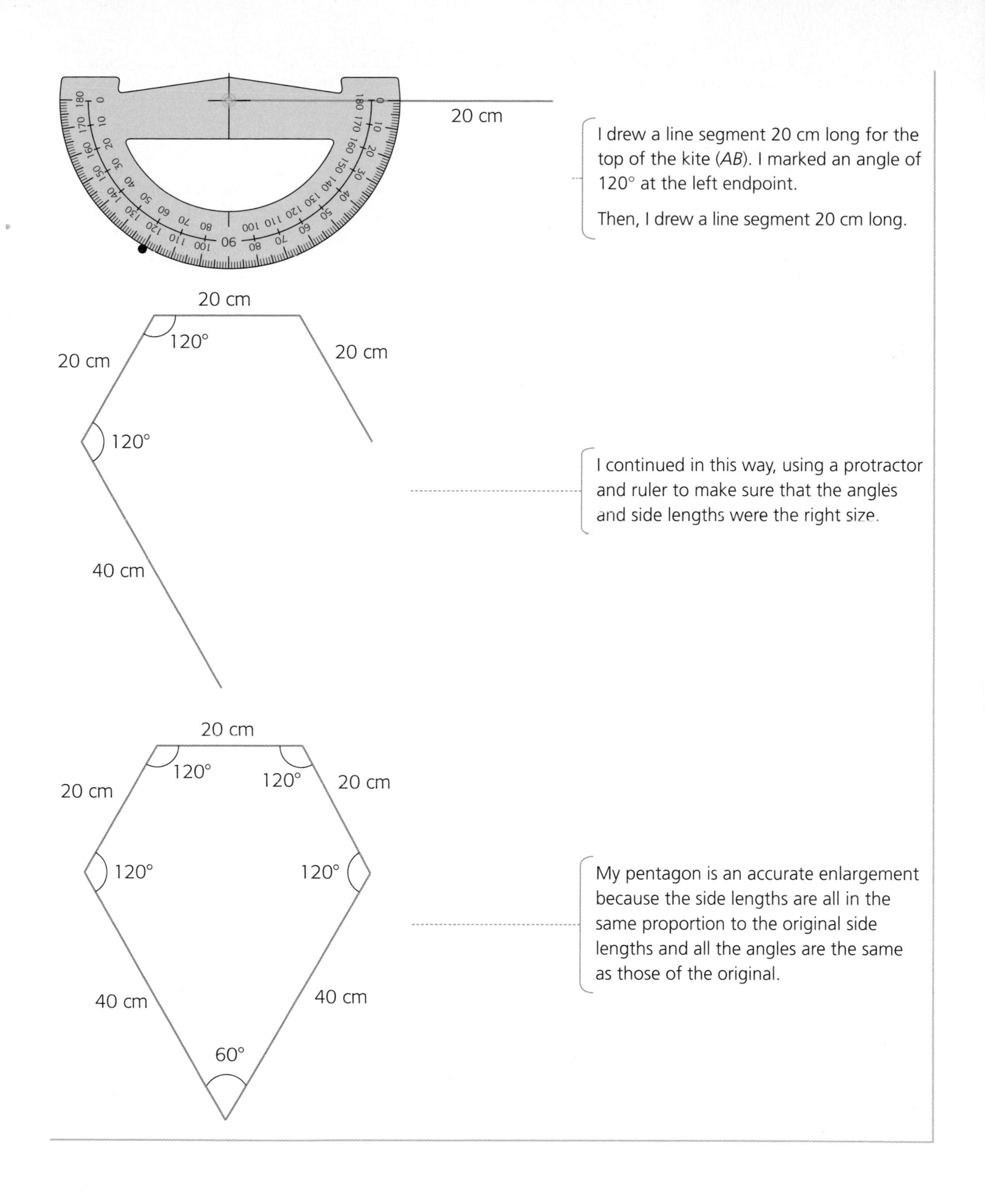

I drew a line segment 20 cm long for the top of the kite (*AB*). I marked an angle of 120° at the left endpoint.

Then, I drew a line segment 20 cm long.

I continued in this way, using a protractor and ruler to make sure that the angles and side lengths were the right size.

My pentagon is an accurate enlargement because the side lengths are all in the same proportion to the original side lengths and all the angles are the same as those of the original.

EXAMPLE 2 | Enlarge using technology

Rachel's Solution

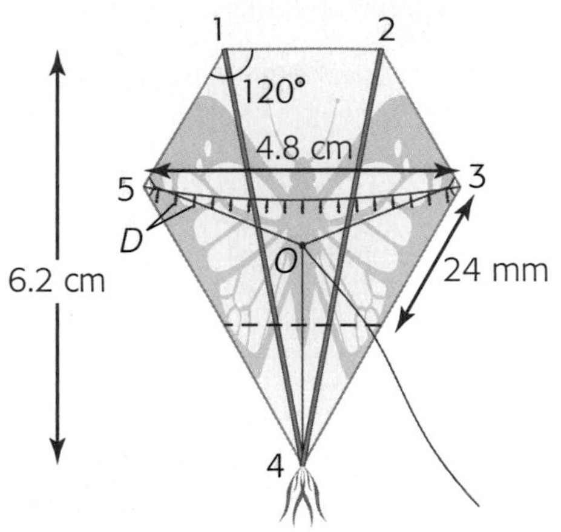
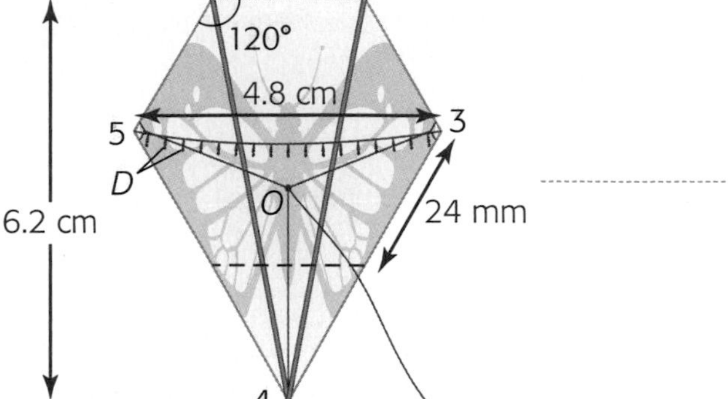

I decided to use a design on paper as a template. I wanted the width of the kite to fit the width of the biggest piece of paper I could print on, which is 22 cm by 28 cm.

My kite looks like a hexagon with a triangular piece added to create a pentagon. The hexagon part looks like it's regular, so I measured the sides and angles to check. Each side is 2.4 cm and each angle is 120°. I was correct. I have software that will let me draw a regular hexagon.

I want to leave about a 1 cm margin on each side of the page, so the widest part of the printed area is 20 cm. The widest part of the hexagon is 4.8 cm.

$20:4.8 = 4.2:1$, to 1 decimal place. I need to use a scale factor of 4.2 or 420%.

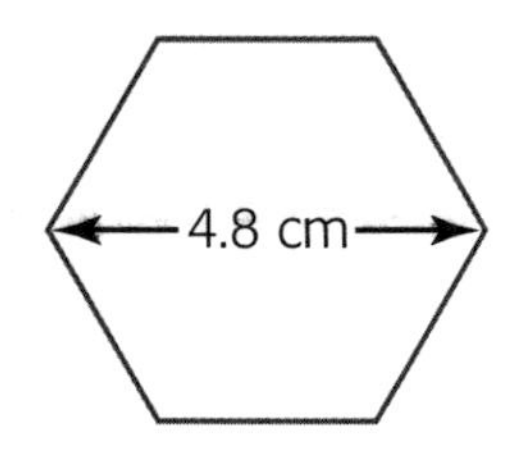

I created a regular hexagon that is 4.8 cm wide.

I set the height scale and width scale to 420%.

$6.2 \times 420\% = 24.9$ cm. That will fit on a 28 cm page.

I checked that the new height will fit on the page.

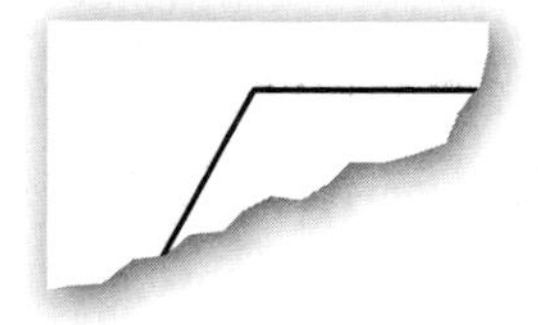

The enlarged kite pattern filled the page. I can extend the lines by hand to add the triangle that makes the pentagon.

Reflecting

A. Why did David need to measure both the angles and the side lengths to draw the enlarged design?

B. How did Rachel know that the scale factor for the widest part of the hexagon would also apply to the sides of the hexagon?

WORK WITH the Math

EXAMPLE 3 | Using a grid to draw a similar shape

Make a reduction of this kite design using a scale factor of 67%.

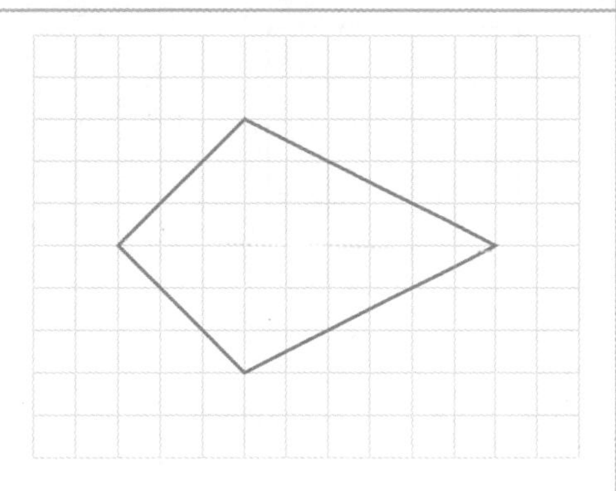

Jia-Wen's Solution

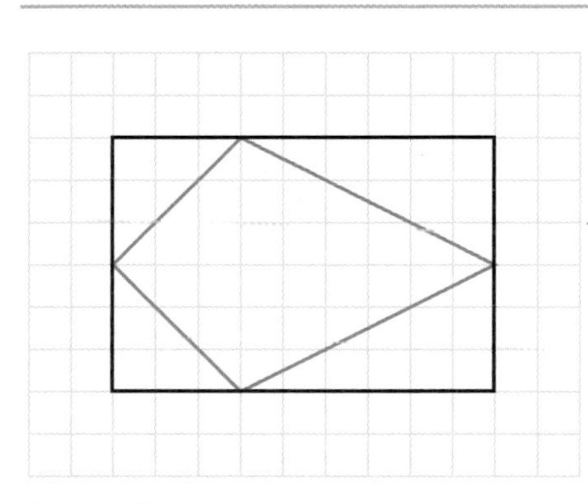

I drew a rectangle around the shape that touched all of the vertices. It measures 6 squares by 9 squares.

I will reduce the rectangle, and then draw the new kite shape inside it.

$6 \times 0.67 \doteq 4$
$9 \times 0.67 \doteq 6$

Each rectangle dimension is multiplied by the scale factor to get the new dimensions.

The new rectangle is 4 squares by 6 squares.

To locate the vertices, I looked at the original picture.

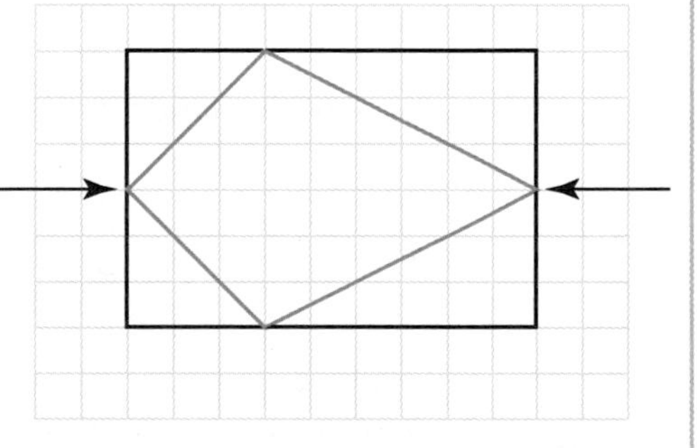

The left and right vertices are in the middle of the left and right sides.

I marked vertices in the middle of the left and right sides.

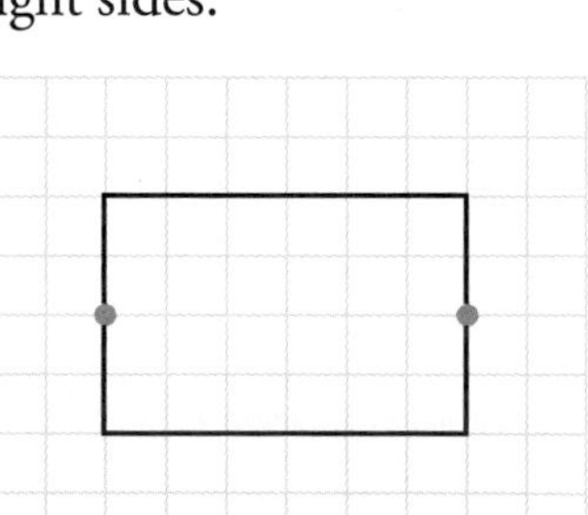

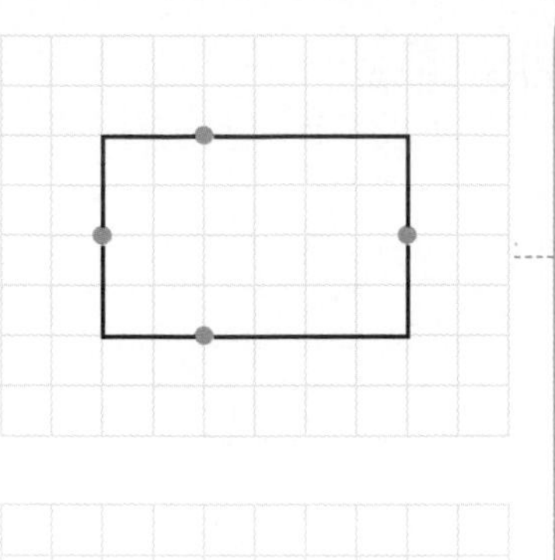

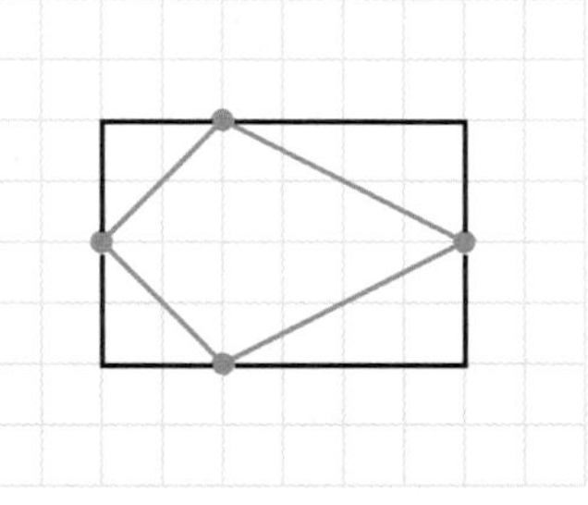

I connected the vertices to finish.

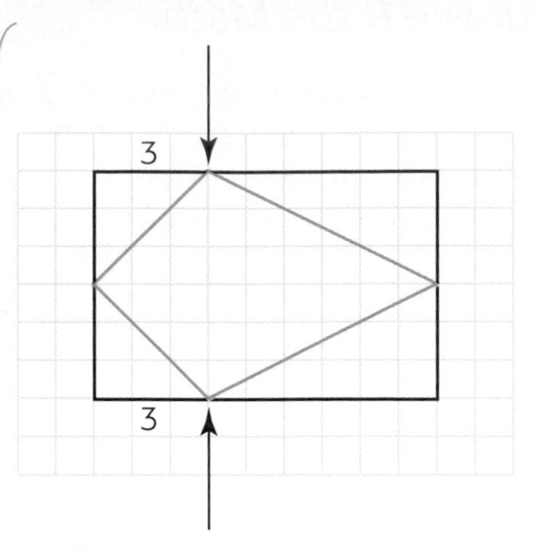

The top and bottom vertices are 3 squares from the left vertices of the rectangles.

In the new rectangle, they will be $3 \times 0.67 = 2$ squares from the left vertices.

In Summary

Key Idea

- When you draw a similar polygon, each side length is enlarged or reduced by the same scale factor and each angle remains the same.

Need to Know

- The scale factor can be calculated using corresponding sides with known lengths.
- Many software programs allow you to create a similar shape using a scale factor expressed as a percent.
- A shape drawn on a grid can be enlarged or reduced by enlarging or reducing a reference rectangle drawn around it.

Checking

1. Measure the dimensions of the quadrilateral. Draw a similar quadrilateral for each scale factor.
   a) an enlargement by a scale factor of 1.5
   b) a reduction by a scale factor of $\frac{3}{4}$
   c) a reduction by a scale factor of 60%

Practising

2. For each polygon, draw a similar shape on grid paper using the given scale factor.
   a) a reduction by a scale factor of 0.5
   b) an enlargement by a scale factor of 3
   c) an enlargement by a scale factor of 2

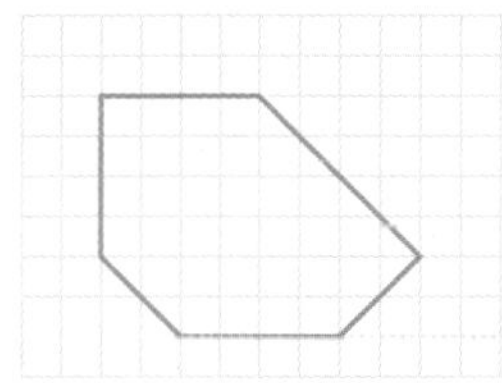
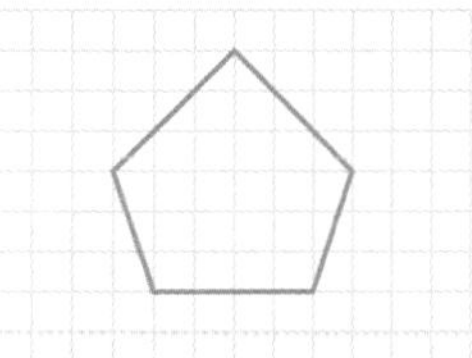
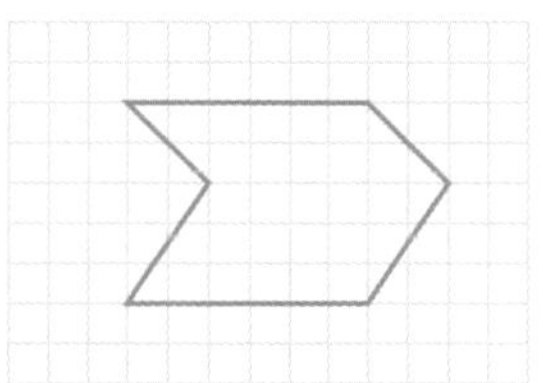

3. For each octagon and scale factor, construct a similar shape.
   a) a reduction by a scale factor of 25%
   b) an enlargement by a scale factor of 2

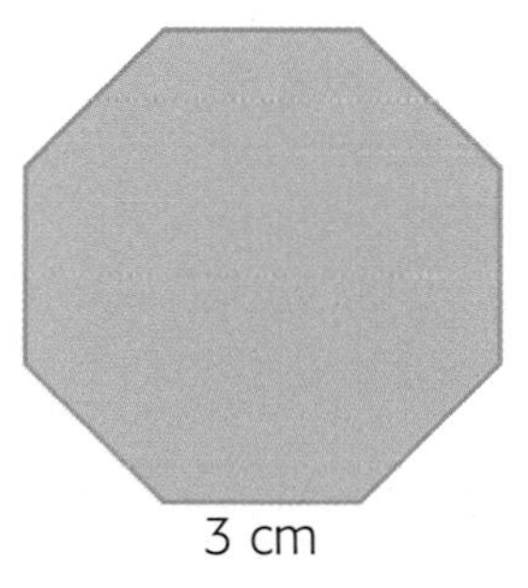

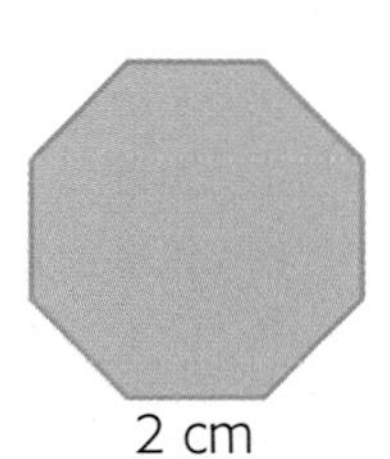

4. Construct a similar polygon for each scale factor.
   a) scale factor 50%
   b) scale factor 1.3
   c) scale factor 200%
   d) Identify each of the polygons you drew as either an enlargement or a reduction of the original.

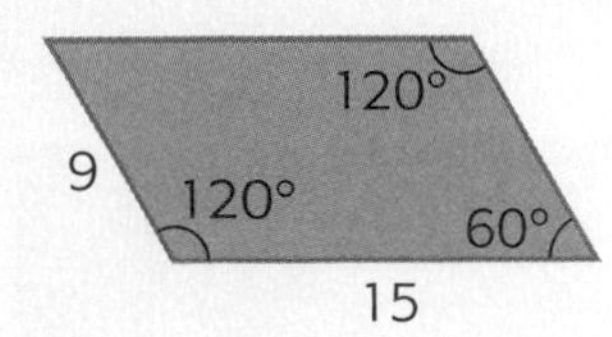

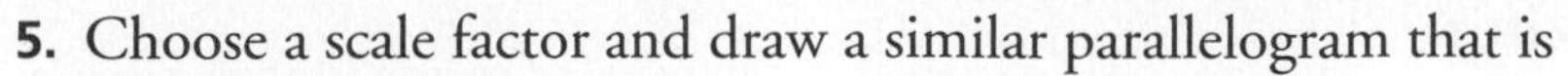

5. Choose a scale factor and draw a similar parallelogram that is
   a) an enlargement
   b) a reduction

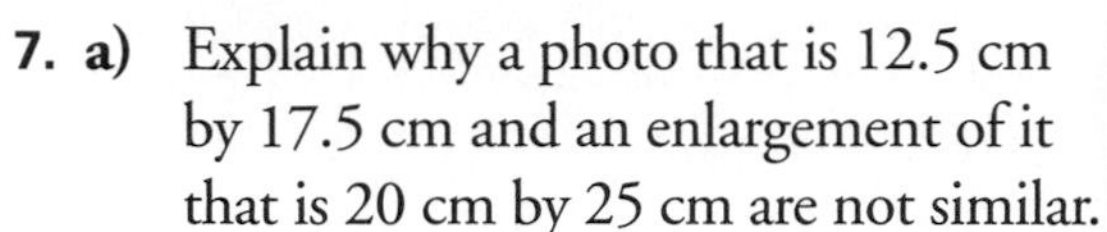

6. Draw any polygon on grid paper. Then, draw two similar polygons, one that is an enlargement and one that is a reduction. State the scale factor for each.

7. **a)** Explain why a photo that is 12.5 cm by 17.5 cm and an enlargement of it that is 20 cm by 25 cm are not similar.
   b) What size is an enlargement of a photo that is 12.5 cm by 17.5 cm that has been increased by a scale factor of 1.4?

$C(1, 3)$
$A(0, 1)$
$B(2, 0)$

8. **a)** Draw a triangle similar to ABC on a grid using a scale factor of 3.
   b) Repeat part a) using a scale factor of $\frac{1}{2}$.

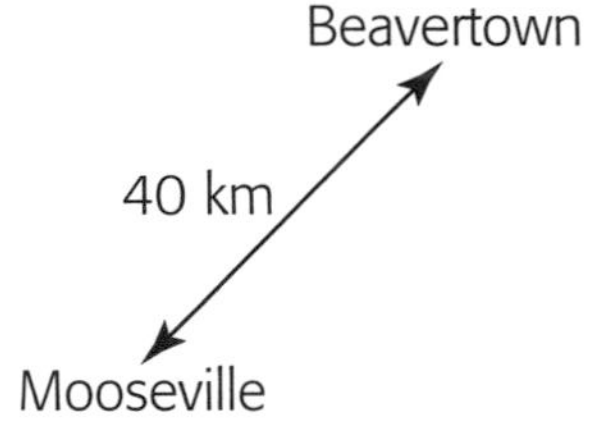

9. On a map, 1 cm represents 10 km.
   a) The distance between two towns is 40 km. How long would you draw the line between the two towns on the map?
   b) If you draw two cities 4.5 cm apart on the map, how far apart are the actual cities?

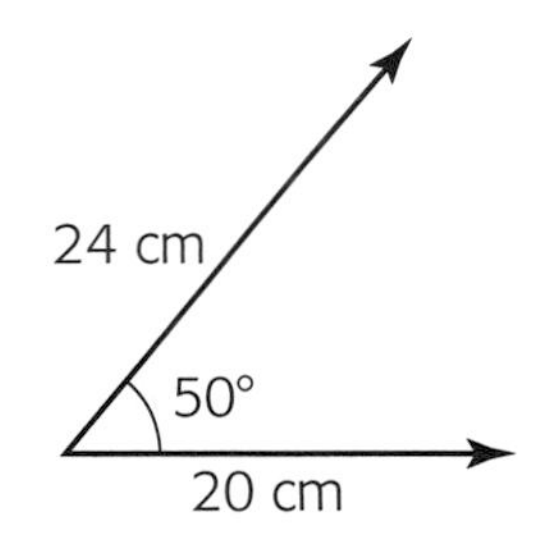

10. Sol made a scale drawing of his triangular vegetable garden so that he could plan how to plant it. Two sides of the garden are 10 m and 12 m and they form an angle of 50°. He drew a 50° angle on paper and drew legs of 20 cm and 24 cm. What is the length of the third side of his garden?

11. Construct two similar hexagons using a scale of 1 : 2.5.

Closing

12. Describe how to enlarge the notepad design using a scale factor of $\frac{5}{3}$. Test your instructions.

3.5 Solving Problems Involving Similar Shapes

GOAL

Use the properties and relationships of similar polygons to solve problems.

YOU WILL NEED

- a ruler

INVESTIGATE the Math

You are going to draw a picture of the flag of the Métis Nation of Saskatchewan on a piece of paper that is 22 cm by 29 cm. You want it to be as large as possible.

Scale factor for reduction from standard size: 11.3%

What are the greatest possible dimensions for your drawing?

A. Calculate the dimensions of the standard size flag in centimetres.

B. Determine the ratio of the length of the flag to the width of the flag.

C. Create a table showing three possible sets of dimensions for the picture of the flag that are similar to the standard size flag.

D. Compare the dimensions in your table with the size of the paper.

E. Determine the largest possible picture of the flag that can be drawn on the paper. Explain your choice.

Reflecting

F. How did the length-to-width ratio of the flag help you determine the possible dimensions for your drawing?

G. How can using a scale factor help you to determine the size of the picture that would fit on the page?

WORK WITH the Math

EXAMPLE 1 | Using similar figures to solve a problem

When the Sun shines on objects that are close to each other, the shadows, the Sun's rays, and the objects form similar triangles. The Sun is shining on a tree and a nearby parking meter. What is the height of the tree?

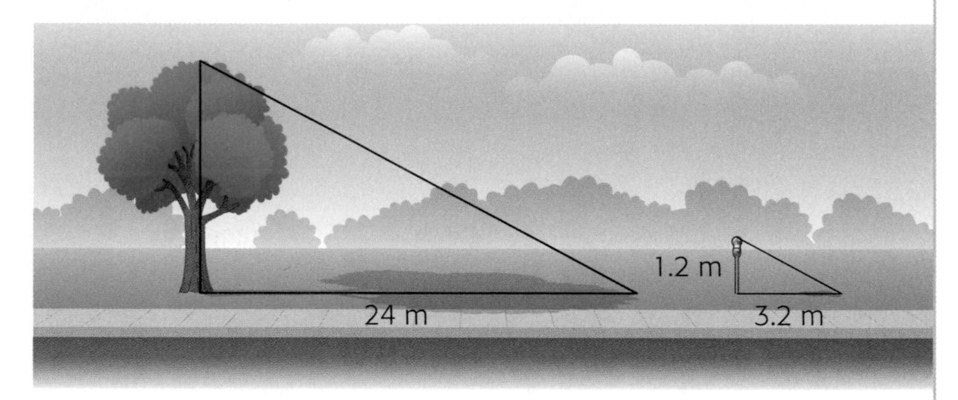

Jia-Wen's Solution

24 : 3.2

$\frac{24}{3.2} = 7.5$

Scale factor = 7.5

Dimensions in similar polygons are related by a scale factor. I wrote the lengths of the shadows of the two triangles as a ratio. I divided 24 by 3.2 to calculate the scale factor.

$1.2 \times 7.5 = 9$ m

The tree is 9 m tall.

I multiplied the height of the parking meter by the scale factor to determine the height of the tree.

EXAMPLE 2 | Using a scale factor to solve a problem

Rachel's family is building a gazebo from these plans. They want to know how much bamboo railing to buy.

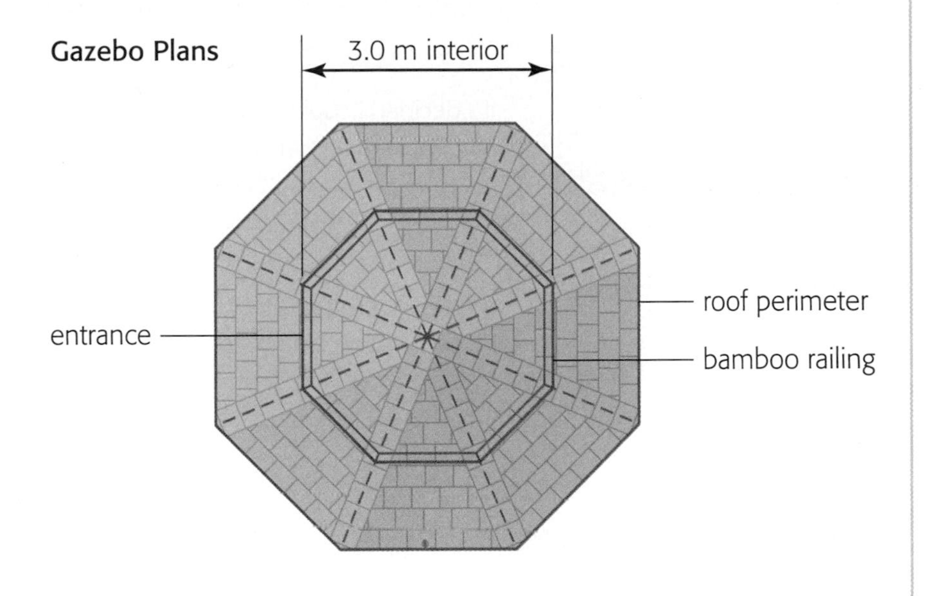

Rachel's Solution

3.3 cm represents 3.0 m, or 300 cm.
Scale factor
$300:3.3 \doteq 900:10$, or 90.

I measured the length that represents 3.0 m. I used it to determine the scale factor.

One side of the octagon railing is 1.4 cm long.
$1.4 \times 90 = 126$ cm

Each railing piece is 126 cm long.

Next, I measured one side of the smaller octagon in the diagram. I used the scale factor to calculate the length it represents in the gazebo.

There are 8 sides but one of them doesn't have a railing.
$126 \times 7 = 882$ cm, or about 8.9 m.

I will buy 8.9 m of bamboo railing.

I multiplied by 7 to determine the bamboo needed for all sides.

I noticed that I could also have calculated the perimeter of the octagon on the plans, multiplied the perimeter by the scale factor, and subtracted an eighth for the missing side.

EXAMPLE 3 | Using similar triangles and scale diagrams

A bridge is going to be built over a gorge. How long will the bridge need to be?

Thomas's Solution

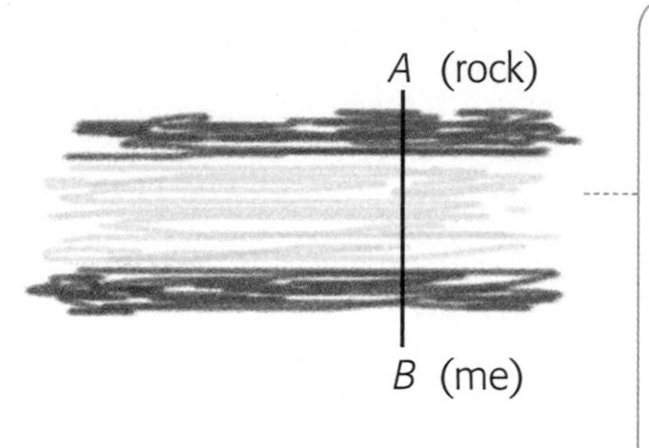

I decided I could solve the problem if I could create two similar triangles. I needed to know some linear measurements for each triangle and the scale factor.

I went to the gorge. I noticed a rock on the other side. I stood directly across from it.
I drew a diagram.

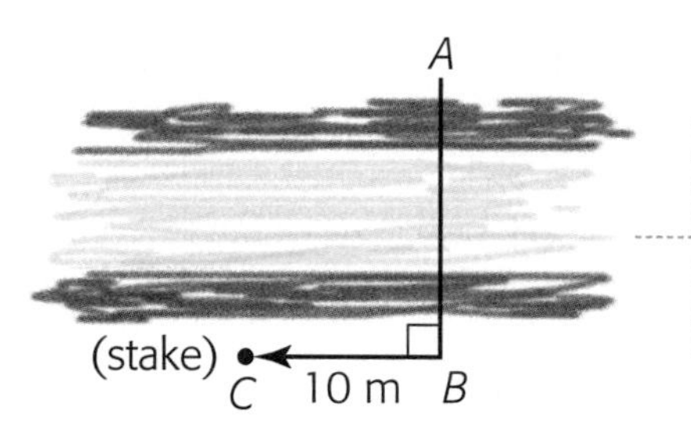

I walked 10 m along the edge of the gorge perpendicular to *AB*. I put a stake in to mark the spot *C* and added it to the diagram.

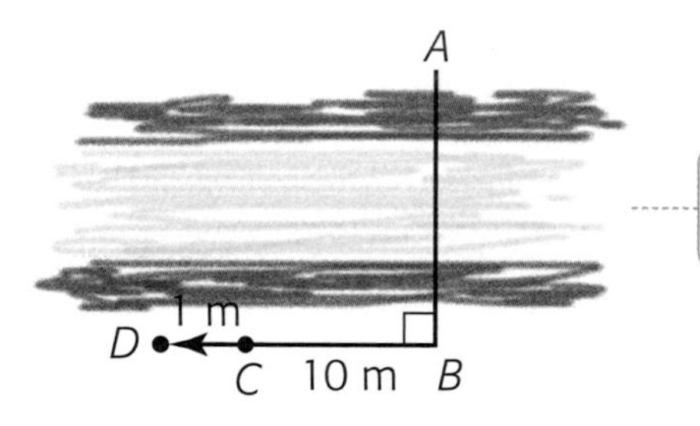

I walked one more metre past *C*, put a stake at *D*, and marked the diagram.

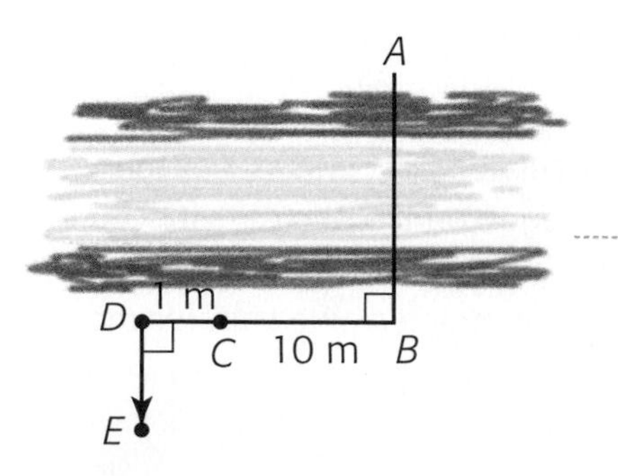

I turned away from the gorge and walked perpendicular to the *BD* line. I put a stake at point *E*, where I could see the top of the stake at *C* and the rock at *A* in a straight line.

$\triangle ABC$ is similar to $\triangle EDC$.

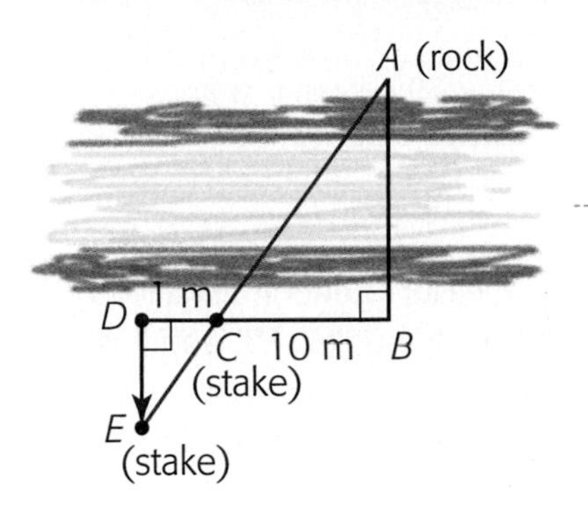

I connected *A*, *C*, and *E* on the diagram with a straight line to create two similar triangles.

I knew the triangles were similar because the corresponding angles in the two triangles are the same. $\angle DCE = \angle BCA$ and there is a right angle in each triangle, so $\angle BAC = \angle DEC$ because the sum of the angles must be 180°.

DC and *BC* are corresponding sides of the two triangles. $DC = 1$ m and $BC = 10$ m, so the scale factor is 10.

Once I knew the scale factor, all I needed to do was measure *DE* to be able to calculate the width of the gorge.

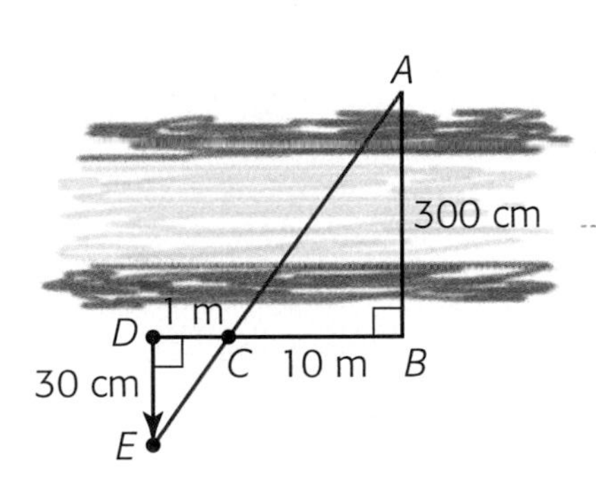

I measured the distance from the *D* stake to the *E* stake. It was 30 cm.

$$\begin{aligned} AB &= 30 \times 10 \\ &= 300 \text{ cm or } 3 \text{ m} \end{aligned}$$

The bridge has to be at least 3 m long.

In Summary

Key Idea

- Scale factors can be used to solve problems involving similar shapes or scale diagrams.

Need to Know

- When you are asked to determine a missing measurement or dimension, it can be helpful to identify similar shapes where the unknown length is a side length.
- You can calculate the scale factor in a diagram using one measurement and the length it represents.
- The perimeters of similar shapes are related by the scale factor.

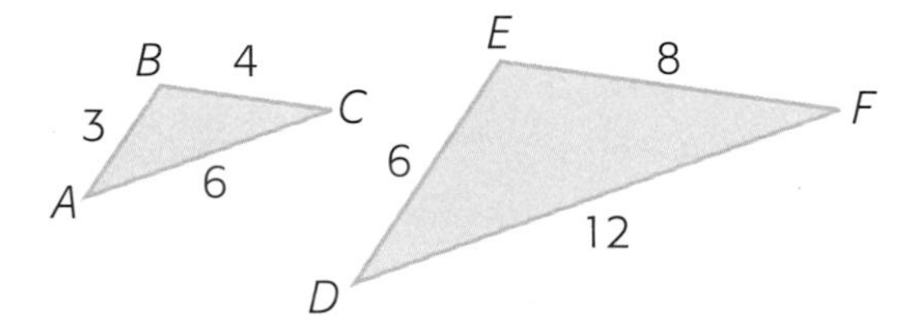

perimeter $\triangle ABC = 3 + 4 + 6$
$= 13$

perimeter $\triangle DEF = 6 + 8 + 12$
$= 26$
$= 2 \times 13$

Checking

1 cm represents 1.4 m

1. A "do it yourself" web page helps people to build backyard ponds. The page says to "Draw a scale diagram of your yard and play with shapes and placement. Then, go outside and outline the shape of your pond with a garden hose." What length of hose will be needed to surround the pond in the scale diagram at left?
2. The principal wants to hang a banner to congratulate the basketball team on its season. The scale drawing for the banner is 20 cm by 38 cm. The actual banner will be 1 m wide. How long will the banner be?

Practising

3. Why might you think these two shapes are similar? If they are similar, what is the length of the blue side?

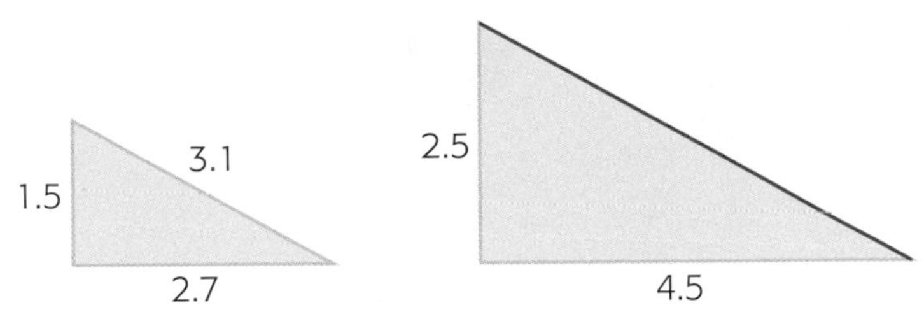

4. a) Measure the height of the head of the person in the picture.
   b) Measure the height of your own head.
   c) Imagine the height of the person's head is similar to yours. What is the scale factor describing the relationship of the head in the photo and your head?
   d) What might the actual height of the dog's head be?

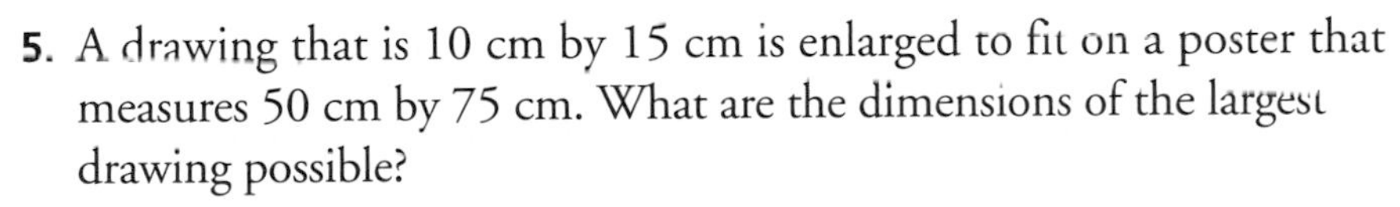

5. A drawing that is 10 cm by 15 cm is enlarged to fit on a poster that measures 50 cm by 75 cm. What are the dimensions of the largest drawing possible?

6. How many similar parallelograms are in the diagram at right? Explain.

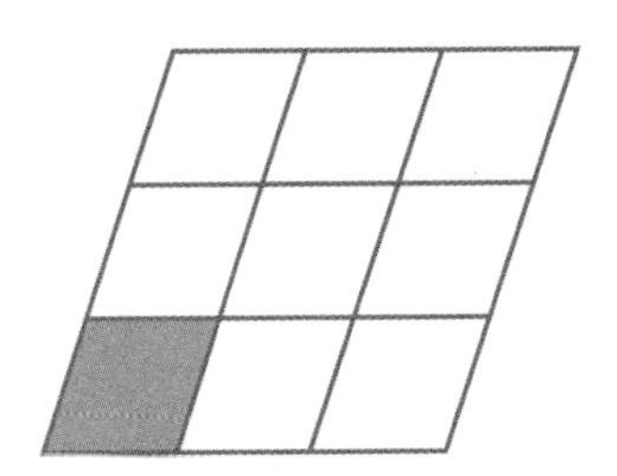

7. **Multiple choice.** The dinosaur robot is a scale model where 1 cm represents 6 cm. How long is the head of the real dinosaur?

A. 2 cm **B.** 48 cm **C.** 144 cm **D.** 24 m

8. **Multiple choice.** Two fire rescue ladders leaning against a wall form similar triangles. The 8 m ladder reaches 7 m up the wall. How much farther up the wall does the 25 m ladder reach?

A. 21 m **B.** 26 m **C.** 12 m **D.** 15 m

9. These kites are similar. Calculate the length of YZ.

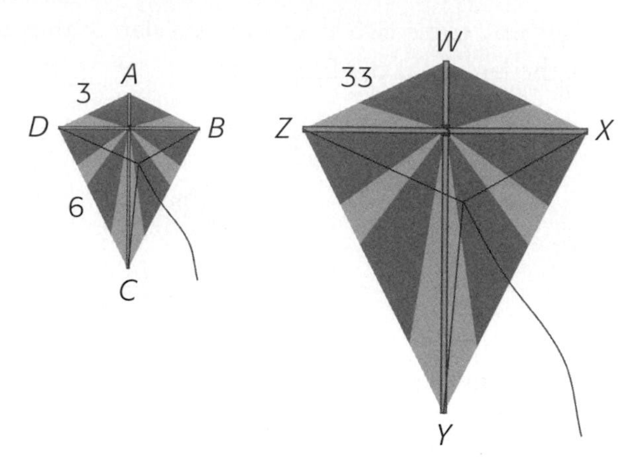

10. Yvonne has entered a contest to design a postage stamp. She designed a large-scale version to show to the committee that will choose the stamp. Her design was selected. What scale factor should be used to reduce the drawing to stamp size?

11. The side lengths of a triangular shade sail are 3.6 m, 3.6 m, and 4.8 m. A landscape architect is making a scale model. If the two equal sides in the model are 9 cm, what is the length of the third side?

12. These two polygons are similar. What is the length of QP?

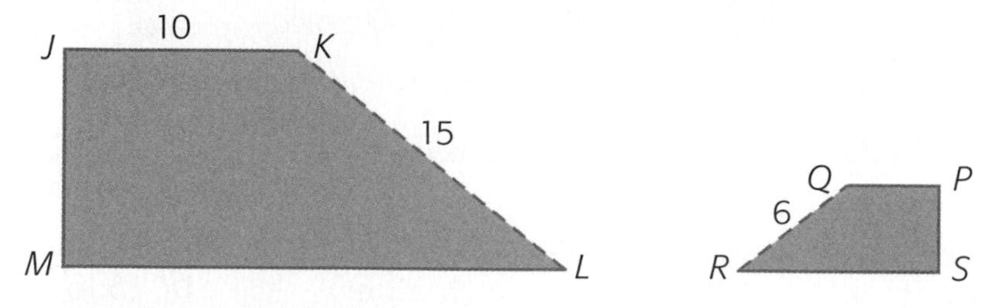

13. Make a scale drawing of the soccer field where 1 mm represents 1 m.

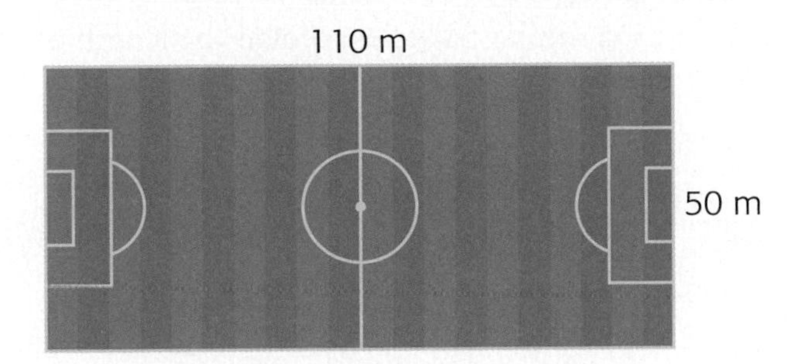

14. Joyce is working on the school yearbook. She must reduce a photo that is 10 cm wide by 12.5 cm long to fit in a space 7.5 cm wide. How long will the reduced photo be?

15. You have been asked to create a poster to promote a new wildlife refuge in your area. You have a photo that is 9 cm by 13 cm to enlarge. You want the enlargement to be 32.5 cm wide. How long will it be?

16. A person 1.63 m tall has a shadow 1.22 m long. At the same time of day, a nearby lamppost has a 4.27 m shadow. Calculate the height of the lamppost.

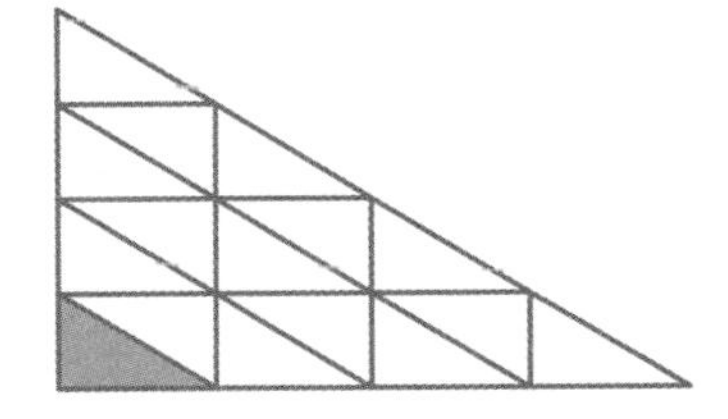

17. What is the scale factor to get from the smallest to the largest triangle in the design at right? Explain your thinking.

18. Taf stands near a lighthouse on a sunny day. What is the height of the lighthouse?

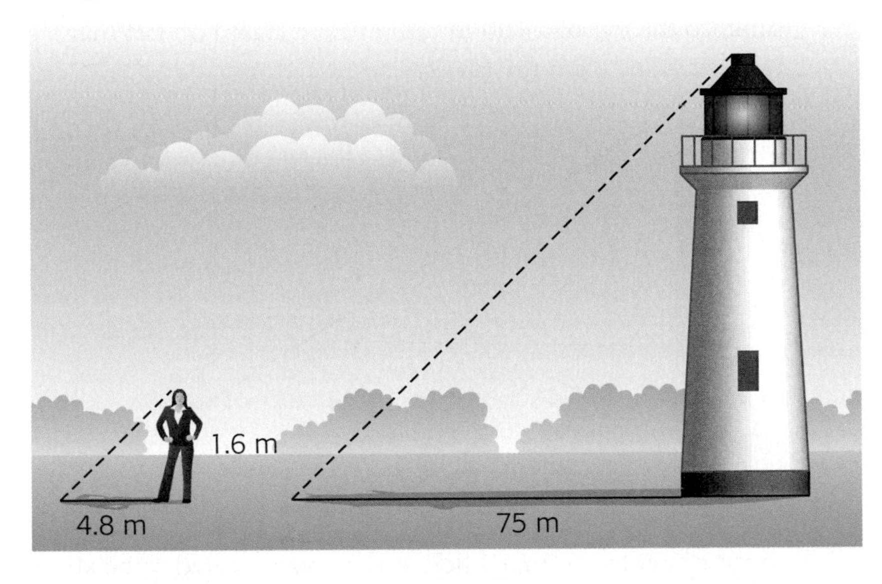

19. Jean Francois Gravelet became famous when he crossed the Niagara Gorge on a tightrope in 1859. Since he couldn't measure across the gorge, Jean used similar triangles to plan the length of the tightrope. How long was tightrope *AB*?

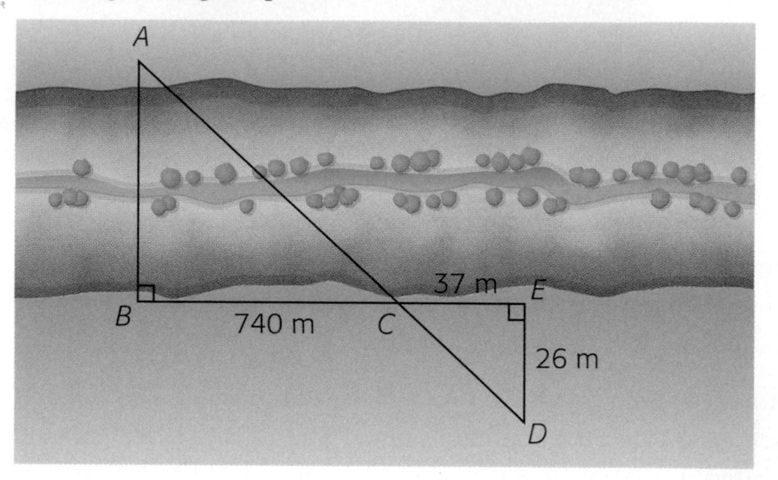

Closing

20. At a certain time of the day, the shadow of a 1.5 m tall boy is 2.4 m long. The shadow of a nearby tree at this same time is 8.5 m long. Describe how can you use similar shapes to solve for the height of the tree.

Extending

21. Victoria, at point *F*, used a 3 m surveyor's pole to sight from the ground to the top of a 100 m radio tower. Based on her diagram, how far was she from the tower?

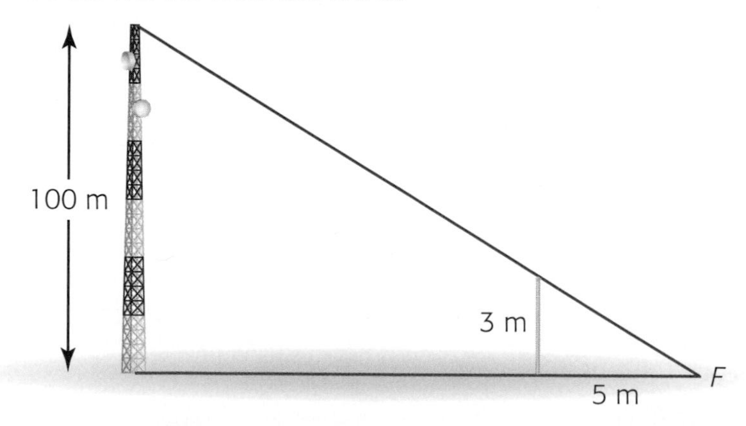

22. Julie knew her hand was 20 cm tall. She held her hand far enough in front of her eye so that a lion at the zoo appeared to be about 30 cm tall. Julie's hand was about 45 cm in front of her eye, and she was standing about 3 m from the lion. Use a scale drawing to estimate the height of the lion.

3.6 Communicate about Similarity

GOAL

Describe situations involving similar shapes and scale diagrams.

YOU WILL NEED

- a ruler
- a calculator
- a protractor

LEARN ABOUT the Math

Sam wants to convince the Nordic Ski committee to include a shorter race for the novice cross-country skiers at the next meet. He thinks novices need a course that is a bit less than half as long as the regular course. He has designed a course that cuts across the frozen lake parallel to part of the original course.

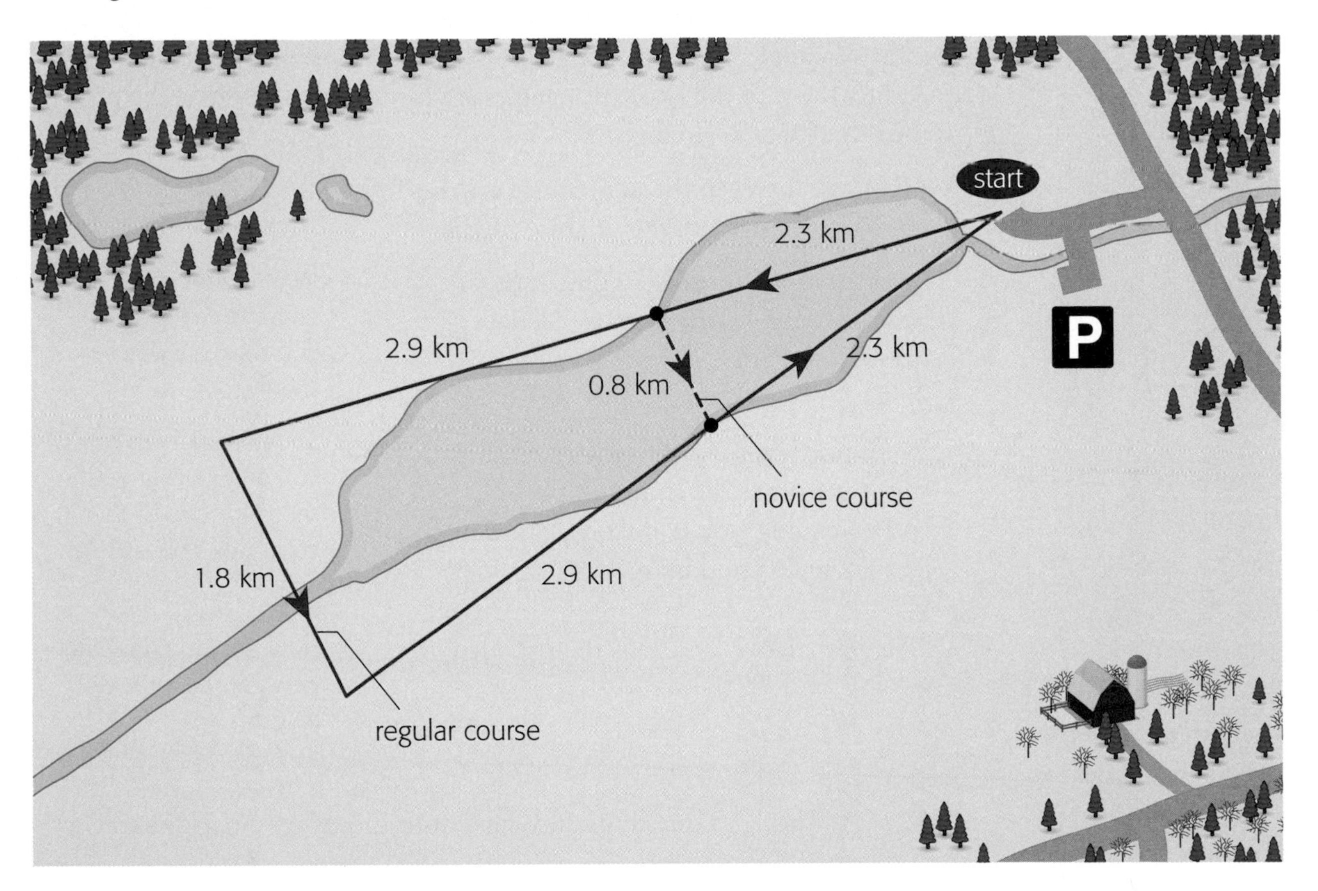

He asked Thomas to make suggestions about the report he has written for the committee.

❓ How can Sam improve his report?

Sam's Report	Thomas's Questions
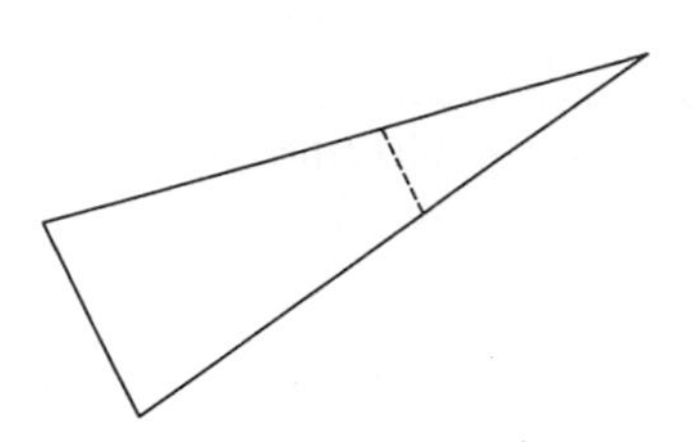	
The new course is a triangle inside the original triangle course.	Would labels on your diagram help?
Both triangles are isosceles and have the same top angle. All of the angles must add to 180°, so the two equal angles are the same for both triangles.	It might help to refer to your diagram here.
All of the angles in the new course are the same as the angles in the original course.	
I made ratios of corresponding side lengths to figure out the scale factor. 2.3:5.2 = 0.44 0.8:1.8 = 0.44	Where does the 5.2 come from? Maybe you should show more steps.
Every side length of the new triangle is about 0.4 times the length of the corresponding side in the original triangle. The triangles are similar.	Should you explain why you only calculated the ratios for two of the corresponding pairs of sides?
The new triangle course is the right length.	How do you know the new course is the right length?

A. Use Thomas's questions and the Communication Checklist to improve Sam's report.

Reflecting

B. What parts of the Communication Checklist did Sam cover well?

C. How did Thomas's questions help you to improve Sam's communication about using similar shapes?

Communication ***Checklist***

✔ Did you explain your solution clearly?

✔ Did you include a clearly labelled diagram?

✔ Did you clearly explain each calculation?

✔ Did you use appropriate math vocabulary?

WORK WITH the Math

EXAMPLE 1 | Explaining how to determine a missing length

Larissa is proofreading her math homework. She revised her solution to the following problem to communicate her thinking more clearly.

Triangles *SNR* and *GNI* are similar. Calculate the length of *IG*.

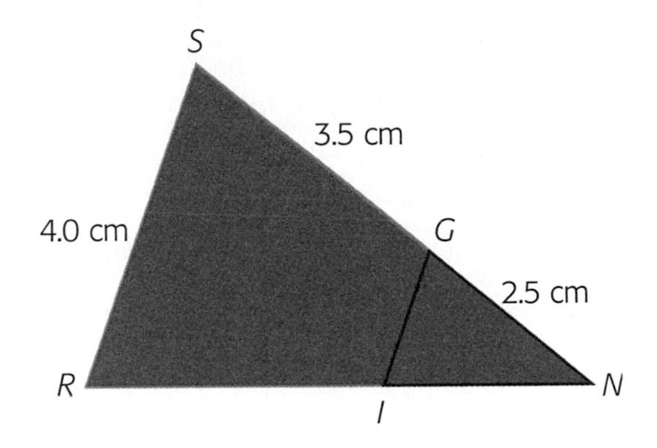

Larissa's Draft Solution

$$\frac{IG}{GN} = \frac{RS}{SN}$$

$$\frac{IG}{2.5} = \frac{4.0}{6.0}$$

$$IG = 1.7$$

Larissa's Improved Solution

I know that the ratio of any two sides of a triangle will be the same as the ratio of their corresponding sides in a similar triangle.

This means that

$$\frac{IG}{GN} = \frac{RS}{SN}$$

$$\frac{IG}{2.5} = \frac{4.0}{(3.5 + 2.5)}$$

$$\frac{IG}{2.5} = \frac{4.0}{6.0}$$

I multiplied both sides by 2.5 to calculate *IG*.

$$IG = \frac{4}{6} \times 2.5$$

$$IG = 1.67$$

The length of *IG* is about 1.7 cm.

I rounded to the tenths place value since the measurements given in the problem were provided to tenths.

In Summary

Key Idea

- Communicating about math ideas requires accurate and precise descriptions of mathematical relationships and reasoning.

Need to Know

- Including diagrams and using them as references supports understanding.
- Using mathematical vocabulary and notation in your solution helps others to understand your reasoning and processes.
- One of the ways to describe a shape is to describe the relationships among its linear dimensions.

Checking

1. Why might it be easier to decide if the shapes on the right are similar than it would to decide if the shapes on the left are similar?

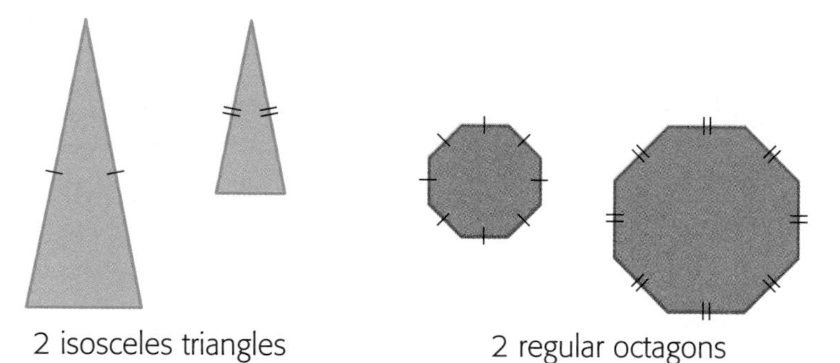

2 isosceles triangles 2 regular octagons

Practising

2. Decide if each statement is true or false. Justify your thinking.
   a) Any two quadrilaterals are similar.
   b) Any two triangles are similar.
   c) Any two squares are similar.

3. Rachel says that all circles are similar. Explain why she might think that is true.

4. Draw a triangle, and then draw a similar triangle using a scale factor of 2. Calculate and compare their areas. What do you notice? Explain why the same thing will happen with other triangles.

5. Triangle *PQS* and triangle *QRS* are similar. What is wrong with the diagram? Explain.

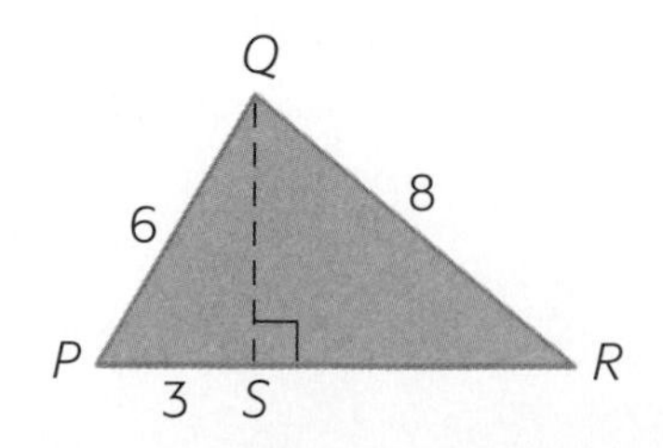

6. Arianna designed an ad for the school musical on paper that is 20 cm by 28 cm. The band asked if she could enlarge it to make a poster using a ratio of 1 : 3 and shrink it to make a postcard using a ratio of 2 : 1. Explain to Arianna what the ratios mean.

7. Diane wants the perimeter of her garden to be 1.75 times longer but still keep the same shape. The garden is currently 4 m by 2 m. Explain how long the new garden needs to be.

8. Draw a parallelogram that is similar to this parallelogram. Explain the steps you used to create your parallelogram.

9. Mayson measures the length of the shadow cast by a fir sapling as 6 paces. A minute later, he measures the length of the shadow cast by a spruce tree as 18 paces. He reasons that the height of the spruce tree is 3 times the height of the fir sapling. Is he correct? Explain.

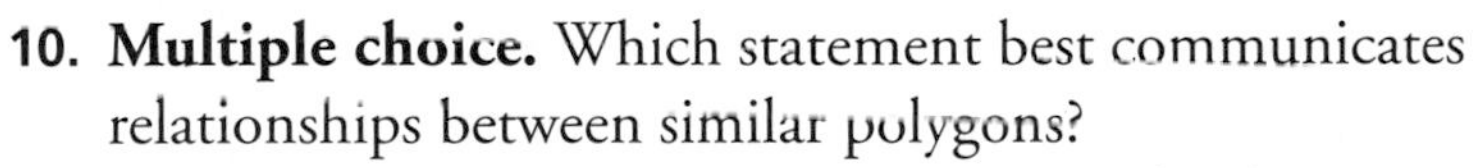

10. **Multiple choice.** Which statement best communicates relationships between similar polygons?
   A. Similar polygons have at least two angles that are equal.
   B. Similar polygons have congruent sides.
   C. Similar polygons look alike, but they are different sizes.
   D. Similar polygons have equal ratios between their corresponding sides.

11. **a)** The photo at right is of a model railway and town in a museum. If the yellow car being held by the hand in the photo were sitting on your desk, about how long do you think it would be? Explain your estimate.
   b) What scale do you think the museum used for its model? Explain how you arrived at your decision.

12. **a)** Write instructions explaining how to calculate the height of a building by measuring the length of its shadow and the length of a metre stick's shadow.
   b) Use your instructions to calculate the height of your school or another building.

Closing

13. Explain how linear dimensions can be used to describe similar shapes. Use examples, words, and diagrams to communicate your thinking.

Chapter Self-Test

1. Which sets of polygons are similar?

Set A

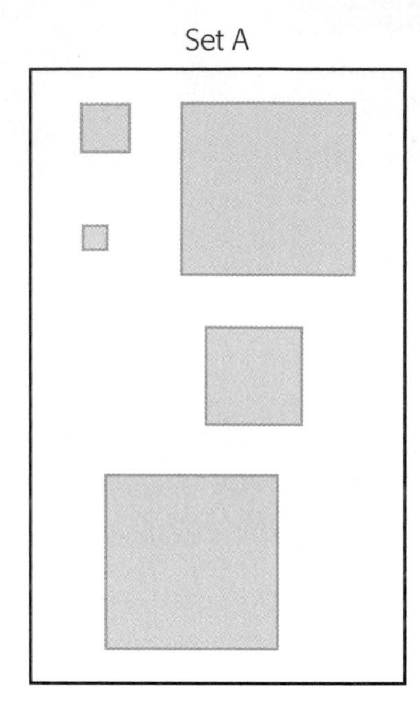

Set B

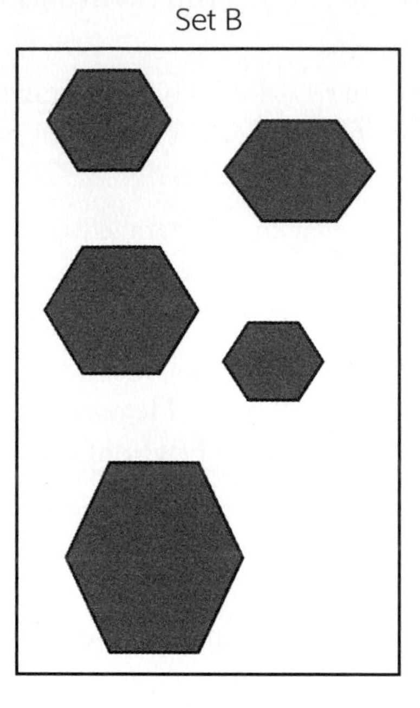

Set C

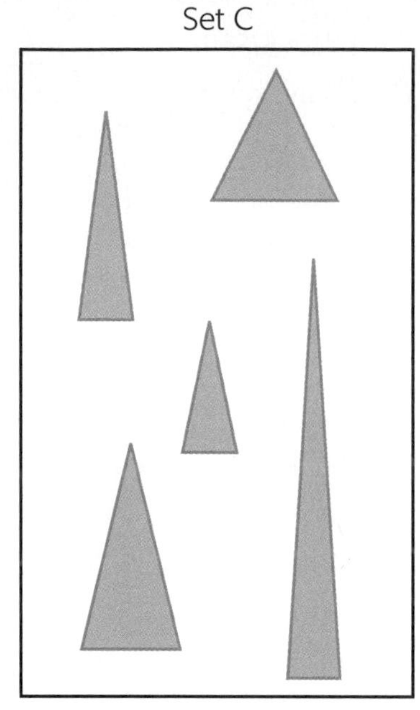

2. Are these two shapes similar? Explain.

3. Measure the dimensions of the two rectangles.

a) Write a statement using a scale factor that describes one rectangle as an enlargement of the other.

b) Write a statement using a scale factor that describes one rectangle as a reduction of the other.

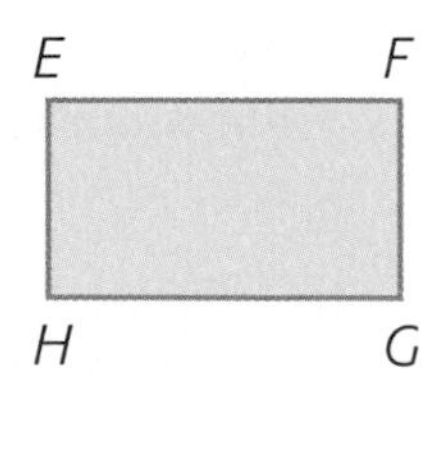

4. Draw a triangle similar to triangle *ABC* using a scale factor of 2.5. Label the dimensions of the new triangle.

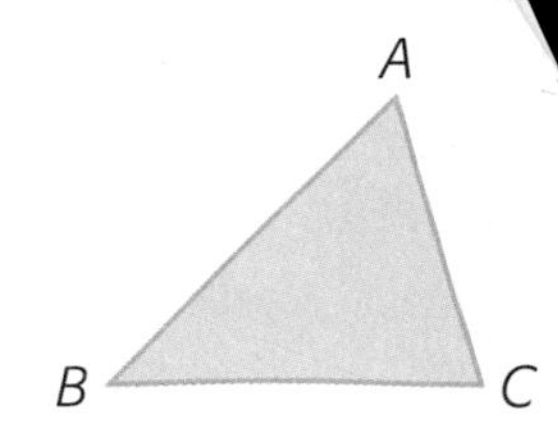

5. Maja is working in a graphic design class. She needs to create posters of her art on paper that is 22 cm by 28 cm, 22 cm by 35 cm, and 28 cm by 43 cm. What are the dimensions of the largest copy of her art that will fit on each size of paper?

6. A camp flagpole 14 m tall casts a shadow 17 m long. Frank is 1.8 m tall. How long is Frank's shadow?

7. A 2 m pole is 95 m from a tree. When a surveyor whose eye level is 1.5 m above the ground stands 5 m from the pole, he can see the tops of the pole and tree aligned. How tall is the tree?

8. David says these two polygons are similar. How would you communicate to David that he has made an error?

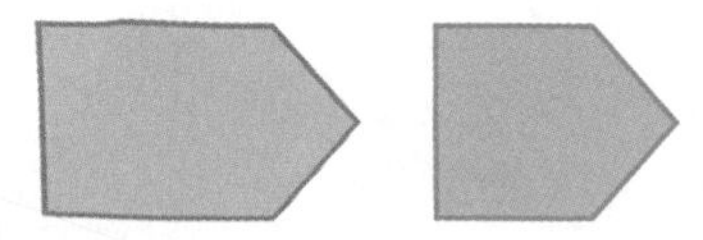

WHAT DO You Think Now?

Revisit What Do You Think? on page 99. Have your answers and explanations changed?

Chapter Review

FREQUENTLY ASKED Questions

Q: How is the scale factor used to draw similar polygons?

A1: Each side length is multiplied by the scale factor. Each angle stays the same.

For example, to create a similar polygon using a scale factor of 1.3, multiply each side length by 1.3 and keep all angles the same.

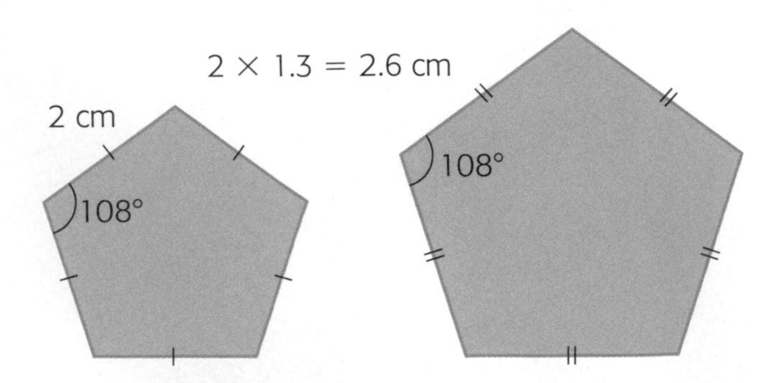

A2: Software packages allow you to use a scale factor to enlarge or reduce images or text boxes. Opening a dialog box reveals the scale for the length and width.

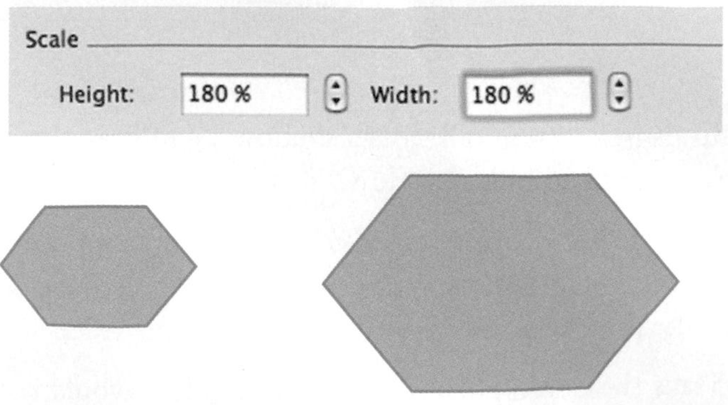

Enlarged by a scale factor of 180%

A3: A shape drawn on a grid can be enlarged or reduced to create a similar shape by drawing a reference rectangle around it, then enlarging or reducing the rectangle and drawing the similar shape inside it.

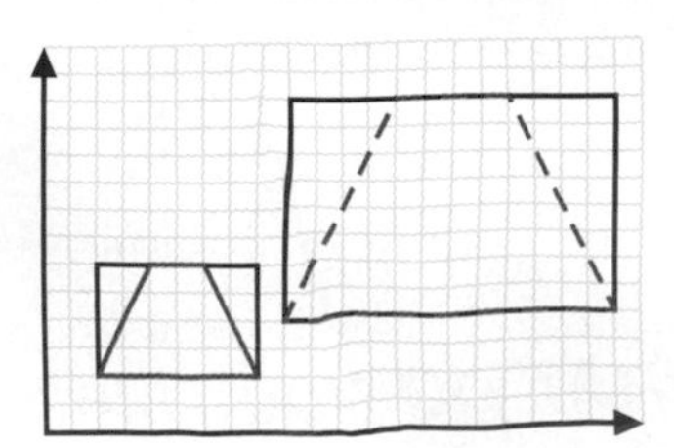

Scale factor: 2
Each dimension is doubled.

...dy Aid

- See Lesson 3.4, Examples 1, 2, and 3.
- Try Chapter Review questions 4, 5, 6, 7, and 9.

Q: How can a scale factor and properties of similar polygons help to solve problems?

A: Properties of similar polygons can be used to calculate unknown dimensions, to determine distances from scaled maps, charts, or diagrams, and to draw reductions or enlargements.

For example, to determine length *EF* in the second similar trapezoid, you would first identify two corresponding sides for which you have measures, in this case *AD* and *EH*.

You can use ratios and a proportion:

The ratio of *AD* to *EH* is $\frac{8}{24}$.

The ratio of *AB* to *EF* will be the same: $\frac{10}{■}$.

A proportion can be created to show the relationship of the ratios:

$$\frac{8}{24} = \frac{10}{■}$$

$$\frac{1}{3} = \frac{10}{■}$$

$$30 = ■$$

Study | *Aid*

- See Lesson 3.4, Examples 1, 2, and 3; and Lesson 3.5, Examples 1, 2, and 3.
- Try Chapter Review questions 3, 4, 6, 7, 8, 9, and 10.

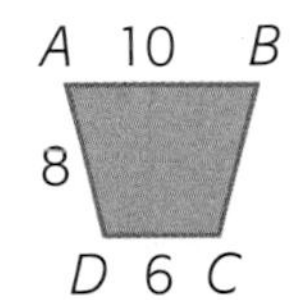

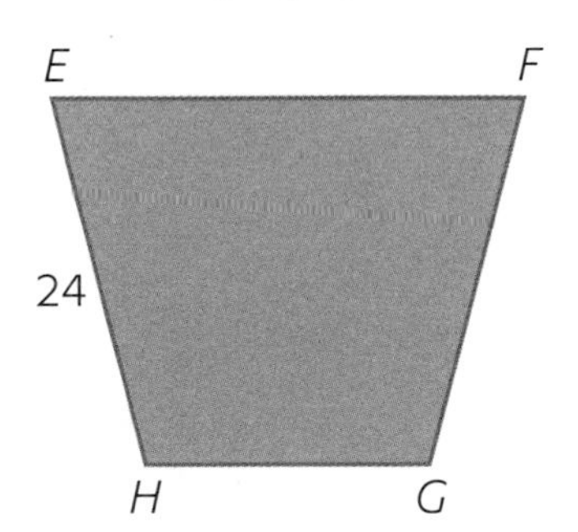

Practice

Lessons 3.1 and 3.2

1. Which polygons are similar? Explain how you know.

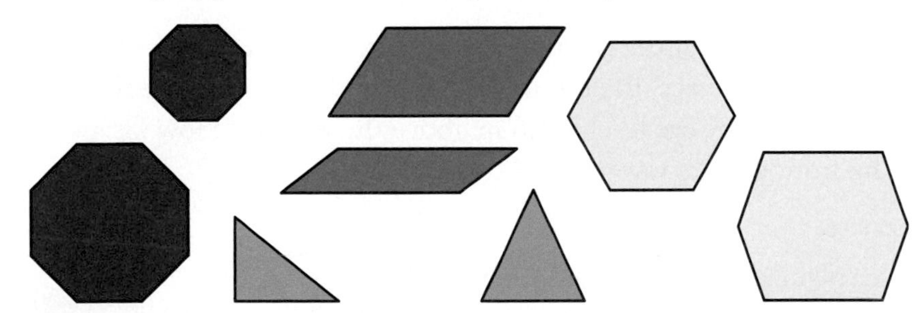

2. How can you verify that two polygons are similar?

Lesson 3.3

3. a) Triangle A is similar to triangle B. Triangle A has a base of 3.0 cm. Triangle B has a base of 7.5 cm. What is the scale factor?

b) Triangle A also has a side that measures 5 cm. How long is the corresponding side of triangle B?

c) Triangle A has a right angle. What is the measurement of the corresponding angle in triangle B?

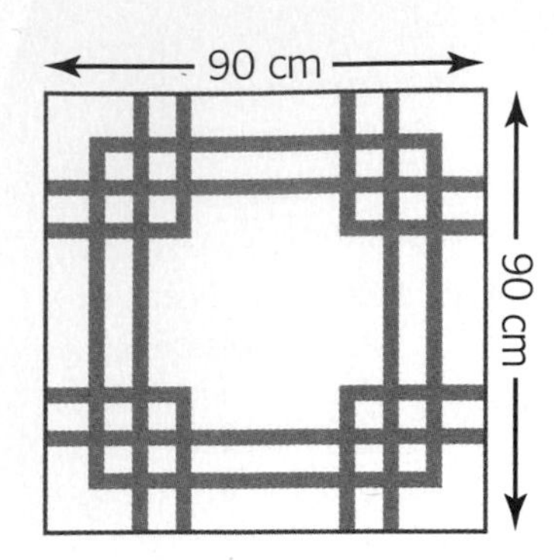

Lesson 3.4

4. Kenzu wants to enlarge this design to make a poster. He decides to enlarge it by 150%.

a) What will the poster dimensions be?

b) Draw the poster design from part a) on a single page at a size you choose. What scale factor did you use?

5. Draw a similar shape to the one at right using a scale factor of $\frac{1}{3}$.

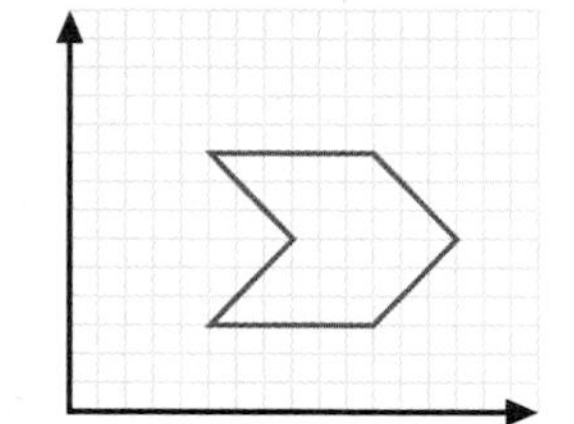

Lesson 3.5

6. A photo that is 12.5 cm by 17.5 cm has been enlarged so that it is now twice as wide and similar to the original. What are the minimum dimensions for a frame that will fit the new enlarged photo?

7. A rectangular garden that is 2 m by 5 m will be enlarged by a scale factor of 5. How long will the fence be around the new garden?

8. The organizing committee for an event is planning to sell T-shirts with a logo printed on the back and the front. The front logo fits inside a rectangle that is 8 cm by 5 cm. The back logo is an enlargement of the front logo by a scale factor of 3. Size small is 40 cm wide and size XL is 80 cm wide. Will the enlarged logo fit on the back of all T-shirt sizes?

9. A tree 12.8 m tall casts a shadow 35.5 m long. Yvonne is 1.7 m tall and she is standing nearby. How long is Yvonne's shadow?

10. Tim knows that the fire tower is 34 m tall. When he stands 1 m from a 2 m fence, the top of the fence and the top of the fire tower line up. Tim's eye level is 1.6 m above the ground. How far away is he from the fire tower?

Lesson 3.6

11. Explain step-by-step how you would show that these triangles are similar.

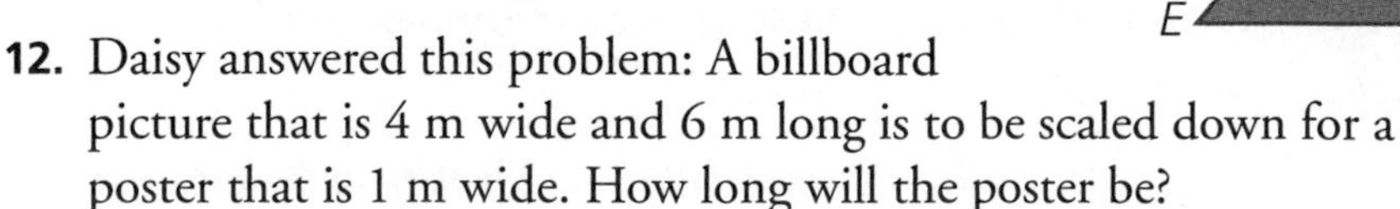

12. Daisy answered this problem: A billboard picture that is 4 m wide and 6 m long is to be scaled down for a poster that is 1 m wide. How long will the poster be?

a) Explain why Daisy's reasoning is not correct.

b) How would you communicate the correct solution?

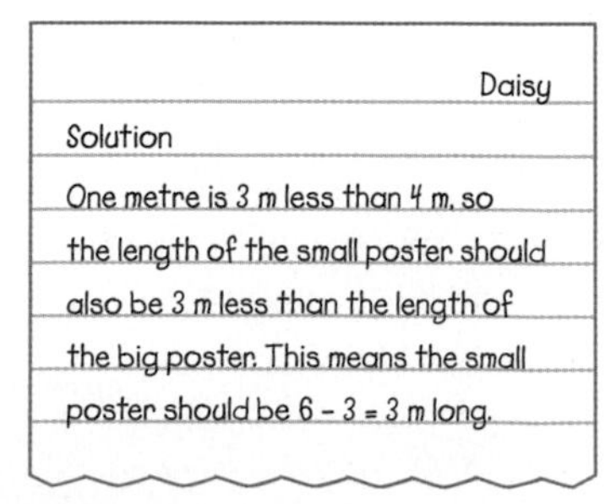
Daisy

Solution

One metre is 3 m less than 4 m, so the length of the small poster should also be 3 m less than the length of the big poster. This means the small poster should be 6 − 3 = 3 m long.

Chapter Task

Painting the School Emblem

The parents' council is deciding on which school projects to fund. You are part of the team that is applying for money to paint the school emblem on the wall of the gymnasium.

? How can you use similarity and scale factor to support your funding application?

A. Measure the length and width of the wall that you want the emblem to cover.

B. Make a diagram of the emblem. Identify the polygons in your diagram.

C. Choose a scale factor to enlarge the emblem.

D. Determine the area to be painted.

E. Research the price of paint and supplies in hardware or lumber supply catalogues.

F. Prepare a report to submit to the parents' council. Include your diagram, a detailed explanation of the materials needed, and the estimated cost of your project.

Task *Checklist*

- ✔ Did you identify similar polygons and determine an appropriate scale factor?
- ✔ Did you prepare a scale drawing to support your plans?
- ✔ Did you explain your thinking and calculations in detail?

CHAPTERS 1–3 Cumulative Review

1. Which of the comparisons below is true?

   A. $-3\frac{2}{3} < -2\frac{7}{8}$
   B. $-5.6 > -3\frac{1}{3}$
   C. $-0.8 < -0.9$
   D. $-7\frac{3}{4} > 6\frac{5}{8}$

2. Calculate. $2\frac{3}{4} - 5\frac{1}{3} = ■?$

   A. $-\frac{30}{12}$
   B. $\frac{31}{12}$
   C. $-3\frac{2}{3}$
   D. $-2\frac{7}{12}$

3. Calculate. $\frac{4}{3} + \left(-\frac{5}{8}\right) = ■?$

   A. $\frac{1}{5}$
   B. $-\frac{17}{24}$
   C. $\frac{17}{24}$
   D. $-1\frac{2}{8}$

4. Calculate. $-3.6 + (-5.4) = ■?$

   A. -9.0
   B. -2.2
   C. 9.0
   D. -8.2

5. Calculate. $-4\left[\frac{2}{3} - \left(-\frac{1}{3}\right)\right] - \frac{6}{2} = ■?$

   A. $-4\frac{1}{3}$
   B. -4
   C. 7
   D. -7

6. Joyce calculated $\frac{4}{5} \div \left(-\frac{3}{5} + \frac{2}{20}\right)$ as $-\frac{2}{5}$. She made a mistake when she

   A. added $-\frac{3}{5} + \frac{2}{20}$
   B. wrote her answer in lower terms
   C. divided $\frac{4}{5}$ by $-\frac{10}{20}$
   D. divided instead of multiplying

7. The sum of three numbers is -2. The first number is equal to (-0.5) multiplied by the second number. The quotient of the second and third numbers is 6. What are the numbers?

   A. $3, -1.5, -3.5$
   B. $3, -6, 1$
   C. $1.5, -3, -0.5$
   D. $1, -2, -\frac{1}{3}$

8. Express $(7^4)(7^3)$ as a single power.

   A. 7^1
   B. 7^{12}
   C. 7^6
   D. 7^7

9. Express $(5^4)^6$ as a single power.

   A. 5^{10}
   B. 5^2
   C. 5^{16}
   D. 5^{24}

10. Which is a simplified form of $(14^3)^3 \div 14^3$?

    A. 14^3
    B. 14^6
    C. 14^9
    D. 1

11. Which is the value of $\frac{(-4^2)(-4^7)}{(-4^2)^3(-4^3)}$?

    A. -4
    B. 4
    C. $\frac{1}{256}$
    D. 1

12. Which expression represents this sequence of operations: square $12x$, divide by 5, add 2, square the result, add $47x$?

A. $\dfrac{(12x)^2 + 2}{5^2 + 47x}$

B. $\left[\dfrac{47x + (12)^2x}{5}\right]^2$

C. $\left[\dfrac{(12x)^2}{5} + 2\right]^2 + 47x$

D. $47x + \left[\dfrac{12x^2 + 2}{5}\right]^2$

13. Which has an exact value?

A. 1.43 **B.** 1.24 **C.** 1.21 **D.** 1.84

14. Which does not have an exact value?

A. 1.44 **B.** 2.89 **C.** 625 **D.** 2.46

15. A square patio has an area of 21.2 m^2. Which is the closest estimate for the length of one side of the patio?

A. 4.0 m **B.** 4.5 m **C.** 5.0 m **D.** 5.5 m

16. Derek creates a new rectangle that is similar to rectangle B using a scale factor of $\frac{1}{3}$. What is the scale factor between rectangle A and Derek's new rectangle?

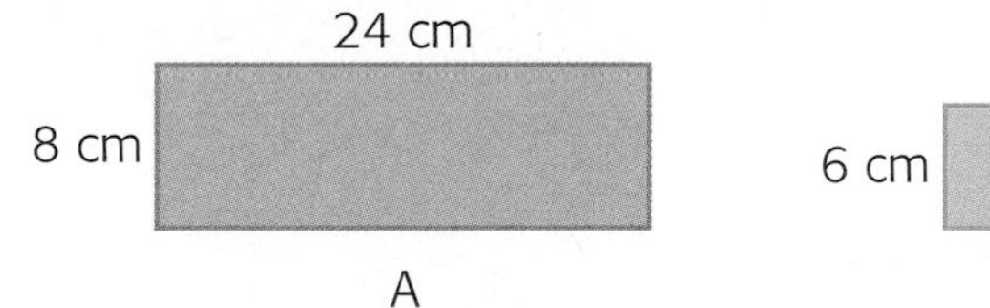

A. 4:9 **B.** 4:1 **C.** 4:3 **D.** 3:1

17. Triangle *ABC* and triangle *DEF* are similar. Which is the best estimate of the length of side *DE*?

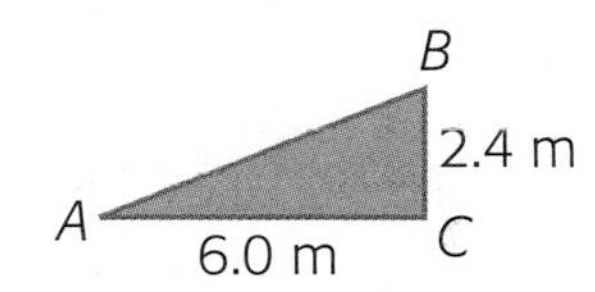

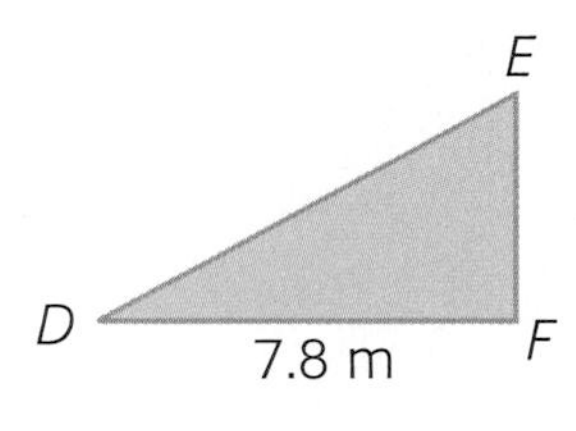

A. 3.1 m **B.** 9.8 m **C.** 5.0 m **D.** 8.4 m

18. How long does a rope need to be to reach across the river from *A* to *B*?

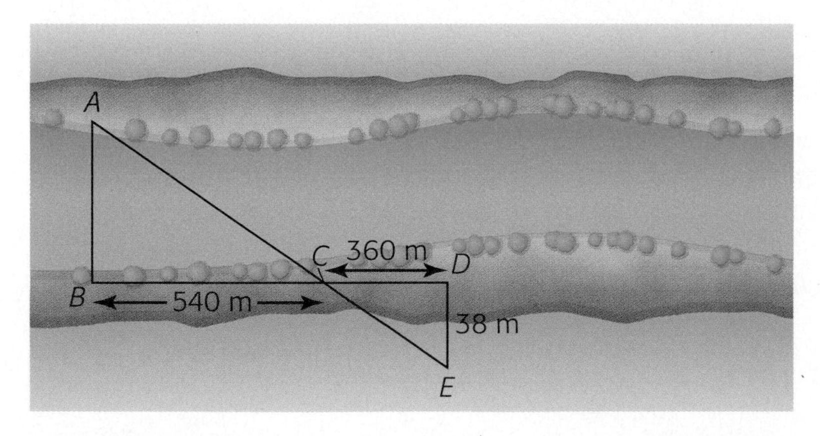

A. 112 m **B.** 57 m **C.** 342 m **D.** 56 m

Chapter

4

Measurement

GOALS

You will be able to

- visualize composite 3-D objects to reason about their surface areas
- solve problems involving surface areas of prisms and cylinders using reasoning

The Royal Canadian Mint in Winnipeg, MB, has a complex shape. How could you estimate how much glass was used to cover the building?

Getting Started

Comparing Surface Areas

Jarrod and Tiffany make custom candy packages for special occasions. They are working with four new tin designs. Each tin holds about 9500 cm^3 of candies.

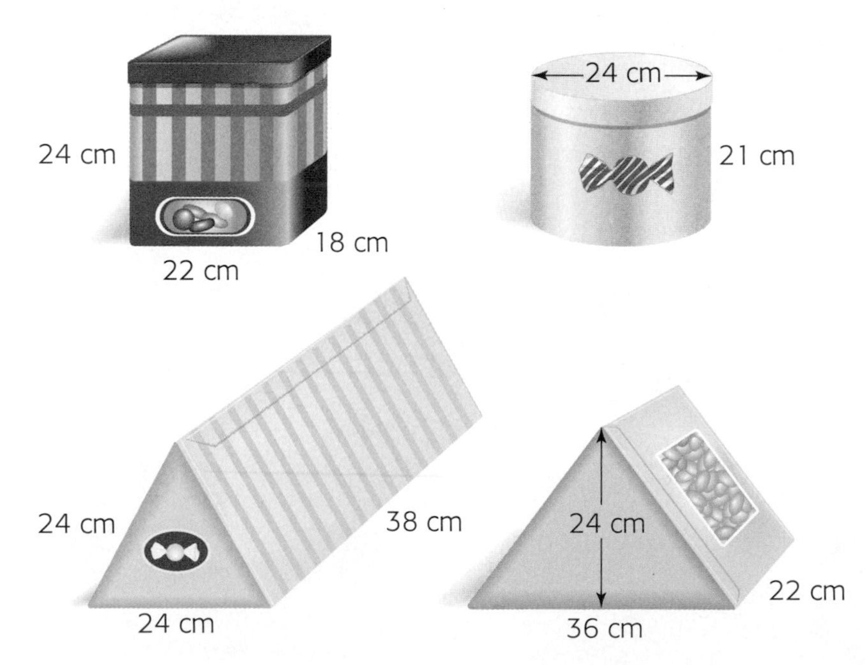

? Which tin uses the least amount of material?

A. The net of the rectangular prism is shown. Draw the nets for the other three tins.

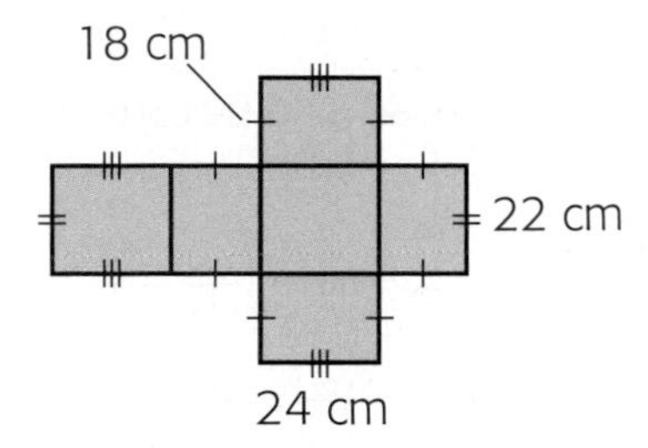

B. Use the nets to calculate the **surface area** of each tin. Which tin uses the least material?

C. What other factors might Jarrod and Tiffany consider when deciding which tin to choose?

surface area

the total area of all the faces of any 3-D object; e.g., the surface area of this rectangular prism is $2(2 \times 4) + 2(2 \times 6) + 2(4 \times 6) = 88 \text{ cm}^2$.

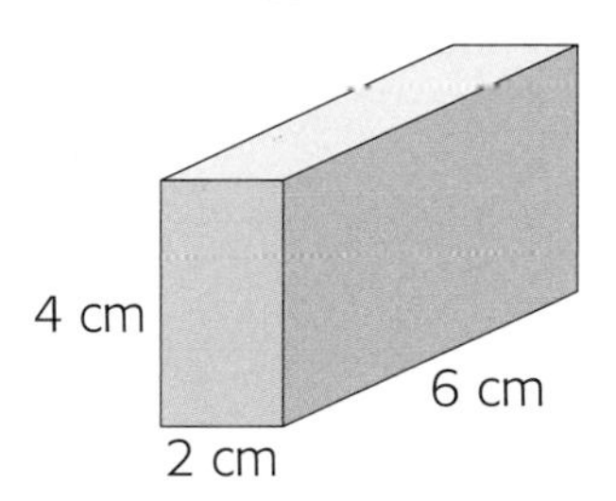

WHAT DO You Think?

Decide whether you agree or disagree with each statement. Explain your decision.

1. Two containers with the same surface area must have the same volume.
2. To calculate the surface area of this object, break it down into two smaller objects and add their surface areas.

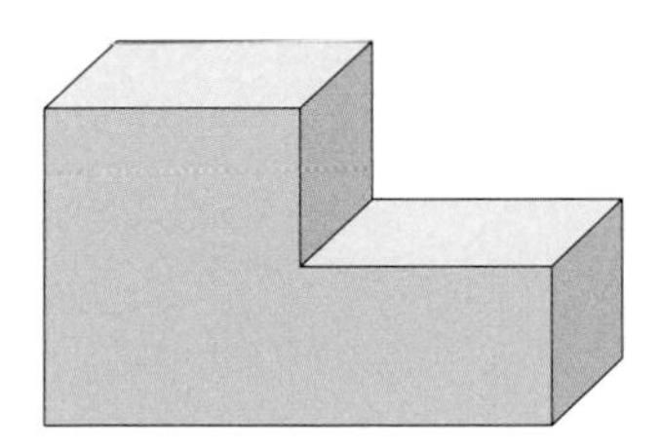

3. The surface area of a rectangular prism is always more than the surface area of a triangular prism with the same length, width, and height.
4. The best way to determine the surface area of this object uses subtraction.

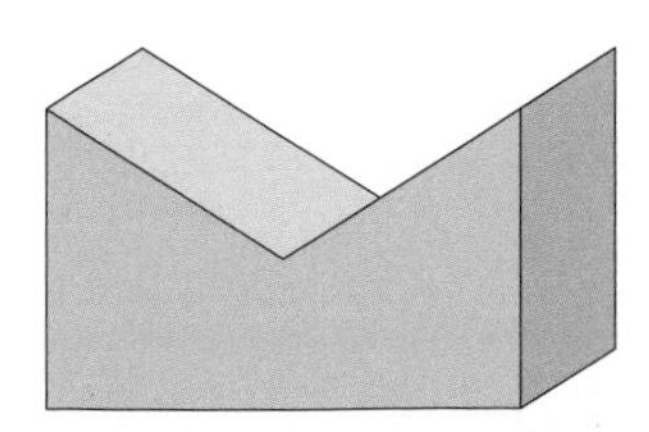

4.1 Exploring Cube Structures

YOU WILL NEED

- linking cubes

GOAL

Build non-prism cube structures and determine their surface areas.

Shelby designs mirrored tables in various artistic shapes.

She builds each table using cubes made from plywood, and then attaches mirrors to every exposed surface. These tables are all built using eight plywood cubes.

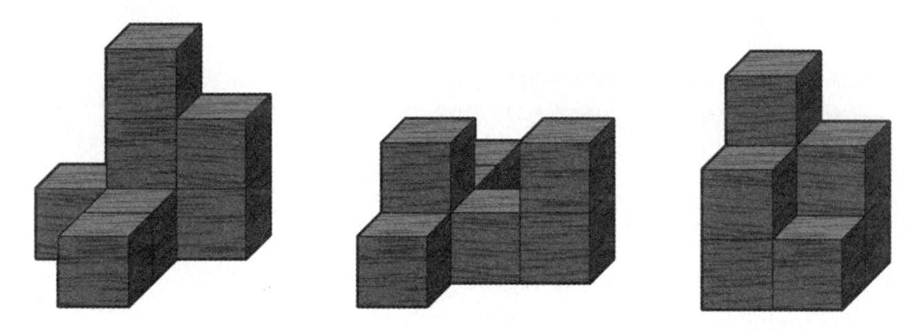

Build four more eight-cube table designs.

? Of all the possible designs using eight cubes, which one uses the most mirrors and which one uses the fewest mirrors?

4.2 Composite Objects and Their Components

GOAL

Decompose objects into right rectangular prisms, right triangular prisms, and right cylinders.

LEARN ABOUT the Math

Yvonne wants to build a set of carpeted pet stairs, as shown. Yvonne could make this **composite object** using rectangular prisms or triangular prisms.

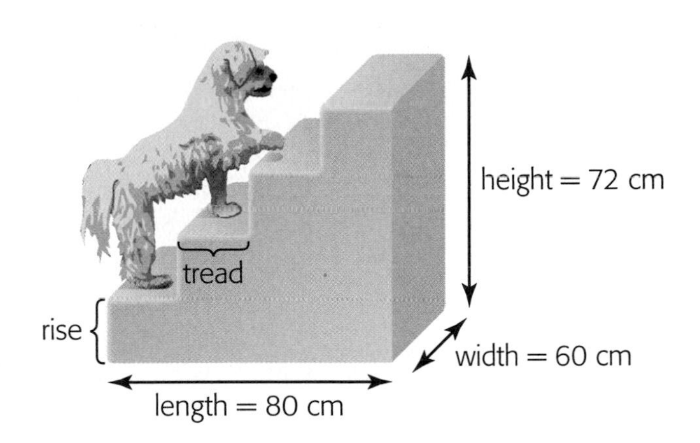

composite object

an object that can be decomposed into component parts, such as prisms and cylinders; e.g., this composite object can be decomposed into two rectangular prisms and one triangular prism.

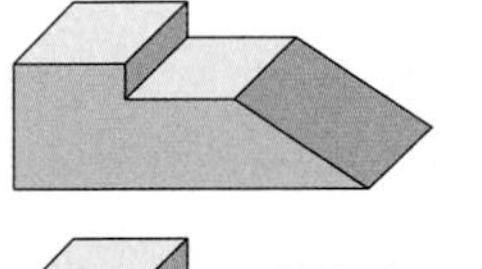

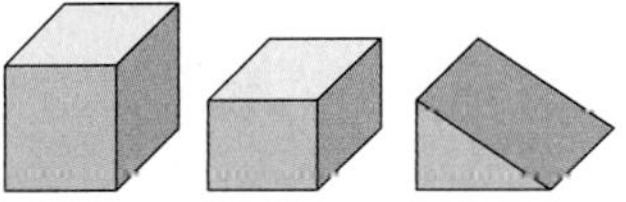

Communication *Tip*

In this book, when you are asked to decompose an object, it means to decompose it into triangular prisms, rectangular prisms, or cylinders.

? What are the dimensions of the components?

EXAMPLE 1 Using different sizes of an object

Nicole's Solution: Using rectangular prisms

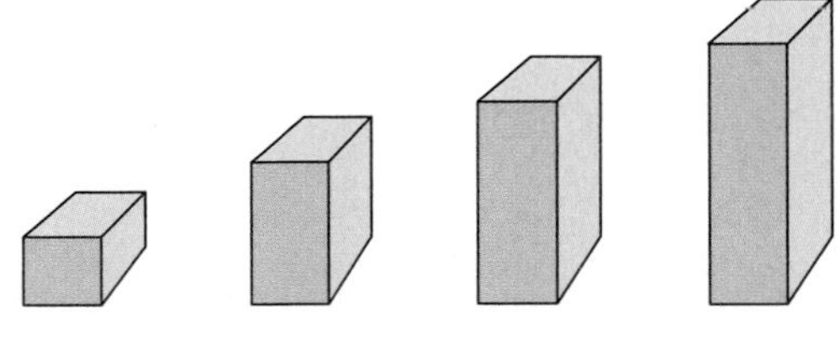

I saw that I could decompose the stairs into four rectangular prisms.

height of 4 steps = 72 cm

rise of each step = 72 ÷ 4 = 18 cm

I determined the rise of each step.
I assumed that each rise was the same.
The shortest prism has a height equal to the rise of the first step, or 18 cm.
Each prism should be 18 cm taller than the previous one.

length of four steps = 80 cm
tread = 80 ÷ 4 = 20 cm

Next, I determined the tread of each step.

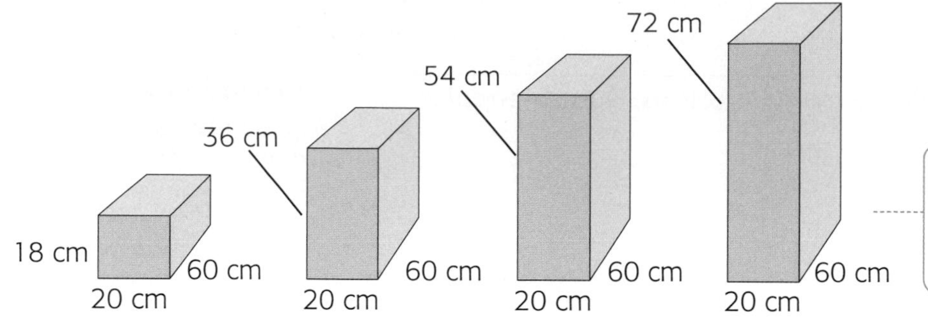

I knew that each step was 60 cm wide, so I could label all the dimensions in my diagram.

Austin's Solution: Using right triangular prisms

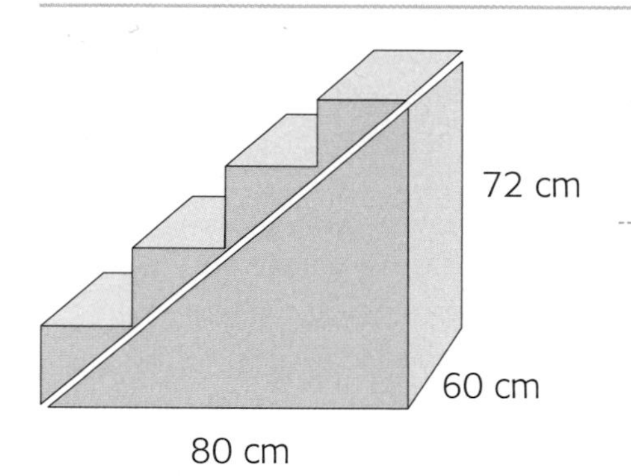

Looking at the side view, I saw that I could decompose the steps to form a large right triangular prism and some smaller ones.
The large prism is 80 cm long, 60 cm wide, and 72 cm high.

$$\text{rise} = \frac{1}{4} \times 72 = 18 \text{ cm} \qquad \text{tread} = \frac{1}{4} \times 80 = 20 \text{ cm}$$

I assumed that all of the steps on the stairs are the same size. Each step must have a rise of $\frac{1}{4}$ of the total height, and a tread of $\frac{1}{4}$ of the total length. The width of each step is 60 cm.

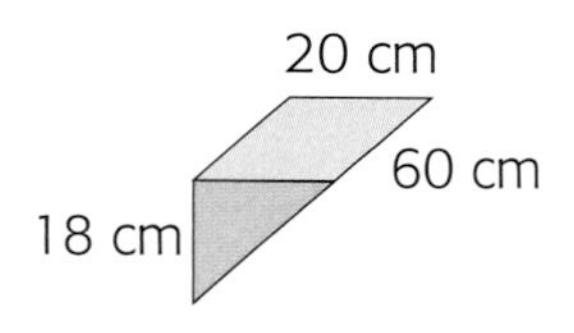

Reflecting

A. Whose solution did you prefer, and why?

B. Suggest another possible solution.

C. Explain how decomposing a composite object makes it easier to determine its volume.

WORK WITH the Math

EXAMPLE 2 | Determining component parts

An aquarium has this object for a base. What component parts make up this base and what are their dimensions?

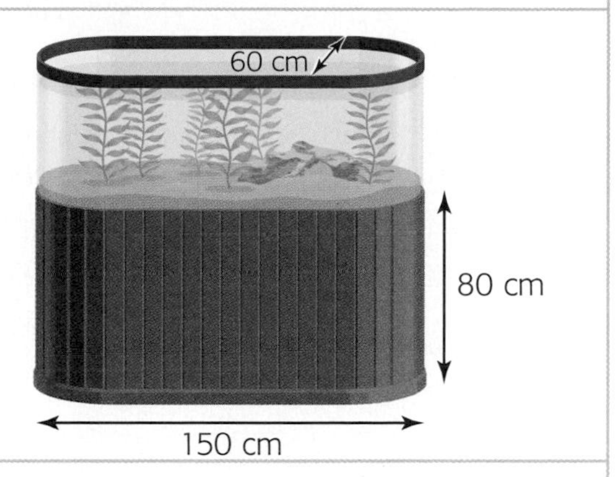

Derek's Solution

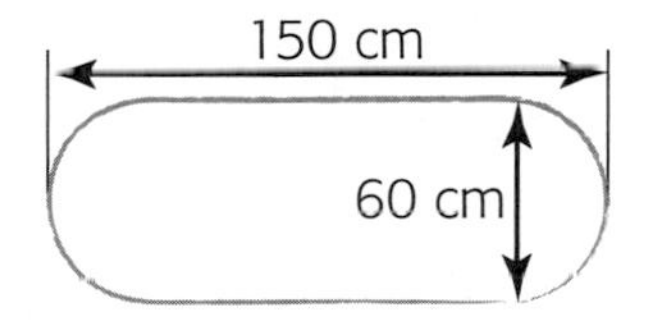

I drew a top view of the base, with its dimensions.
I noticed that each end is semicircular.

The width is a diameter, so the radius of the semicircles is 30 cm.

$150 - 30 = 120$
$120 - 30 = 90$ cm

I subtracted the radius twice from the overall length to calculate the distance between the two semicircles.

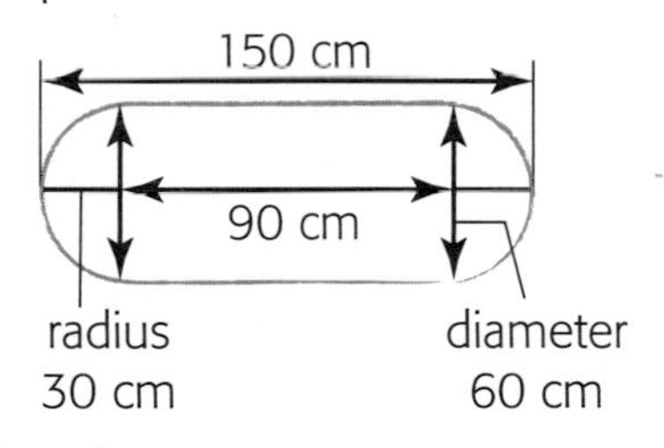

I added the new dimensions to my diagram.

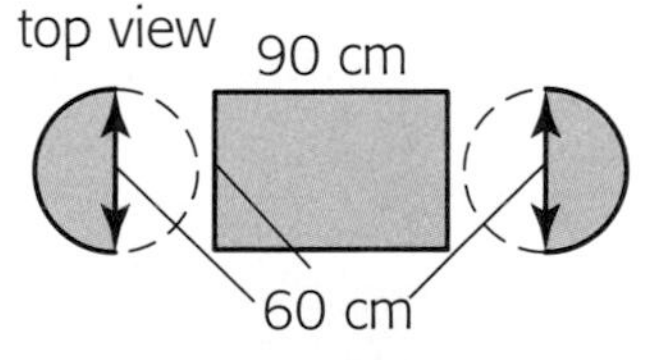

I drew the diagram again, decomposing it into two semicircles and a rectangle.

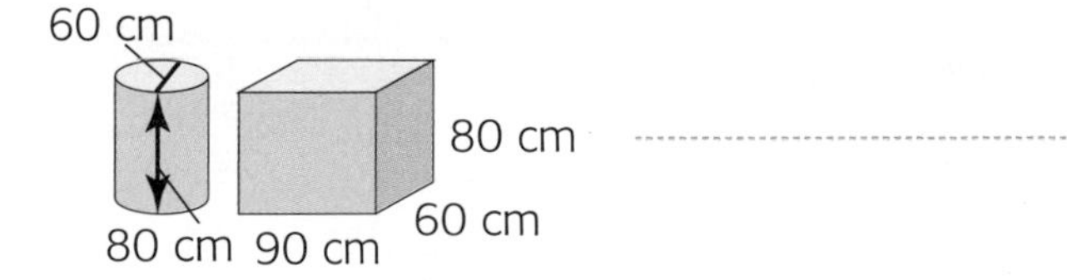

The semicircles in my diagram are the tops of half-cylinders in the actual object. I joined them to form a whole cylinder. The rectangle is the top of a prism.

The components are a rectangular prism and two half-cylinders, which are like a single cylinder.

In Summary

Key Idea

- It is possible to decompose a composite object in more than one way.

Need to Know

- When decomposing a composite object, look for the following component parts: triangular prisms, rectangular prisms, and cylinders.

Checking

1. Sketch two different ways to decompose each object. Include dimensions of each part.

a)

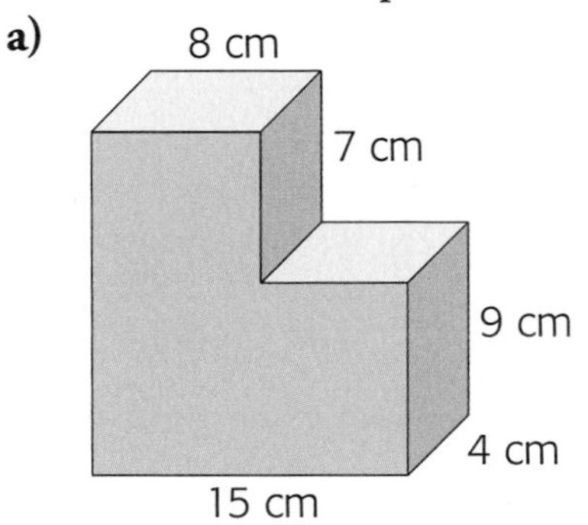

b)

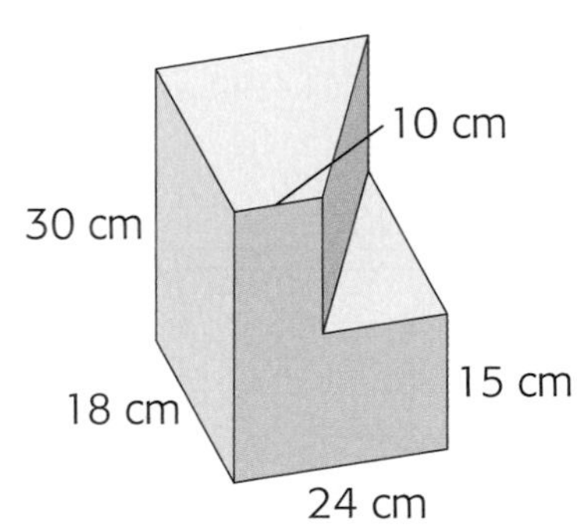

Practising

2. Sketch two different ways to decompose each object. Include dimensions of each part.

a)

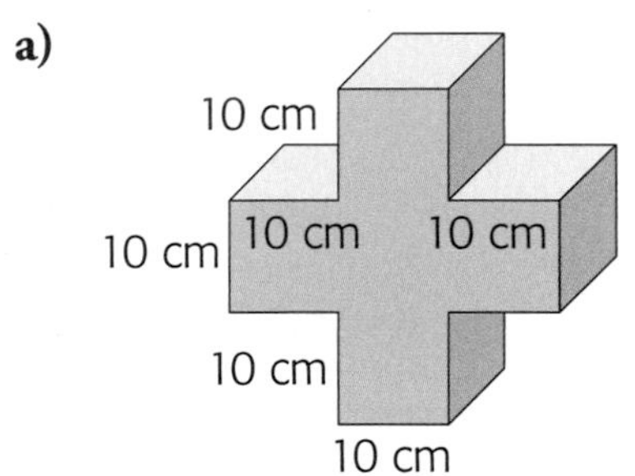

b)

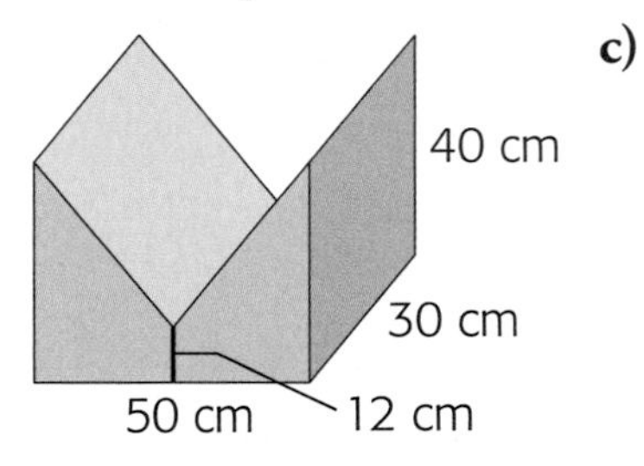

c)

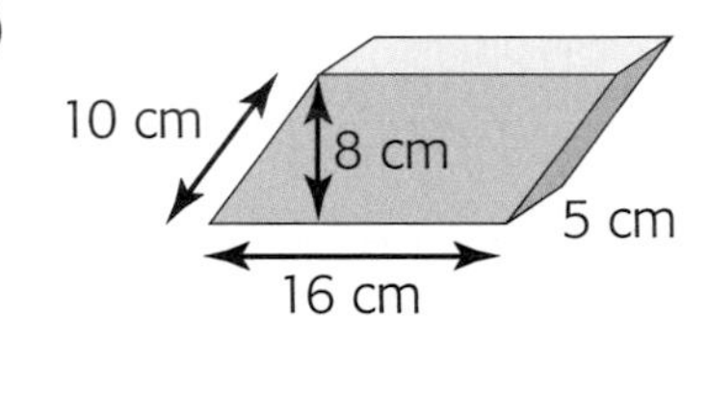

3. Decompose each object into two components. Include dimensions of each part.

a)

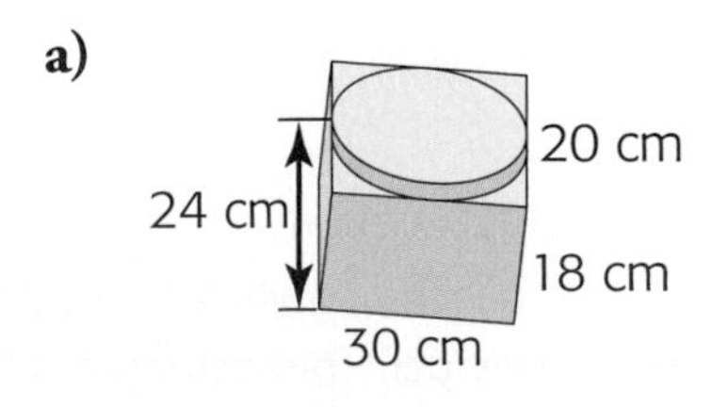

b)

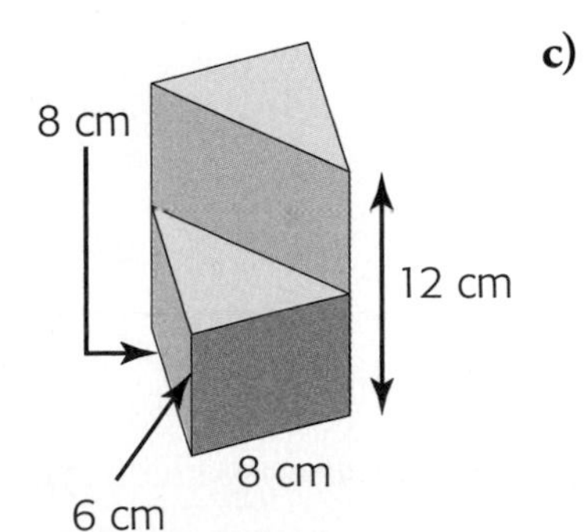

c)

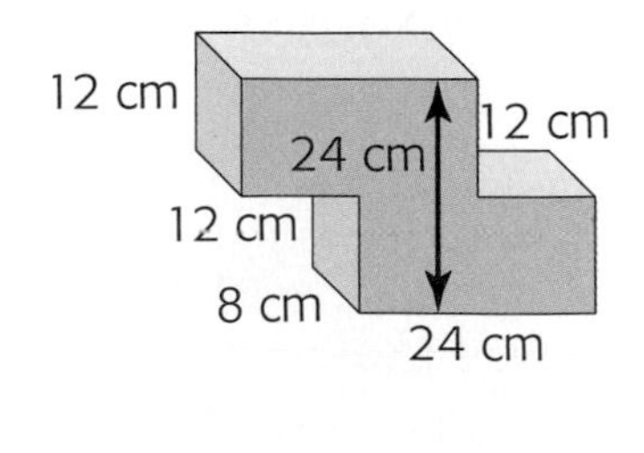

4. Sketch one way to decompose the red object at right.

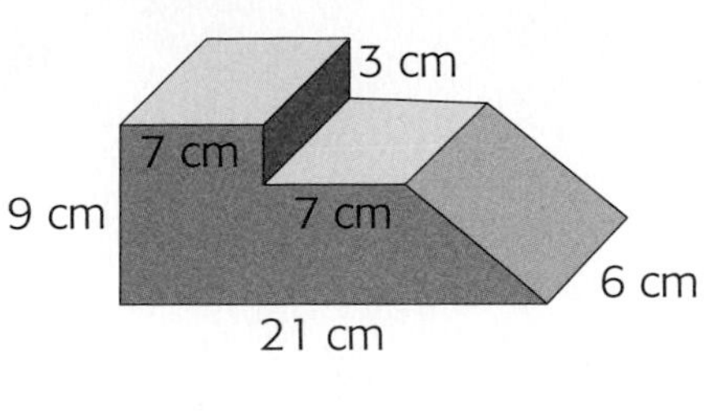

5. William wants to make a set of bookends, one of which is shown. The triangular-prism support is inset by 2 cm on all sides. What are the dimensions of the components for each bookend?

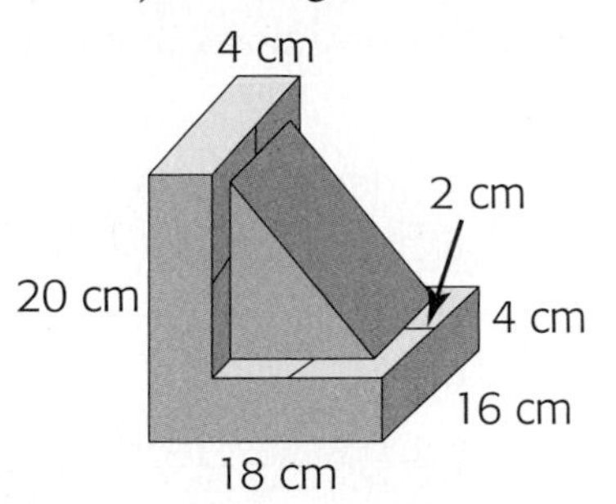

6. Multiple choice. A video game involves filling a space using the following four objects. Each individual cube measures 1 unit on each edge. Which one of these objects cannot be decomposed into two prisms, each with two cubes?

A. **B.** **C.** **D.**

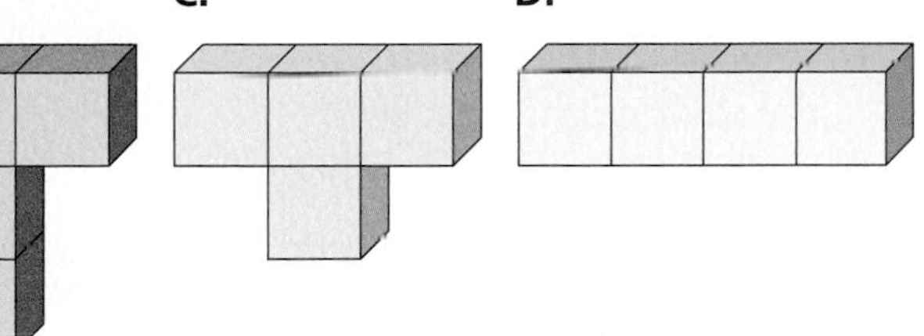

7. Multiple choice. What is the least number of triangular or rectangular prism components in this object?

A. 3
B. 4
C. 5
D. 6

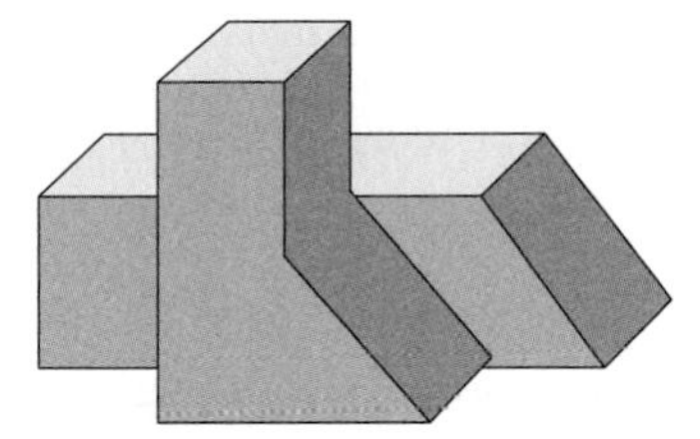

8. Sketch one way to decompose the picture frame shown at right.

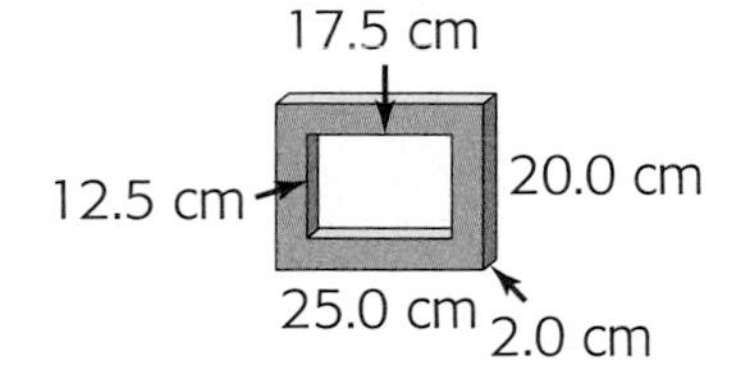

9. Describe one way to decompose this desk.

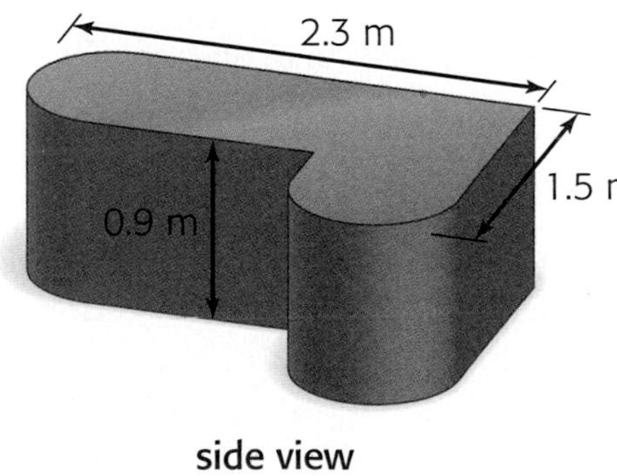

side view

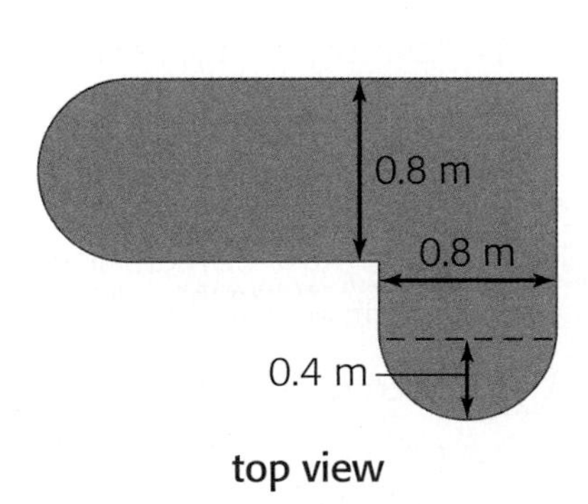

top view

10. Describe one way to decompose this television stand. Assume that the cylindrical posts do not go through the bottom shelf.

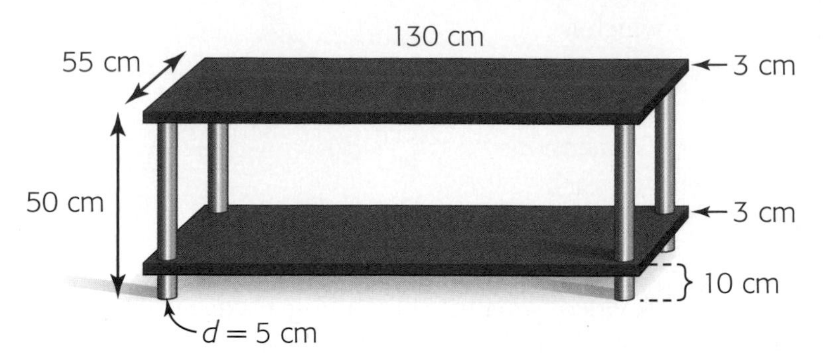

11. This chair was made by combining foam blocks and covering them with upholstery.
    a) Describe three ways in which the chair might have been made from component pieces of foam. State the dimensions of each component part.
    b) Could the chair have been made from a single foam block? Explain.

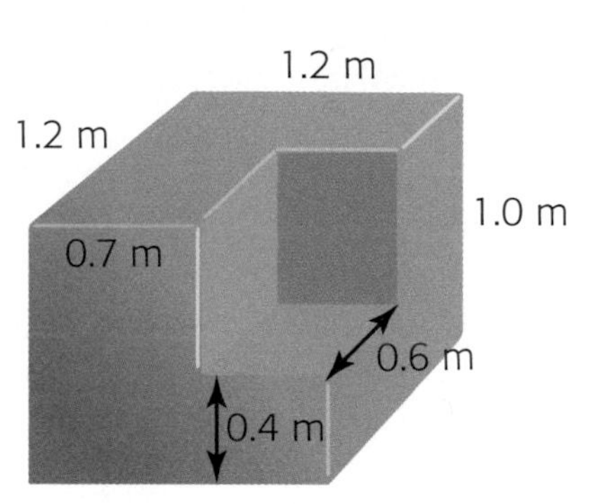

12. Determine the component objects and their dimensions for this grain elevator.

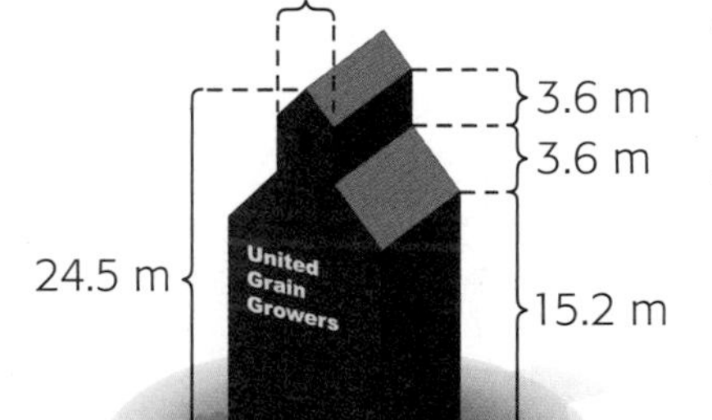

13. a) Find an example of a composite object in your school, at home, or in your town. Sketch the object and its component parts.
    b) Exchange your example with a classmate. Sketch the component parts of your classmate's composite object.
    c) Compare your solutions for both objects. Did both of you decompose them in the same way?

Closing

14. Composite objects can be decomposed in more than one way. Explain with an example why one way might be preferable to another.

Extending

15. This piece of foam is packed around a circular vase for shipping. What are the component parts and what are their dimensions?

30 cm
24 cm
24 cm

16. Sketch a set of component parts, including their dimensions, for this model of a toy.

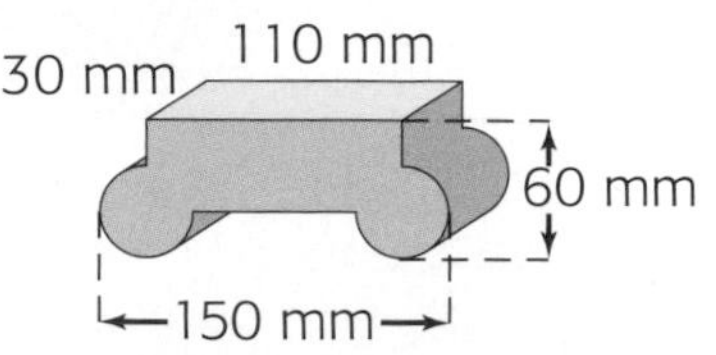

4.3 Area of Overlap

YOU WILL NEED

- two different rectangular prisms
- a cylinder
- linking cubes
- isometric dot paper

GOAL

Determine the area of overlap for the components of 3-D objects.

LEARN ABOUT the Math

Amanda is building a lamp in her woodworking class, using three different pieces of wood as shown. She will glue the bases of the top two pieces to attach them to the piece underneath.

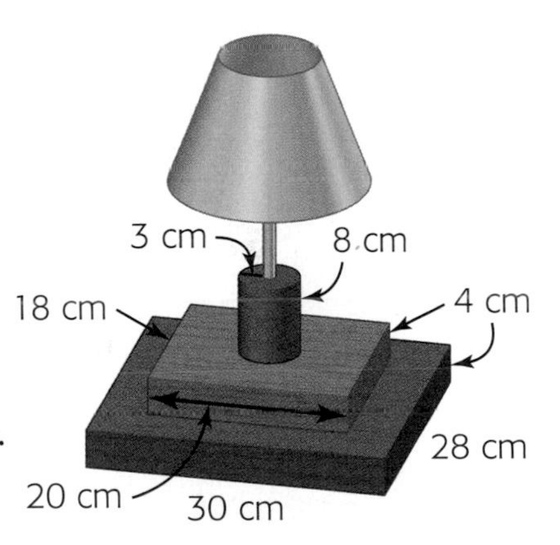

? What is the total area of the surfaces that will be glued?

A. Build a model of the lamp by stacking the prisms and the cylinder.

B. Examine the model. Trace around the cylinder onto the smaller rectangular prism, then trace around the smaller prism onto the larger prism.

C. Label on your diagrams the **areas of overlap** with their dimensions.

D. What is the total area of overlap?

area of overlap

the area covered when two component parts are joined to form a composite object

Reflecting

E. Why might you need to know the area of overlap if you were making 100 of these lamps?

F. When you are determining the area of overlap for two objects, do you have to think about the shapes of both objects?

WORK WITH the Math

EXAMPLE 1 | Building and decomposing a model

Decompose this structure into rectangular prisms and determine the total area of overlap. Each edge of each cube is 2 cm long.

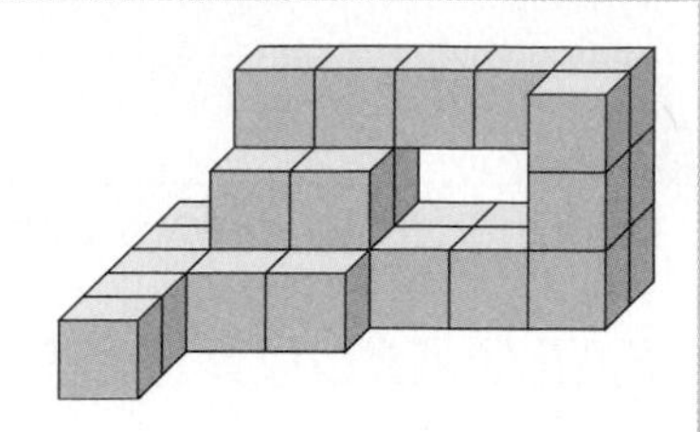

Shelby's Solution

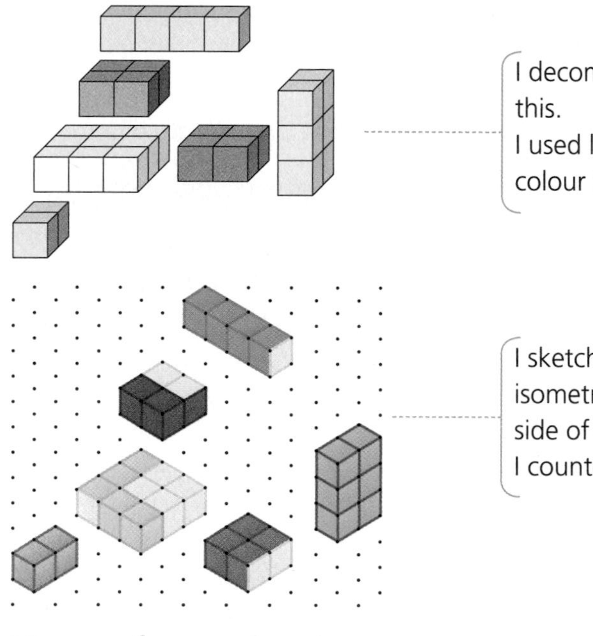

I decomposed the structure like this.
I used linking cubes of the same colour for each prism.

I sketched each prism on isometric paper and shaded one side of each connecting surface.
I counted the shaded surfaces.

12 square faces on the prism surfaces are connected to other prisms, so the total area of overlap is $12 \times 4 = 48$ cm^2.

I knew the face of each cube has an area of $2 \times 2 = 4$ cm^2.

EXAMPLE 2 | Decomposing an object using different prisms

Decompose this object and determine the area of overlap.

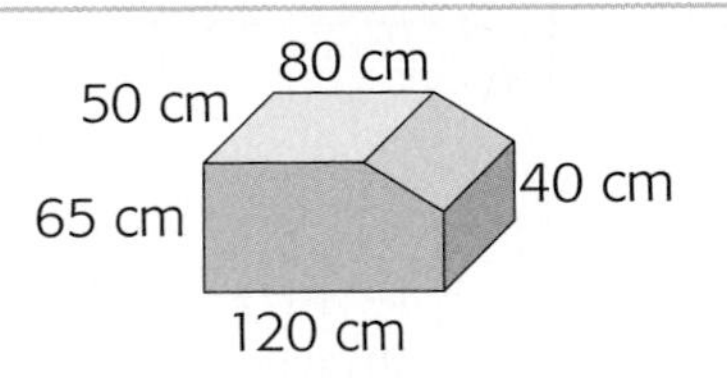

Bay's Solution

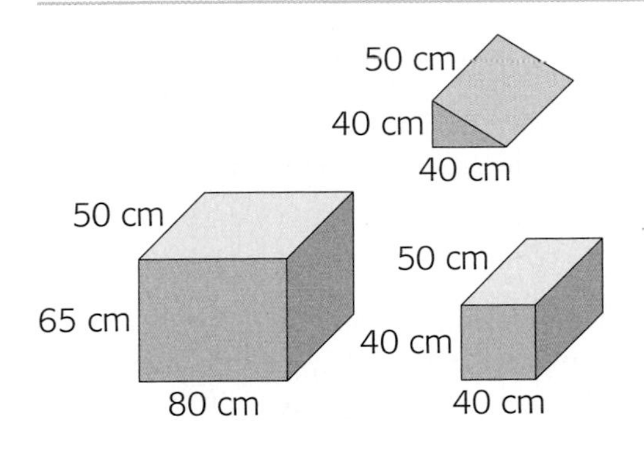

I visualized separating the object into two rectangular prisms and a triangular prism. I determined the dimensions of the prisms using given measurements and calculations.

The base of the original object is 120 cm long, and the large rectangular prism is 80 cm long. So the small rectangular prism and the triangular prism are $120 - 80 = 40$ cm wide.

The height of the original object is 65 cm, and the height of the small rectangular prism is 40 cm. So the height of the triangular prism is $65 - 40 = 25$ cm.

I noticed that the small rectangular prism and the triangle overlap the complete side of the large rectangular prism. The triangular prism overlaps the top side of the small rectangular prism.

Area of overlap:

Right side of large rectangular prism

$A = l \times w$
$= 65 \times 50$
$= 3250 \text{ cm}^2$

Top of small rectangular prism

$A = l \times w$
$= 40 \times 50$
$= 2000 \text{ cm}^2$

The total area of overlap is $3250 + 2000 = 5250 \text{ cm}^2$.

EXAMPLE 3 | Determining partial area of overlap

Brenda makes custom jewellery from metal cubes that are 15 mm on each side. This design has three cubes, as shown. What is the area of overlap?

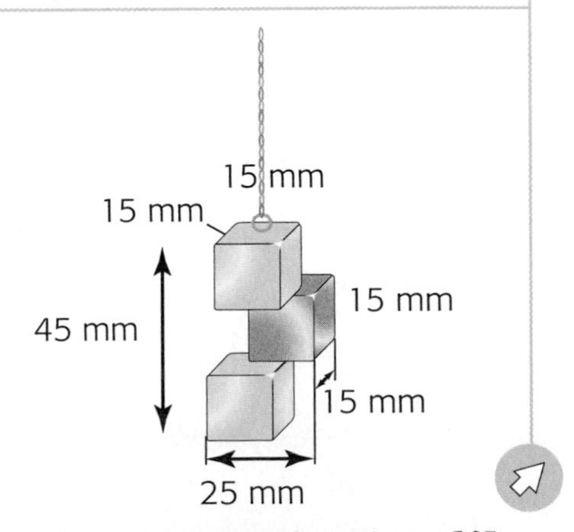

Yvonne's Solution

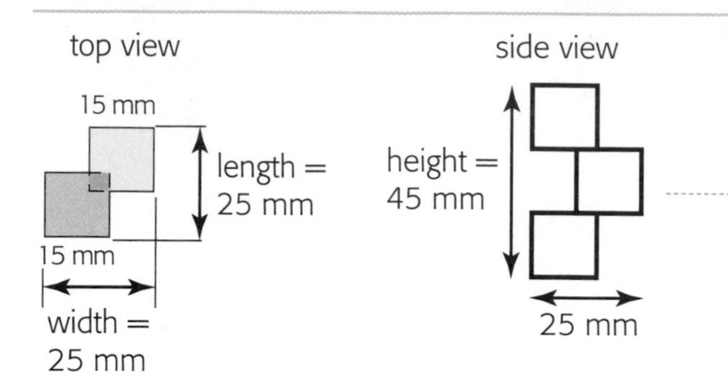

I knew that if I placed two metal cubes side by side, the total width would be 30 mm.

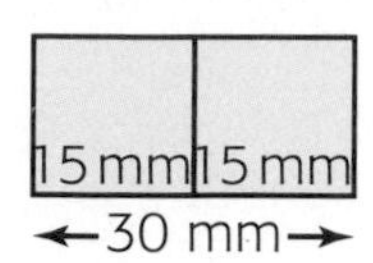

But the design is 25 mm wide, so I could calculate the width of the overlap. The length of the design was also 25 mm.

The cubes overlap by
$30 - 25 = 5$ mm in both directions.

Area of overlap per cube $= (5)^2$
$= 25 \text{ mm}^2$

Total area of overlap $= 2 \times 25$
$= 50 \text{ mm}^2$

Each cube overlapped another cube by a square that is 5 mm by 5 mm. There were two identical areas of overlap.

EXAMPLE 4 Determining area of overlap

Speakers in the shape of triangular prisms are attached on either side of a television screen. The entire unit is then connected to a base. Determine the total area of overlap.

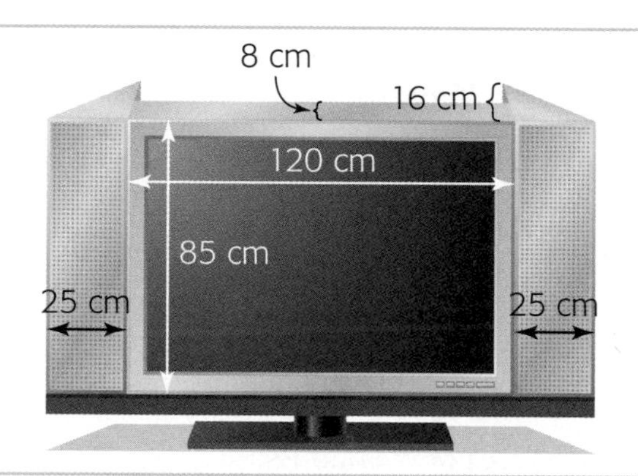

Derek's Solution

Area of overlap between screen and speakers
$= 2 \times (l \times w)$
$= 2 \times (85 \times 8)$
$= 1360 \text{ cm}^2$

Area of overlap between screen and base
$= 120 \times 8$
$= 960 \text{ cm}^2$

First, I decided to determine the area of overlap between the television screen and the speakers. The screen is 85 cm high, and 8 cm deep. Its edges are rectangular. There is an area that size on either side of the screen. I also wanted to determine the area where the screen touches the base. The width of the screen is 120 cm.

Area of overlap between base and both speakers
$= 2 \times \left(\frac{1}{2}(b \times h)\right)$
$= 2 \times \left(\frac{1}{2}(25 \times 16)\right)$
$= 400 \text{ cm}^2$

Next, I needed to calculate the area of overlap between the two speakers and the base. They overlap in right triangular shapes. The base of each triangle is 25 cm, and the height is 16 cm.

Total area of overlap
$= $ area between screen and speakers
$+$ area between screen and base
$+$ area between base and speakers
$= 1360 + 960 + 400$
$= 2720 \text{ cm}^2$

I added all of the areas of overlap together.

EXAMPLE 5 | Determining circular area of overlap

A washer is to be used with a screw. What is the area of overlap between the washer and the screw head?

Amanda's Solution

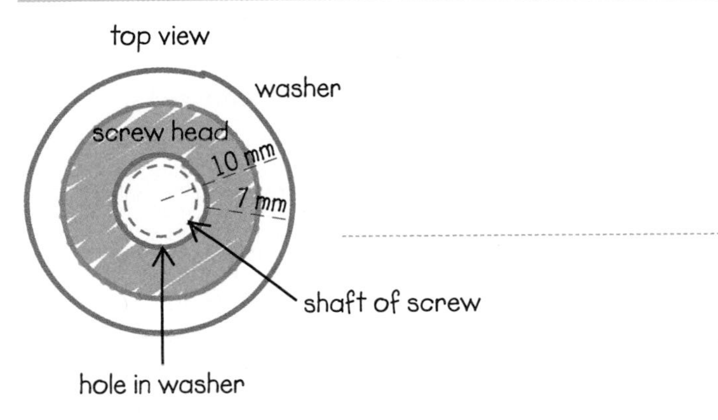

I drew a diagram showing how the washer and screw would line up.

The area of overlap between the washer and the screw head is an outer circle the size of the screw head, with an inner circle the size of the hole in the washer removed.

I knew that the outer radius is half of the outer diameter of the screw head.
I calculated the radius of the hole in the washer.

I need to calculate the area of the orange part in my diagram.

Washer dimensions:
Full radius $= 10$ mm
Radius of hole $= 10 - 7$
$= 3$ mm

Area of screw head
$= \pi r^2$
$= \pi(7)^2$
$= \pi 49$

Area of washer hole
$= \pi r^2$
$= \pi(3)^2$
$= \pi 9$

I determined expressions for the area of the outer circle (the screw head) and the inner circle (the washer hole).

Area of overlap $= \pi 49 - \pi 9$
$= \pi 40$
$\doteq 126 \text{ mm}^2$

I subtracted to determine the area of overlap.

The area of overlap is about 126 mm^2.

In Summary

Key Ideas

- When two objects are combined, there will be an area of overlap.
- The way in which a composite object is decomposed may affect its area of overlap.

Need to Know

- The area of overlap can be all or part of the face of a component part.

Checking

1. Sketch component parts of each object. Indicate the areas of overlap.

a)

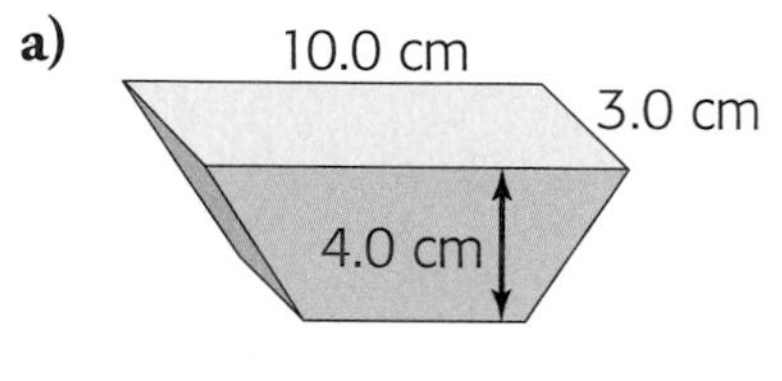

b)

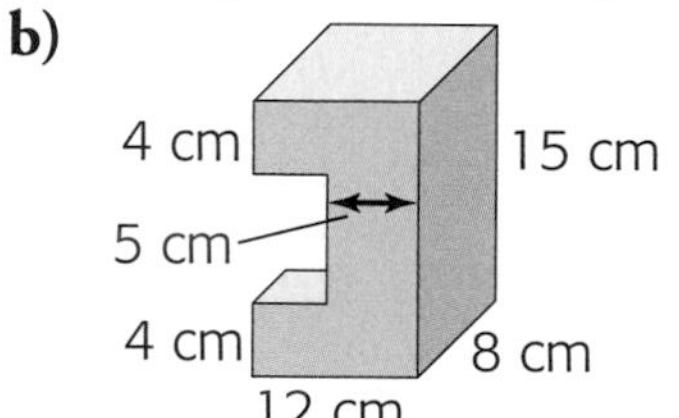

c)

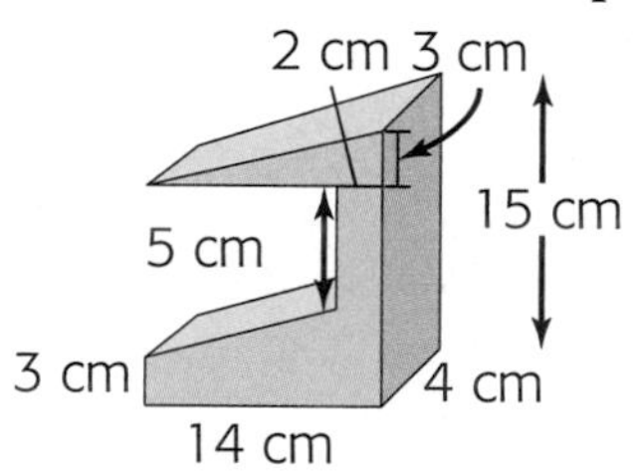

2. Calculate the total area of overlap for the components you identified in question 1.

Practising

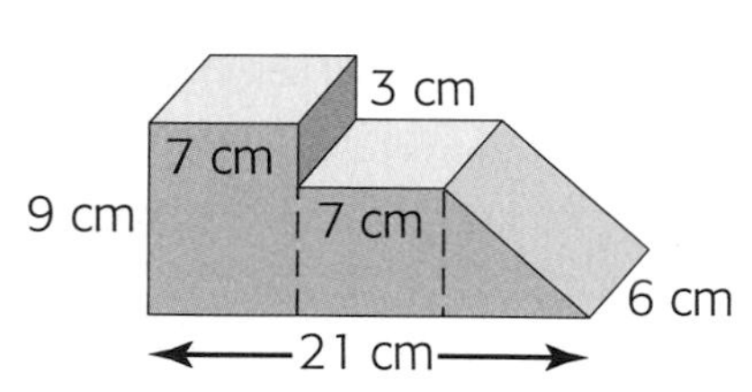

3. This object is decomposed into two rectangular prisms and a triangular prism, as shown. Calculate the area of overlap.

4. **Multiple choice.** A set of three planters is assembled as shown. What is the area of overlap of the exteriors of the planters?

   A. 2000 cm^2 **B.** 2400 cm^2 **C.** 2500 cm^2 **D.** 4000 cm^2

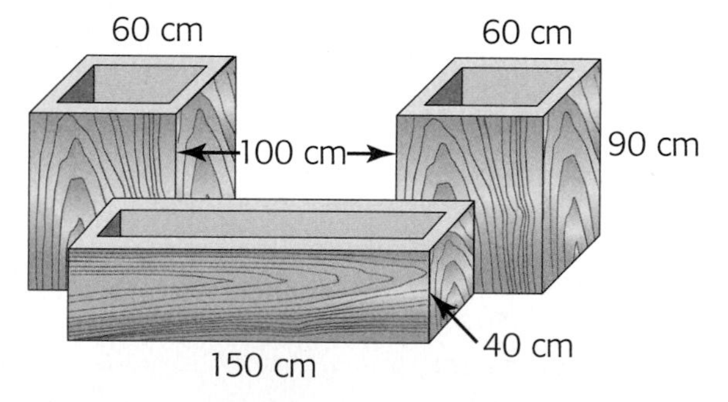

5. **Multiple choice.** A barbell is set up as shown. What is the total area of overlap of the plates?

   A. 3620 cm^2
   B. 452 cm^2
   C. 1232 cm^2
   D. 904 cm^2

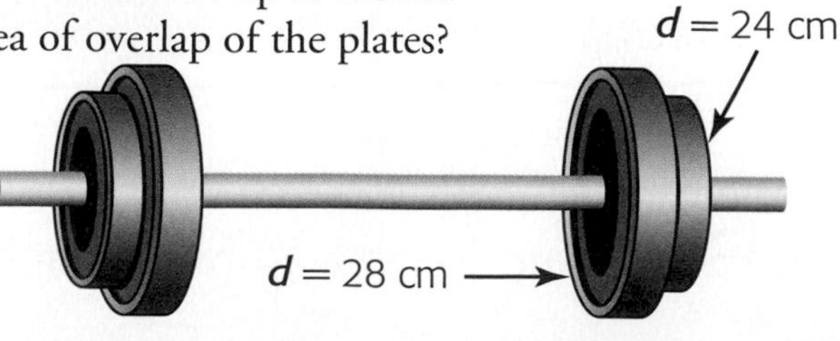

6. Calculate the areas of overlap in this cat toy. Each cylindrical post has a radius of 3.0 cm.

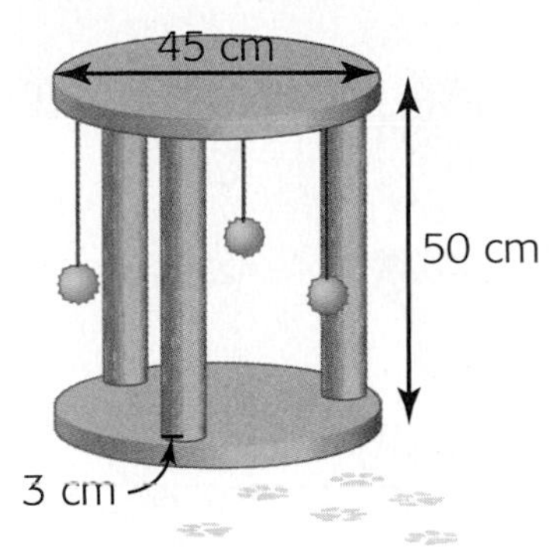

7. A store display is designed with rectangular prisms, as shown. The top of each prism is a square 0.3 m on each side. Calculate the total area of overlap of the prisms.

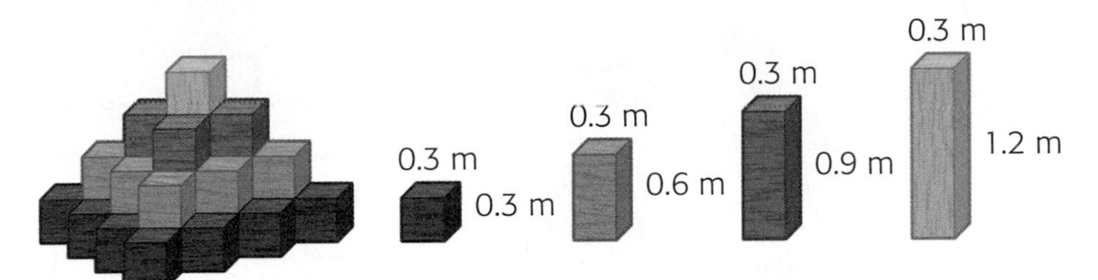

8. Amanda decides to add a fourth triangular piece of wood to the top of her lamp as shown. How would you determine the area of overlap between the new triangular prism and the cylinder?

Reading Strategy

Predicting

Use sketching and decomposing to help predict and confirm the area of overlap.

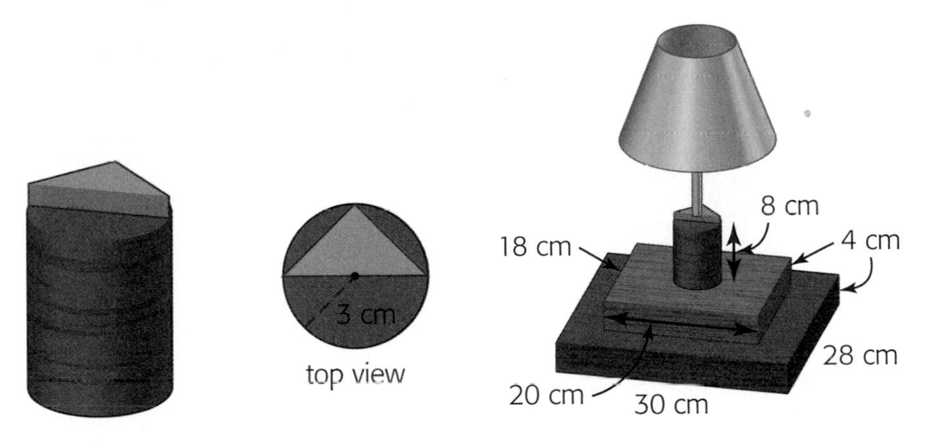

9. Build a composite structure with linking cubes. Exchange your object with a partner. Decompose your partner's object and determine the area of overlap.

10. A Kransekake is a Norwegian wedding cake. It is constructed using cookie rings that increase in diameter from top to bottom. Meaghan wants to bake a Kransekake using six cookie rings. The outer diameters for the cookies are 6.0 cm, 7.0 cm, 8.0 cm, 9.0 cm, 10.0 cm, and 11.0 cm. The inner diameter of each cookie ring is 2 cm less than its outer diameter. Calculate the total area of overlap of the cookies when assembled.

cookie ring

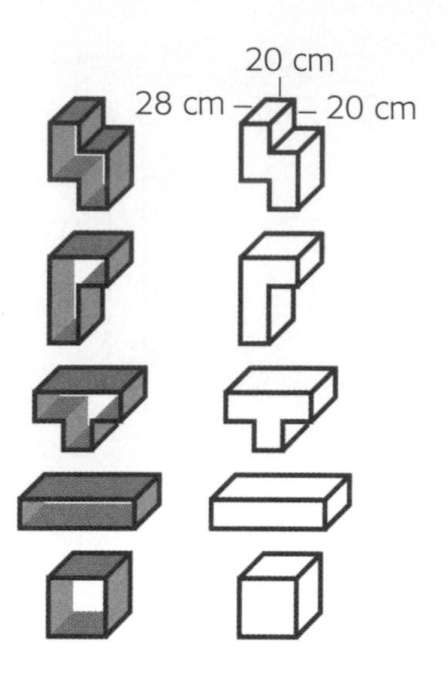

11. A wall unit is made using objects from a popular video game, as shown. Each object consists of four rectangular prisms that are 20 cm long, 20 cm wide, and 28 cm high.

a) This wall unit was built using nine of these objects. Calculate the area of overlap.

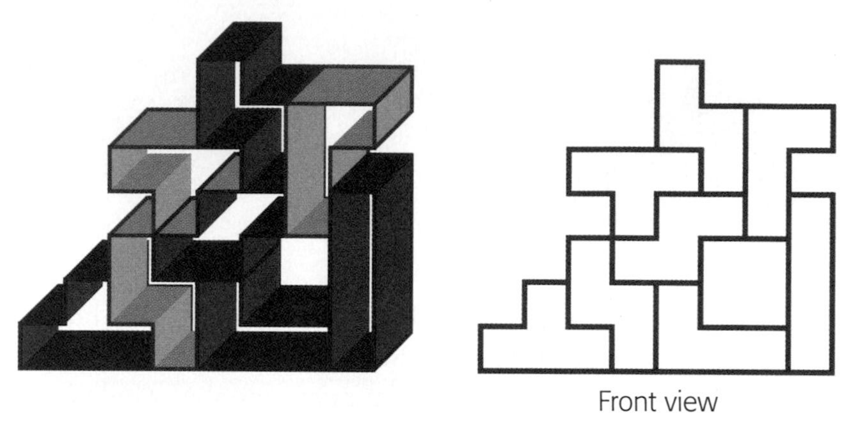

Front view

b) Use linking cubes to create your own wall unit with 12 of these objects. Calculate the area of overlap.

c) Exchange your design with a partner and calculate the area of overlap in your partner's design.

Closing

12. Is it possible for the overlap when two rectangular prisms touch to be the same as the overlap when two triangular prisms or two cylinders touch? Explain.

Extending

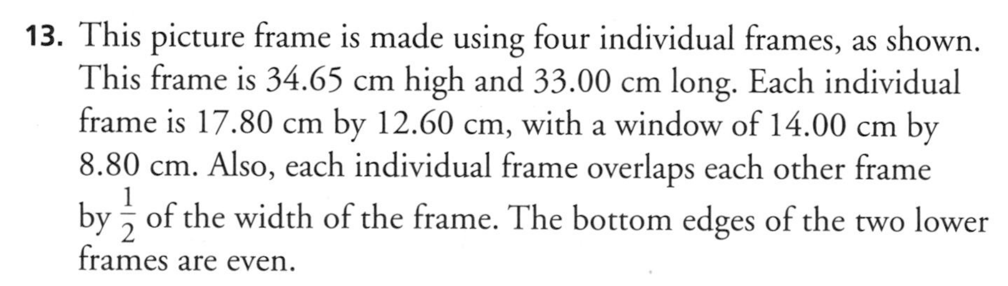

13. This picture frame is made using four individual frames, as shown. This frame is 34.65 cm high and 33.00 cm long. Each individual frame is 17.80 cm by 12.60 cm, with a window of 14.00 cm by 8.80 cm. Also, each individual frame overlaps each other frame by $\frac{1}{2}$ of the width of the frame. The bottom edges of the two lower frames are even.

a) Determine the dimensions of the open space between the frames.

b) Determine the area of overlap of the four individual frames.

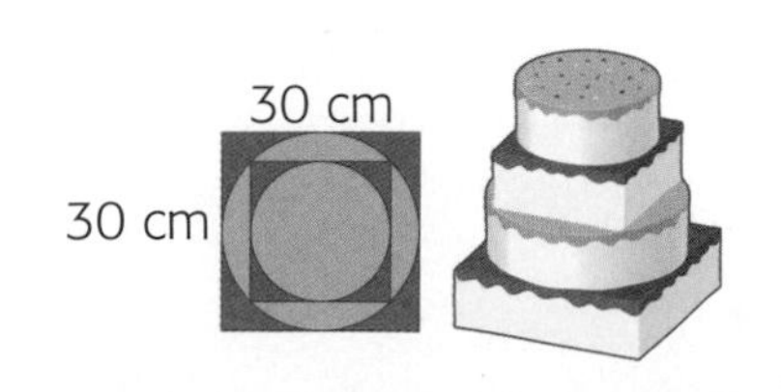

14. A party cake consists of four layers, each the same height. There are two square layers, and two circular layers, as shown. Determine the area of overlap to the nearest square centimetre.

Mid-Chapter Review

FREQUENTLY ASKED Questions

Q: How can you decompose a composite object?

A: Examine the object for component rectangular prisms, triangular prisms, and cylinders. There may be more than one way to do this. For example, this kitchen cabinet can be decomposed into a triangular prism, one square prism, and one rectangular prism. Or, it can be made of a triangular prism and three square prisms.

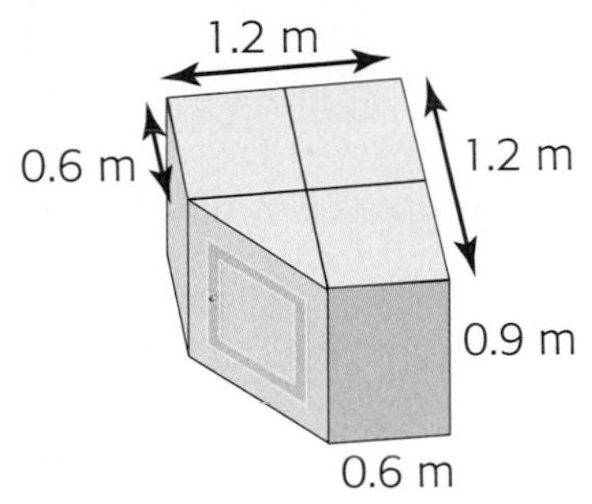

Study Aid

- See Lesson 4.2, Examples 1 and 2.
- Try Mid-Chapter Review questions 1 and 2.

Q: How can you determine the area of overlap for a composite object?

A: Separate the object into component parts and calculate the areas of the faces they share. For example, the areas of overlap for this composite object are a semicircle and a rectangle. The rectangle is 20 cm long $(\sqrt{12^2 + 16^2} = 20)$.

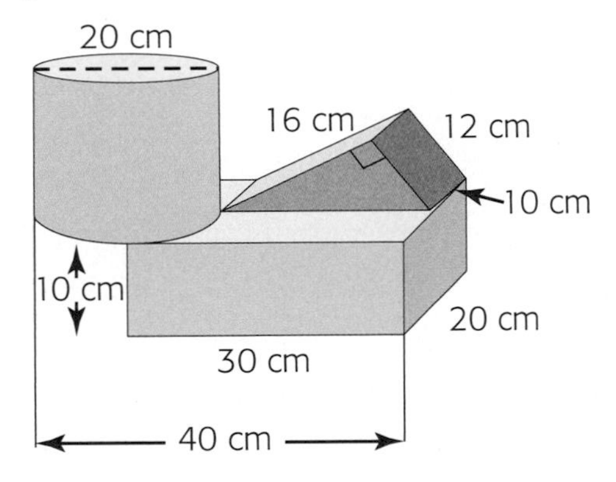

Total overlap area

$= \text{area of semicircle} + \text{area of rectangle}$

$= \pi r^2 \div 2 + (lw)$

$\doteq 3.14 \times (10)^2 \div 2 + (20 \times 10)$

$\doteq 157 + 200$

$\doteq 357 \text{ cm}^2$

Study Aid

- See Lesson 4.3, Examples 1, 2, 3, 4, and 5.
- Try Mid-Chapter Review questions 3, 4, and 5.

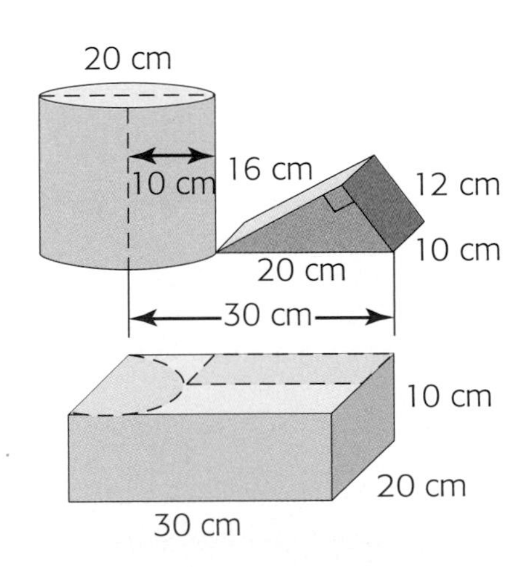

Practice

Lesson 4.2

1. Which components can you identify in the International Space Station?
   - cylinder
   - rectangular prism
   - triangular prism

2. Sketch one way to decompose each object. Include dimensions of each part.

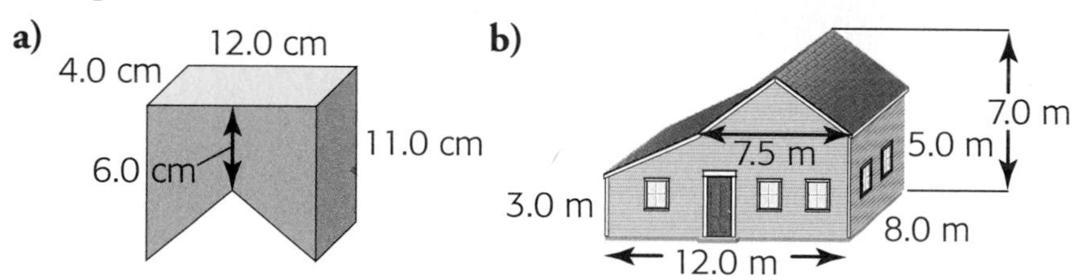

Lesson 4.3

3. Determine the area of overlap for each object in question 2.
4. A child's toy has four wheels, as shown. Determine the area of overlap between the wheels and the body of the toy.

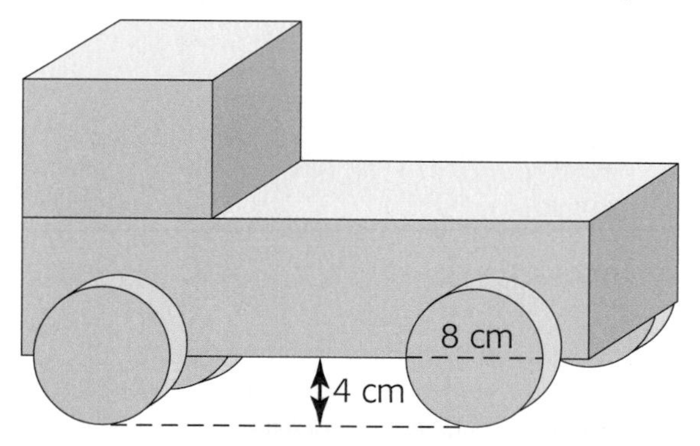

5. A child made this toy from building blocks. Determine the area of overlap.

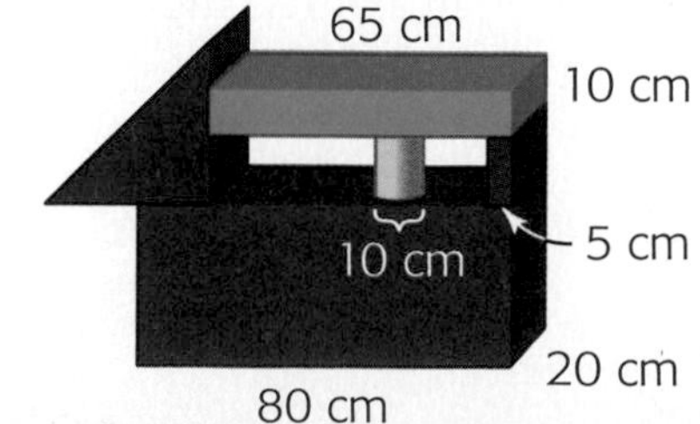

4.4 Calculating the Surface Area of Composite Objects

GOAL

Determine the surface area of composite 3-D objects.

LEARN ABOUT the Math

Derek must assemble an entertainment unit and then paint it.

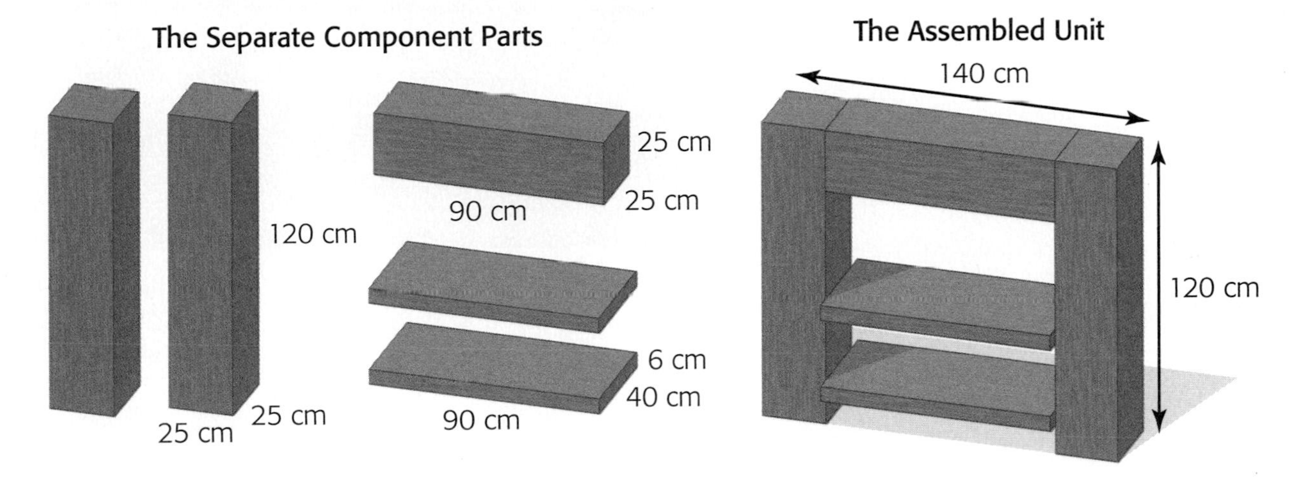

? What is the total area Derek needs to paint?

A. Calculate the total surface area of the components.

B. Calculate the area of overlap of the components when the unit is assembled.

C. What is the total area of the components that will not be painted? Explain your answer.

D. The ends of the stand that touch the floor will not be painted. Determine the total area to be painted.

Reflecting

E. How can you use the area of overlap to determine the surface area of a composite shape?

F. Suppose the assembled unit had been cut into component parts in a different way. Would the total surface area change?

WORK WITH the Math

EXAMPLE 1 | Calculating surface area of a composite object

A farmer wants to paint a building on his farm, and needs to know the total area to be painted. Determine the total area of the building, including the shutters covering the windows.

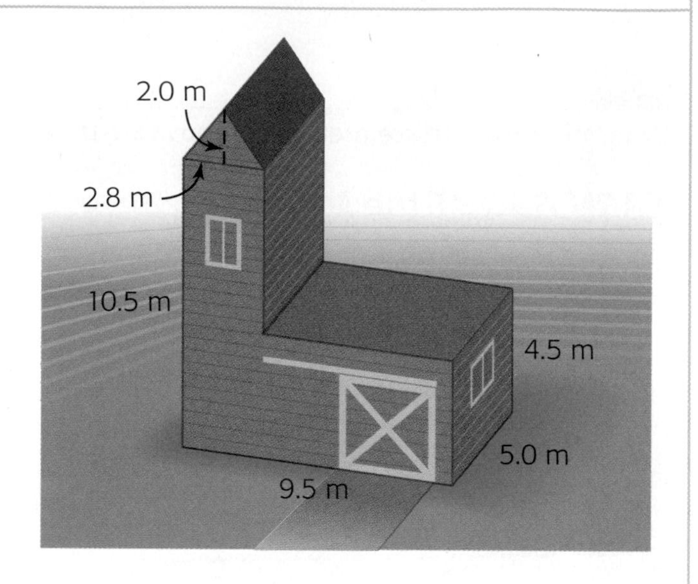

Shelby's Solution: Using area of overlap

I'll divide the building into component parts.

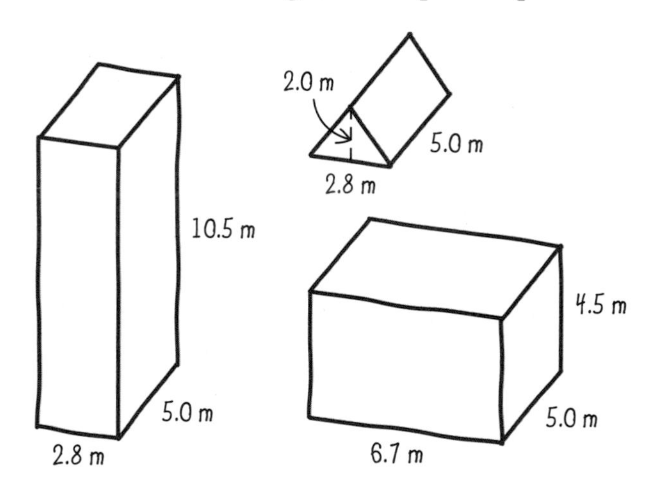

I sketched each part. I knew that each part was 5.0 m wide.

The building is 9.5 m long and the tall rectangular prism is 2.8 m long, so the short rectangular prism is $9.5 - 2.8 = 6.7$ m long.

Surface area of tall rectangular prism

$$= 2lw + 2lh + 2wh$$
$$= 2(2.8 \times 5.0) + 2(2.8 \times 10.5) + 2(5.0 \times 10.5)$$
$$= 191.8 \text{ m}^2$$

I calculated the surface area of each rectangular prism by thinking about all of the faces. I knew that there were three sizes of faces and two of each of those sizes.

Surface area of short rectangular prism

$$= 2lw + 2lh + 2wh$$
$$= 2(6.7 \times 5.0) + 2(6.7 \times 4.5) + 2(5.0 \times 4.5)$$
$$= 172.3 \text{ m}^2$$

Surface area of the triangular prism
Half of the base of the triangle is 1.4 m.
Let the hypotenuse be c.

First, I needed to calculate the dimensions of the triangular prism. I used the Pythagorean theorem.

$c^2 = (1.4)^2 + (2.0)^2$
$c^2 = 5.96\ \text{m}^2$
$c \doteq 2.4\ \text{m}$

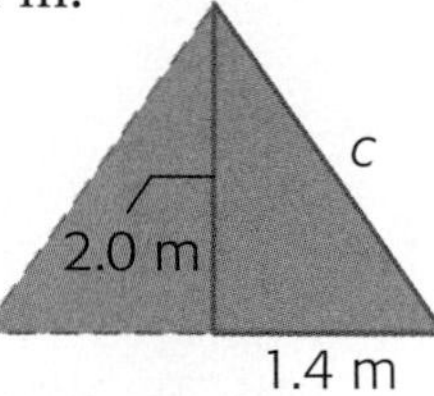

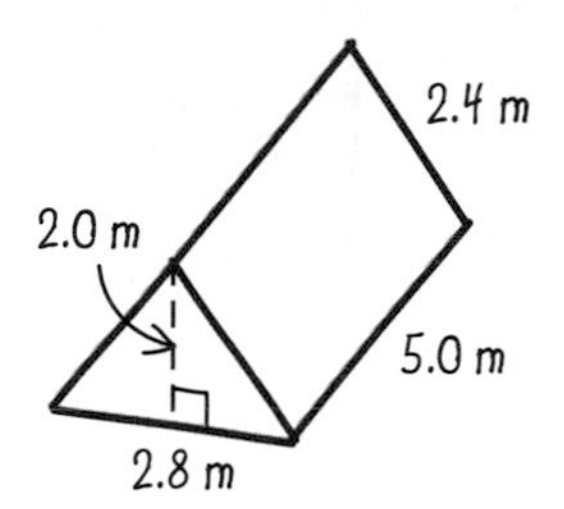

Area of two triangles
$= 2(bh \div 2)$
$= bh$
$= 2.8 \times 2.0$
$= 5.6\ \text{m}^2$

Area of two roof faces
$= 2(2.4 \times 5.0)$
$= 24.0\ \text{m}^2$

Area of base
$= 2.8 \times 5.0$
$= 14.0\ \text{m}^2$

Total area of triangular prism
$= 5.6 + 24.0 + 14.0$
$= 43.6\ \text{m}^2$

Total surface area of the three prisms
$= 191.8 + 172.3 + 43.6$
$= 407.7\ \text{m}^2$

Areas of overlap

I needed to calculate the areas of overlap that wouldn't be painted. There are areas of overlap where the triangular prism and the tall rectangular prism meet, and where the tall and short rectangular prisms meet.

Tall rectangular prism and triangular prism
$= 2.8 \times 5.0$
$= 14.0\ \text{m}^2$

Tall and short rectangular prisms
$= 5.0 \times 4.5$
$= 22.5\ \text{m}^2$

Surface area of building
$= 407.7 - 2(14.0) - 2(22.5)$
$= 334.7\ \text{m}^2$

I had included the area of overlap between the triangular prism and the tall prism in both calculations of surface area, so I had to subtract the overlap area twice. The same was true of overlap of the tall and short rectangular prisms.

Surface to be painted
$= 334.7 - (2.8 \times 5.0) - (6.7 \times 5.0)$
$= 287.2\ \text{m}^2$

Since the farmer won't paint the bases of the two rectangular prisms, I needed to subtract those areas.

The farmer needs enough paint to cover 287.2 m^2.

Derek's Solution: Using exposed faces

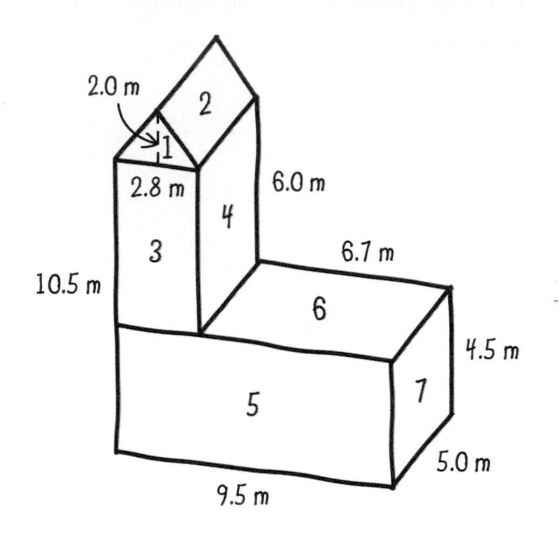

The sides and roof were made of rectangles and triangles. I decided to calculate the area of each shape that is visible, and then add. I numbered the visible shapes that make up the building.

height of sections 3 and 4 $= 10.5 - 4.5$
$= 6.0$ m

I calculated the missing dimensions and included them in my diagram.

width of section 2, c

$c^2 = (1.4)^2 + (2.0)^2$
$= 5.96 \text{ m}^2$
$c \doteq 2.4$ m

For section 2, I calculated the dimension I needed using the Pythagorean theorem $c^2 = a^2 + b^2$.

Area of section 1
$= \frac{1}{2}(2.8 \times 2.0)$
$= 2.8 \text{ m}^2$

Section 1 is a triangle. I used $A = \frac{1}{2}bh$.

Area of section 2
$= 5.0 \times 2.4$
$= 12.0 \text{ m}^2$

Area of section 3
$= 6.0 \times 2.8$
$= 16.8 \text{ m}^2$

All of the other sections are rectangles. I used $A = lw$.

Area of section 4
$= 6.0 \times 5.0$
$= 30.0 \text{ m}^2$

Area of section 5
$= 9.5 \times 4.5$
$= 42.75 \text{ m}^2$

I kept the hundredths in the answer for section 5 because I knew that I was going to have to do another calculation with the number.

Area of section 6
$= 6.7 \times 5.0$
$= 33.5 \text{ m}^2$

Area of section 7
$= 5.0 \times 4.5$
$= 22.5 \text{ m}^2$

Area to be painted
$= 2(\text{section } 1) + 2(\text{section } 2) + 2(\text{section } 3)$
$+ 2(\text{section } 4) + 2(\text{section } 5) + \text{section } 6 + 2(\text{section } 7)$
$= 2(2.8) + 2(12.0) + 2(16.8) + 2(30.0)$
$+ 2(42.75) + 33.5 + 2(22.5)$
$= 287.2 \text{ m}^2$

I needed to include two of all the sections except section 6.

The farmer needs enough paint to cover 287.2 m^2.

EXAMPLE 2 | Calculating surface area of objects with cylinders

Austin's sister builds tables to sell at craft fairs. Austin helps her by painting them. This design has legs of diameter 16 cm. A 1 L can of paint covers 7 m^2. How many cans of paint will Austin need to paint 12 tables?

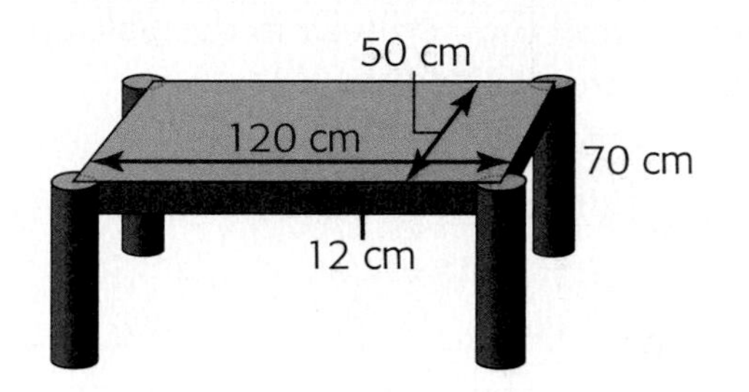

Austin's Solution

The tabletop is a rectangle plus four $\frac{3}{4}$ circles.

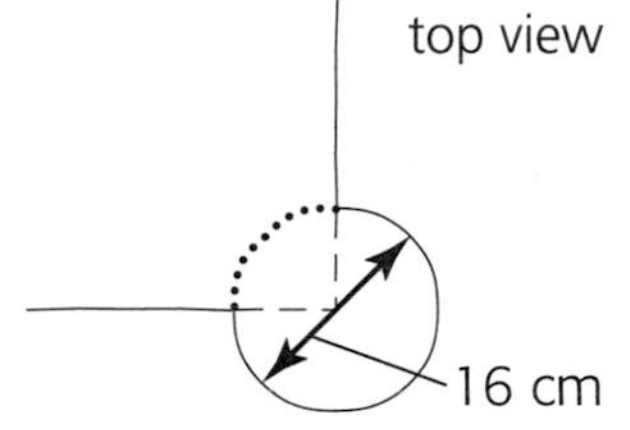

I imagined the tabletop as a rectangle with its corners at the centre of each leg. I drew a diagram of the top.
I decided to paint only the visible surfaces.

Area of rectangle
$= lw$
$= 120 \times 50$
$= 6000 \text{ cm}^2$

Area of $\frac{3}{4}$ of circle
$= \left(\frac{3}{4}\right)\pi r^2$
$= \left(\frac{3}{4}\right)\pi (8)^2$
$\doteq 151 \text{ cm}^2$

Each corner overlaps $\frac{1}{4}$ of the circular legs. I calculated the area of the rectangle and the area of $\frac{3}{4}$ of one circle.

Area of top of table
$\doteq 6000 + 4(151)$
$\doteq 6604 \text{ cm}^2$

I added all the areas. I multiplied the area of the $\frac{3}{4}$ circle by 4 since there are four legs.

Width of end rectangle
$= 50 - 2 \times 8$
$= 34 \text{ cm}$

Length of side rectangle
$= 120 - 2 \times 8$
$= 104 \text{ cm}$

50 cm
12 cm
34 cm
70 cm
58 cm
16 cm

view of end of table

I determined the areas of the rectangular sides of the table. The legs overlapped the edges of the table, reducing the width of the side rectangles by $2r$.

Total area of sides
$= 2(34 \times 12 + 104 \times 12)$
$= 3312 \text{ cm}^2$

I multiplied the 34 and the 104 both by 12 because the height of the sides is 12 cm.

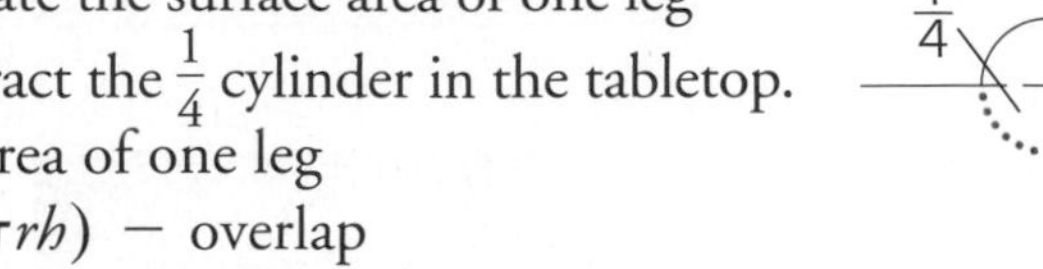

I'll calculate the surface area of one leg and subtract the $\frac{1}{4}$ cylinder in the tabletop.

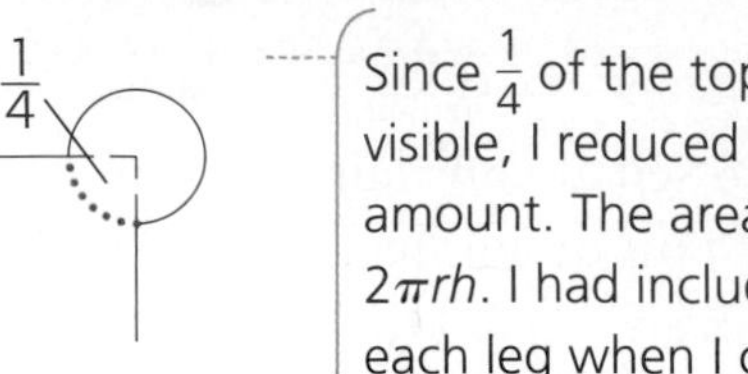

Surface area of one leg

$= (2\pi rh) - \text{overlap}$

$= (2\pi(8) \times 70) - \frac{1}{4}(2\pi(8) \times 12)$

$= 1120\pi - 48\pi$

$\doteq 3368 \text{ cm}^2$

Since $\frac{1}{4}$ of the top 12 cm of each leg was not visible, I reduced the area of each leg by that amount. The area of the side of a cylinder is $2\pi rh$. I had included the area for the top of each leg when I calculated the area of the tabletop, and I wouldn't paint the bottom of the legs.

Surface area of one table

$= \text{top} + \text{sides} + 4 \text{ legs}$

$\doteq (6604 + 3312 + 4(3368))$

$\doteq 23\ 388 \text{ cm}^2$

The underside of the table is not visible, so I decided not to paint it.

Surface area of 12 tables

$\doteq 12 \times 23\ 388$

$\doteq 280\ 656 \text{ cm}^2$

To calculate the paint needed for 12 tables, I multiplied by 12.

Surface area in m^2

$\doteq 280\ 656 \div (100)^2$

$\doteq 28 \text{ m}^2$

I wrote this value in square metres since the paint coverage was given in square metres. I knew 100 cm = 1 m, so $100^2 \text{ cm}^2 = 1 \text{ m}^2$.

Number of cans needed $= \frac{28}{7} = 4$

I need 4 cans of paint.

I divided the total area by the area that one can of paint covers.

In Summary

Key Ideas

- One way to determine a composite shape's surface area is to calculate the surface area of each component, and then subtract twice the area of overlap of each component.
- Another way is to determine the area of each exposed surface and add.

Need to Know

- When you are determining surface area, keep the context in mind. For example, to determine how much paint is needed to paint a flat-bottom dresser, omit the area of the bottom because it would not be painted.
- The area of overlap of component parts cannot be seen on the outside of the composite object.
- No matter how you decompose an object, its surface area will be the same.

Checking

1. Calculate the surface area of each shape.

   a) 26 cm, 6 cm, 30 cm, 10 cm

   b) 16 cm, 20 cm, 5 cm, 5 cm, 10 cm, 9 cm

2. Determine the surface area of the rounded aquarium stand shown at right, not including the bottom.

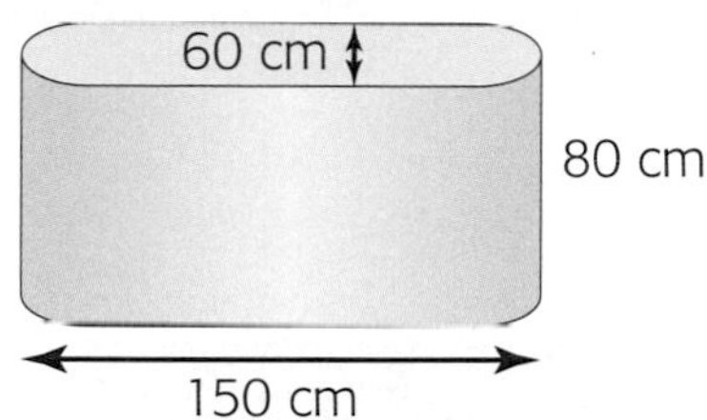

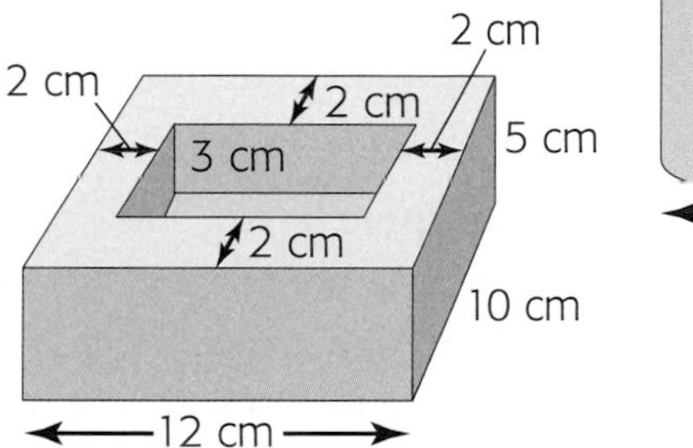

Practising

3. Determine the surface area of the paperclip holder shown at right.

4. Jordy is making a mailbox, as shown. Calculate the amount of metal required, not including the flag and the top catch.

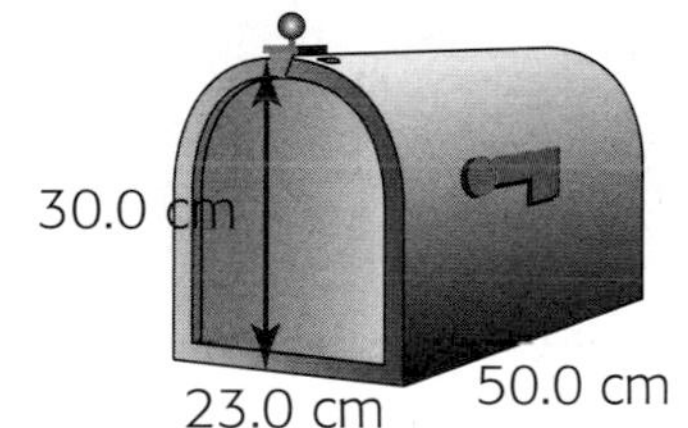

5. A Bundt cake has a cylindrical hole in the centre as shown. Calculate the amount of icing required to ice the top and exposed sides of the cake.

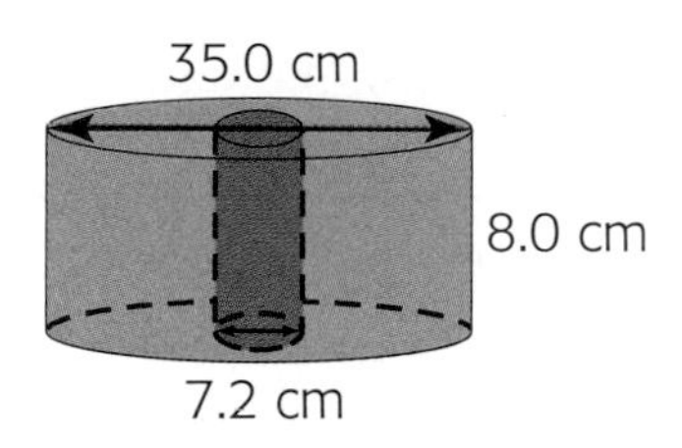

6. Determine the amount of carpeting needed to cover the entire surface of these pet stairs.

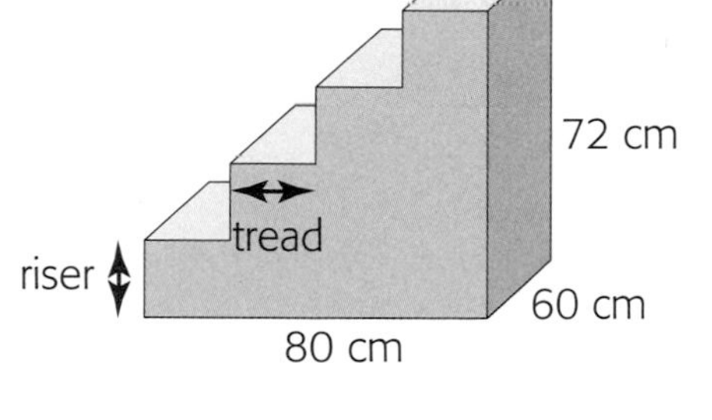

7. The hand grip on this dumbbell has a circumference of 10 cm. Calculate the total surface area of the dumbbell.

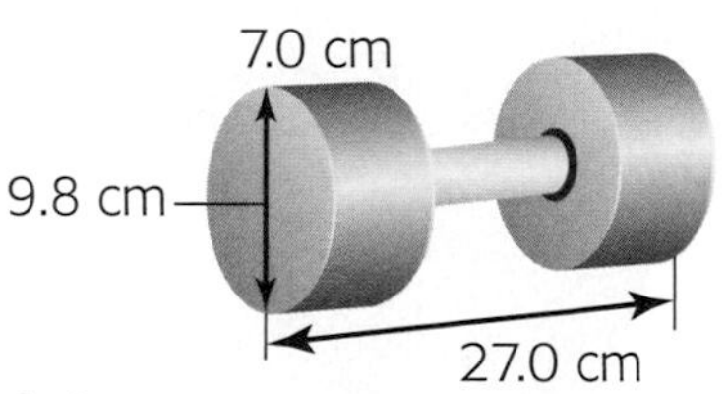

8. A wooden tea light candle holder is in the shape of an isosceles right triangle. Each insert for a tea light is 3.5 cm in diameter and 1.5 cm deep. The entire holder, including the inserts, is to be stained. Calculate the total area that will be stained.

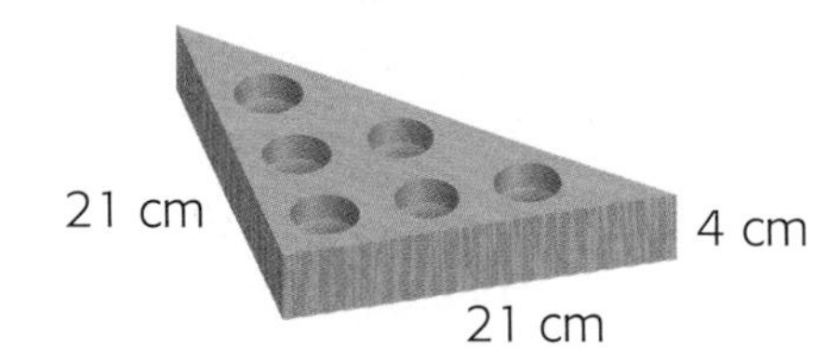

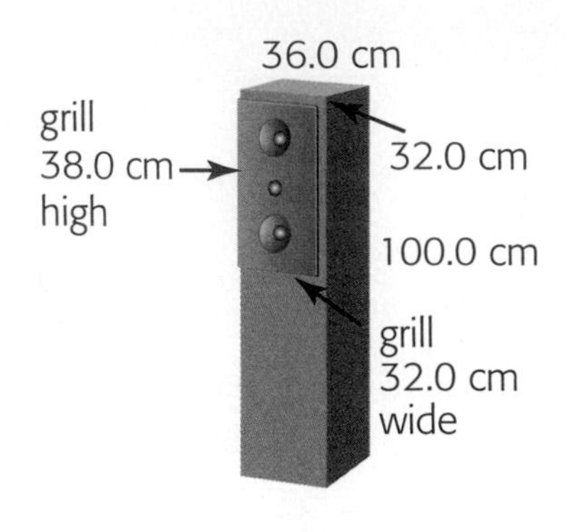

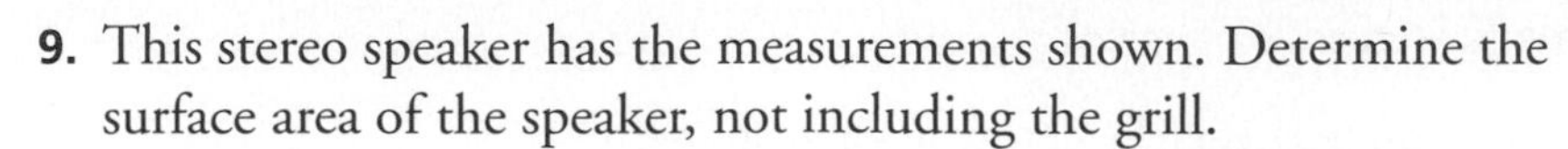

9. This stereo speaker has the measurements shown. Determine the surface area of the speaker, not including the grill.

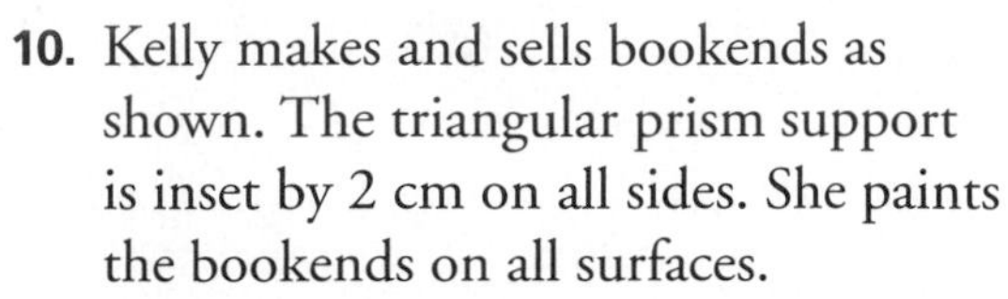

10. Kelly makes and sells bookends as shown. The triangular prism support is inset by 2 cm on all sides. She paints the bookends on all surfaces.

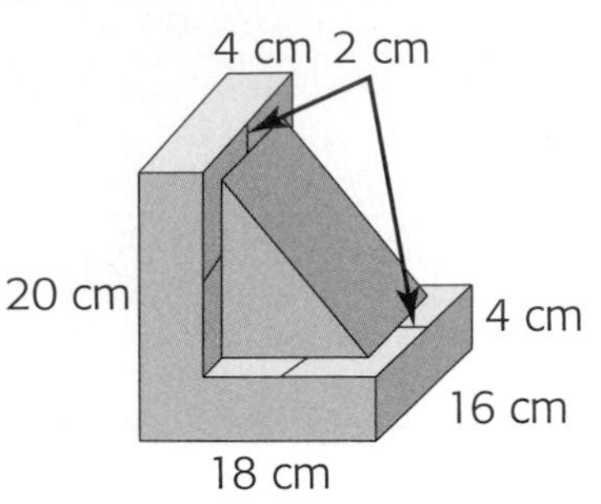

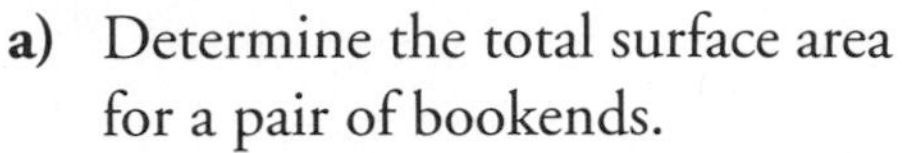

a) Determine the total surface area for a pair of bookends.

b) One litre of the paint Kelly uses covers 5 m^2. Determine how many litres of paint she will need to paint 100 pairs of bookends.

11. **Multiple choice.** The metal frame of a greenhouse is covered with polycarbonate panels. It is 3.6 m long and 2.4 m wide, with walls 1.5 m high and a total height of 2.3 m. Which choice is the best estimate for total area of polycarbonate needed?

A. 30 m^2 **B.** 40 m^2 **C.** 50 m^2 **D.** 60 m^2

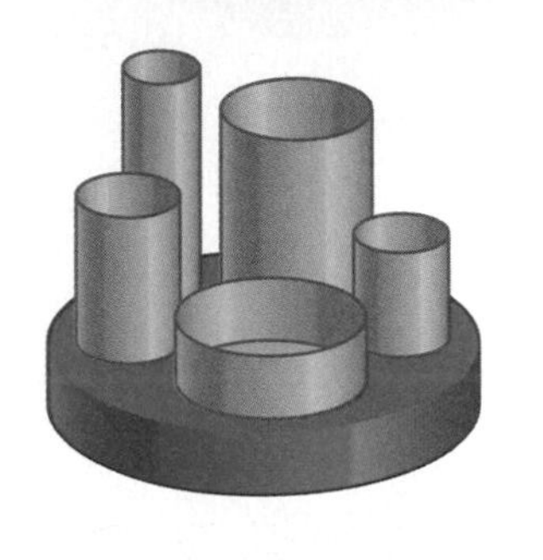

12. **Multiple choice.** A desk organizer has a circular base with diameter of 16 cm, and height of 2.5 cm. The organizing cylinders have diameters of 3 cm, 3.5 cm, 4 cm, 5.5 cm, and 7 cm.

Which choice is the best estimate for the exposed dark green surface area of the base of the organizer, including the bottom?

A. 690 cm^2 **B.** 420 cm^2 **C.** 325 cm^2 **D.** 235 cm^2

13. Determine the total surface area of the heart-shaped box.

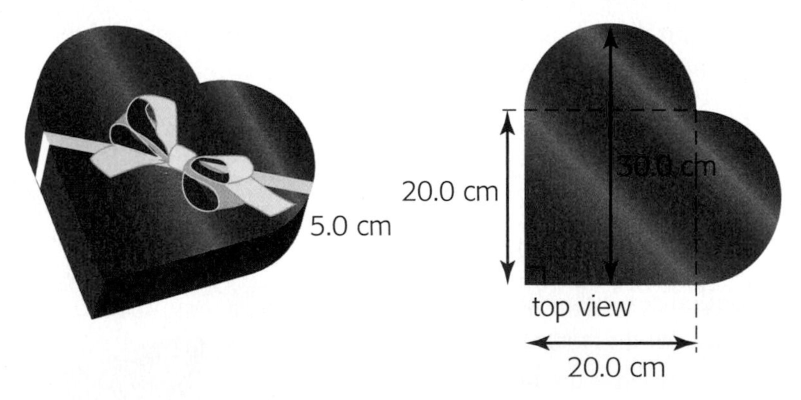

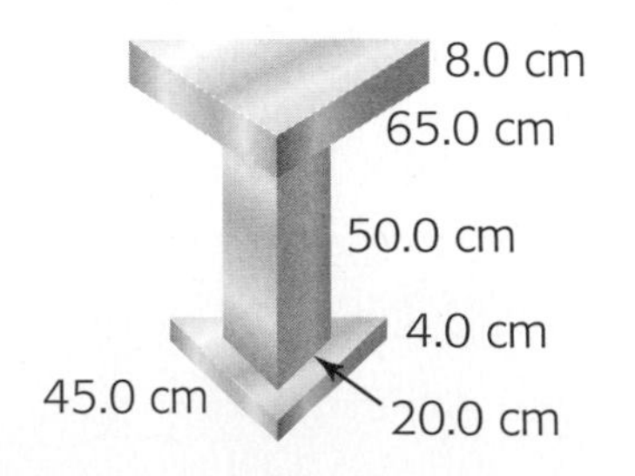

14. Each section of the acrylic table shown is an isosceles right triangular prism. Determine the total surface area, including the undersides of the top and the base.

15. The carrying case of a portable video game is 18.0 cm long by 8.0 cm wide by 4.0 cm high. The hinge on one side and the clasp on the other side are both 10.0 cm long by 0.5 cm wide by 1.5 cm high. Calculate the total surface area of the case.

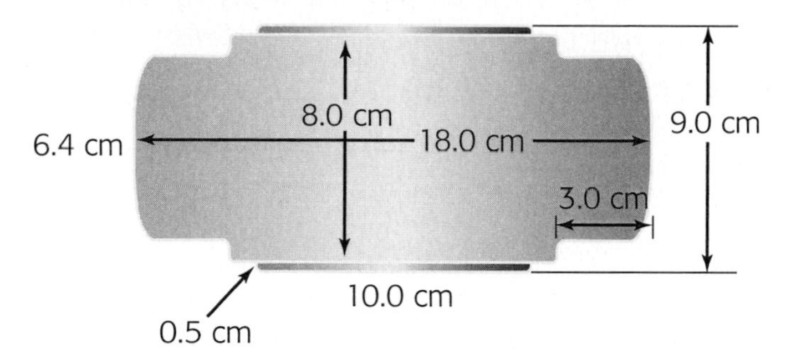

16. A swimming pool is 12.7 m long, 6.0 m wide, and 1.5 m deep. Its circular corners have a radius of 0.7 m. Explain how you would determine the surface area of the pool's vinyl liner.

Closing

17. When you are determining the surface area of a composite object, do you always need to know the area of the overlapping faces? Explain with an example.

Extending

18. This door frame is 315 cm high, 140 cm wide, and 6 cm deep. Determine the surface area of the frame that will be painted, not including the pieces in the window.

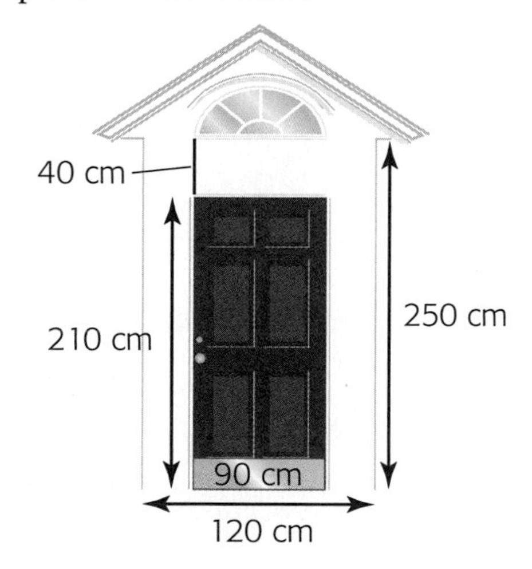

19. This inground pool is 1.4 m deep. Calculate the area of the vinyl liner for the pool.

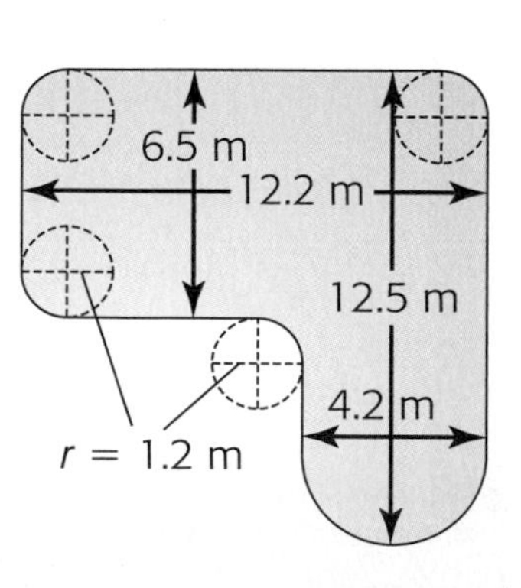

Math GAME

Greatest Areas

YOU WILL NEED
- linking cubes in different colours

In this game, you will build, as a team, a three-dimensional composite object, then determine the surface area of the portion that you built.

Number of players: 2 to 4

How to Play

1. Each player selects eight cubes of one colour, a different colour for each player.
2. Player 1 places a cube in the centre of the table.
3. Player 2 links one cube to Player 1's cube.
4. Each player, in turn, adds a cube to the structure. The game continues until all of the cubes have been used.
5. Each player estimates the number of visible surfaces in their colour, and then counts the surfaces to check his or her estimate.
6. The player with the most exposed surfaces wins.

Sample Game

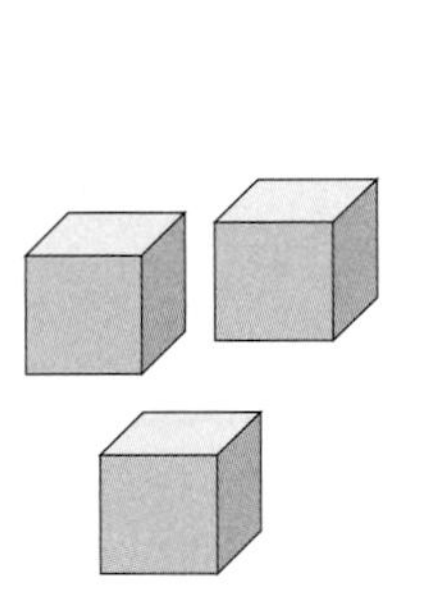

Player 1 is orange.

Player 1 has 19 exposed faces, and Player 2 has 21 exposed faces, so Player 2 is ahead.

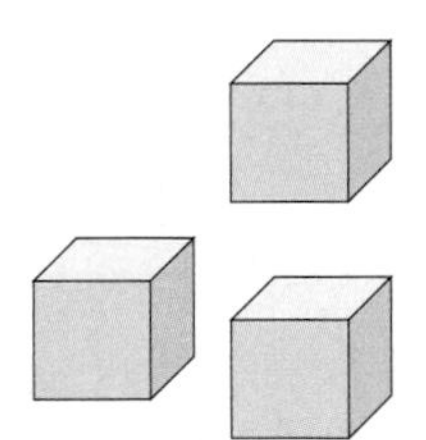

Player 2 is blue.

Curious MATH

The Art of Reutersvärd

YOU WILL NEED

- linking cubes

Swedish artist Oscar Reutersvärd is the "father of impossible figures." He drew figures that cannot be made in three dimensions. For example, he drew this triangle in 1934, which was honoured in 1982 on a Swedish stamp.

The sculpture shown here was created by Peter Quigley of Adelaide University in Australia, and is based on Reutersvärd's work.

1. Build several cubes, each consisting of eight linking cubes, as shown.

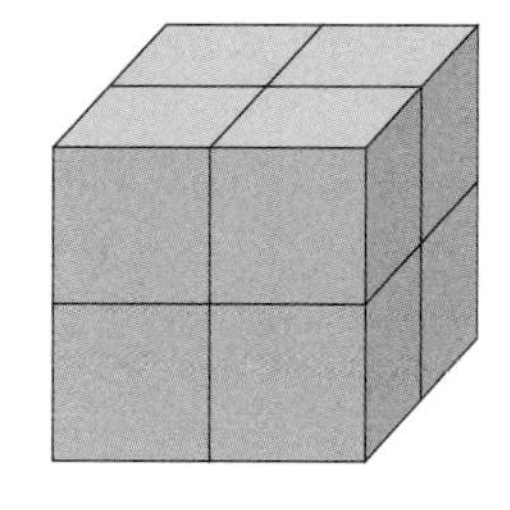

2. Assemble your cubes to reproduce Peter Quigley's sculpture.

3. The face of one linking cube is 4 cm^2. Determine the area of overlap of your structure.
4. Determine the total surface area of your structure.

4.5 Solve Problems Using Logical Reasoning

inner diameter = 150 cm
depth = 61 cm
height = 64 cm
outer diameter = 180 cm

GOAL

Solve problems involving surface areas of prisms and cylinders using reasoning.

LEARN ABOUT the Math

A company makes portable cylindrical hot tubs with hard foam coated in vinyl. One model has these dimensions. Vinyl is sold in square metres.

? How much vinyl is needed to coat the tub?

EXAMPLE 1 | Using logical reasoning to estimate surface area

Bay's Solution

1. Understand the Problem
I need to determine the entire surface area. The hot tub is like two cylinders, one inside the other. I need to calculate the surface of the inner cylinder, the surface of the outer cylinder, and the area of the top edge of the tub.

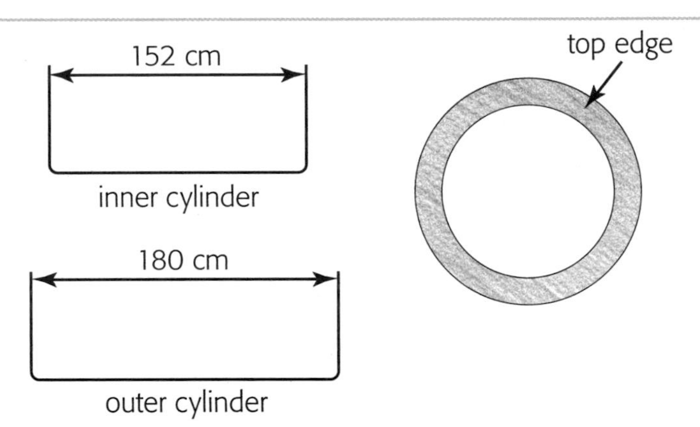

2. Make a Plan
I'll calculate the area of the outer sides and bottom, and the inner sides and bottom using the formula for the area of a cylinder.
I can think of the top edge as a large circle with a smaller inside circle cut out. I'll add these three areas to determine the total area.
Vinyl is sold in square metres, so I'll change the measurements to metres before calculating.
I think an estimate will be good enough, so I'll use convenient values to do the calculation.

3. Carry Out the Plan
I'll calculate the outer and inner radii of the tub.

Outer diameter = 2.0 m　　Inner diameter = 1.6 m
Outer radius = 1.0 m　　Inner radius = 0.8 m

The outer diameter is 180 cm, so I used 2 m. The inner diameter is 152 cm, so I used 1.6 m, because it's easier to work with than 1.5 m.

Area of outer cylinder
$= \pi(1.0)^2 + 2\pi(1.0)(0.6)$
$\doteq 6.6 \text{ m}^2$

Area of inner cylinder
$= \pi(0.8)^2 + 2\pi(0.8)(0.6)$
$\doteq 5.0 \text{ m}^2$

I determined the area of the sides and the bottom for both the outside and the inside. The surface area of a cylinder is $SA = 2\pi r^2 + 2\pi rh$. The hot tub has a bottom but no top, so I used $SA = \pi r^2 + 2\pi rh$. The outside of the tub is 64 cm high and the inside is 61 cm deep, so I used 0.6 m for both.

Area of top edge
$=$ area of large circle $-$ area of small circle
$= \pi(1.0)^2 - \pi(0.8)^2$
$\doteq 1.0 \text{ m}^2$

I calculated the area of the top edge.

$SA =$ area of outer cylinder
$+$ area of inner cylinder $+$ area of top edge
$\doteq 6.6 + 5.0 + 1.0$
$\doteq 12.6 \text{ m}^2$

I added up all areas to estimate the total amount of vinyl required.

About 12 m^2 of vinyl is needed to cover the foam in the hot tub.

I used numbers that were mostly greater than the actual measurements. So I decided to round down.

Reflecting

A. Was Bay justified in estimating to solve the problem? Explain.

B. How did Bay use logical reasoning to solve the problem?

WORK WITH the Math

EXAMPLE 2 | Using logical reasoning to determine surface area

Nicole is building this bookshelf. She is enclosing one section with a door that is 32 cm wide and 2 cm thick. Determine the total area of wood she must finish with stain and varnish.

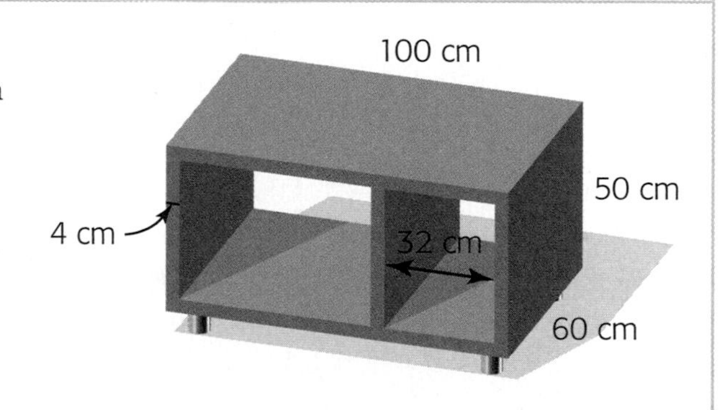

Nicole's Solution

1. Understand the Problem
I'll stain every surface except the underside, which won't be seen. I can use the dimensions of the shelf to determine the area to stain.

2. Make a Plan

I should use measurements in metres rather than centimetres because varnish cans usually give coverage in square metres. This way I will avoid the conversion from square centimetres to square metres later. Also, I really only need an estimate, because I will buy the stain and varnish in cans, so I need to know only which size of can I need. I can solve a simpler problem to get my estimate.

3. Carry Out the Plan

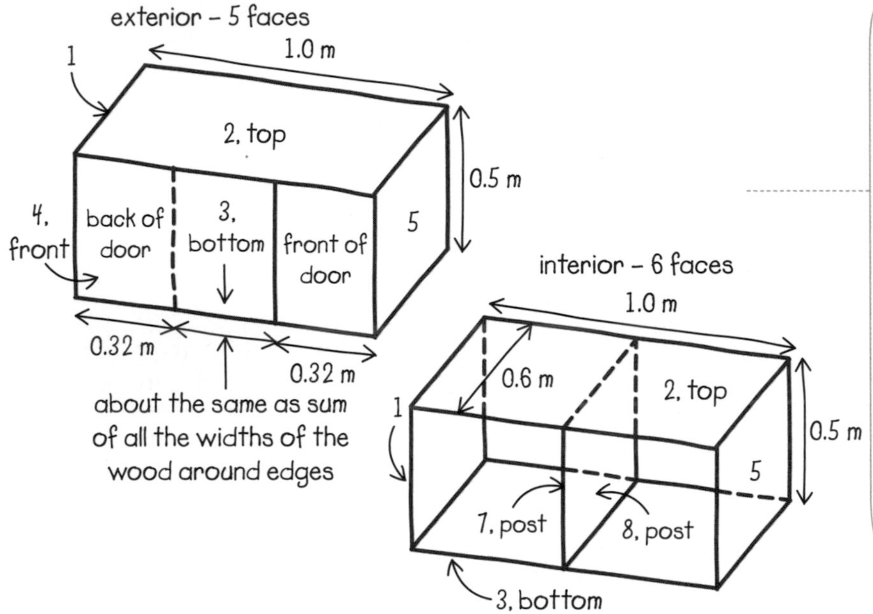

The door is to be finished on both sides, so I visualized the bookshelf as having two doors, but being finished on only one side. The gap left over would be about the same area as the edges of the doors.

To make my estimate easier, I decided to use the same measurements for interior and exterior, even though I knew the interior length and height were less than the exterior length and height because of the 4 cm width of the wood.

$$\begin{aligned}\text{Surface area of exterior} &= 2(\text{face } 1) + 2(\text{face } 2) + (\text{face } 4)\\ &= 2(0.6 \times 0.5) + 2(1.0 \times 0.6)\\ &\quad + (1.0 \times 0.5)\\ &= 2(0.3) + 2(0.6) + 0.5\\ &= 0.6 + 1.2 + 0.5\\ &= 2.3 \text{ m}^2\end{aligned}$$

Faces 1 and 5 are the same; faces 2 and 3 are the same.

$$\begin{aligned}\text{Surface area of interior} &= 4(\text{face } 1) + 2(\text{face } 2)\\ &= 2(0.6) + 1.2\\ &= 1.2 + 1.2\\ &= 2.4 \text{ m}^2\end{aligned}$$

I had already calculated the area of two of face 1 and two of face 2.

$$\begin{aligned}\text{Total surface area} &= \text{exterior} + \text{interior}\\ &= 2.3 + 2.4\\ &= 4.7 \text{ m}^2\end{aligned}$$

I need enough stain and varnish to coat about 5 m^2.

4. Look Back

My estimate is greater than the actual value, because the area of the sums of all the widths of the wood plus the front and back of the door is probably less than the full face 4 that I visualized. Also, I used greater measurements for the interior than the actual values. However, it's better to estimate a little high and have enough of the stain and varnish than to estimate low and not have enough.

Checking

1. A silicone muffin pan is used to make cylindrical muffins with a 7.5 cm diameter. The pan is 4.0 cm deep. Calculate the surface area of silicone poured into a mould to make the muffin pans.

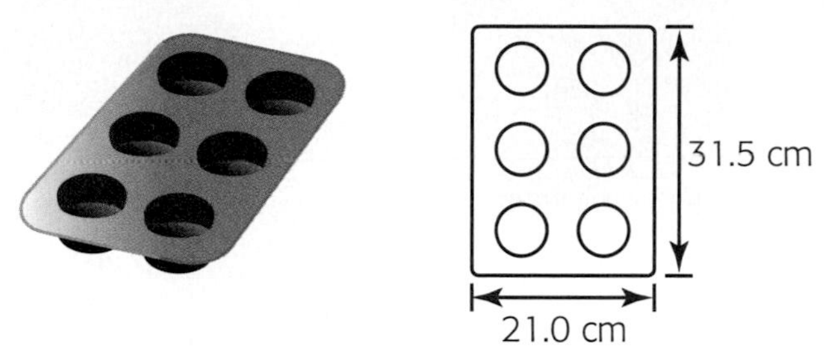

Practising

2. Johanna builds sets for her school theatre. One set uses giant linking cubes. Each cylindrical connector is 0.20 m in diameter and 0.15 m high. Calculate the total area Johanna must paint for each piece.

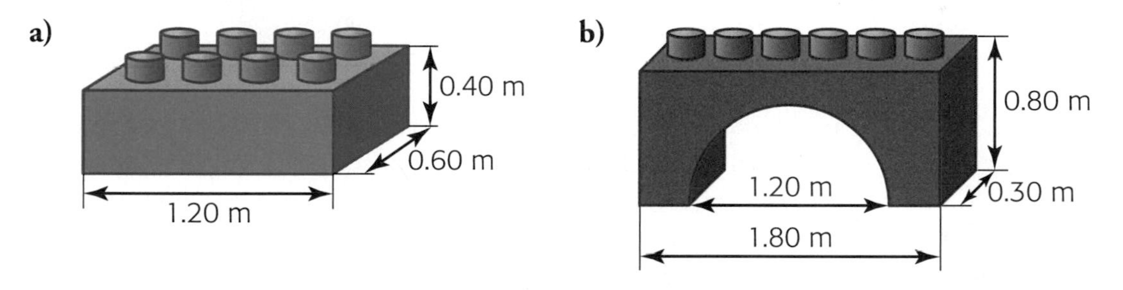

3. Alexis wants to spray a protective coating on the interior of her truck's cargo box. The box is rectangular with semicircular wheel wells, having a diameter of 0.60 m. It is 1.08 m between the wheel wells. Determine the total area that Alexis must spray.

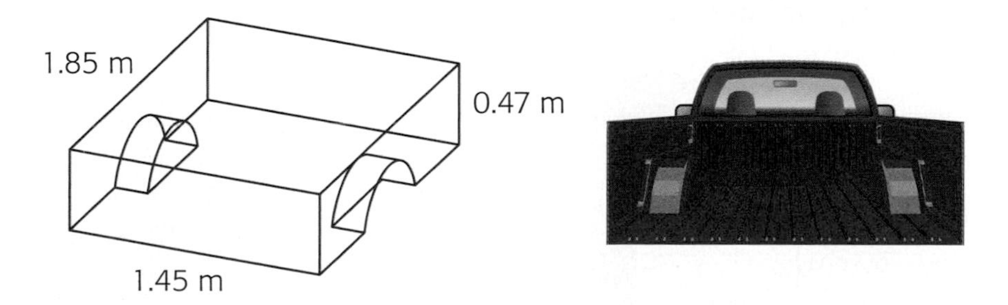

4. A semicircular tub chair is upholstered in one fabric. Calculate the amount of fabric used to cover the chair.

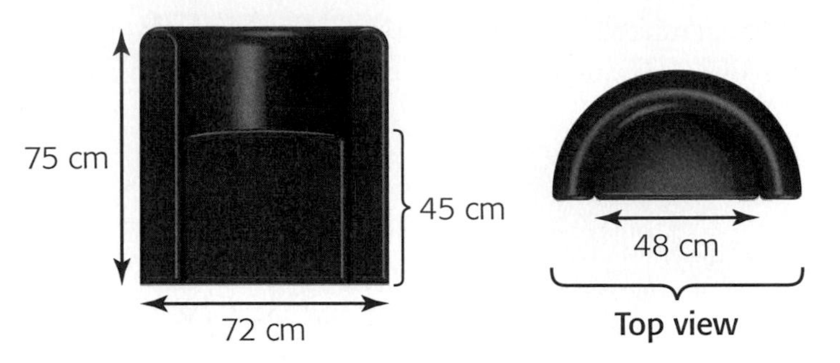

5. Benjamin designs modern furniture. He finishes each piece with colourful paint. Each drawer has a height of 24 cm. What surface area must he paint?

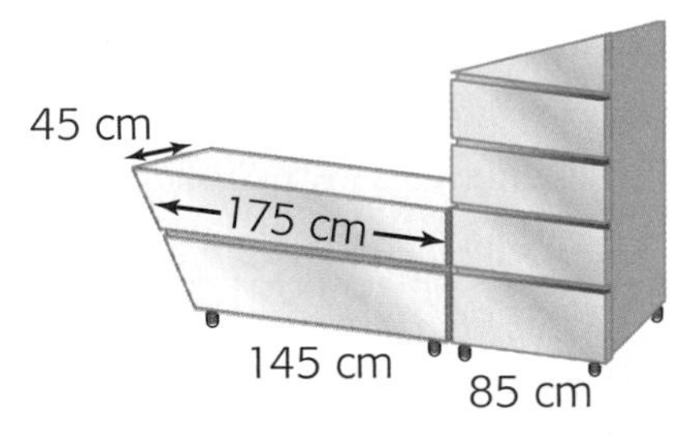

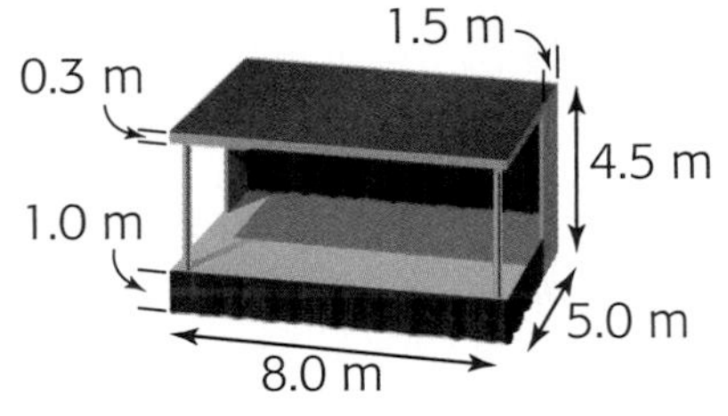

6. An outdoor stage is to be built as shown. The back and side walls are 10 cm thick. The cylindrical posts are 20 cm in diameter. Determine the surface area of the stage, not including the area touching the soil.

Closing

7. A child's table is built with three separate pieces as shown. The base has a diameter of 30 cm. The post is square: 8 cm each side. Determine the surface area of the whole table, including the base. Explain your reasoning.

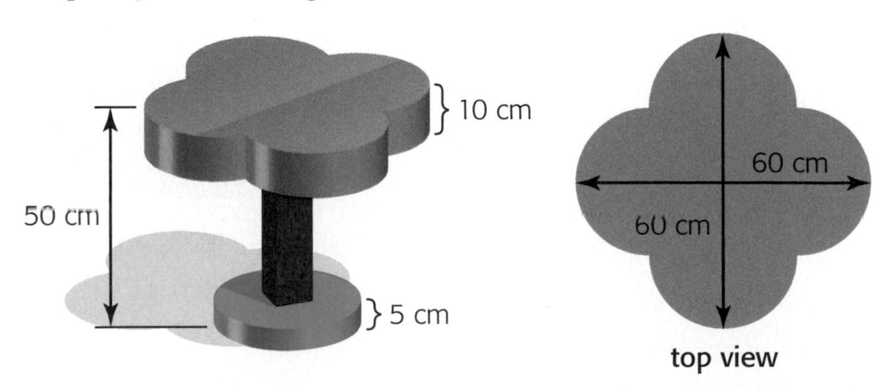

Extending

8. A leather stool is in the shape of a regular hexagon. Calculate the amount of leather required to cover the entire stool.

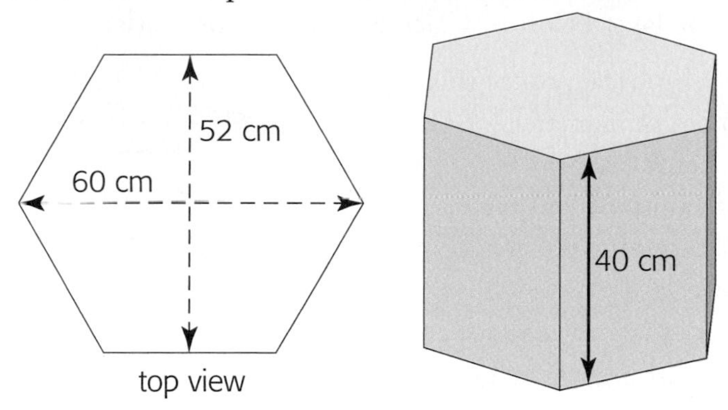

9. When this alarm clock goes off, three objects pop out. To turn off the alarm, you need to replace the objects. The hole for each object is 2 cm deep.

a) The green cylinder is 5 cm in diameter. The base of the blue rectangular prism is 5 cm by 3 cm. The legs of the base of the red right triangular prism are each 4 cm. Each object is 5 cm high. Determine the total surface area of each object.

b) Determine the total surface area of the alarm clock when the objects are in place.

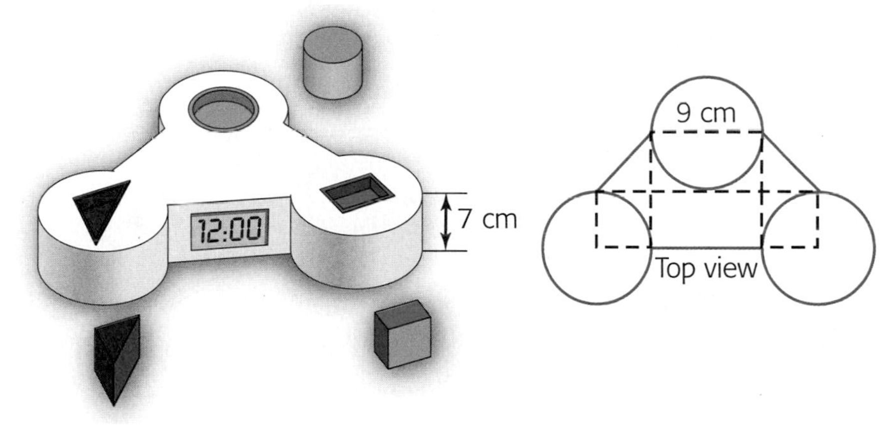

Chapter Self-Test

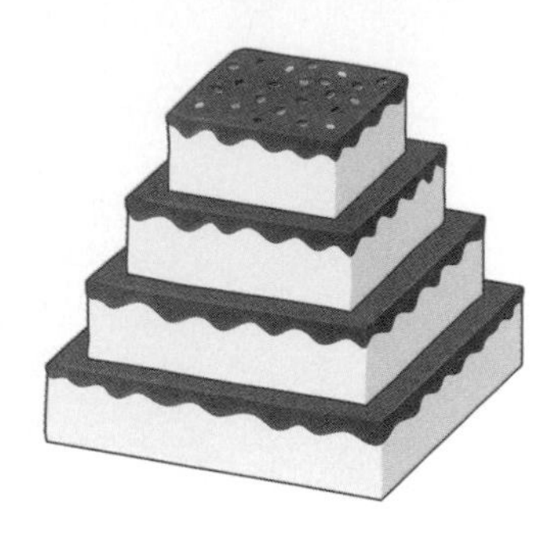

1. A cake has four square layers. The sides of each layer are 5 cm less than the layer below it. Calculate the area of overlap.

2. The cylindrical post of this table is 15 cm in diameter.
   a) Sketch one way to decompose this table.
   b) Determine the area of overlap.
   c) Calculate the surface area of the table, not including the underside of the base.

110 cm
5 cm
76 cm
5 cm
$d = 36$ cm

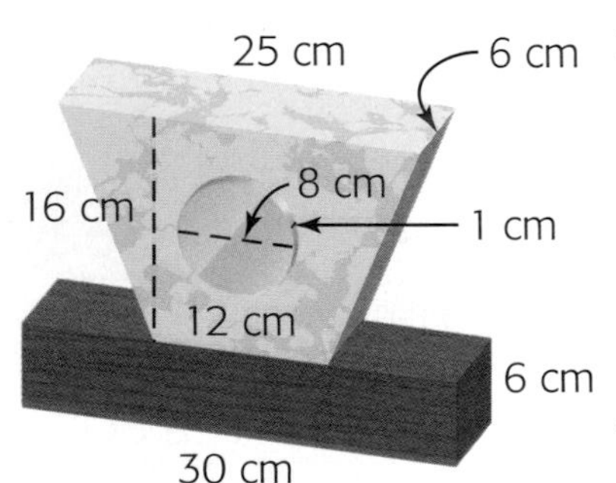

3. Jovana built a trophy with dimensions as shown. She plans to protect the entire trophy with a urethane finish.
   a) Explain how you would decompose the trophy into component parts, and determine their dimensions.
   b) Determine the area of overlap.
   c) Calculate the surface area of the trophy. Show your work.

4. Jasa made a table saw push stick for his wood shop using a piece of wood 8.9 cm wide and 3.8 cm high. Calculate the surface area.

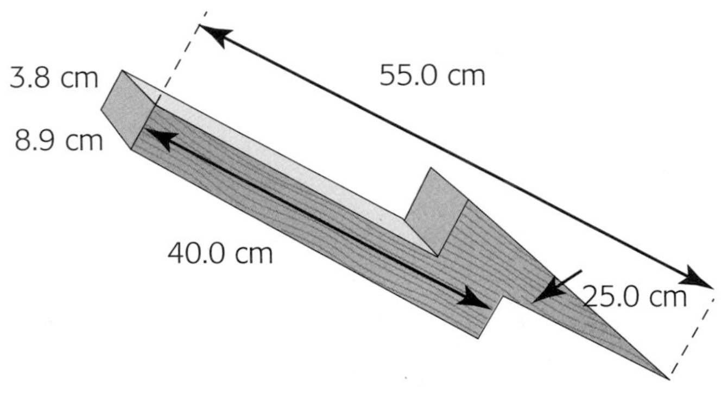

5. This canvas tent is 6.0 m wide, 10.0 m long, and 3.0 m high, with side walls that are 2.0 m high. There are 12 windows, each 1.5 m by 1 m.
   a) Explain two different methods you can use to determine the surface area.
   b) Calculate the total area of canvas, including the roll-up door.
   c) Which method did you use? Explain your choice.

6. Timothy is building a skateboard ramp, as shown. He will cover the top and sides of each section with plywood. Determine the total area of plywood required.

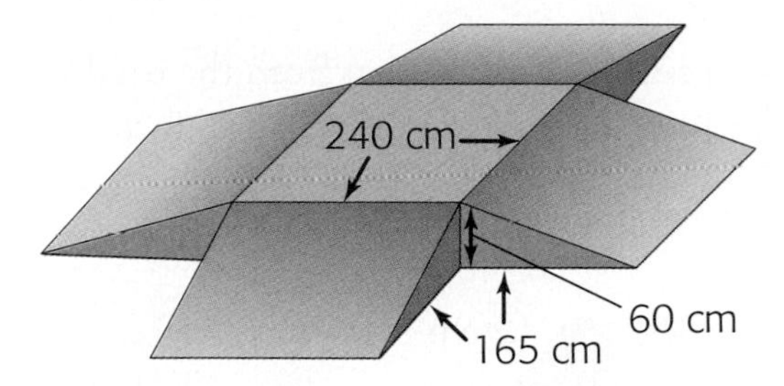

7. A garden shed is 2.4 m wide, 3.1 m long, and 2.5 m high. All of the sides, the roof, and the floor are made with plywood. Calculate the total area of plywood needed to build the shed.

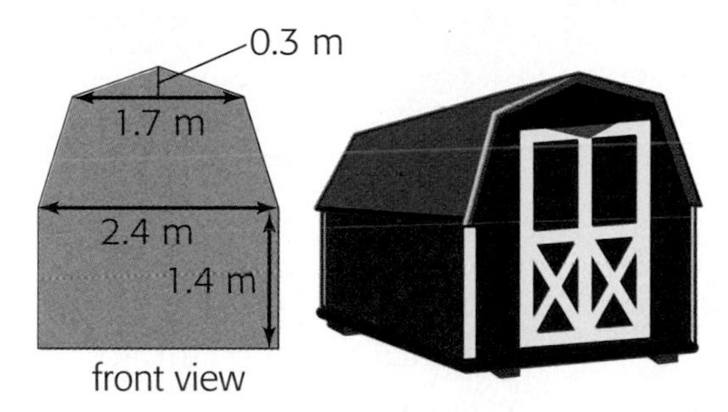

8. A toolbox is designed to fit over the wheel well in the cargo area of a truck. Calculate the total area of metal needed to make the box.

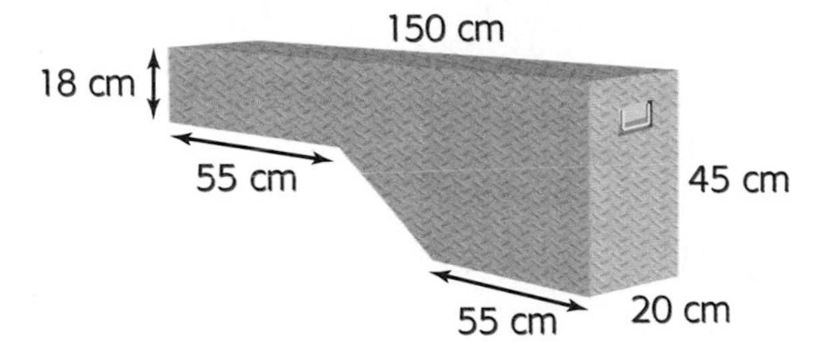

WHAT DO You Think Now?

Revisit What Do You Think? on page 155.
How have your answers and explanations changed?

Chapter Review

FREQUENTLY ASKED Questions

Study Aid

- See Lesson 4.4, Examples 1 and 2.
- Try Chapter Review questions 6, 7, 8, 9, and 10.

Q: How can you determine the surface area of a composite object?

A1: Subtract twice the area of overlap from the total surface area of the component parts. For example, for this object,

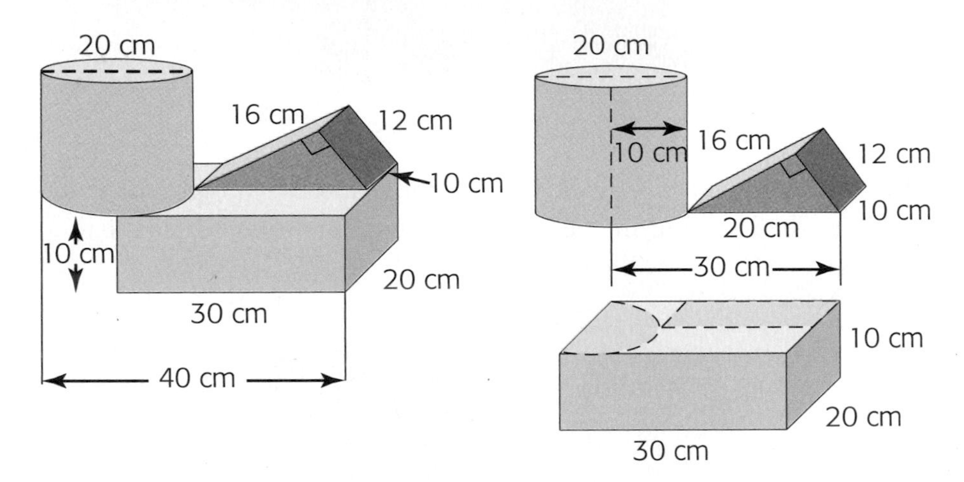

Total Surface Area = surface area of cylinder + surface area of triangular prism + surface area of rectangular prism − 2(area of semicircle) − 2(area of rectangle)

A2: Calculate the visible surface area, which includes any areas you can see by turning the objects. For example, for the object above,

① Visible surface area of red prism
= 2(area of triangular faces)
+ area of long rectangle
+ area of short rectangle

② Visible surface area of blue prism
= 2(area of bottom + area of front + area of side)
− area of semicircle
− area of rectangle

③ Visible surface area of cylinder
= surface area of cylinder − area of semicircle

Total surface area
= area 1 + area 2 + area 3

Practice

Lesson 4.2

1. Sketch one way to decompose each object. Include dimensions.
   a) b)

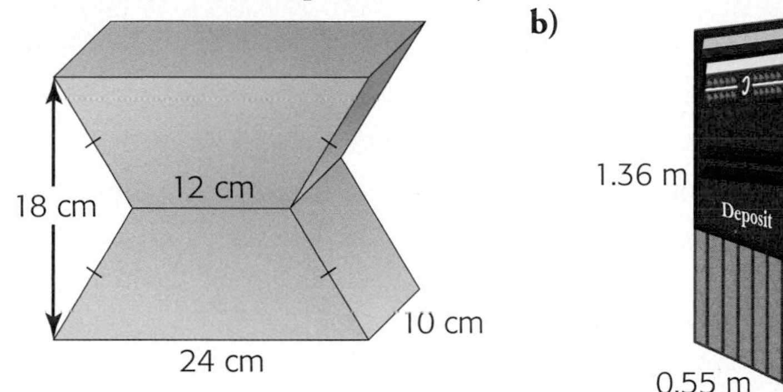

Lesson 4.3

2. A case for badminton equipment is decomposed as shown. Determine the area of overlap.

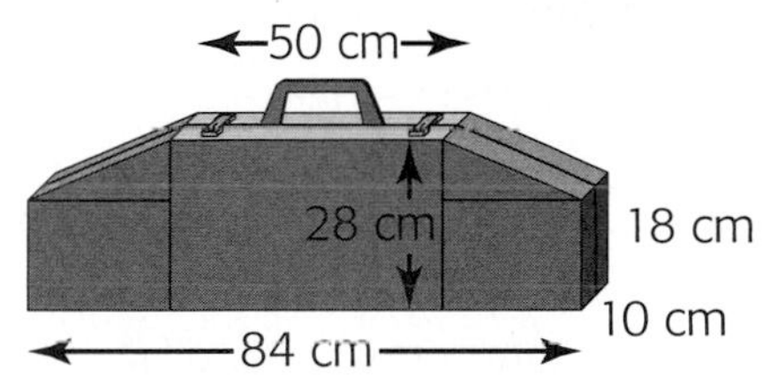

a case for badminton equipment

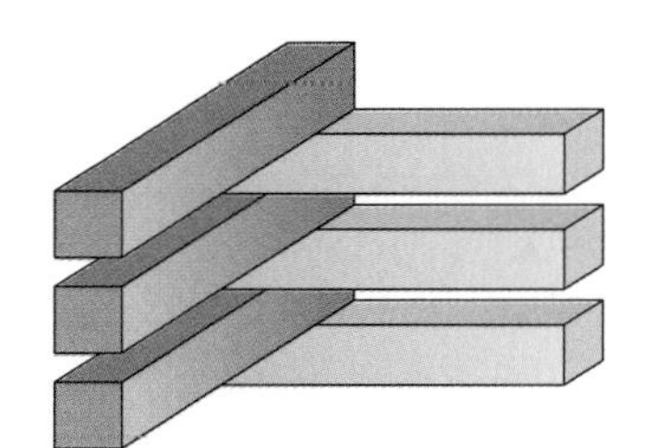

3. The corner of a garden fence is made with six posts, as shown. Each post is 9 cm by 9 cm by 365 cm. Calculate the area of overlap.
4. A support for a highway overpass is made with 2 m diameter cylindrical concrete pillars. The pillars are set between two rectangular prisms. Calculate the area of overlap of this support.

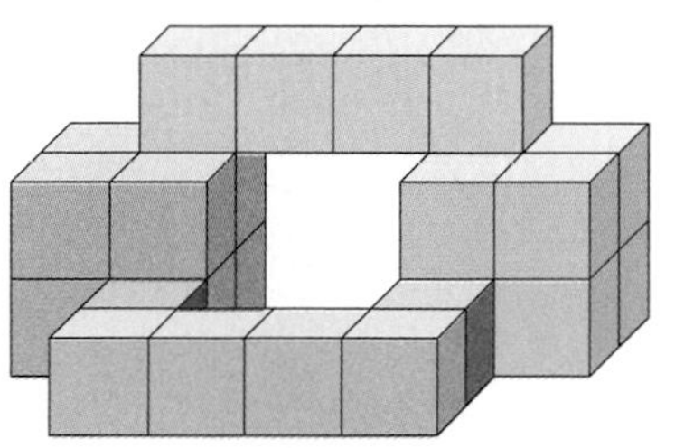

5. Teresa built this structure with 2 cm cubes using different colours for each rectangular prism. Determine the area of overlap.

Lesson 4.4

6. A "For Sale" sign is made with two posts. Each post is 9 cm square and painted brown. The vertical post stands 210 cm above ground, and the horizontal post is 70 cm long. Calculate the surface area of the posts to be painted.

7. A cake is made up of three layers, each 15 cm high. The radii for the layers are 19 cm, 15 cm, and 11 cm. Determine the surface area of the decorative icing. Explain any assumptions you made.

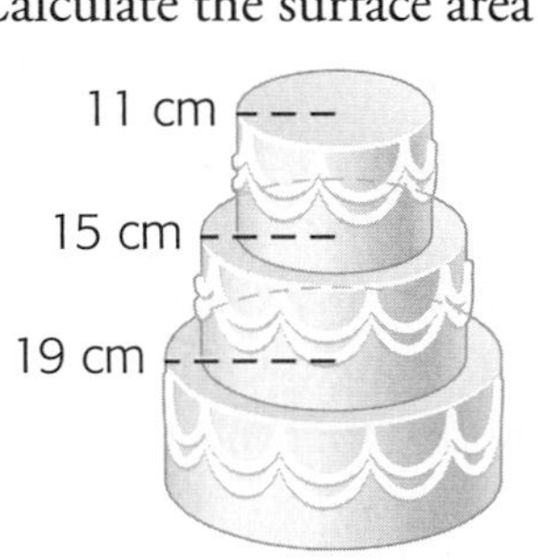

8. Determine the surface area of each object.

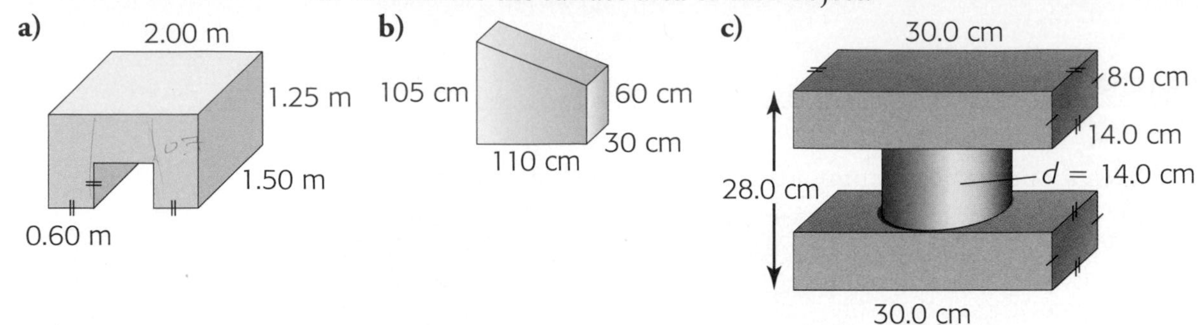

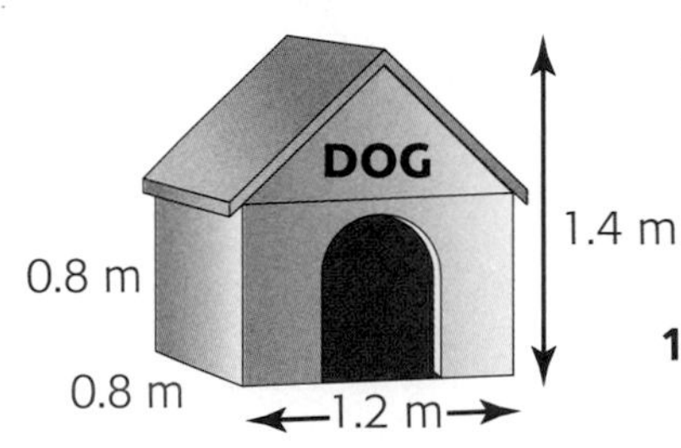

9. The roof of this doghouse has an overhang of 0.10 m on all sides. The doghouse also has a floor. Calculate the surface area of the doghouse, if the area of the doorway is 0.3 m^2. Explain your calculations.

10. A solar laptop case provides power for a laptop computer. It is made of waterproof canvas. The main case is 43 cm by 35 cm by 9 cm, and the solar panels are attached to a pocket that is 35 cm by 25 cm by 5 cm. Calculate the total amount of canvas in the case. Explain any assumptions you made.

Lesson 4.5

0.2 m
1.3 m
1.8 m
1.8 m
3.0 m
2.4 m

11. Cody is building a playhouse out of plywood for his sister. It will be 2.2 m high and include the roof and floor. Calculate the total surface area of plywood Cody needs before he cuts out the windows.

12. A frame for a semicircular window is shown. Estimate the surface area of the frame. Explain what you did.

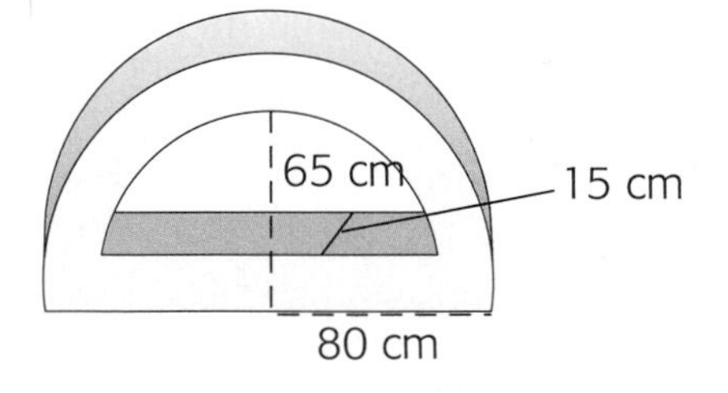

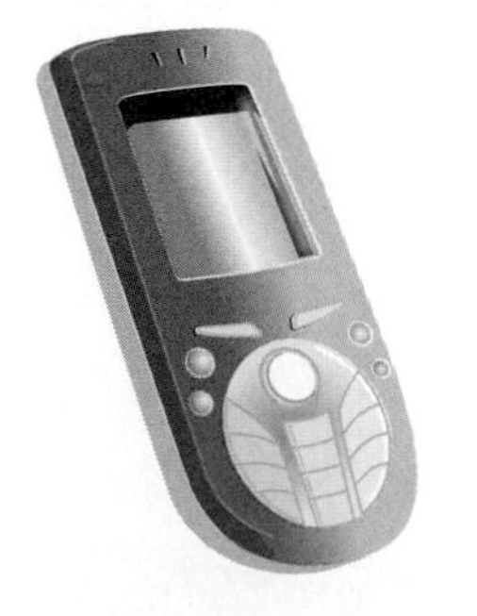

13. Morgan makes hard cases for cell phones that cover everything except the screen and the keypad. This cell phone is 16 cm long, 5.5 cm wide, and 1.4 cm thick. The screen is 5.8 cm by 4.2 cm and the keypad is 4.5 cm in diameter. Determine the surface area of the phone that the case must cover.

CHAPTER 4

Chapter Task

Designing a Cat Play Structure

Cats enjoy climbing, hiding, and looking through the window from a high platform. Play structures allow cats to do all three activities.

These structures often have a wooden base and wooden platforms. Large cardboard tubes are often used for hideaways and posts. The entire structure is then covered with carpeting.

Your task is to design an original cat play structure.

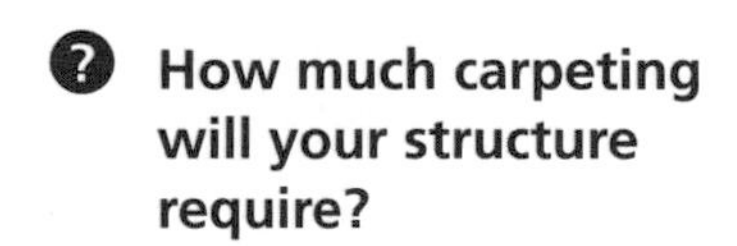

How much carpeting will your structure require?

A. Research cat play structures to get ideas for your structure. Your design must have at least one hideaway and two platforms.

B. Determine what objects you will use. Sketch each object, indicating its dimensions. Be sure that your objects are large enough for a cat to use.

C. Sketch your design, including all dimensions.

D. Calculate the total area to be carpeted. If you plan to use two different types of carpeting, calculate the amount of each type required.

Task | ***Checklist***

- ✔ Did you draw an accurate diagram of each component and the complete play structure?
- ✔ Did you make sure your objects were large enough for a cat?
- ✔ Did you include all dimensions on your diagrams?
- ✔ Did you calculate the surface area, and explain your methods?

AQUATICA

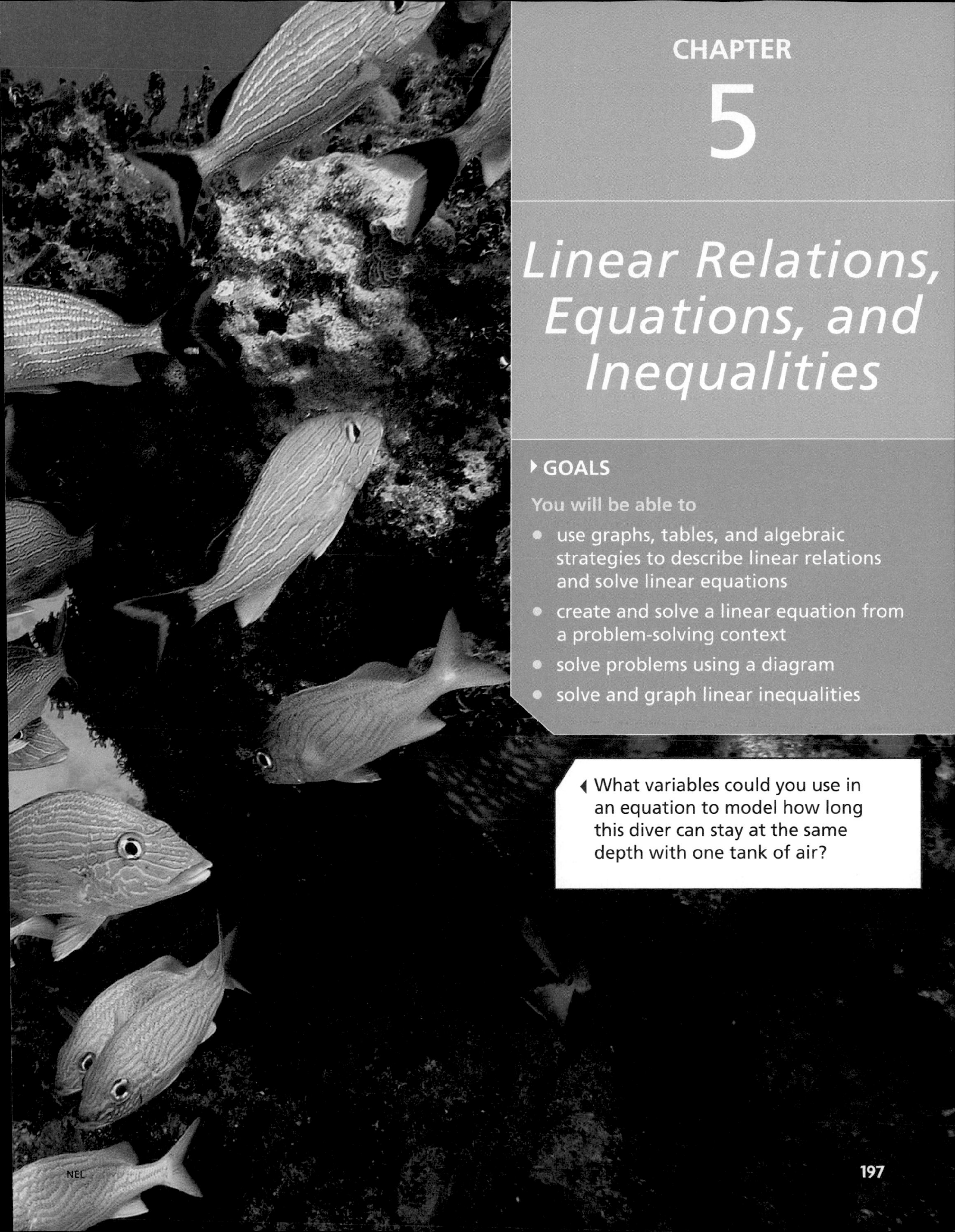

CHAPTER

5

Linear Relations, Equations, and Inequalities

GOALS

You will be able to

- use graphs, tables, and algebraic strategies to describe linear relations and solve linear equations
- create and solve a linear equation from a problem-solving context
- solve problems using a diagram
- solve and graph linear inequalities

What variables could you use in an equation to model how long this diver can stay at the same depth with one tank of air?

Getting Started

Dragon Boats

Fifty-six people have registered for an upcoming dragon boat race, resulting in two full boats and another one that is one-third full. All of the boats hold the same number of people.

How many more people do they need to fill the remaining dragon boat?

A. If you know the number of people in a full dragon boat, how can you determine the number of people in three full boats?

B. How does $2\frac{1}{3}$ describe the current number of full boats in this race?

C. Write a **relation** between the number of people, n, in each full boat and the total number of people in all the boats, t.

D. What equation can you solve to determine the number of people in one full boat?

E. Solve your equation to determine the number of people in one full boat.

F. How many more people do they need to fill the third boat?

WHAT DO You Think?

Decide whether you agree or disagree with each statement.
Be ready to explain your decision.

1. The graphs of the relations $y = 4x - 5$ and $y = 3x - 5$ are alike.
2. To solve the equation $\frac{x}{2} + 5 = \blacksquare$, you have to subtract 5 from both sides of the equation.
3. You can use the equation $y = 25 - x$ to describe an addition situation.

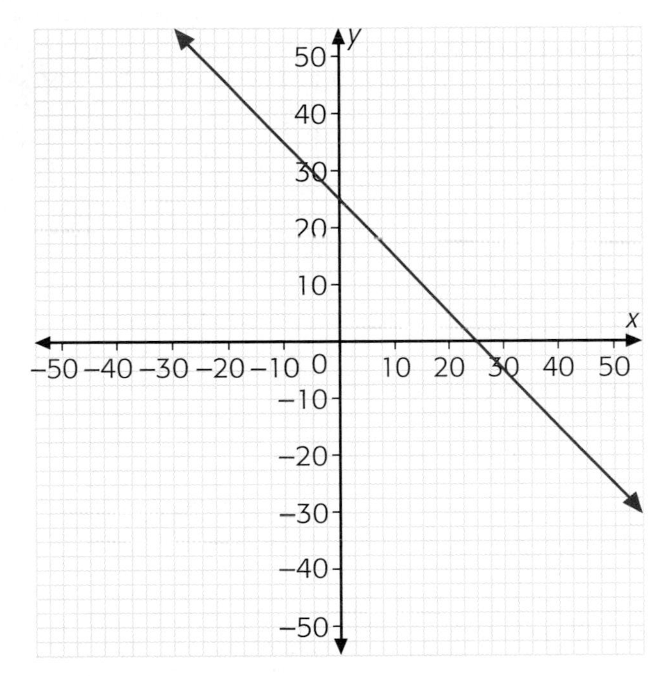

4. If a graph passes through the points (1, 3), (2, 5), and (3, 7), it has to also pass through (4, 9).

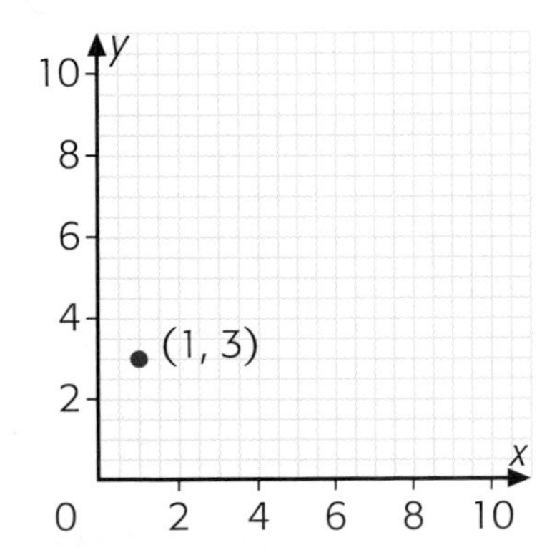

5.1 Describing Relations Algebraically

GOAL

Use symbols to describe a pattern that changes at a constant rate.

LEARN ABOUT the Math

Rani and Erin run a dog-walking service.

? How can Rani and Erin calculate what to charge?

EXAMPLE 1 | Representing a relation using a picture

Rani's Solution

I drew pictures. This one shows the price to walk a dog for 15 min.

The price to walk a dog for 15 min is $7.50.

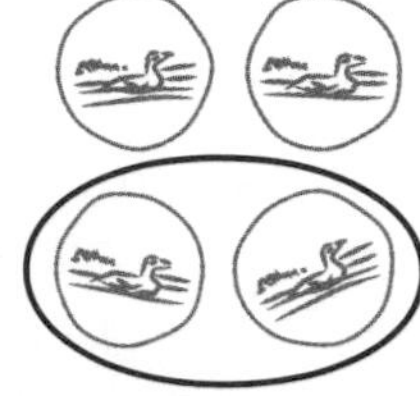

This picture shows the price to walk a dog for 30 min. I circled the part that increases with time. $5.50 is constant, so it is the same in each picture.

The price to walk a dog for 30 min is $9.50.

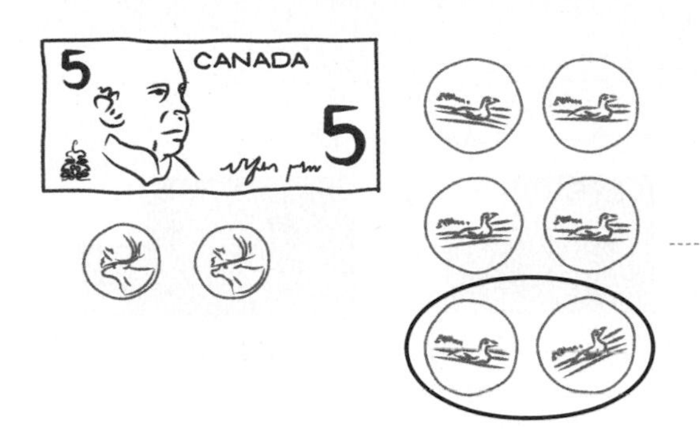

This picture shows the price for a 45 min walk. I added two loonies for the extra 15 min.

The price to walk a dog for 45 min is $11.50.

An expression for the price is
$5.50 + 2 × (number of 15 min periods).

With each additional 15 min period, the price rises by $2.

An equation for the price, P, is
$P = 5.50 + 2t$, where t is time.
Each unit of t is 15 min.

I wrote an equation for the relation between time and price.

EXAMPLE 2 | Representing a relation using a table

Erin's Solution

Number of 15 min periods, t	Total price ($), P
1	7.50
2	9.50
3	11.50

goes up by 2
goes up by 2

I created a table of values.
The price increases by 2 each time.
I decided to write an algebraic expression to describe the pattern rule. I chose the variables t and P to represent each quantity in the relation.

The price goes up by $2 each time.
The number of 15 min periods, t, multiplied by the rate of change, is $2t$.

The rate of change of the price tells how much the price increases for each change of 1 in the number of 15 min periods. In this case, it is $2. This part of the pattern rule tells me the additional price to walk a dog for any multiple of 15 mins.

An expression for the price is $5.50 + $2t$, where t is the number of 15 min periods.

I have to add $5.50 because it is a fixed price.

An equation for the price, P, is $P = 5.50 + 2t$, where t is the number of 15 min periods.

Reflecting

A. How do the picture and table of values help to determine the algebraic representation of a relation that changes at a constant rate?

B. Why might it be more useful to represent a relation algebraically than with pictures or tables?

Communication | *Tip*

An expression that describes a relation using symbols and letters is often called an algebraic representation.

WORK WITH the Math

EXAMPLE 3 | Determining a value algebraically

Determine the number of squares in Figure 20.

Figure 1

Figure 2

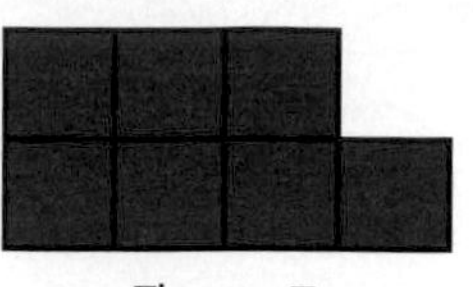
Figure 3

Francis's Solution

Figure 1

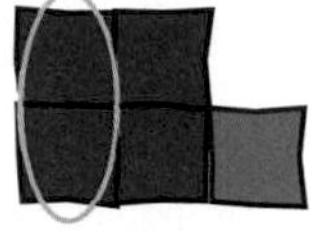
Figure 2

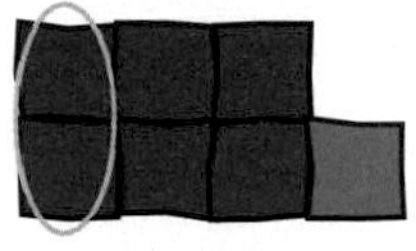
Figure 3

I redrew each diagram, so that the single square on the right was a different colour, since it was different from the rest of the shape. I also used an oval to mark the new shapes in each new figure.

Each time the figure number, n, increases by 1 there are 2 more red squares. In Figure n, there are $2n$ red squares.

> I looked at how the figures changed.
> In Figure 1, there are 2 red squares.
> In Figure 2, there are 4 red squares.
> In Figure 3, there are 6 red squares.

An expression for the number of squares in Figure n is $2n + 1$.

> There is one blue square in each figure, so I added 1 to the expression.

An equation for the number of squares, S, in Figure n is $S = 2n + 1$.

> I used the expression to write the equation.

$$S = 2(20) + 1$$
$$= 41$$

> I substituted 20 for n to determine the number of squares in Figure 20.

In Figure 20, there are 41 squares.

EXAMPLE 4 | Determining the rate of change from an algebraic representation

Determine the rate of change for $y = -3.4x + 1$.

Luc's Solution

x	$y = -3.4x + 1$
0	$y = -3.4(0) + 1$ $= 1$
1	-2.4
2	-5.8
3	-9.2

goes down by 3.4
goes down by 3.4
goes down by 3.4

> I created a table to see how the y-values change. I chose x-values that were 1 unit apart and substituted them into the relation to calculate the y-values.

The relation has a constant rate of change of -3.4.

> The y-value decreases by 3.4 each time the x-value increases by 1. Since it is decreasing, the rate of change is negative.

EXAMPLE 5 | Connecting a relation to a situation

Create a problem that can be solved using $y = 1300 - 25x$.

Viktor's Solution

x	$y = 1300 - 25x$
0	1300
1	1275
2	1250
3	1225

goes down by 25
goes down by 25
goes down by 25

I made a table to help me understand the relation.
The y-value starts at 1300 and decreases by 25 when the x-value increases by 1.

Let x be the number of days and let y be the remaining distance to Banff. The equation $y = 1300 - 25x$ can represent the kilometres remaining in my bike trip from Winnipeg to Banff.

I need a situation in which something starts at 1300 and then decreases with a constant rate of change of -25.

- It's about 1300 km from Winnipeg to Banff.
- I can cycle about 25 km per day.

The situation can be about a bike trip from Winnipeg to Banff.

Problem: How long will the bike trip take?

Solution:

$$0 = 1300 - 25x$$
$$25x = 1300$$
$$x = \frac{1300}{25}$$
$$= 52$$

I tried to think of something I would want to know about the bike trip.

The distance remaining will be 0 when the trip is finished. I set $y = 0$ and solved for x.

The bike trip will take 52 days.

In Summary

Key Idea

- A pattern that changes at a constant rate can be expressed in a variety of ways such as: a picture, a table of values, or an algebraic expression.

Figure 1 Figure 2 Figure 3

Figure number, n	Number of circles, C
1	3
2	5
3	7

$C = 2n + 1$

Need to Know

- An algebraic representation of a relation allows you to substitute any number to calculate a value.

  For example, you can let $n = 18$ in the relation $t = \frac{1}{2}n - 3$:

$$t = \frac{1}{2}(18) - 3$$
$$t = 9 - 3$$
$$t = 6$$

  When $n = 18$, $t = 6$.
- You can use a table of values to investigate the rate of change for a relation.
- If the y-values are decreasing as x increases, the rate of change is negative. If the y-values are increasing as x increases, the rate of change is positive.

Checking

1. Match each pattern with its equation.

a)

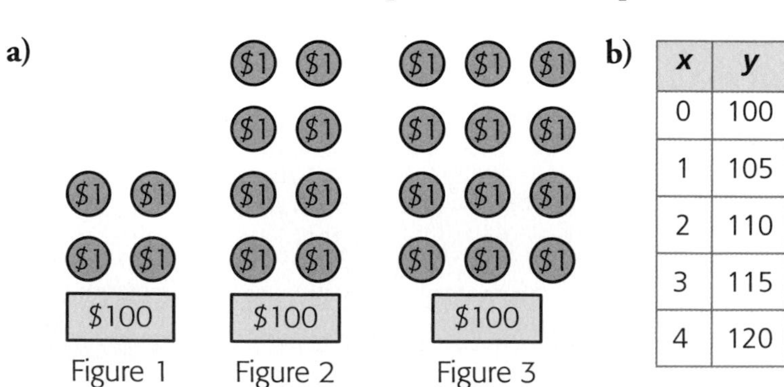

Figure 1 Figure 2 Figure 3

b)

x	y
0	100
1	105
2	110
3	115
4	120

c) Don has $100 in a bank account and withdraws $5 each week.

A. $y = 100 - 5x$ **B.** $y = 100 + 5x$ **C.** $y = 100 + 4x$

2. Jim pays a one-time fee of \$5 to download songs plus \$0.25 for each song. An equation for this is $C = 0.25s + 5$, where C is the cost to download s songs.

a) Represent this situation with a picture.

b) Complete the table.

s	1	2	3	4
C				

c) Determine the rate of change using the table.

Practising

3. Liz can ride at 15 km/h for a bike marathon.

a) Describe the relation between time and distance using a table.

b) Represent the relation between time and distance algebraically.

c) Determine how far Liz can ride in 8 h.

d) Determine how long Liz will take to ride 100 km.

Figure 1

Figure 2

Figure 3

4. Describe each relation using an algebraic representation.

a) the perimeter of an equilateral triangle in terms of its side length

b) the amount John pays for a taxi ride in which the fare is \$0.50/km plus a flat rate of \$2.50

c) the number of red squares in each figure in the pattern at right

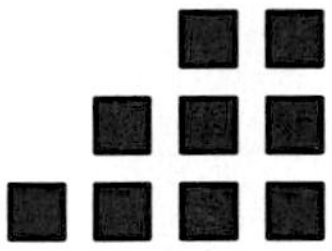

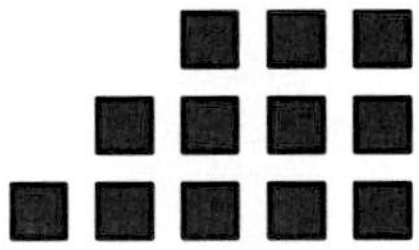

5. Eli created this toothpick pattern.

Figure 1

Figure 2

Figure 3

a) Make a table of values for the number of toothpicks in each figure.

b) Write an equation for the number of toothpicks in Figure n.

c) Determine the number of toothpicks in Figure 8. Verify your answer.

d) Which figure will require 46 toothpicks?

6. Multiple choice. Allan mows the grass at a golf course. He charges \$5/h plus a flat fee of \$12.50. One day, he earned \$84. Which equation represents this?

A. $84 + 5h = 12.50$

B. $5h \times 12.50 = 48$

C. $5h + 12.50 = 84$

D. $84h + 5 = 1250$

7. Multiple choice. The relation between Celsius, C, and Fahrenheit, F, temperatures is shown in the table. Which equation represents this pattern?

Reported Temperatures	
°F	°C
0	−18
20	−7
40	4
60	16
80	27
100	38

A. $C = \frac{5(F - 32)}{9}$

B. $F = \frac{5(C - 32)}{9}$

C. $C = 5F - 18$

D. $F = 2C + 24$

8. **Multiple choice.** This table of values shows the details of a phone plan.

Cost ($)	25	26	27
Time (min)	0	10	20

Assuming this pattern continues, how many minutes can you buy for $50?

A. 50 min **B.** 100 min **C.** 150 min **D.** 250 min

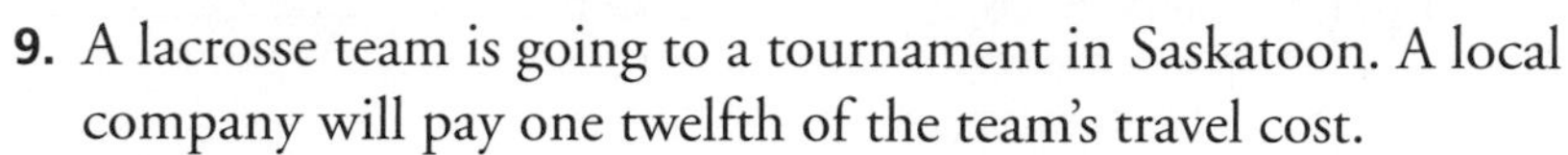

9. A lacrosse team is going to a tournament in Saskatoon. A local company will pay one twelfth of the team's travel cost.
   a) Relate the company's cost to the team's travel cost using an expression.
   b) The travel cost is $1800. How much will the company pay?

10. Determine the rate of change for the relation in each table. Write an equation to represent each relation.

a)

x	*y*
1	5
2	11
3	17
4	23

b)

x	*y*
1	120.0
2	115.5
3	111.0
4	106.5

11. Create a table of values for each relation. Use the values 1, 2, and 3 for x.
   a) $y = x - 3$
   b) $y = 5x$
   c) $y = 5 - 4x$
   d) $2.5x + 1.25 = y$
   e) $y = \frac{3x}{5}$
   f) $y = 2\frac{1}{4}x - 9\frac{1}{3}$

12. Determine the rate of change for each relation in question 11. What do you notice?

13. Describe a situation you can represent by $y = 3.5x + 1.75$.

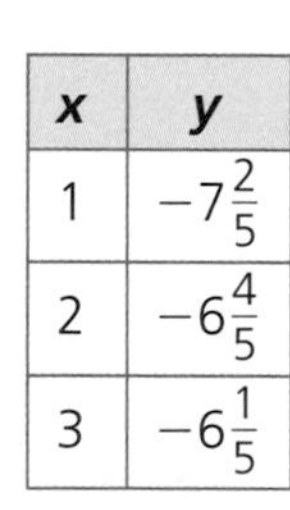

x	*y*
1	$-7\frac{2}{5}$
2	$-6\frac{4}{5}$
3	$-6\frac{1}{5}$

14. Mika created the equation $y = \frac{3}{5}x - 8$ for this table of values.
   a) Determine the rate of change using the table values.
   b) Mika thinks the values $x = 35$ and $y = 19$ fit the relation. Is he correct? Explain your thinking.

15. Jaime pays $30 per month for 50 MB of data for her smart phone. After the first 50 MB, it costs $1.15 per MB.
   a) Copy and complete the table of values.
   b) What is the difference between the monthly cost for 60 MB and for 70 MB?
   c) The rate of change in Jaime's monthly cost is $1.15. Explain why your answer to part b) is different.
   d) Create an algebraic representation for this situation.
   e) Verify your answer to part d) by using it to calculate the monthly cost for 80 MB.

Number of MB	Monthly cost ($)
50	
60	
70	
80	

16. Kristina is building a dog run against her house that is twice as long as it is wide.

a) Create a relation to show the amount of fencing needed in terms of the width, x.

b) Determine the amount of fencing needed for a width of 5 m.

c) Determine the dimensions of a dog run that uses 105 m of fencing.

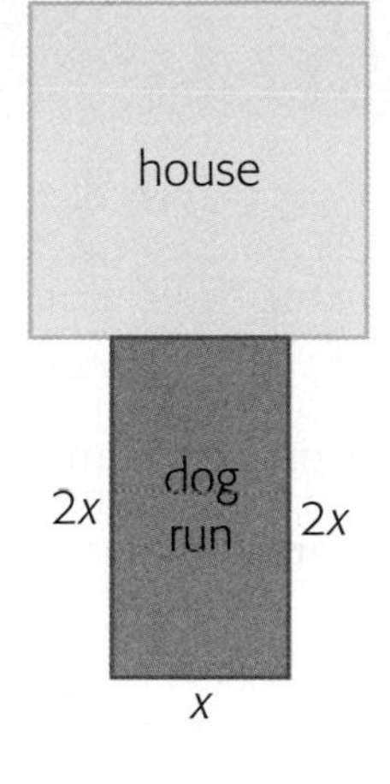

17. Consider the relation $y = \frac{x}{3} - 5$.

x	y
1	
2	
3	

a) Predict the rate of change by using the algebraic representation.

b) Copy and complete the table. Determine the rate of change.

c) Compare your answers to parts a) and b). How accurate was your prediction?

d) What other values of x could you choose to make creating a table of values easier? Explain.

Closing

18. What are the benefits of describing a relation using a table of values? What are the benefits of describing it using an algebraic representation? Support your answers with examples.

Extending

19. Write an algebraic representation for each relation.

a)

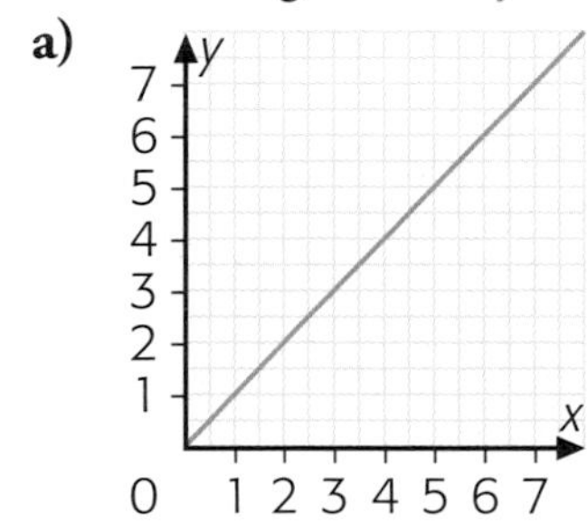

b)

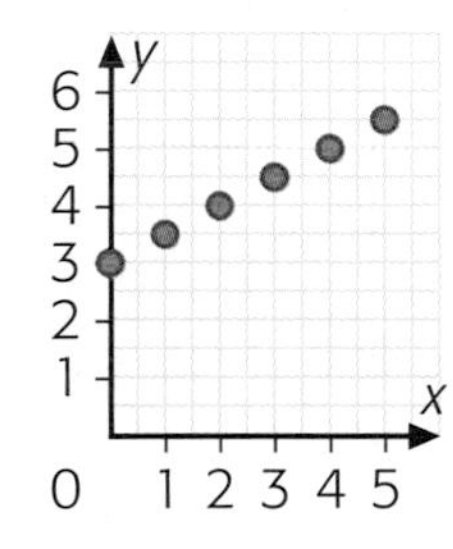

20. Allan has changed his fees for cutting grass. Now he charges a flat fee of \$20, with the first hour free. For the next three hours after that, he charges \$5/h. For every hour after that, he charges \$4/h.

a) Create a table of values for 10 h.

b) Write an algebraic relation for each group of hours.

c) Will the table of values or the algebraic representation be more useful to determine Allan's cost to cut grass? Justify your choice.

Curious MATH

Crossing the T

Francis told Erin that if she shaded a letter T on a number grid and told him the sum of all the numbers, he could tell her where the T is located.

Erin: "My sum is 320."

Francis: "Your numbers are 57, 58, 59, 68, and 78!"

How did Francis know what numbers Erin chose?

1	2	3	4	5	6	7	8	9	10
11	12	13	14	15	16	17	18	19	20
21	22	23	24	25	26	27	28	29	30
31	32	33	34	35	36	37	38	39	40
41	42	43	44	45	46	47	48	49	50
51	52	53	54	55	56	57	58	59	60
61	62	63	64	65	66	67	68	69	70
71	72	73	74	75	76	77	78	79	80
81	82	83	84	85	86	87	88	89	90
91	92	93	94	95	96	97	98	99	100

1. What expression can you use to describe the sum of the numbers in a T?
2. Try this trick with a partner.
3. Create another trick that would predict the numbers that form a letter E on the hundred chart if you know the sum.

5.2 Graphing Linear Relations

GOAL

Represent a linear relation using a graph.

YOU WILL NEED

- grid paper
- a ruler

LEARN ABOUT the Math

Zachary got a new cell phone and $50 for his birthday. Text messages cost $0.15 each on his phone plan, and he must pay a monthly fee of $5. He made a table to compare the number of text messages he might send each month and the cost.

Number of text messages sent in a month, x	Monthly cost ($), y
0	5.00
20	8.00
40	
60	
80	
100	
120	

? How many text messages can Zachary send each month for $50?

A. Copy and complete the table of values.

B. Graph the **linear relation** between the number of text messages sent and the monthly cost.

C. **Interpolate** using the graph to estimate the cost of sending the following number of text messages each month: 10, 50, and 115.

D. **Extrapolate** to determine the cost of sending 160 and 200 text messages each month. Plot these points on the graph using a ruler.

E. Zachary's cost to send text messages increases at a constant rate of $0.15 per message. How can you use this rate of change to extend the pattern and determine the cost of sending 260 text messages each month?

F. Determine an algebraic representation of the linear relation.

G. Determine the number of text messages he can send with his $50 in birthday money using your graph. How do you know your answer is correct?

linear relation

a relation whose plotted points lie on a straight line

interpolate

to estimate a value between two known values

extrapolate

to predict a value by extending a pattern beyond known values

Reflecting

H. How does the rate of change help you decide where to place new points on the graph?

I. Why does the y-value decrease by 3.50 each time the x-value increases by 20, no matter where you are on the line?

J. Why might you use a graph to extrapolate or interpolate, instead of using an algebraic representation or a table of values?

WORK WITH the Math

EXAMPLE 1 | Connecting a real-life situation to a graph

Erin's family wants to rent a generator for their camping trip in the Rocky Mountains. The cost is a flat rate of $25 for insurance plus $5 per week. Which graph should they use to estimate the cost of renting the generator?

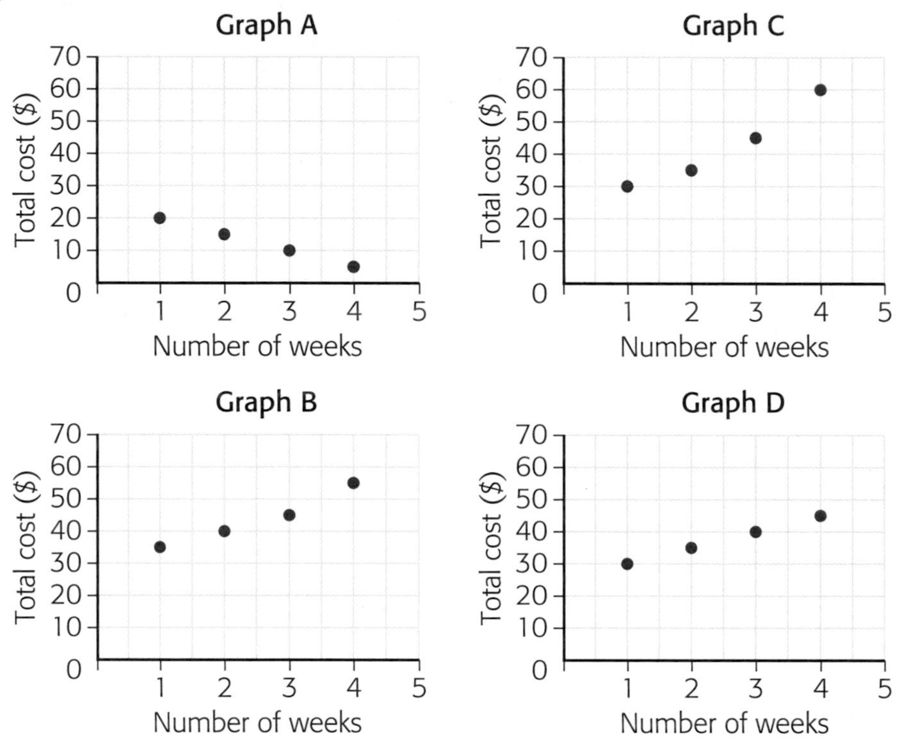

Erin's Solution

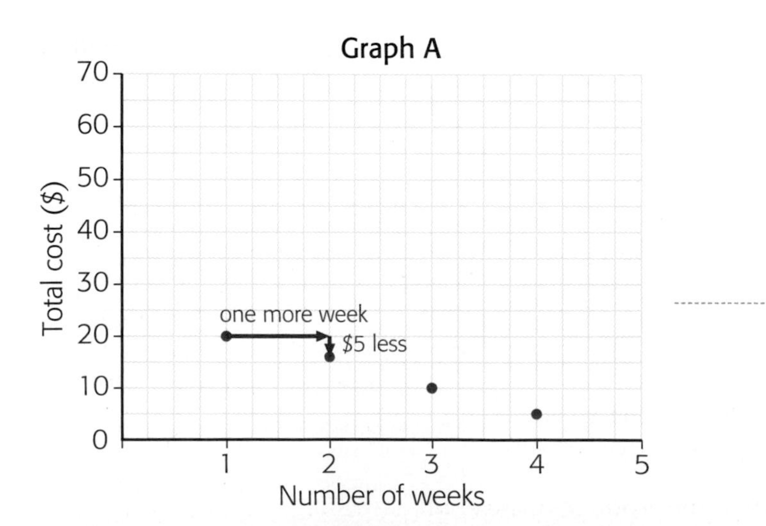

Each additional week the cost increases by $5, so the rate of change is constant at $5 per week. I think the points of the correct graph will lie on a straight line. I used my ruler to check: the points in Graph A lie on a straight line, but the cost is not increasing.

Graph A is incorrect, because the cost is decreasing.

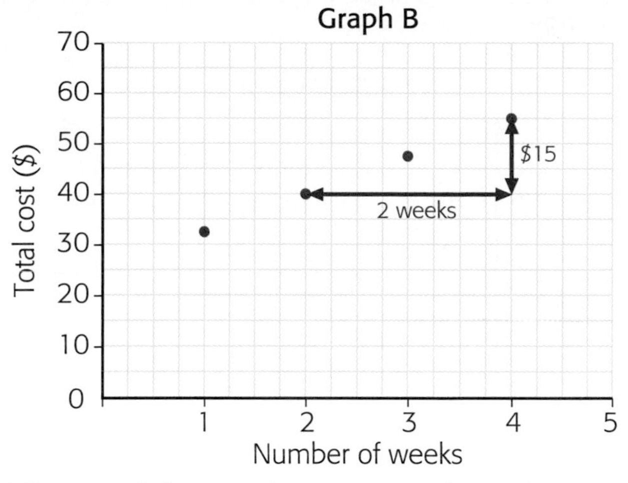

The points in Graph B lie on a straight line and the cost is increasing at a constant rate. It might be correct.

The points for weeks 2 and 4 fall right on the grid, so I used them to determine the rate of change.

The rate of change is $15 over 2 weeks, or $7.50 per week. Graph B is incorrect, because the rate of change is not $5 per week.

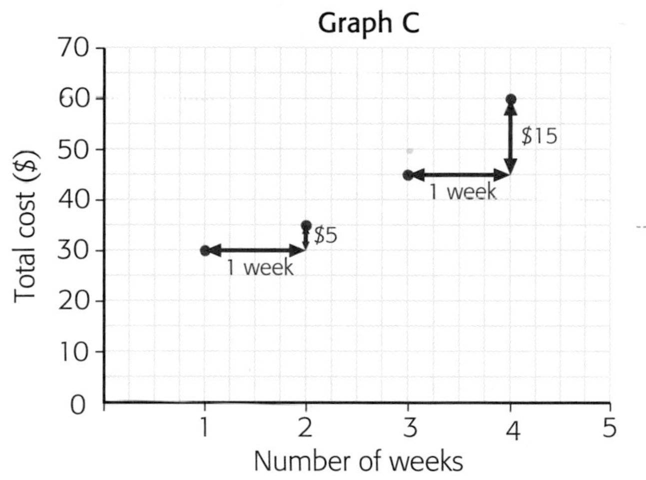

The points in Graph C of this graph do not to lie on a straight line. I think the rate of change is not constant.

I calculated the rate of change for different parts of the graph to see if they were different. The change is $5 from week 1 to week 2 but it's $15 from week 3 to week 4.

Graph C is incorrect, because the rate of change is not constant.

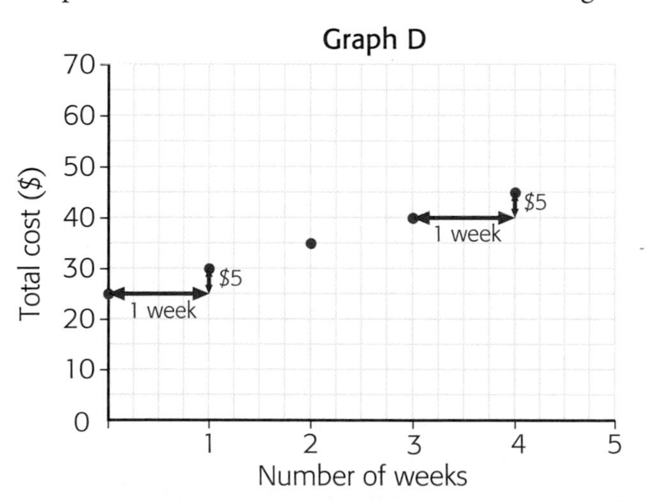

Graph D must be correct, but I checked to make sure.
The points in Graph D lie on a straight line, so the rate of change is constant. Each week there is an additional cost of $5.
I used the rate of change to extrapolate to 0 weeks. At week 1, the cost was $30, so at 0 weeks it has to be $5 less. The initial cost is $25, the cost of insurance.

The cost increases by $5 each week and starts at $25. We can use this graph to estimate our costs.

EXAMPLE 2 | Solving a problem using the rate of change

Rani saw this graph on a package of energy-saving light bulbs. How much will the savings be for the entire 6000 h lifespan of one of the bulbs?

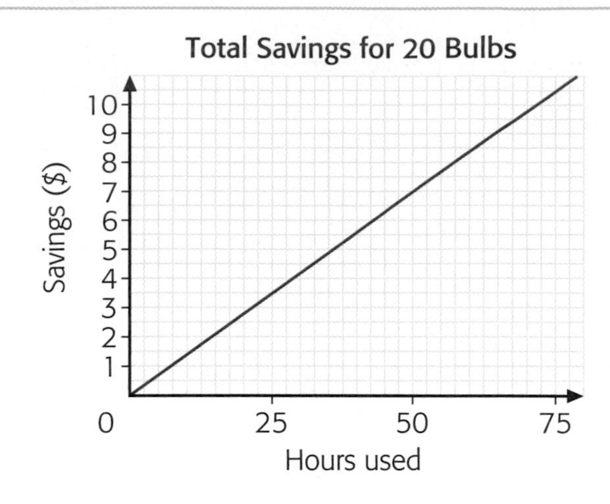

Rani's Solution

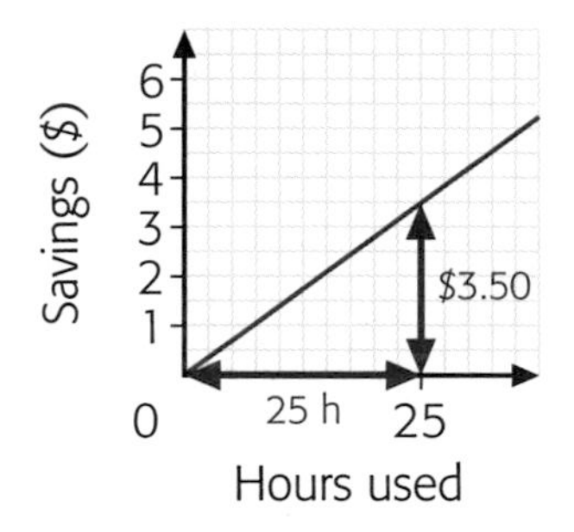

The graph is linear, so the rate of change is constant.

I looked at the first 25 h to calculate the rate of change.

For every 25 h, you save $3.50 for 20 bulbs.

$6000 \div 25 = 240$

I calculated the number of 25 h time periods in the 6000 h lifespan of the 20 bulbs.

$240 \times \$3.50 = \$840$

You will save $840 for 20 light bulbs.

I multiplied the number of 25 h time periods by the savings for 25 h.

$\$840 \div 20 = \$42$

One light bulb will save $42 in energy costs over its 6000 h lifespan.

I divided this amount by 20 to get the savings for one light bulb.

EXAMPLE 3 | Solving a problem using a linear relation

A solar water-heating system can reduce carbon emissions by 400 kg each year. How long will it take for a solar water-heating system to reduce the equivalent of, or offset, a year's worth of carbon emissions?

Average Canadian household produces 11 tonnes of carbon emissions each year

Francis's Solution

Years	Carbon emissions (tonnes)
0	11.0
1	10.6
2	10.2
3	9.8

I created a table of values and calculated the amount of carbon emissions left to offset. 1 tonne is equal to 1000 kg, so 400 kg is the same as 0.4 tonnes.

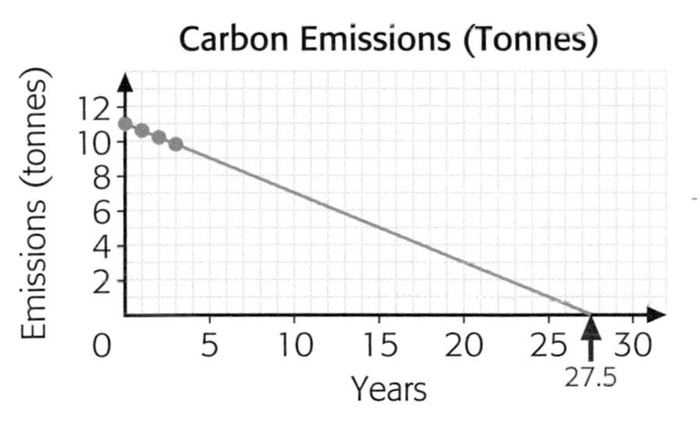

I plotted the points on a graph. Then, I used a ruler to connect the points and extrapolate.

The carbon emissions are offset when the y-value is 0.

It will take about 27.5 years to offset one year of carbon emissions by installing a solar water-heating system.

In Summary

Key Idea

- If the points of a graph lie on a straight line, then the rate of change is constant. A linear relation has a constant rate of change. The rate of change of this relation is constant, at $3 for each pen.

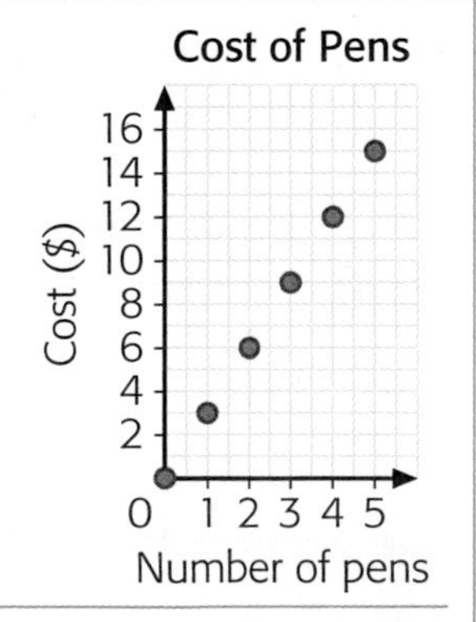

(continued)

Need to Know

- You can draw a line through the plotted points of a linear relation to determine other points on the graph.
- You can use the rate of change to determine new points on the graph of a linear relation by calculating the change in the y-value for a given change in the x-value. In this graph the y-value goes up by 2 for every unit increase in the x-value. The point (10, 21) is on the graph because $x = 10$ is 9 units more than $x = 1$, so its y-value is $2 \times 9 = 18$ units more than 3, or 21.

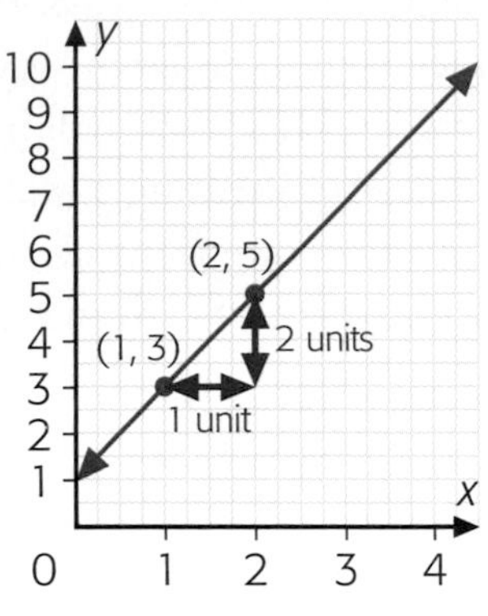

Checking

1. Match each situation with its graph.
   a) Chantel earns \$7.50/h babysitting.
   b) Derek earns \$9.00/h painting.
   c) Corey earns \$7.00/h shovelling snow.

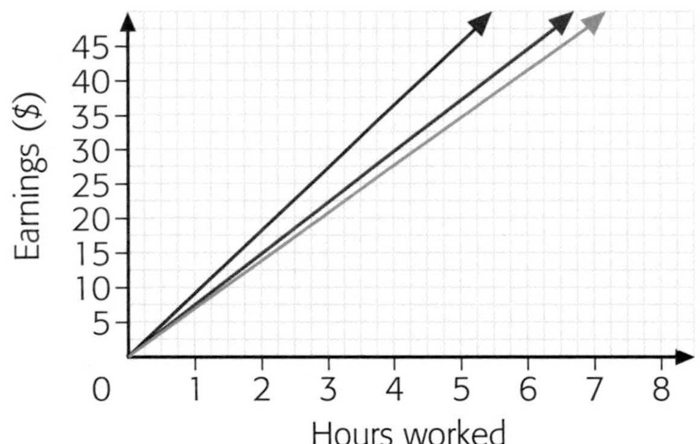
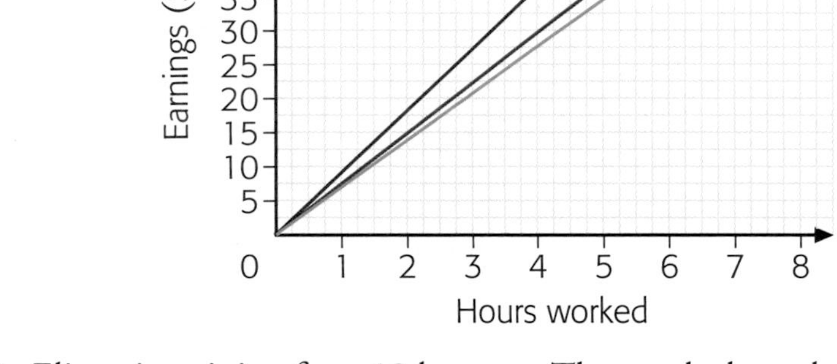

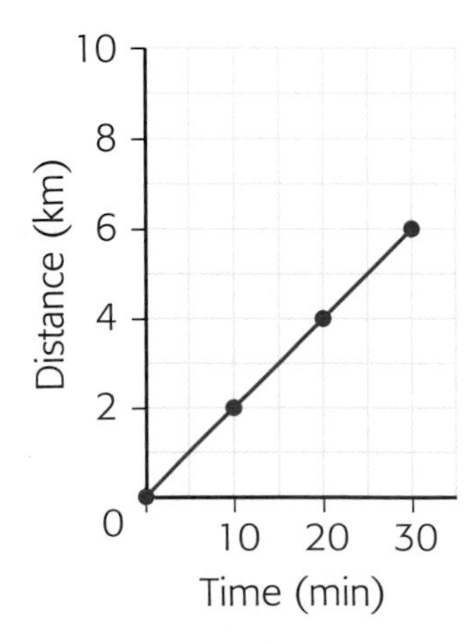

2. Elinor is training for a 10 km race. The graph shows her times and distances.
   a) Determine how long she takes to run 3 km.
   b) Determine how far she can run in 45 min if she maintains this speed.
   c) Is she running at a constant rate? Explain how you know.
   d) Determine how fast she is running.

Practising

3. Match each situation with its graph.
   a) Wilson has a calling card with \$100 on it. The company charges \$0.10/min to make calls with the card.
   b) Andrew has a calling card with \$50 on it. His company charges \$0.15/min to make calls with the card.

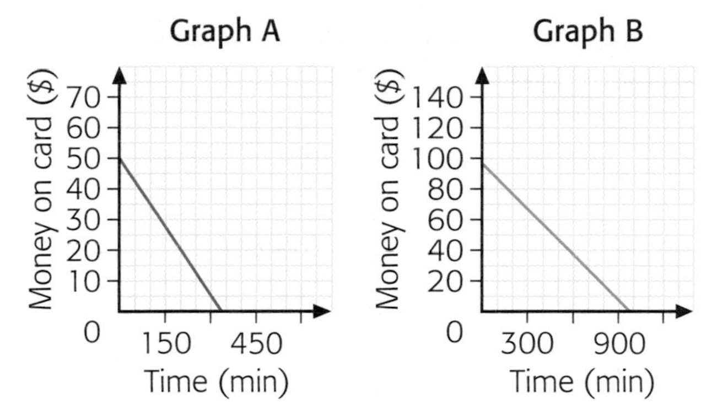

4. a) Create a table of values and draw the graph of the relation $y = \frac{1}{2}x - 1$.
   b) Determine the rate of change of the linear relation.

5. A linear relation passes through $(-3, 2)$ and $(5, -1)$. What is the rate of change?

6. **Multiple choice.** A hot-air balloon is launched from a hill 1500 m above sea level. It rises at 35 m/min. Which graph shows the balloon's height in relation to time?

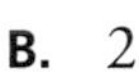

A. 1 **B.** 2 **C.** 3 **D.** 4

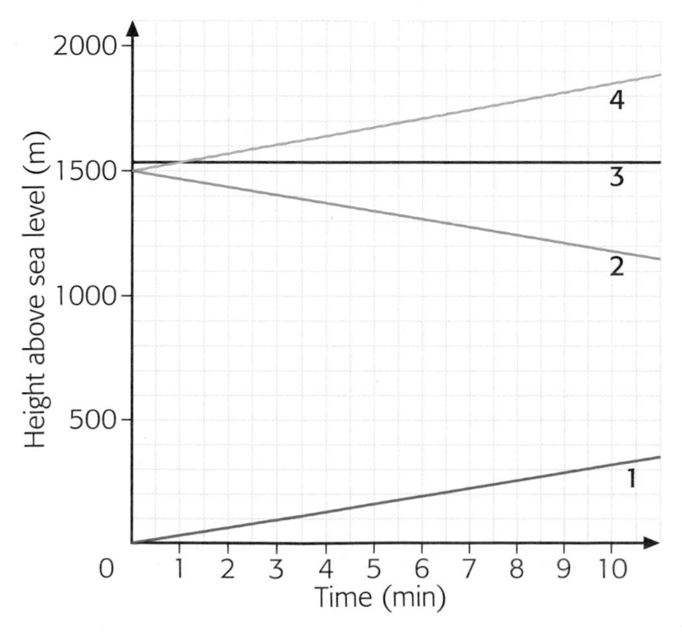

7. **Multiple choice.** Which graph represents the linear relation $y = \frac{-2}{5}x + 1$?

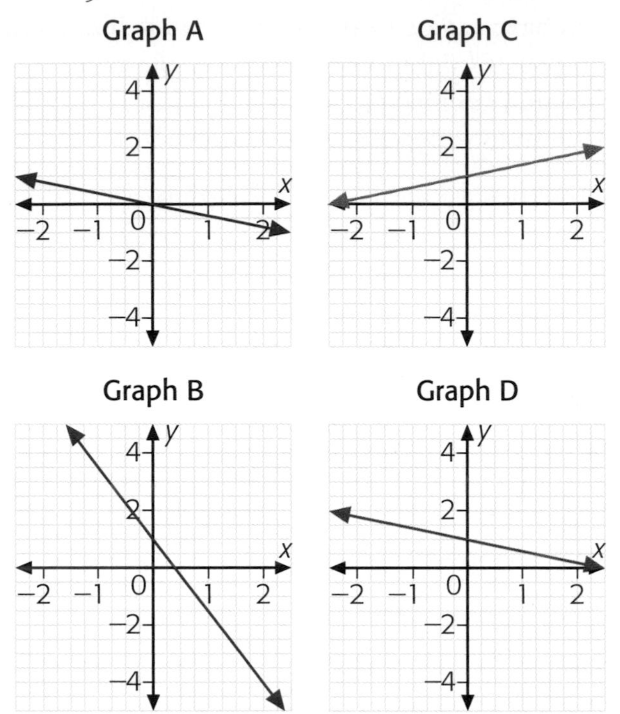

8. Describe or draw a linear relation that has a rate of change of zero and passes through (0, 2). Describe a situation that would have a rate of change of zero.

9. a) Create a table of values for $y = -2x + 10$ using x values of 0, 5, 10, 15, and 20.
   b) Use your table of values to graph $y = -2x + 10$.
   c) Use your graph to predict the value of y when $x = 4$, 18, and 75.

10. A restaurant charges these amounts for parties.
    a) Explain the meaning of the coordinate (20, 250).
    b) Estimate the cost for 35 people.
    c) Determine how many people can be invited for $500.
    d) What is the difference in cost between 10 people and 20 people?
    e) Divide your answer in part d) by 10. What does this value mean?

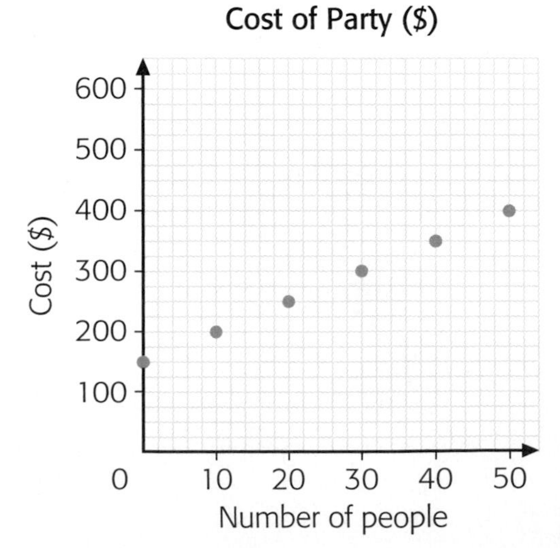

11. A computer decreases in value as shown.

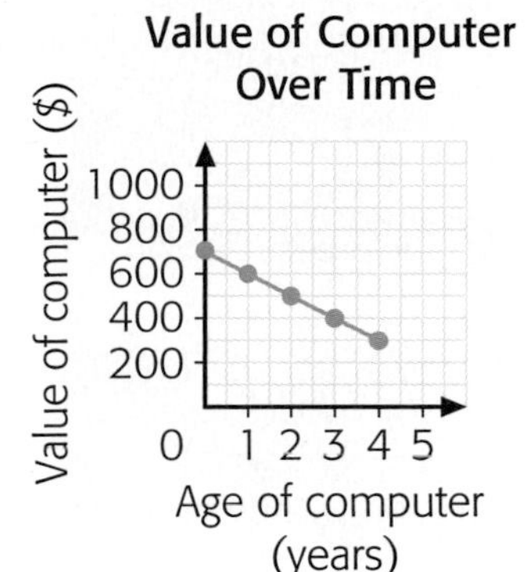

a) Explain the meaning of the coordinate (2, 500).
b) Estimate the value of the computer at 1.5 years.
c) About when will it be worth $100?
d) About when will it be worth $0?
e) What is the difference in the value between years 3 and 4?
f) How does the graph show that the decrease between years 1 and 2 was the same as between years 2 and 3?

12. **a)** Graph this table of values.
b) Is the relation between x and y linear? Explain.
c) How is this graph different from other graphs in this lesson?

x	2	2	2	2
y	5	3	0	−4

13. **a)** Graph this table of values.
b) Is the relation between x and y linear? Explain.
c) How is this graph different from other graphs in this lesson?

x	−1	0	1	2
y	2	2	2	2

14. A weather balloon recorded these temperatures.

Altitude (km)	6.5	7.4	8.7	9.0	9.8
Temperature (°C)	20	5	−18	−23	−37

a) Graph the relation between altitude and temperature.
b) Interpolate to estimate the temperature at 7 km.
c) Extrapolate to estimate where the temperature is −50 °C.
d) Is this relation linear? Explain.
e) Estimate the rate of change in temperature for an increase of 1 km in altitude.

15. An equation for a house's value is $y = 7500x + 125\,000$, where y is the value in dollars and x is the time in years, starting now.
a) Predict how the graph of cost versus time will look. Explain your reasoning.
b) Create a table of values for the first five years.
c) Determine the value of the house in year 7.
d) By how much does the house increase in value between years 4 and 5?
e) How does your answer to part d) relate to the equation?

16. **Multiple choice.** Marie earns $1 for every 4 papers she delivers. Which ordered pair is not on the graph of the relation between Marie's earnings and the number of papers she delivers?
A. (4, 1) **B.** (8, 2) **C.** (12, 3) **D.** (4, 16)

17. Kim uses her cell phone about 10 minutes each day and wants to choose a new rate plan.

a) Graph the cost of each plan for one month (30 days).

b) Compare the two graphs. How are they similar? How are they different?

c) Which plan would you recommend?

Closing

18. How does the rate of change help you to estimate and predict values in a linear relation?

Extending

19. Recall Elinor from question 2 who was training for a 10 km race. Can the pattern you created be used to predict how far she will run in 100 min and 200 min? Why or why not?

20. The graph below represents the cost to make long distance calls within Canada on a land line for a particular phone company.

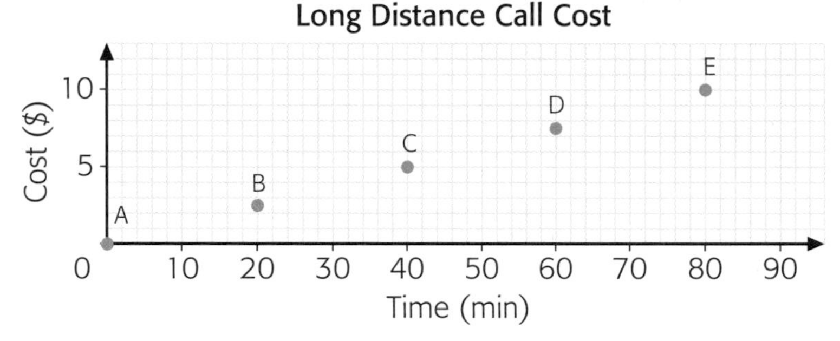

a) Interpret the ordered pair E(80, 10) in this situation.

b) What is the rate of change between points A and E? What does this value mean in this situation?

c) What is the rate of change between points C and D? What does this value mean in this situation?

d) Compare your answers for parts b) and c). What does this indicate about the type of relationship that exists between Cost and Time in this situation?

21. Graph the linear relations $y = \frac{1}{2}x + 1$, $y = x + 1$, $y = 2x + 1$, and $y = 3x + 1$.

a) Determine the rate of change for each relation.

b) What point is common to all of the linear relations?

c) How does the equation help you to determine the rate of change of the linear relation?

d) Write a linear relation that has a rate of change of -3 and passes through $(0, 1)$.

5.3 Interpreting the Solution of a Linear Equation

GOAL

Relate equations to tables of values and graphs.

YOU WILL NEED

- grid paper

LEARN ABOUT the Math

Nola wants U-Host to host her website.

U-Host's Charges per Month
\$19.00 monthly charge
\$1.15/megabyte (MB) of storage used

? How many megabytes of storage can Nola buy for \$60 per month?

EXAMPLE 1 | Solving a problem using different representations

Nola's Solution: Using a table of values

Amount of storage (MB)	Total cost (\$)
0	$19 + 0 \times 1.15 = 19.00$
10	$19 + 10 \times 1.15 = 30.50$
20	$19 + 20 \times 1.15 = 42.00$
30	$19 + 30 \times 1.15 = 53.50$
40	$19 + 40 \times 1.15 = 65.00$

I made a table to estimate the storage I can buy for \$60. I knew the charge for each MB is the sum of the monthly charge and 1.15 times the number of megabytes.

I used multiples of 10 to make the calculations easier.

The amount of storage for \$60 is between 30 MB and 40 MB. I interpolated from the table.

I can afford about 35 MB of storage for \$60.

\$60 is almost halfway between \$53.50 and \$65.

Check:
$19 + 1.15 \times 35 = 59.25$

I can buy about 35 MB of storage.

Viktor's Solution: Using a graph

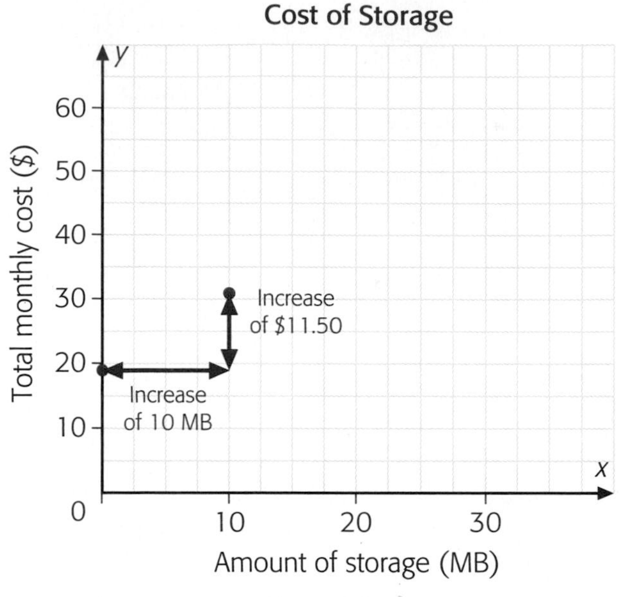

I drew a set of axes with storage on the x-axis and cost on the y-axis.

If Nola uses 0 MB, she will still have to pay \$19. I plotted this point (0, 19) on the graph.

For every 10 additional MB, the cost increases by $10 \times 1.15 = 11.50$. I used this data to plot another point.

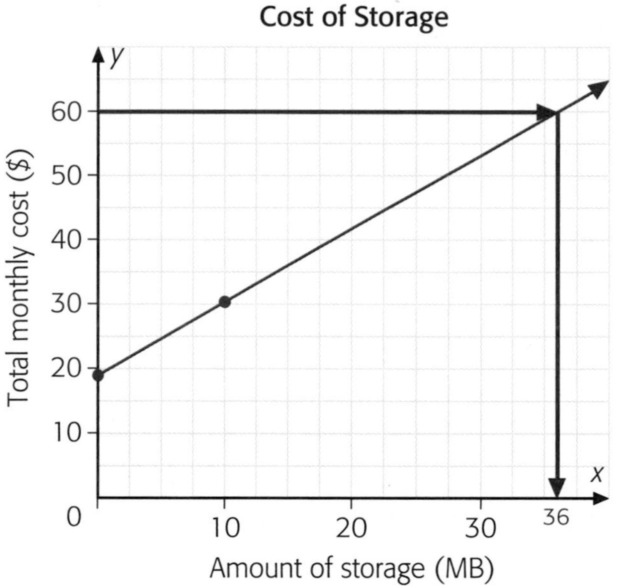

The rate of change is constant, so the points will lie on a straight line. I need only two points to make a straight line.

I used a ruler to extend the line past the point where $y = 60$.

Then, I drew a horizontal line from \$60 on the y-axis to my graph and a vertical line from my graph down to the x-axis to determine the amount of storage it buys.

Based on the graph, Nola can buy about 36 MB of storage.

I extrapolated from the graph that \$60 would pay for about 36 MB of storage.

Erin's Solution: Using an equation

cost = monthly charge + cost per MB × number of MB
cost = 19 + 1.15 × number of MB

I wrote a word equation to see how the amount of storage was used to calculate the cost.

Let n represent the amount of storage that Nola can buy.
Let C represent the cost.

I used variables to represent the quantities in the relation.

$C = 19 + 1.15n$

I used my word equation to create a **linear equation**.

$$60 = 19 + 1.15n$$
$$60 - 19 = 19 + 1.15n - 19$$
$$41 = 1.15n$$
$$\frac{41}{1.15} = \frac{1.15n}{1.15}$$
$$35.65 = n$$

Nola can buy 35.65 MB.

I substituted 60 for C. I subtracted the monthly cost of $19 from both sides. $41 is the amount of money Nola can spend on storage.
I divided both sides of the equation by 1.15 to determine the amount of storage Nola can buy.

Check:
$19 + 1.15n$
$\rightarrow 19 + 1.15 \times 35.65$
$= 59.9975$ or 60.00 to the nearest cent

I checked. I substituted 35.65 into the left side of the equation.

If U-Host charges for each megabyte and not a portion of 1 MB, Nola can buy 35 MB.

36 MB would cost more than $60.

Reflecting

linear equation
an equation involving numbers and variables

A. Nola's problem was solved using a table, a graph, and an equation. What are the advantages and disadvantages of each method?

B. Which method do you prefer? Why?

WORK WITH the Math

EXAMPLE 2 | Solving an equation using a graph

Solve $3x + 2.5 = -3.5$.

Rani's Solution

When $x = -1, y = 3(-1) + 2.5 = -0.5$
When $x = 0, y = 3(0) + 2.5 = 2.5$
When $x = 1, y = 3(1) + 2.5 = 5.5$
$(-1, -0.5)$, $(0, 2.5)$, and $(1, 5.5)$ are points on the graph.

I decided to graph $3x + 2.5 = y$ because I can think of the equation $3x + 2.5 = -3.5$ as $3x + 2.5 = y$ when $y = -3.5$. To do so, I determined three points on the graph by letting $x = -1$, 0, and 1 and solving for y in each case.

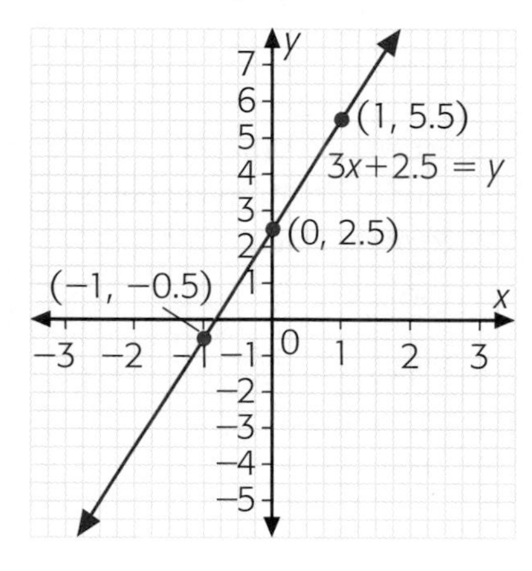

I plotted the points and saw they all lie along a straight line. I joined these points using a ruler. The linear relation $3x + 2.5 = y$ will include the point I need, at $y = -3.5$.

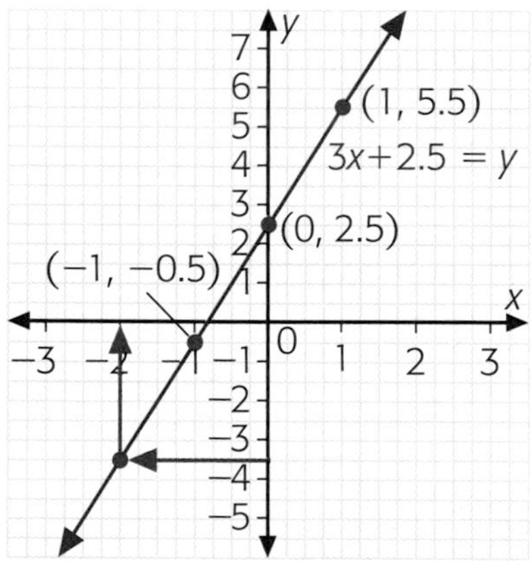

I drew a horizontal line from $y = -3.5$. It met the graph at $x = -2$.

The solution is $x = -2$.

Check:

I substituted the solution back into the equation to verify.

$3x + 2.5$
$\rightarrow 3(-2) + 2.5$
$= -3.5$

The solution checked.

In Summary

Key Idea

- You can estimate an approximate solution to an equation using a table of values or a graph, or determine an exact solution by working backward. For example, for $2\frac{3}{4} = \left(\frac{1}{2}\right)x + 2$,

From the table, the solution is between $x = 1$ and $x = 2$, so it is about $1\frac{1}{2}$.

x	$\frac{1}{2}x + 2$
0	2
1	$2\frac{1}{2}$
2	3
3	$3\frac{1}{2}$
4	4

From the graph, it is about $1\frac{1}{2}$.

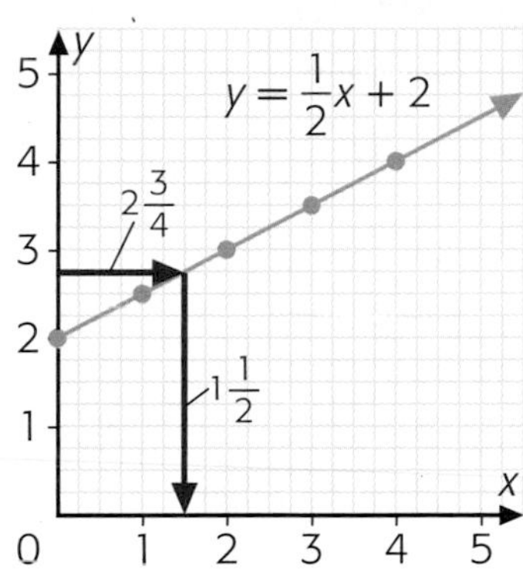

From the equation, it is exactly $1\frac{1}{2}$.

$$2\frac{3}{4} = \frac{1}{2}x + 2$$
$$2\frac{3}{4} - 2 = \frac{1}{2}x + 2 - 2$$
$$\frac{3}{4} = \frac{1}{2}x$$
$$2\left(\frac{3}{4}\right) = 2\left(\frac{1}{2}x\right)$$
$$x = \frac{6}{4} \text{ or } 1\frac{1}{2}$$

Need to Know

- The solution to a linear equation is the x- or y-coordinate of a point on the graph of its corresponding linear relation. Sometimes you have to extend the graph beyond given points to solve the equation.
- To check a solution, substitute it into the equation and evaluate. If both sides work out to the same number, the solution is correct.

For example, check that $x = 5$ is a solution to $3 = \frac{1}{5}x + 2$.

$$\frac{1}{5}(5) + 2 = 1 + 2 = 3$$

Checking

1. Write an equation you can graph to estimate the solution of each linear relation.

a) $4.25x - 3 = 9.5$ **b)** $-2 = 5 - \left(\frac{1}{4}\right)x$

2. Estimate a solution to each equation in question 1.

3. A cell phone company charges a flat fee of \$9 per month plus \$0.15 per minute. How many minutes can you buy for \$20 each month?

Practising

4. Estimate a solution to each equation.

a) $-3x - 11 = 7$ **c)** $\frac{2}{3}x + 9 = 4$ **e)** $3 - 2t = -5.5$

b) $1.5 = 2.75x - 4$ **d)** $\frac{-2}{9}x + 1 = \frac{2}{3}$ **f)** $3(x - 7) = -8$

5. Verify each solution.

a) $2a - 5 = 12; a = 3$

b) $12 - 4c = 20; c = -2$

c) $\frac{1}{3} = 3 - 5x; x = \frac{8}{15}$

d) $7y + 2 = -30; y = -4$

6. Nick solved two equations as shown.

A. $4w + 8 = 22$

w	4*w* + 8
1	12
2	16
3	20
4	24

The solution is $w = 3.5$, since 22 is halfway between 20 and 24.

B. $3 - 5x = 1$

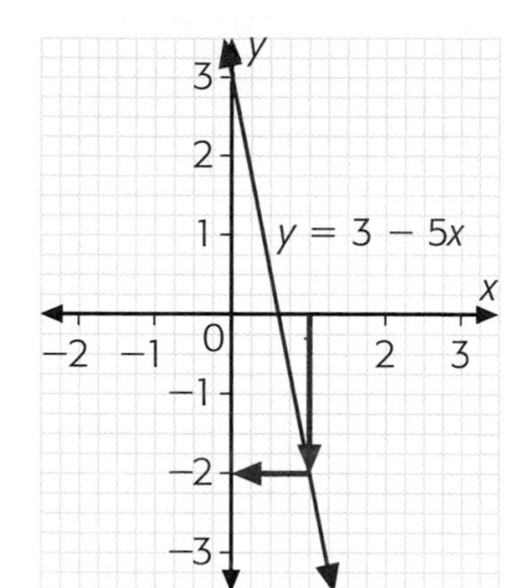

The solution is $x = -2$.

a) Verify each solution using another method.

b) Correct any errors Nick might have made. Explain.

7. To cater a party, Party Planners charges $25 per guest with a minimum of 50 guests, but does not charge for the first 10 guests.

a) Create a linear relation for the cost to cater a party for n guests.

b) Graph your linear relation.

c) Determine the cost for 50 guests and for 75 guests.

d) Write an equation to determine how many people are at a party that costs $1500. Estimate the solution using the graph.

8. This graph shows Kim's earnings for hours worked.

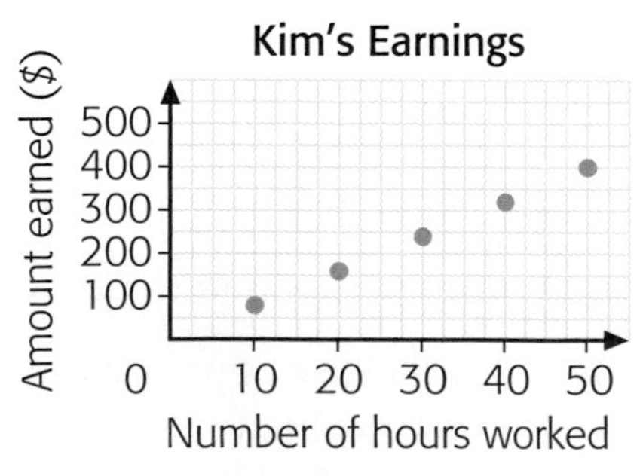

a) Write a linear relation to model the graph.

b) Suppose Kim earned $720. Write an equation you can solve to determine the number of hours she worked.

c) Kim worked for 90 h. Write an equation you can solve to determine her earnings.

d) How are the equations in parts b) and part c) alike and different?

e) Estimate each solution using the graph. Verify your solutions.

f) Solve each equation algebraically.

9. A passport to the Carnaval d'hiver is \$24 per person. School groups receive a free adult pass for every 10 students who attend. The parent-teacher committee has given \$500. How many students and adults can attend?

10. Multiple choice. A cell-phone company offers this plan:
- \$9.95/month
- the first 50 min free
- \$0.09/ minute after the first 50 min

Each month, after 50 min of airtime, the company uses the exact airtime to calculate the monthly bill. About how many minutes can you buy each month for \$40?

A. 495 **B.** 445 **C.** 335 **D.** 385

11. Multiple choice. A rectangular field 100 m long is enclosed by 500 m of fencing. Which equation can be used to determine the width, w, of the field?

A. $500 = 2(100) + w$ **C.** $500 = 100 + w$

B. $500 = 2(100) + 2w$ **D.** $500 = 100 + 2w$

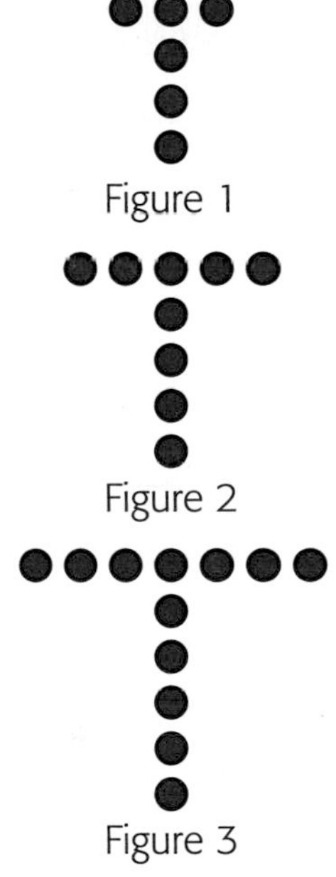

12. a) For the counter pattern shown at right, write an equation for the relation between figure n and the number of counters in it.

b) Determine the number of counters in Figure 12.

c) Determine which figure has exactly 60 counters.

d) Does any figure in this pattern have exactly 100 counters? Explain.

Closing

13. Compare the steps you would use to estimate the solutions to $\frac{x}{3} - 5 = \frac{13}{3}$ and $2x - 5 = 21$ using either a table of values or graph. How are they alike and different?

Extending

14. Estimate the solutions to the following equations.

a) $\frac{(x + 1)}{5} - 2x = 12$

b) $\frac{-3}{5}(x + 1) + 2\left(x - \frac{1}{2}\right) = 0$

c) $4x - 3 = 7x + 1$

15. The equation $ax + \frac{4}{5} = 9$ has the solution $x = 3$. What is the value of a?

5.4 Solving Linear Equations Using Inverse Operations

GOAL

Solve equations by working backward.

LEARN ABOUT the Math

Francis delivered paper to a recycling centre. His net earnings were $34.20.

Francis's Cost ($)	Francis's Earnings ($)
$12.00 for gas	$82.50/t of paper

? How much paper did Francis deliver?

A. Explain why you can determine Francis's earnings for x tonnes of paper using the expression $82.50x - 12.00$.

B. Evaluate the expression in part A for 1 t of paper. What does this value mean?

C. List the operations you used in part B, in the order you used them.

D. Explain why you can determine the amount of paper Francis delivered using the equation $82.50x - 12.00 = 34.20$.

E. What operation will **isolate** the term $82.50x$? Perform this operation and record an **equivalent equation**.

F. Isolate the variable x and solve the equation.

isolate

to show the same equation in an equivalent way so that the variable or term is alone on one side

equivalent equation

an equation that has exactly the same solution as another; e.g., $y = 3x + 4$ and $2y = 6x + 8$ are equivalent equations.

Reflecting

G. Why is "working backward" a good name for the process used to solve the equation?

H. How does evaluating $82.50x - 12.00$ for $x = 1$ help to determine the **inverse operations** needed to solve the equation $82.50x - 12.00 = 34.20$?

I. Would the solution be affected if you did the inverse operations in a different order? Explain.

inverse operations

operations that undo, or reverse, each other; e.g., subtraction is the inverse of addition; division is the inverse of multiplication.

WORK WITH the Math

EXAMPLE 1 | Solving an equation using inverse operations

Solve $\frac{2w}{3} + 14 = 9$.

Luc's Solution

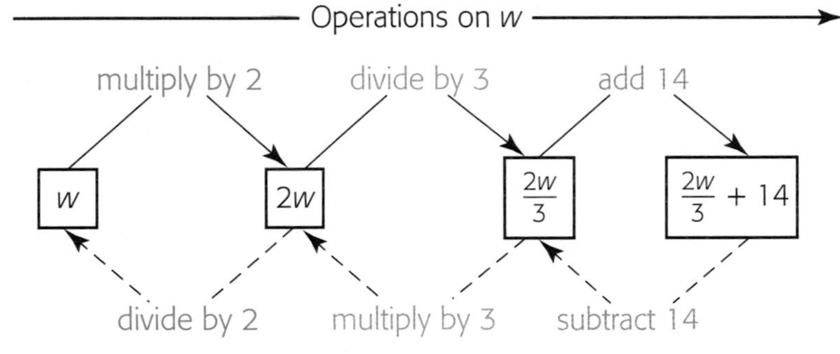

I used a diagram to show the operations I would use if I substituted a value into $\frac{2w}{3} + 14$.

Working backward, I listed the inverse operations I need to use to solve the equation.

$$\frac{2w}{3} + 14 - 14 = 9 - 14$$
$$\frac{2w}{3} = -5$$

I used my diagram to determine which operation to do first. I isolated the term $\frac{2w}{3}$ by subtracting 14. I did the same thing to both sides, so I knew that the original and new equations would be equivalent.

$$\frac{2w}{3} \times 3 = -5 \times 3$$
$$2w = -15$$

I multiplied both sides of the equation by 3 and got another equivalent equation.

$$2w \div 2 = -15 \div 2$$
$$w = \frac{-15}{2} \text{ or } -7.5$$

I divided by 2 to isolate w and solve the equation.

Check:

Left side:	Right side:
$\frac{2w}{3} + 14$	9
$\rightarrow \frac{2(-7.5)}{3} + 14$	
$= -5 + 14$	
$= 9$	

I substituted to verify the answer.

Both sides were the same, so I knew it was correct.

Zachary's Solution

$$\frac{2w}{3} + 14 = 9$$

I read the equation aloud and realized that the variable *w* was divided by 3.

$$3\left(\frac{2w}{3} + 14\right) = 3(9)$$

Multiplication is the inverse of division, so I multiplied both sides by 3.

$$3 \times \frac{2w}{3} + 3 \times 14 = 27$$

I used the distributive property on the left side of the equation.

$$2w + 42 = 27$$

I created an equivalent equation.

$$2w + 42 - 42 = 27 - 42$$
$$2w = -15$$

I subtracted 42 to isolate the variable term.

$$2w \div 2 = -15 \div 2$$
$$w = -7.5$$

The inverse of multiplying by 2 is dividing by 2.

Check:

Left side:

$\frac{2w}{3} + 14$

$\rightarrow \frac{2(-7.5)}{3} + 14$

$= \frac{-15}{3} + 14$

$= -5 + 14$

$= 9$

Right side:

9

I verified the answer by substituting it for the variable in the equation.

It worked out to be the same value as the right side of the equation, so I knew that it was correct.

EXAMPLE 2 | Connecting a real-life situation to solving equations

Noreen works for a special effects company. She is building a scale model of the Lion's Gate Bridge in Vancouver, British Columbia, to be used for a movie. The distance between the vertical supports on the bridge is 473 m, and those towers are 111 m tall. She needs to make the towers on her model 2 m tall. Determine the distance between the two towers in the model to one decimal place.

Erin's Solution

Let x represent the distance between the towers on the model.

I used a variable to represent the unknown distance.

$$\frac{\text{height of tower (actual)}}{\text{height of tower (model)}} = \frac{\text{distance between towers (actual)}}{\text{distance between towers (model)}}$$

$$\frac{111}{2} = \frac{473}{x}, \text{ where } x \neq 0.$$

I wrote a proportion to compare the measurements of the actual bridge to the measurements of the model. Then I substituted the measures that I knew. I indicated that *x* can't be equal to zero. If it were zero, the equation would have no meaning.

$$x\left(\frac{111}{2}\right) = x\left(\frac{473}{x}\right)$$
$$\frac{111x}{2} = 473$$

I multiplied by x on both sides so that the variable would be in the numerator.

$$2\left(\frac{111x}{2}\right) = 2(473)$$
$$111x = 946$$

I multiplied by 2 on both sides.

$$111x \div 111 = 946 \div 111$$
$$x \doteq 8.5$$

I divided by 111 on both sides to isolate the variable.

The distance between the towers in the model must be about 8.5 m.

In Summary

Key Ideas

- Using inverse operations, you can isolate individual terms or variables to solve linear equations.
- You can create equivalent equations by applying the same operation to both sides of an equation.

Need to Know

- You can figure out which inverse operations to use by
  - reading the equation
  - noting the operations you would use to estimate the solution in a diagram or list
- There is usually more than one way to solve an equation using inverse operations. As long as you perform the same operations on both sides of the equation, the solution will be correct.
- You can verify your solution by substituting it into the original equation. The solution is correct if both sides work out to the same number.

Checking

1. List the inverse operations and the order in which you would apply them to isolate the variable in each equation.

a) $-3x + 2 = 15$ **b)** $12.4x - 3.2 = 21.5$ **c)** $\frac{x}{2} + 5 = 11$

2. Solve each equation in question 1. Show all of your steps.

3. An author is paid a $5000 advance, plus $1.25 for every book sold.

a) Write an equation for the number of books the author needs to sell to earn $10 000.

b) Solve the equation using inverse operations. Show all of your steps.

c) Verify your solution.

Practising

4. List the operations you would use to isolate each variable.
   a) $6b - 10 = -2$
   b) $2.5c + 1.0 = 1.5$
   c) $3.5f = 10$
   d) $\frac{x}{12} = -100$
   e) $-2e = 6$
   f) $\frac{-3}{x} = -2,\ x \neq 0.$
5. Solve each equation in question 4. Show all of your steps and verify each solution.
6. The relation $C = 8.00 + 0.50T$ is the cost of a pizza in dollars, where T is the number of toppings.
   a) Write an equation to represent a $10 order with T toppings.
   b) Determine the number of toppings on a $10 pizza. Show all of your steps.
   c) How would your equation change if the first two toppings were free?

7. A submarine that is 600 m deep begins rising at 4 m/s.
   a) Write a linear relation to show the relationship between depth and time.
   b) Write an equation you can solve to determine when the submarine will be 486 m deep.
   c) Solve the equation. Show all of your steps.
   d) Verify your solution.
8. Caroline and Marc were asked to solve $8 - 4d = 52$. Caroline divided both sides by 4, and then subtracted 2. Marc subtracted 8, and then divided by 4.
   a) Solve the equation using Caroline's strategy.
   b) Solve the equation using Marc's strategy.
   c) Explain why Marc and Caroline both got the same solution.
9. Solve each equation.
   a) $\frac{x}{4} + 1 = 3$
   b) $\frac{x}{2} - 10 = 3$
   c) $5 - \frac{y}{3} = 3$
   d) $\frac{5}{b} = -1,\ b \neq 0.$
   e) $\frac{w}{3} + 5 = 1$
   f) $3 - \frac{d}{6} = -1$
10. **Multiple choice.** A hot-air balloon that is 500 m high begins descending at 60 m/min. How long will it take the balloon to reach a height of 20 m?
    A. 6 min **B.** 8 min **C.** 13 min **D.** 22 min
11. **Multiple choice.** Liz gave Jane this problem: "When you divide me by 7, and then add 13, you get 32. What number am I?" Which equation solves the problem?
    A. $\frac{x}{7} + 13 = 32$
    B. $\frac{x}{7} = 32 + 13$
    C. $x = \frac{32}{7} + 13$
    D. $x = \frac{32 + 13}{7}$

12. Solve each equation.

a) $3(x + 1) = 12$ c) $\frac{w + 3}{4} = 2$ e) $\frac{2a + 3}{3} = 5$

b) $2(x - 4) = 4$ d) $\frac{y - 5}{3} = 6$ f) $-2 = \frac{5}{2c}$, $c \neq 0$.

13. Kahlil's Restaurant charges $22.95 for brunch, but lets one person eat for free if there are two or more people at a table. To figure out how many people attended the Sunday brunch, Kahlil collected these data.

a) Why is it reasonable for Kahlil to use $22.95(x - 1) = T$ to determine the number of people at each table? What do the variables x and T represent?

b) Write and solve an equation for each table.

c) How many people in total sat at the five tables?

Table Number	Bill Total ($)
1	137.70
2	68.85
3	160.65
4	91.80
5	91.80

14. The relation between Celsius and Fahrenheit is $C = \frac{5}{9}(F - 32)$.

a) Determine what Celsius temperature is equivalent to 58 °F.

b) List the operations you used in part a).

c) List the inverse operations you would use to isolate F.

d) Determine what Fahrenheit temperature is equivalent to 25 °C.

Closing

15. When you use an inverse operation to isolate a variable, why can you say that the equation you get at each step is equivalent to the original one?

Extending

16. Which equation is equivalent to $\frac{-3}{x} + 1 = \frac{2}{5}$? Assume that $x \neq 0$.

A. $\frac{3}{x} - 1 = \frac{2}{5}$ **C.** $\frac{-3 + 1x}{x} = \frac{2}{5x}$

B. $-3 + 1x = \frac{2x}{5}$ **D.** $\frac{-x}{3} + 1 = \frac{5}{2}$

17. Solve the following equations, where $x \neq 0$.

a) $\frac{-3}{x} + 1 = \frac{2}{5}$ c) $0 = \frac{5}{x}$

b) $1 + \frac{4}{x} = 7$ d) $-2\frac{1}{5} - \frac{1}{3x} = -2$

18. Determine the value of x in each diagram.

a)

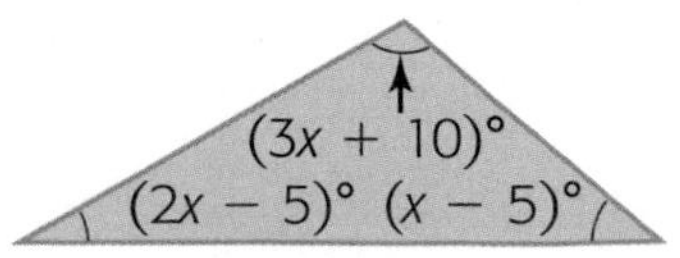

b)

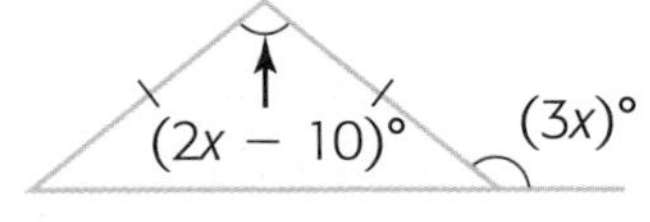

Mid-Chapter Review

FREQUENTLY ASKED Questions

Study | *Aid*

- See Lesson 5.1, Examples 2 and 3.
- Try Mid-Chapter Review Questions 1, 2, and 8.

Q: How can you determine if a pattern or situation represents a linear relation?

A: Graph the values of the situation. If they lie on a straight line, then the relation is linear. Also, determine the rate of change. If it is constant, the relation is linear.

Study | *Aid*

- See Lesson 5.2, Examples 2 and 3.
- Try Mid-Chapter Review questions 3, 4, and 5.

Q: How can you interpolate or extrapolate using a graph?

A: To interpolate a value between two known points, draw a line through the points and use it to estimate the value.

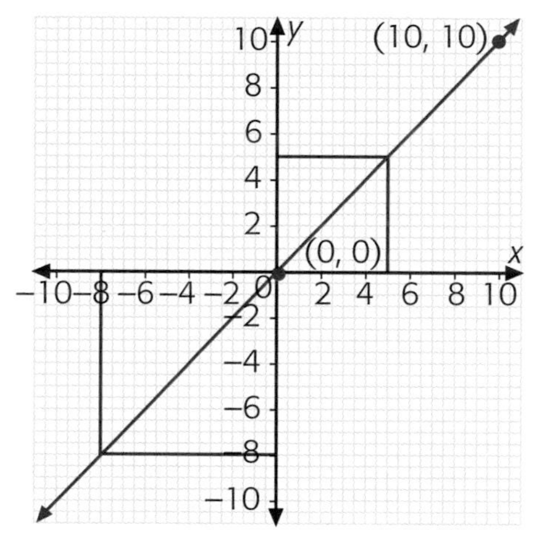

To extrapolate a value beyond two known values, extend the graph, and use it to predict the value. For example, if you know that $(0, 0)$ and $(10, 10)$ are points in a linear relation, then you can interpolate that $y = 5$ when $x = 5$ and extrapolate that $y = -8$ when $x = -8$.

Study | *Aid*

- See Lesson 5.3, Example 1 and Lesson 5.4, Example 1.
- Try Mid-Chapter Review questions 6, 9, and 11.

Q: How can you solve a linear equation?

A1: You can estimate using a table of values. For example, the solution to $2x + 3 = 8$ is about 2.5.

x	$2x + 3$
1	5
2	7
3	9

Since 8 is between 7 and 9, the solution must be between 2 and 3.

A2: You can estimate using a graph of the corresponding linear relation. For example, the solution to $2x + 3 = 8$ is about 2.5.

Graph $y = 2x + 3$.

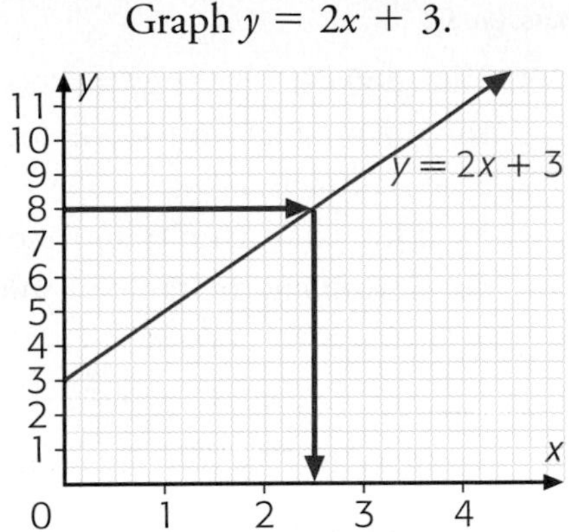

Draw a horizontal line from $y = 8$ to the graph. Then, draw a vertical line from the graph to the x-axis.

A3: You can determine the exact solution using inverse operations. Identify the operations used in the equation. Remember to follow the order of operations. Then, isolate the variable by undoing each operation in the reverse order. Keep the equations equivalent by performing the same operation on both sides of the equation. For example, the solution to $2x + 3 = 8$ is 2.5.

$$2x + 3 = 8$$
$$2x + 3 - 3 = 8 - 3 \quad \text{Subtract 3.}$$
$$2x = 5$$
$$2x \div 2 = 5 \div 2 \quad \text{Divide by 2 to isolate } x.$$
$$x = 2.5$$

Practice

Lesson 5.1

1. Which of these patterns represent a linear relation? Explain how you know.

	Figure 1	**Figure 2**	**Figure 3**
Pattern 1	◆	◆ ◆	◆ ◆ ◆
Pattern 2	◆	◆	◆
Pattern 3	◆ ◆ ◆ ◆	◆ ◆ ◆ ◆ ◆ ◆	◆ ◆ ◆ ◆ ◆ ◆ ◆ ◆

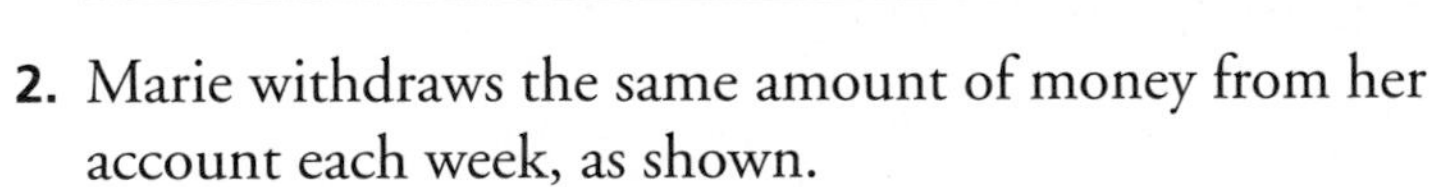

2. Marie withdraws the same amount of money from her account each week, as shown.
   a) What does the ordered pair $(1, 1200)$ mean?
   b) Estimate the amount of money in Marie's account in week 3.
   c) Predict the amount of money in Marie's account in week 8.

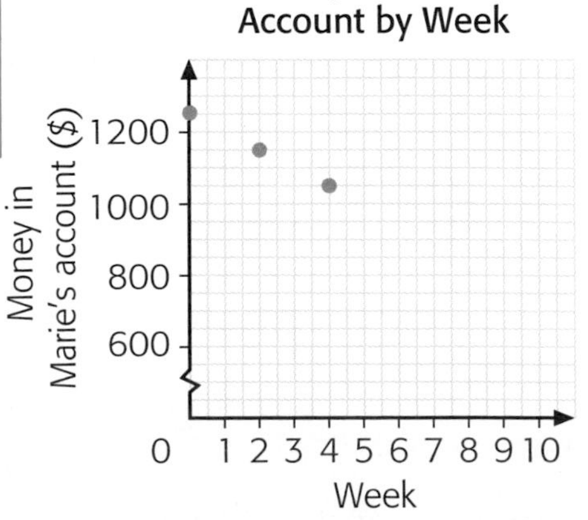

Lesson 5.2

3. Kim downloads songs for a one-time fee of \$10 plus \$1.50 for each song. An equation for the cost, C, in dollars to download s songs is $C = 1.50s + 10$.

a) Draw a picture to represent this situation.

b) Complete the table of values.

s	0	2	4	6
C				

c) Graph this situation.

d) Determine the cost to download 5 songs.

e) Determine the number of songs Kim can download for \$75.

4. Match each situation with its graph.

a) A long distance phone call from a hotel room costs a flat rate of \$2 and \$0.25 per minute.

b) Florence pays \$2 per hour for dog sitting.

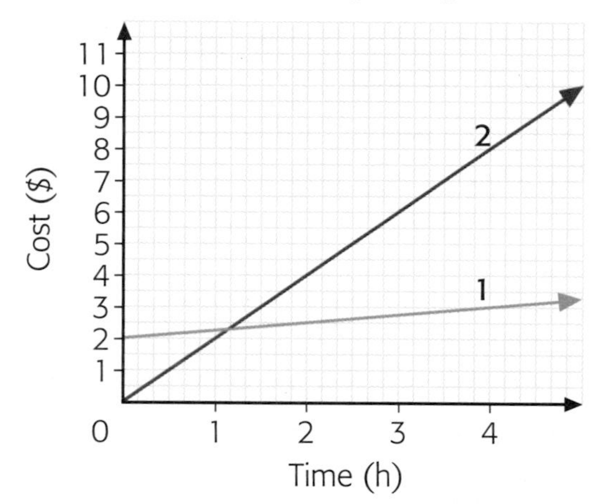

5. The circumference, C, of a circle with radius r is given by $C = 2\pi r$.

a) Graph this relation.

b) Estimate the circumference of a circle with a radius of 3 cm.

c) Estimate the radius of a circle with a circumference of 12 cm.

Lesson 5.3

6. Estimate a solution to each equation. Justify your estimate.

a) $-8 = 2x - 5$

b) $\frac{1}{3}x + 4 = 7$

c) $\frac{-3}{5} + \frac{1}{4}x = 8$

d) $\frac{9}{11} = 2 - 2x$

7. Verify each solution.

a) $2a + 7 = 12;\ a = 1$

b) $9 - 3c = 15;\ c = -2$

c) $\frac{1}{3} = 3 + 4x;\ x = \frac{8}{15}$

d) $7 - \frac{3}{5}y = -30;\ y = -25$

8. A submarine starts at sea level and descends 50 m every 5 min.

a) Make a table of values of the submarine's depth, using intervals of 5 min, up to 30 min.

b) Graph the submarine's depth using the table of values.

c) What patterns do you see in the table and the graph?

d) Suppose the submarine had started to descend from a depth of 219 m. What relation would model the submarine's location over time?

e) Write an equation to show how long the submarine would take to go from sea level to a depth of 428 m.

f) Solve this equation using your graph.

g) How does the equation connect to the graph?

Lesson 5.4

9. State whether you would solve each equation using a table of values, a graph, inverse operations, or some other method. Justify your choice. Solve and verify each equation.

a) $2x - 5 = 7$

b) $\frac{3}{5x} + \frac{4}{9} = \frac{10}{3}, x \neq 0.$

c) $-6 = \frac{3}{2} + \frac{3}{2x}, x \neq 0.$

d) $-2.1k + 5.6 = -20.2$

e) $-8.75z + 12.5 = 12.5$

f) $-501 + 3x = 27$

10. Amit joined a book club. The first six books are free, but after that he pays $8.98 per book.

a) Write an expression for the cost of b books.

b) How much would Amit pay for eight books?

c) Amit ordered some books for $53.88. Write, solve, and verify an equation to determine how many books he ordered.

11. Write an equivalent equation you can use to solve each equation. Solve and verify each equation.

a) $\frac{k}{3} + 1 = 4$

b) $\frac{x}{2} - 3 = 1\frac{1}{6}$

c) $\frac{7}{a} = 5, a \neq 0.$

d) $\left(-1\frac{2}{3}\right)g + \frac{7}{9} = 0$

e) $\frac{2}{3}h + \frac{1}{4} = 3\frac{1}{2}$

f) $\frac{3}{x} = \frac{2}{3}, x \neq 0.$

12. a) Create a situation or pattern that you can model using the linear relation $y = 3x + 6$.

b) Locate and interpret one point on the graph of the linear relation.

c) Are there any values that do not fit the relation? Explain.

5.5 Equation-Solving Strategies

GOAL

Solve equations that contain the variable in more than one place.

LEARN ABOUT the Math

Viktor has a 20 m roll of fencing to make a rectangular dog kennel. He has decided that the kennel must be 2 m longer than it is wide.

? How can Viktor determine the dimensions of the kennel?

EXAMPLE 1 Selecting a strategy to solve

Viktor's Solution

Let w represent the width of the kennel and $w + 2$ its length

I used the letter w to represent the width.

Since the length is 2 m longer than the width I used the expression $w + 2$ for the length.

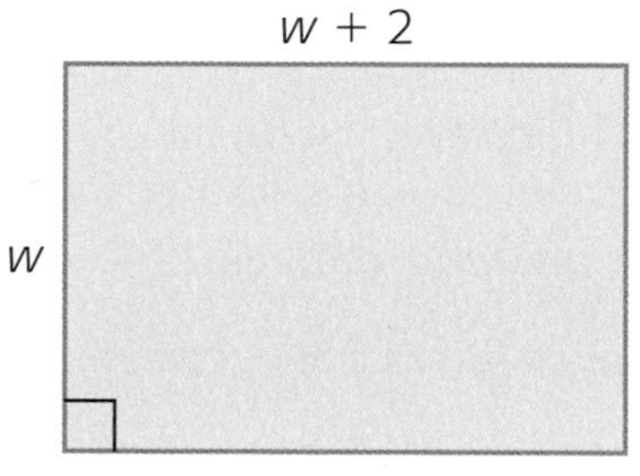

$P = 2(l + w)$
$\rightarrow 2(w + 2 + w)$

I drew a diagram of the kennel, then wrote the formula for the perimeter of a rectangle.

I substituted my expressions for length and width in the formula.

$20 = 2(w + 2 + w)$

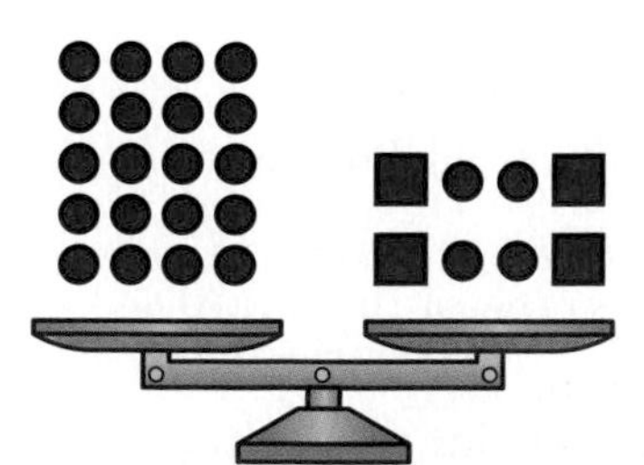

The perimeter of the rectangle equals the 20 m of fencing I have. I substituted this for P in the perimeter equation.

I used red cubes to represent w and round counters for numbers.

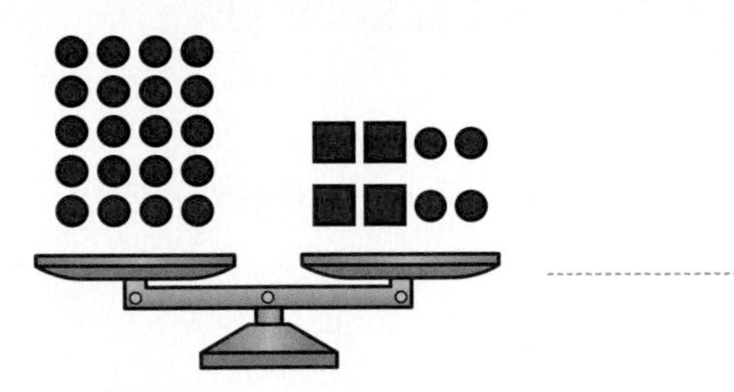

$20 = 2(2w + 2)$
$20 = 4w + 4$

Looking at my model I reasoned that I could add the two variables inside the brackets.

I also noticed that the right side of the equation in the model was $4w + 4$ and that this was the result of multiplying 2 by $2w + 2$ in the equation.

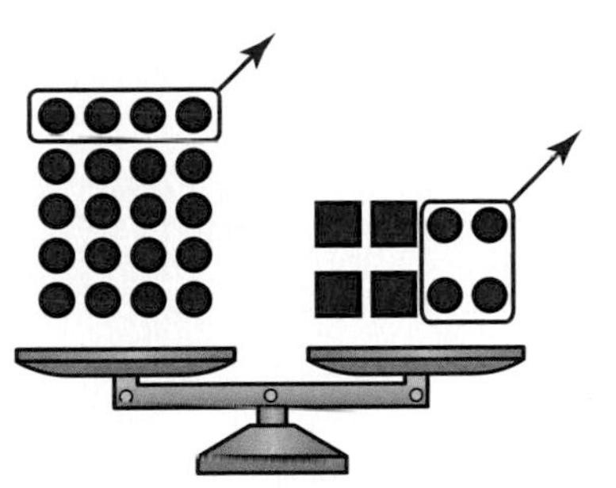

$20 - 4 = 4w + 4 - 4$
$16 = 4w$

To isolate w, I removed 4 red counters from both sides of the model.

This is the same thing as subtracting 4 from both sides of the equation.

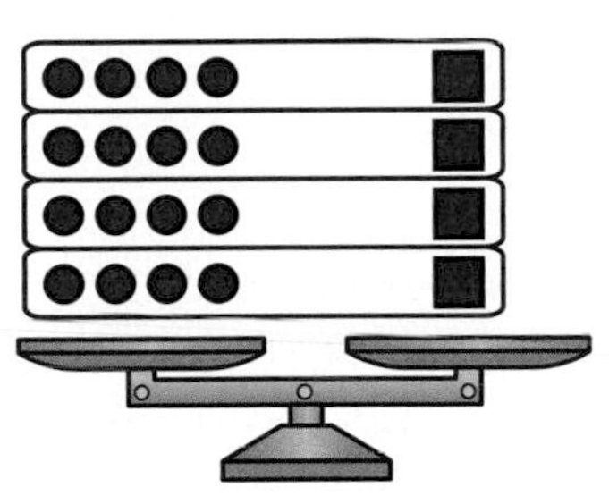

$16 \div 4 = 4w \div 4$
$4 = w$

4 w cubes are worth 16 counters. Each w cube must be worth 4, so $w = 4$.

This is the same as dividing by 4 on both sides of the equation.

Check:

Left Side	Right Side
20	$2(w + 2 + w)$
	$\rightarrow 2(4 + 2 + 4)$
	$= 2(10)$
	$= 20$

I verified my solution by substituting 4 for w in the original equation.

The left and right sides are equal, so the solution is correct.

The dimensions of my kennel must be 4 m by 6 m.

I added 2 to the width to determine the length. My answer seems reasonable since the perimeter of this rectangle $(4 + 6 + 4 + 6)$ equals the 20 m of fencing available.

Reflecting

A. How did Viktor deal with the brackets in his equation?

B. How is solving an equation with the variable in more than one place like solving equations with the variable in only one place?

C. Could he have chosen another strategy to solve the problem? Explain.

WORK WITH the Math

EXAMPLE 2 | Solving an equation with variables on both sides

Solve $4 - 2x = -5x - 8$.

Zachary's Solution: Using a model

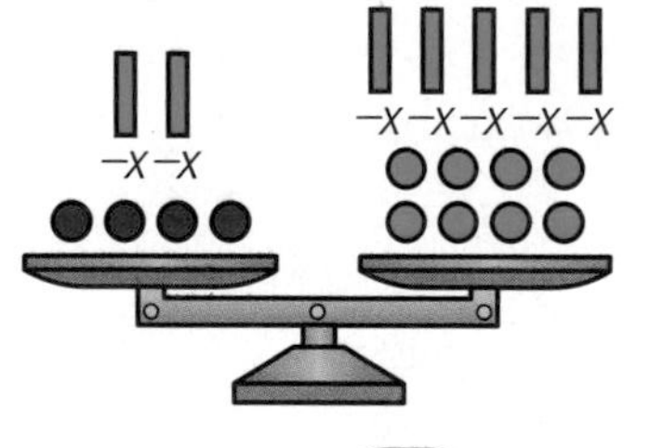

I used a balance scale to represent the equation and inverse operations to solve it.

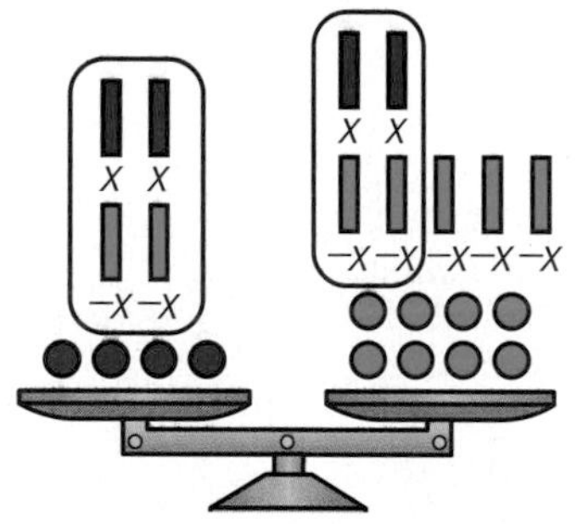

$4 - 2x + 2x = -5x - 8 + 2x$

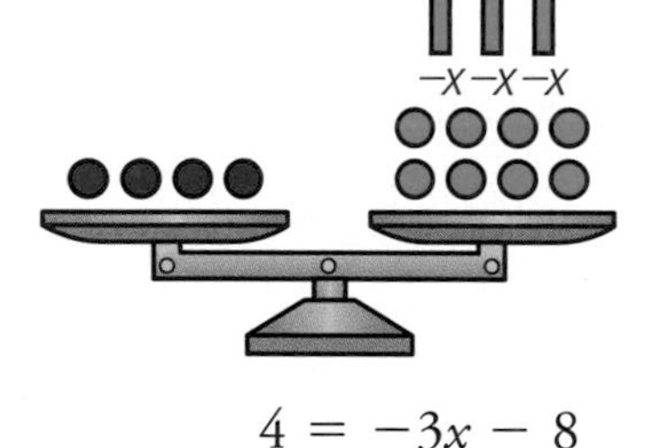

$4 = -3x - 8$

I added $2x$ to both sides to group the variables on one side of the equal sign. The circled tiles have a value of zero.

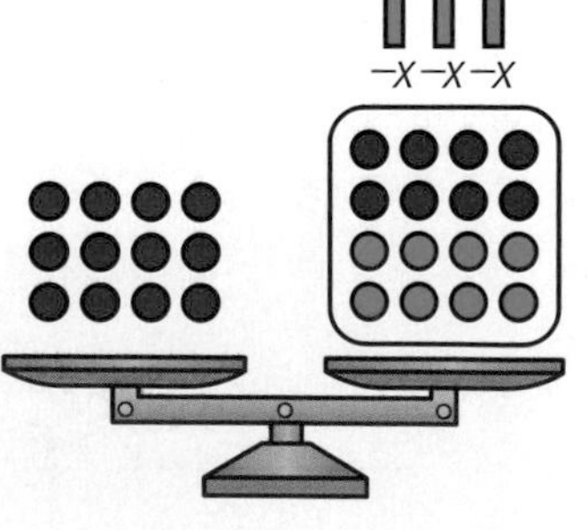

$4 + 8 = -3x - 8 + 8$

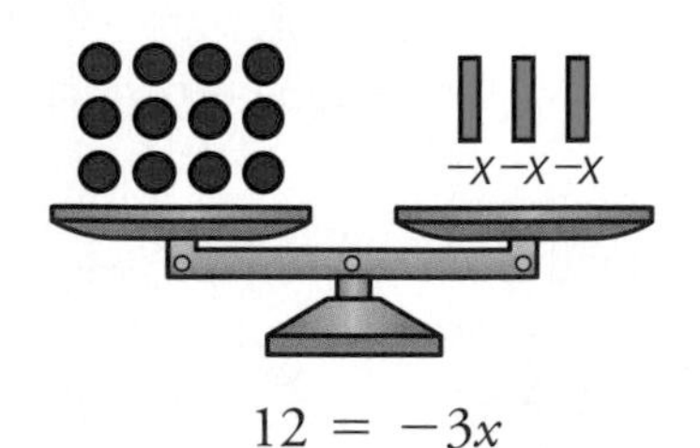

$12 = -3x$

I added 8 to both sides to group the numbers on one side of the equal sign and isolate the variable. The circled counters have a value of zero.

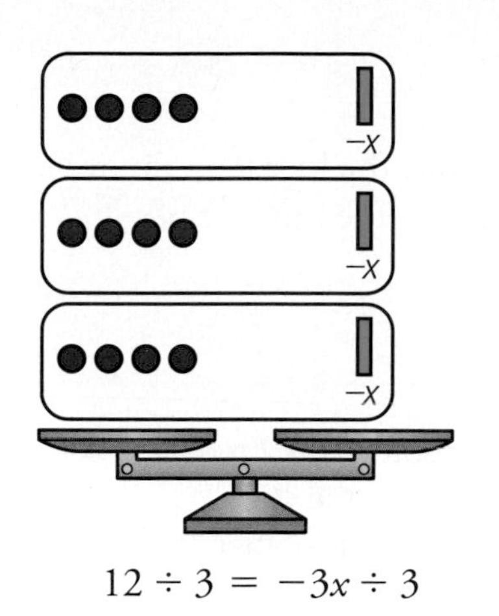

$12 \div 3 = -3x \div 3$

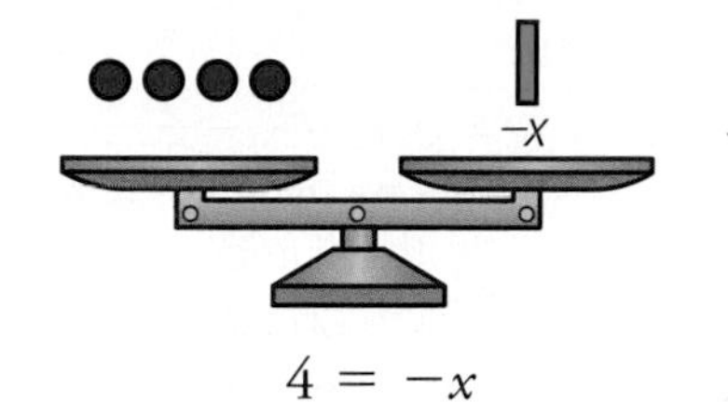

$4 = -x$

I made 3 equal groups on each side to determine the value of $-x$.

If $-x = +4$, then $+x = -4$.
The solution is $x = -4$.

Check:

I verified my answer by substituting the value into both sides of the equation.

Left Side:	Right Side:
$4 - 2x$	$-5x - 6$
$\rightarrow 4 - 2(-4)$	$\rightarrow -5(-4) - 8$
$= 12$	$= 12$

LS = RS

Rani's Solution: Using Algebra

$$4 - 2x = -5x - 8$$
$$4 - 2x + 5x = -5x - 8 + 5x$$
$$4 + 3x = -8$$

I decided to collect the variables on the left side of the equation. I added $5x$ to both sides since $5x$ is the opposite of $-5x$.

$$4 + 3x - 4 = -8 - 4$$
$$3x = -12$$

I subtracted 4 from both sides to isolate the variable term.

$$3x \div 3 = -12 \div 3$$
$$x = -4$$

I divided both sides by 3.

Check:

I verified my answer by substituting the value into both sides of the equation.

Left Side:	Right Side:
$4 - 2x$	$-5x - 6$
$\rightarrow 4 - 2(-4)$	$\rightarrow -5(-4) - 8$
$= 12$	$= 12$

LS = RS

EXAMPLE 3 | Connecting a real-life problem to solving equations

Café Star and Tim's Café are Internet cafés. Café Star charges 85¢ a minute, with the first ten minutes free. Tim's Café charges 60¢ a minute, with the first five minutes free. Determine the number of minutes of Internet use when both cafés charge the same amount.

Erin's Solution

Café Star: $C = 0.85(n - 10)$
Tim's Café: $C = 0.60(n - 5)$

$$0.85(n - 10) = 0.60(n - 5)$$

I wrote linear relations for both cafés, in which n is the number of minutes and C is the cost.
I reasoned that if the costs are equal, then the expressions should be equal.

$$0.85(n - 10) = 0.60(n - 5)$$
$$0.85(n) - 0.85(10) = 0.60(n) - 0.60(5)$$
$$0.85n - 8.5 = 0.6n - 3$$

I simplified each side using the **distributive property**.

$$0.85n - 8.5 - 0.6n = 0.6n - 3 - 0.6n$$
$$0.25n - 8.5 = -3$$
$$0.25n - 8.5 + 8.5 = -3 + 8.5$$
$$0.25n = 5.5$$

I used inverse operations to collect the variable terms on the left side.
I added 8.5 to collect the constants.

$$0.25n \div 0.25 = 5.5 \div 0.25$$
$$n = 22$$

I solved for n by dividing both sides by 0.25.

Café Star:
$C = 0.85(n - 10)$
$\rightarrow 0.85(22 - 10)$
$= 10.20$

Tim's Café:
$C = 0.60(n - 5)$
$\rightarrow 0.60(22 - 5)$
$= 10.20$

I verified my answer.

The cafés charge the same amount for 22 min of Internet time.

EXAMPLE 4 | Solving an equation involving rational coefficients

Solve $\frac{1}{2}x + \frac{3}{4} = x - \frac{1}{2}$

Luc's Solution

$$\frac{1}{2}x + \frac{3}{4} = x - \frac{1}{2}$$

I decided to get an equivalent equation with integer coefficients and constants. I knew that I could multiply by 4 or any multiple of 4 since the denominators in the equation are all factors of 4.

$$4\left(\frac{1}{2}x + \frac{3}{4}\right) = 4\left(x - \frac{1}{2}\right)$$

I expanded using the distributive property.

$$4\left(\frac{1}{2}x\right) + 4\left(\frac{3}{4}\right) = 4(x) + 4\left(\frac{-1}{2}\right)$$
$$2x + 3 = 4x - 2$$
$$2x + 3 - 3 = 4x - 2 - 3$$
$$2x = 4x - 5$$

I got an equation with variables and constants on both sides.
I used inverse operations and subtracted 3 from both sides of the equation.

$$2x - 4x = 4x - 5 - 4x$$
$$-2x = -5$$

I reasoned that subtracting $4x$ from both sides would give me an equivalent equation with the variable term on the left side of the equation.

$$-2x \div (-2) = -5 \div (-2)$$
$$x = \frac{5}{2}$$

I solved for x.

Check:

Left Side	Right Side
$\frac{1}{2}x + \frac{3}{4}$	$x - \frac{1}{2}$
$\rightarrow \frac{1}{2}\left(\frac{5}{2}\right) + \frac{3}{4}$	$\rightarrow \frac{5}{2} - \frac{1}{2}$
$= \frac{5}{4} + \frac{3}{4}$	$= \frac{4}{2}$
$= \frac{8}{4}$	$= 2$
$= 2$	

I verified the solution by entering $\frac{5}{2}$ into the left and right sides.

Since the left side and right side both gave the same result, I knew my solution was correct.

In Summary

Key Idea

- You can solve an equation that contains the variable in more than one place using the same strategies as you would to solve an equation that contains the variable in only one place.

Need to Know

- You can use these methods to simplify an equation to make it easier to solve.

If an equation has fractional coefficients or constants, you can use a common denominator to write an equivalent equation with integer coefficients.

Solve:

$$\frac{1}{2}x + \frac{2}{3} = \frac{1}{4}$$

$$12\left(\frac{1}{2}x + \frac{2}{3}\right) = 12\left(\frac{1}{4}\right)$$

$$6x + 8 = 3$$

You can simplify an equation that contains brackets using the distributive property.

Solve:

$$2.8(x - 3) = -1.3(x + 2)$$

$$2.8x - 8.4 = -1.3x - 2.6$$

You can collect like terms on one side of an equation before using inverse operations.

Solve:

$$x + 3x + 4 + 2 = 8$$

$$4x + 6 = 8$$

- You can check your solution to any equation by substituting the value in each side of the equation and calculating the result. If you get the same result on both sides, then your solution is correct.

Checking

1. Solve using inverse operations.

a) $2x + 3x - 5 = 10$ **b)** $2x + 4 = 4x - 2$

2. Florence was asked to determine the dimensions of a rectangle with a perimeter of 44 cm and a width 3 cm less than its length. She drew a diagram as shown.

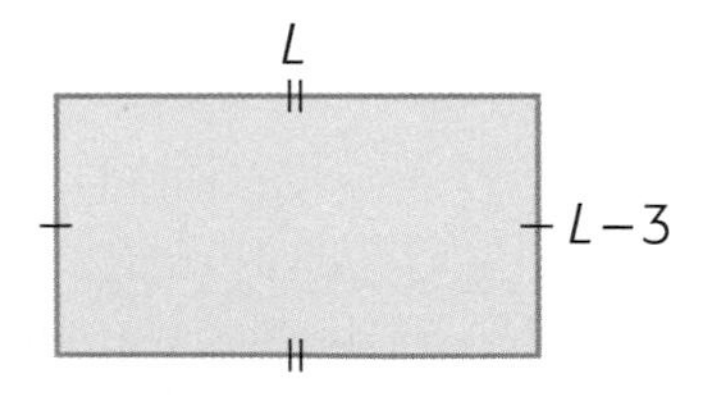

a) Florence labelled the width "$L - 3$" instead of using another variable. Why is this reasonable?

b) Write an equation to represent the perimeter of the rectangle.

c) Determine the dimensions of the rectangle.

Practising

3. Explain the reasoning in each solution step.

a)
$$\begin{aligned} 2x + 8 &= 4x - 18 \\ 2x + 8 - 2x &= 4x - 18 - 2x \quad \text{Step A} \\ 8 &= 2x - 18 \\ 8 + 18 &= 2x - 18 + 18 \quad \text{Step B} \\ 26 &= 2x \\ \frac{26}{2} &= \frac{2x}{2} \quad \text{Step C} \\ 13 &= x \end{aligned}$$

b)
$$\begin{aligned} \frac{1}{2}x + \frac{2}{3} &= 5 \\ 6 \times \left(\frac{1}{2}x + \frac{2}{3}\right) &= 5 \times 6 \quad \text{Step A} \\ 3x + 4 &= 30 \\ 3x + 4 - 4 &= 30 - 4 \quad \text{Step B} \\ 3x &= 26 \\ \frac{3x}{3} &= \frac{26}{3} \quad \text{Step C} \\ x &= 8\frac{2}{3} \end{aligned}$$

4. Explain why the equations in each group are equivalent.

a) $5x + 8 = 2(2x - 3)$

$5x + 8 = 4x - 6$

$5x - 4x = -6 - 8$

b) $\frac{x}{4} + 5 = \frac{1}{3}$

$\frac{3x}{12} + \frac{60}{12} = \frac{4}{12}$

$3x + 60 = 4$

c) $5x - 8 = 12$

$\frac{5x}{6} - \frac{4}{3} = 2$

$\frac{5x}{6} - \frac{8}{6} = \frac{12}{6}$

5. Solve each equation. Verify each solution.

a) $5x + 24 = 2x$

b) $2k = 4k - 15$

c) $-4x - 1 = -3x + 5$

d) $2x - 3x + 6 = 7 - x + 2$

e) $3b - 4 - 5b = -3b - 2$

f) $a + 2a + 3a - 6 = 7a - 6$

6. Write and solve the equation for each model.

a) **b)**

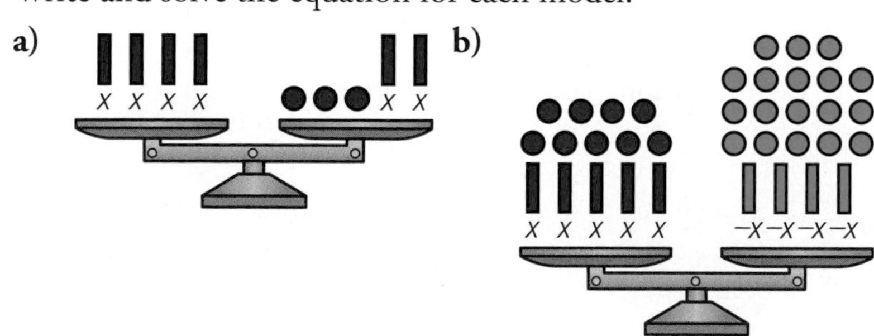

Reading Strategy

Finding Important Information

Find and record the essential information needed to solve the problem.

7. Choose which equations are equivalent to $2(x + 3) = 8x$. Justify your choices.

a) $x + 3 = 6x$
b) $x + 3 = 16x$
c) $x + 3 = 4x$
d) $-6x = -6$
e) $2x + 6 = 8x$
f) $x = 1$

8. A square has sides of length $2k - 1$ units. An equilateral triangle has sides of length $k + 2$ units. The square and the triangle have the same perimeter. What is the value of k?

9. Solve each equation. Verify each solution.

a) $3(x - 5) = 6$
b) $-5 = 5(3 + 2d)$
c) $-3(5 - 6m) = 39$
d) $2(x - 0.2) = 3x - 1.4$
e) $0.3(c + 5) = 0.4(1 - 2c)$
f) $0.04(x - 0.2) = -0.03(2x + 0.6)$

10. **Multiple choice.** A number, n, after being decreased by 5, is equal to 3 times the number plus another 1. Determine the number.

A. 4.5 **B.** -4 **C.** 3.5 **D.** -3

11. **Multiple choice.** The perimeter of a rectangle is 36 cm. The width is 5 cm less than the length. Determine the dimensions of the rectangle.

A. 11.5 cm by 6.5 cm
B. 12 cm by 6 cm
C. 10.25 cm by 5.25 cm
D. 20.5 cm by 15.5 cm

12. **Multiple choice.** George is three times as old as Sam. Five years from now, the sum of their ages will be 46. How old is George now?

A. 20 **B.** 30 **C.** 9 **D.** 27

13. Express each equation with integer coefficients and constants.

a) $\frac{3x}{4} + \frac{2}{3} = 2$
b) $\frac{1}{2} - \frac{x}{3} = \frac{1}{3}$
c) $\frac{2}{3} = 5 + x$
d) $\frac{x - 5}{4} + 1 = \frac{1}{2}$
e) $-16 = \frac{x}{5} + \frac{x}{3}$
f) $\frac{-2}{5}(x - 8) = 4$

14. Solve each equation. Verify each solution.

a) $\frac{x}{3} = 2$
b) $\frac{d}{4} + 3 = 2$
c) $\frac{x}{2} + \frac{x}{3} = 10$
d) $\frac{c}{3} - \frac{c}{4} = 3$
e) $\frac{3k}{5} - 6 = \frac{k}{3}$
f) $\frac{2x + 1}{3} = 5$

15. True or false? $q + 5 = 6$ is an equivalent equation to

$\frac{1}{3}\left(q + \frac{3}{5}\right) = \frac{8}{15}$. Justify your choice.

16. Write and solve an equation for each situation.

a) Eli takes 4 h to paint a room, while Mia takes 3 h to paint a room. How long would it take them to paint the room together?

b) Amir can put together a puzzle in 30 min, while Bob takes twice that long. How long will it take them to do it together?

c) A jet leaves Toronto for Vancouver, travelling at 600 km/h. At the same time, a jet leaves Vancouver for Toronto, travelling at 800 km/h. It is 3500 km from Toronto to Vancouver. How long after their departure will the jets pass each other?

17. a) Verify that $x = 2$ is a solution to

$$\frac{10 - 6x}{2} = 5 - 3x$$

b) Verify that $x = -5$ is a solution to

$$\frac{10 - 6x}{2} = 5 - 3x$$

c) Graph $y = \frac{10 - 6x}{2}$

and $y = 5 - 3x$

on the same axes. What do you notice?

d) What is the solution to the equation?

Closing

18. How can you convince someone that there are several ways to solve $\frac{1}{2}x + \frac{3}{4} = x - \frac{1}{2}$.

Reading Strategy

Evaluating

Prepare your arguments for every possible solution.

Extending

19. Solve each equation for the variable shown in red.

a) $x + y = 100$

b) $P = 2l + 2w$

c) $I = prt$

d) $ax + by = c$

e) $A(Bx - C) = D$

f) $s = 2\pi rh + 2\pi r^2$

20. Explain how to solve $A = \frac{1}{2}(b_1 + b_2)h$ for h.

21. Solve.

a) $\frac{3}{2x} + 1 = \frac{2}{x}$

b) $\frac{3}{4x} = \frac{1}{x + 1}$

5.6 Solve Problems Using Diagrams

YOU WILL NEED

- a ruler

GOAL

Use diagrams to solve problems about polygons.

LEARN ABOUT the Math

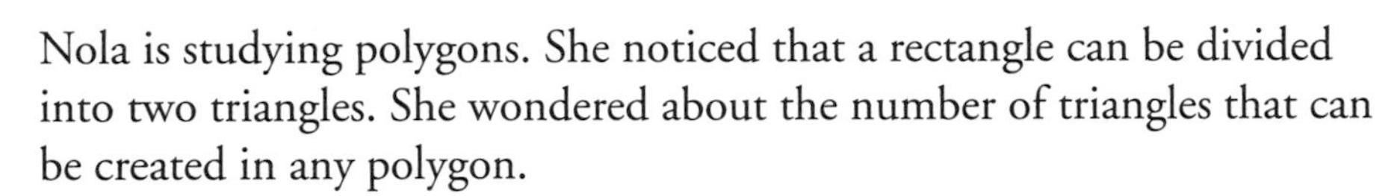

Nola is studying polygons. She noticed that a rectangle can be divided into two triangles. She wondered about the number of triangles that can be created in any polygon.

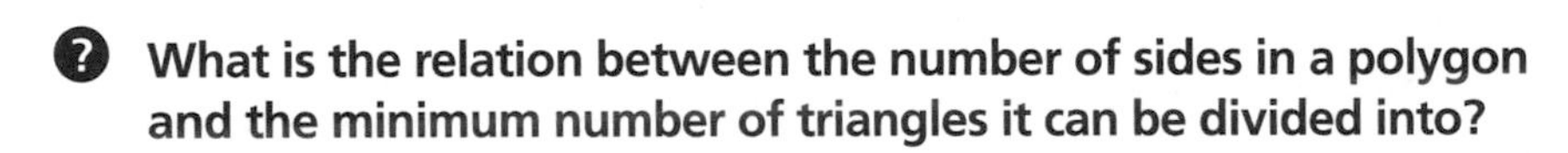

? What is the relation between the number of sides in a polygon and the minimum number of triangles it can be divided into?

EXAMPLE 1 | Using a diagram to solve a geometry problem

Nola's Solution

1. Understand the Problem
I need to see if there is a relation between the number of sides in a polygon and the number of triangles in it, and if there is a relation, express what it is.

2. Make a Plan
I'll draw polygons with different numbers of sides and divide them into triangles that have a common vertex. I'll make a table to compare the number of sides to the number of triangles.

3. Carry Out the Plan

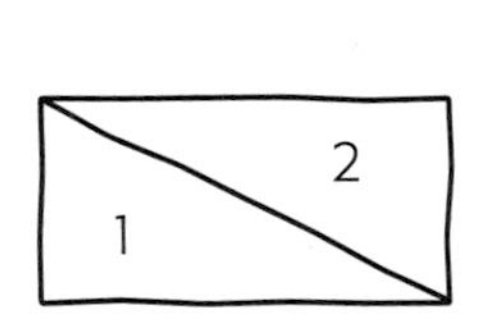

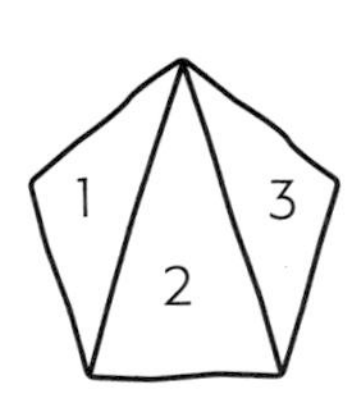

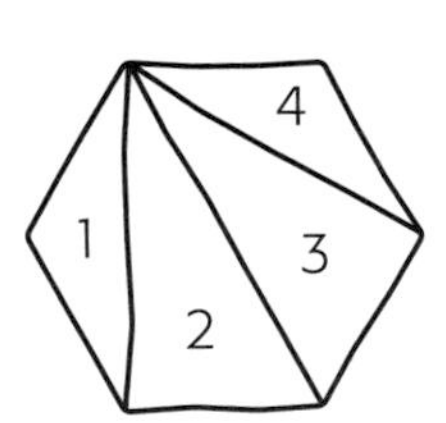

I drew a rectangle, pentagon, and hexagon and separated them into triangles. The rectangle has two triangles, the pentagon has three, and the hexagon has four.

Number of Sides	Number of Triangles
4	2
5	3
6	4

I recorded the results. There are always two fewer triangles than the number of sides.

S represents the number of sides, T represents the number of triangles.
$T = S - 2$

I wrote a relation between the number of sides and the number of triangles.

The number of triangles a polygon can be divided into is 2 less than the number of sides the polygon has.

4. Looking Back

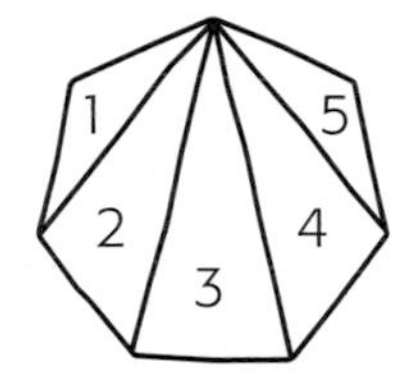

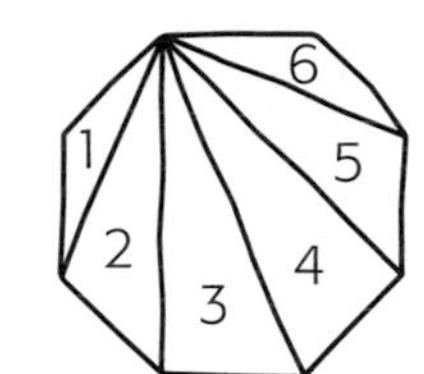

I used my formula to predict. A polygon with 7 sides should have $7 - 2 = 5$ triangles and a polygon with 8 sides should have $8 - 2 = 6$ triangles. They do. The pattern continues, so I think that my answer is right.

Reflecting

A. Is the relation between the number of sides in a polygon and the number of triangles it can be divided into linear? Explain.

B. How did Nola's diagrams help her solve this problem?

WORK WITH the Math

EXAMPLE 1 | Visualizing a problem using a diagram

Luc is building a bookcase with three shelves. The shelves should be 3 times as long as the height of the bookcase. Luc has 5.5 m of wood. What should the dimensions of the bookcase be?

Luc's Solution

1. Understand the Problem
I have to figure out the width and height of the bookcase.
I'll use plywood to cover the back, so I don't need to use any of the 5.5 m of wood for that.

2. Make a Plan

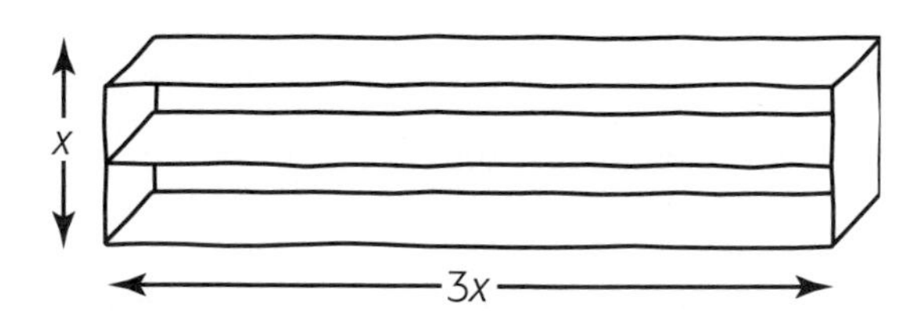

I drew a diagram to help me visualize the bookcase. I used a variable for the dimensions that I need to know. I labelled the height as x and the length of each shelf as 3 times that, $3x$. I need to represent the total length of wood.

3. Carry Out the Plan

$2 \times$ height of case $+ 3 \times$ length of each shelf $=$ total length of wood

I used the diagram to create an equation where the total length was 5.5 m.

$$2x + 3(3x) = 5.5$$
$$2x + 9x = 5.5$$
$$11x = 5.5$$

I solved the equation using inverse operations.

$$\frac{11x}{11} = \frac{5.5}{11}$$

$x = 0.5$ m, so $3x = 1.5$ m

The bookcase should be 0.5 m high and the shelves should be 1.5 m in length.

In Summary

Key Idea

- Many linear relations can be modelled using a diagram and the diagram can suggest how to solve a problem about the relation.

Need to Know

- A diagram can help to create an equation that models a particular situation.

Checking

1. A group of students went on a hike. First they walked 1 km east, then 2 km south, then 3 km west, then 1 km north, and finally 2 km east before stopping for a rest. How far are they from their starting position?

2. Luc, Erin, Rani, Zachary, and Nola all live next to each other on the same side of the street. Erin lives in the middle. Zachary lives in the first building. Rani lives between Erin and Luc. Who lives in the second building?

Practising

3. Intersection Q is three blocks east and three blocks north of intersection P. How many different routes are there from P to Q?

4. Kris and Dion are running a race. Kris has run $\frac{2}{3}$ of the way and is 12.5 m behind Dion, who has run $\frac{4}{5}$ of the race. How long is the race?

5. A picture frame that contains a photo is 20 cm long and 15 cm wide. A mat that surrounds the photo is 2.25 cm wide on all sides. Determine the dimensions of the photo.

6. Mary is training for a marathon on an oval racetrack. She takes 15 s to run from the first light standard to the third light standard. She needs to pass 37 standards to complete her training session. How long would it take her to run the entire distance?

7. Twenty-two people have reserved seats for a high school reunion at a restaurant. The small square tables will seat only one person on each side. If the tables are placed side by side to form one long table, how many tables are needed to seat all 22 people?

8. $\angle$AOB is 60°, and 3 lines are drawn from vertex O that divide $\angle$AOB into 4 equal angles. How many acute angles are there?

9. Two cars are 200 km apart on Yellowhead Highway and are moving directly toward each other. One car is travelling at 100 km/h and the other is travelling at 88 km/h. How long does it take for the two cars to pass?

10. There are 20 students in a classroom. The teacher wants them in 3 groups, with an even number of students in each group. How many ways can the teacher accomplish this?

Closing

11. Create and solve a problem in which drawing a diagram is useful for determining an equation to model the problem.

Extending

12. Katrina is on a camping trip in the Rockies. She must help an ill camper reach a hospital. The campground is 50 km from a roadway, which is 90 km from the local hospital. Katrina's ATV can go 50 km/h and the ambulance can go 140 km/h. At what point should they meet to get to the hospital as quickly as possible?

13. There are 900 fence posts, each 1.2 m apart, between Michelle's farm and Martin's farm. Michelle and Martin bike toward each other, starting at the same time. Michelle bikes at 3 m/s and Martin bikes at 4 m/s. At which fencepost will they meet?

5.7 Graphing Linear Inequalities

YOU WILL NEED

- a ruler

GOAL

Use a number line to represent a solution to a linear inequality.

LEARN ABOUT the Math

Victoria bought a coffee stand. She needs to earn more than \$150 per day to make a profit. She sells coffee for \$1.25 per cup and she regularly sells \$75 of cookies, muffins, and snacks per day.

? How can Victoria represent the number of cups of coffee she needs to sell each day to earn more than \$150?

EXAMPLE 1 | Using a number line to represent the solution

Rani's Solution

$\$1.25 \times (\text{cups of coffee sold}) + \$75$ — I wrote an expression to calculate Victoria's earnings.

$1.25c + 75 > 150$ — I used an **inequality** because she must earn more than \$150 to make a profit.

$1.25c + 75 = 150$ — Since I don't know how to solve an inequality I used an equation to determine how much she needs to earn exactly \$150, the sales where she "breaks even."

inequality
a statement that two quantities or expressions are related using the symbols $<$, $>$, $\leq$ or $\geq$; for example, $2x + 5 < 4$, $3 - 2x \geq 7$, or $14 > 7$

$$1.25c + 75 - 75 = 150 - 75$$
$$1.25c = 75$$
$$1.25c \div 1.25 = 75 \div 1.25$$
$$c = 60$$

I solved the equation using inverse operations.

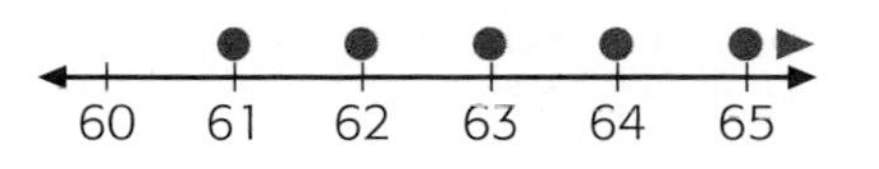

$c > 60$, where c is a whole number, is the solution to the inequality $1.25c + 75 > 150$.

I drew a number line to represent the number of cups of coffee she must sell to make a profit. I reasoned that, if she must sell 60 cups to break even, then she will earn a profit when she sells more than 60 cups. I indicated this by drawing solid dots on the places where the numbers are greater than 60.

Cups Sold	Earnings ($)
61	$1.25(61) + 75 = 151.25$
62	152.50
63	153.73

I verified that selling more than 60 cups each day satisfied the inequality by calculating the earnings for some of the indicated numbers on my number line. The daily earnings were greater than $150.

Victoria must sell more than 60 cups of coffee each day to earn more than $150.

Communication *Tip*

The solution to an inequality is often called a solution set because it is the set of values that make the inequality true.

Reflecting

A. Why is it reasonable to use an inequality to represent this situation?

B. Why does it not make sense for Rani to draw solid dots at numbers like 62.5 or $64\frac{3}{4}$ on her number?

C. Why does $1.25c + 75 > 150$ have more solutions than $1.25c + 75 = 150$?

WORK WITH the Math

Communication | *Tip*

An arrowhead or ray on a number line means the solution set continues in that direction.

An arrowhead is used for integers, natural numbers, and whole numbers because the solution set doesn't include the gaps between the numbers.

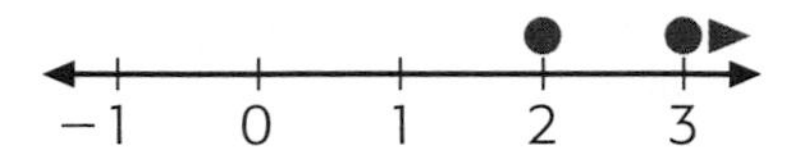

$x \geq 2$, where x is an integer

The graph above can also be read as $x > 1$.

A ray is used when the solution set is rational numbers, to show that the solution set includes numbers between marks on the line.

An open dot shows that a value is not included, and a closed dot shows that it is.

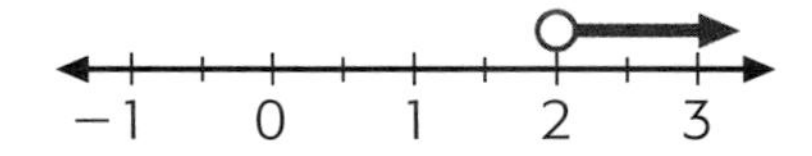

$x > 2$, where x is a rational number

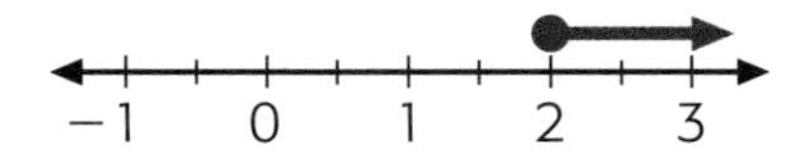

$x \geq 2$, where x is a rational number

EXAMPLE 2 | Interpreting a number line

What does the speed limit sign to a new provincial roadway show?

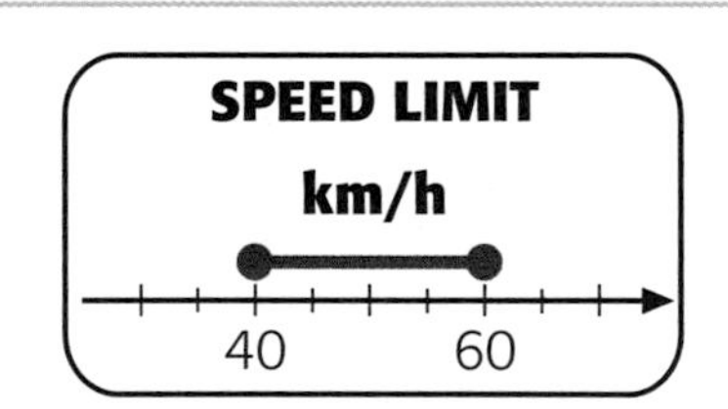

Zachary's Solution

The sign shows that vehicles must travel between 40 km/h and 60 km/h on the road. A car may travel at exactly 40 km/h and exactly 60 km/h since both ends of the line segment have closed dots. It may not travel less than 40 km/h or more than 60 km/h.

EXAMPLE 3 | Representing a situation using a number line

At the West Edmonton Mall, ride tickets cost \$1.25 and each ride requires between 1 and 7 tickets. If you have \$6.00 to spend on a single ride, how many tickets can the ride require?

Francis's Solution

Number of tickets	1	2	3	4	5	6	7
Cost (\$)	\$1.25	\$2.50	\$3.75	\$5.00	\$6.25	\$7.50	\$8.75

I made a table showing the costs for the different rides. I need to solve $c < 6$, where c is the cost.

\$0 \$1.25 \$2.50 \$3.75 \$5.00 \$6.25

I drew four dots on a number line to represent the four possible costs less than \$6. In-between amounts are not possible because partial tickets are not accepted.

EXAMPLE 4 | Connecting inequalities to a real-life situation

The surface temperature of a local lake is 15 °C. The expression $15 - \frac{d}{4}$ can be used to determine the temperature at various depths, d, in metres. Verify that the number line shown represents the solution set to $15 - \frac{d}{4} < 10$ and interpret the results.

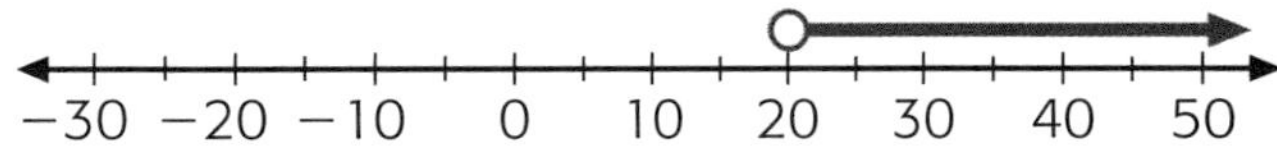

Viktor's Solution

For $d = 21$

Since the number line indicates that the solution is $d > 20$, I chose a test value of 21. It should be a solution to the inequality.

Left Side: Right Side:

$15 - \frac{d}{4}$ 10

$\rightarrow 15 - \frac{21}{4}$

$= 15 - 5.25$

$= 9.75$

$9.75 < 10$, so 21 is in the solution set.

For $d = 19$

I also chose a test value of 19 because it's close to 20 but less than it. I don't expect it to be a solution.

Left Side: Right Side:

$15 - \frac{d}{4}$ 10

$\rightarrow 15 - \frac{19}{4}$

$= 15 - 4.75$

$= 10.75$

$10.75 > 10$, so 19 isn't in the solution set.

For depths greater than 20 m, the temperature will be less than 10 °C.

In Summary

Key Idea

- The solution set for a linear inequality can be represented on a number line.

Need to Know

- Use closed dots to represent integers, whole numbers, and natural numbers on a number line. If the solution set continues indefinitely, use an arrowhead to indicate the direction.

$-5 \leq x \leq -2$, where x is an integer

$7 \leq x$, where x is an integer

- Use a solid ray or line segment to represent rational numbers on a number line. Use an open dot for an endpoint that isn't in the solution set and a closed dot for an endpoint that is.

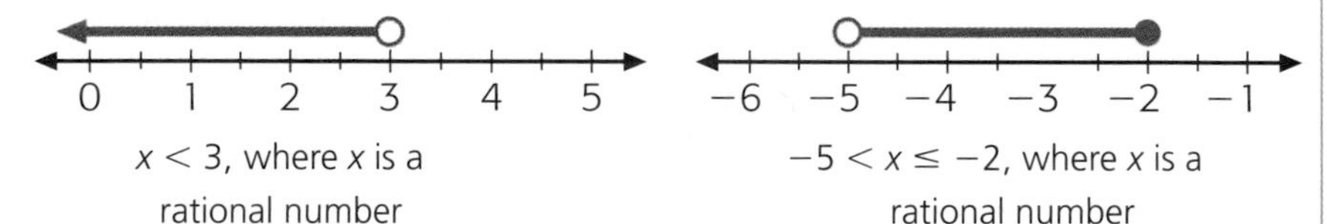

$x < 3$, where x is a rational number

$-5 < x \leq -2$, where x is a rational number

Checking

1. Match each inequality with its graph.

a) $x > -2$, where x is a rational number

b) $-3 < x \leq 0$, where x is a rational number

c) $x \geq -2$, where x is an integer

d) $x > 2$, where x is a whole number

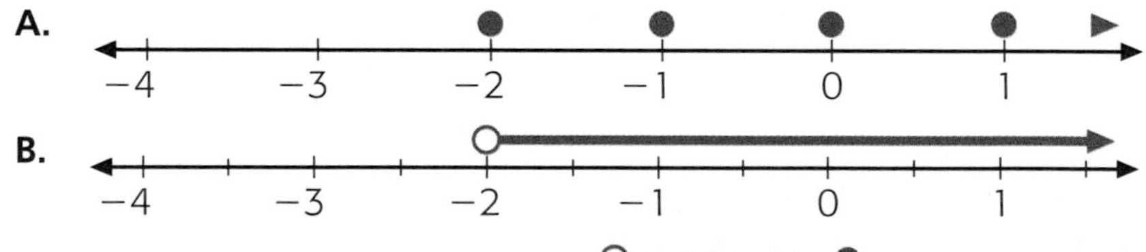

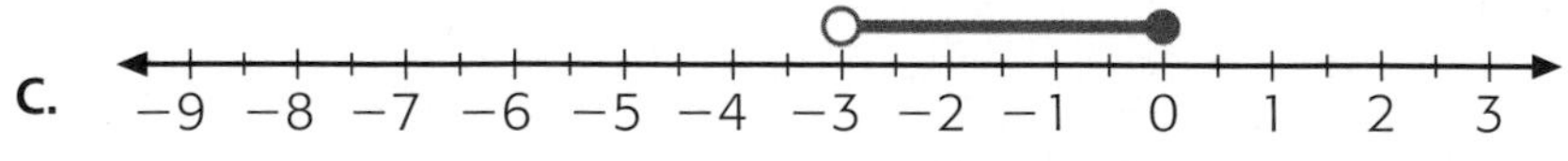

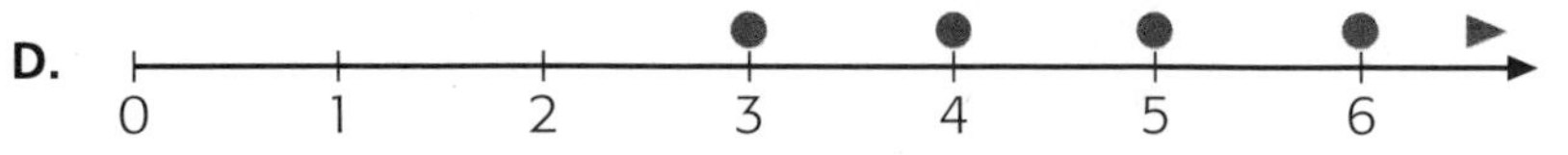

2. Graph each situation.

a) The maximum mass an elevator can carry is 1400 kg.

b) To make a profit for a concert at the Calgary Stampede, Jack must sell more than 150 tickets. The venue seats only 275 people. How many tickets must he sell?

3. Match each statement and inequality.

Statement	Inequality
a) A number is less than 6.	**A.** $x > 6$
b) James rode more than 12 km on his bike.	**B.** $x < 6$
c) The T-shirts cost more than 6 dollars.	**C.** $x \leq 12$
d) A number is less than or equal to 12.	**D.** $x > 12$

Practising

4. For each number line, write the inequality represented.

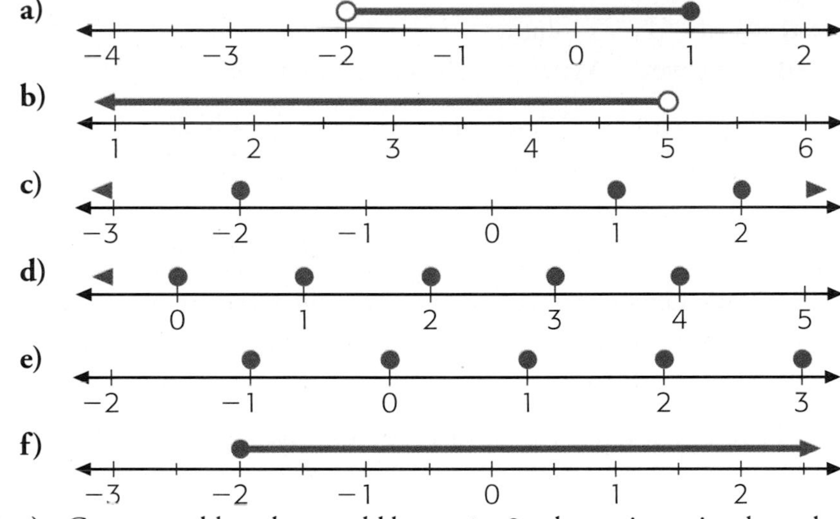

5. a) Create a problem that would have $x > 9$, where x is a rational number, as its solution.
   b) Create a problem that would have $x > 9$, where x is a natural number, as its solution.

6. Graph each inequality.
   a) $x > 3$, where x is a natural number
   b) $-1 < a \leq 5$, where a is a rational number
   c) $h \leq -5$, where h is an integer
   d) $x < -0.5$, where x is a rational number
   e) $-22 < p < -8$, where p is an integer
   f) $h \leq -5$, where h is a rational number

7. In 5 years, Adele will be older than 17. Write an inequality to represent Adele's current age and graph the solution.

8. Consider the inequality $x - 3 > -2$, in which x is an integer.
   a) Explain why you would use a series of dots to graph the solution set.
   b) Solve and graph the inequality.

9. Write the inequality and tell whether the solution set is integers, rational numbers, natural numbers, or whole numbers.

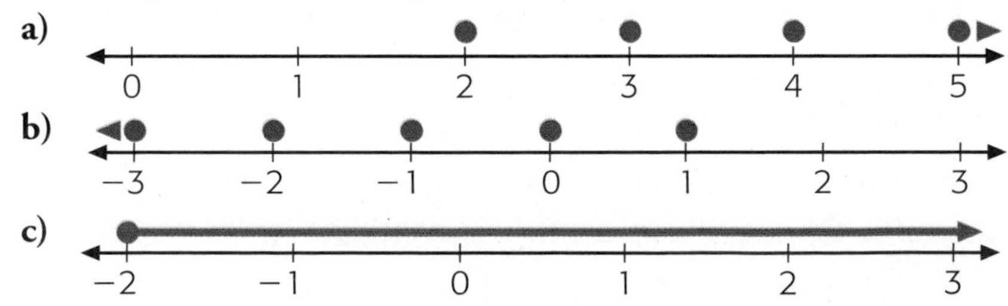

10. Create a problem that has a solution that is an inequality and where the solution set contains only natural numbers.

11. Marie solved the inequality $9 > 5 - 2a$, where a is a rational number, as shown. She represented her solution on a number line.

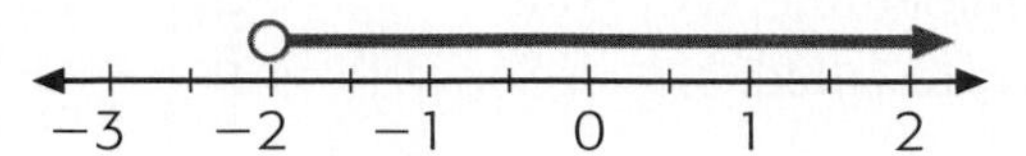

a) Verify Marie's solution.
b) How would Marie's graph change if a were an integer?

12. **Multiple choice.** A fraction is written as $\frac{m}{n}$. Which is a correct description of the relationship between m and n when $\frac{m}{n} > 1$ and m and n are both positive?

A. $m = n$ **B.** $m > n$ **C.** $m < n$ **D.** no relationship

13. **Multiple choice.** Suppose that x is a positive integer and y is a negative integer. Express the relation between x and y as an inequality.

A. $x = y$ **B.** $x > y$ **C.** $x < y$ **D.** no relationship

14. **Multiple choice.** The perimeter of a square is to be less than 80 cm. What is the solution to the inequality to determine the length, l, of one side?

A. $l > 20$, where l is a rational number
B. $l < 80$, where l is a natural number
C. $0 < l < 20$, where l is a rational number
D. $0 < l < 20$, where l is a natural number

Closing

15. How does using a number line help you to solve an inequality?

Extending

16. Jonah solved $2(2 - 3x) \geq 4(x + 2)$ and graphed his solution as shown.

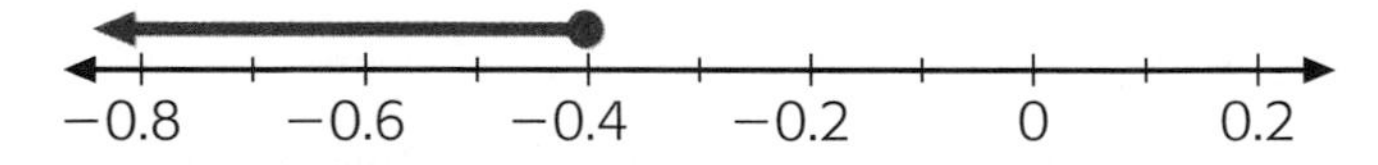

a) Verify Jonah's solution.
b) How do you know the solution set consists of rational numbers?

17. Consider the linear relation $y = 2x + 4$.

a) Draw the graph of the linear relation.
b) Choose ordered pairs on either side of the line to determine the set of values that solves the inequality $y \geq 2x + 4$.
c) Solve the inequality $y < -3x + 1$.

5.8 Exploring Operations with Inequalities

GOAL

Interpret the solution to a linear inequality.

EXPLORE the Math

When you apply the same operation to each side of an equation, the resulting equation is equivalent to the original equation.

For example,

$$5x + 4 = 4x + 20$$
$$5x + 4 - 4 = 4x + 20 - 4$$

are equivalent equations, and the expression on the left is still equal to the expression on the right.

Zachary wondered if something similar is true of inequalities.

He started with the inequality $5 > 3$.

When he added 3 to each side, the new inequality was still true: $5 + 3 > 3 + 3$ because $8 > 6$.

$5 > 3$
$5 + 3 > 3 + 3$
$8 > 6$ ✓

$5 > 3$
$5 - 3 >$

When you apply the same operation to each side of an inequality, is the resulting inequality always true?

5.9 Solving a Linear Inequality

GOAL

Solve linear inequalities using algebraic strategies.

LEARN ABOUT the Math

An outdoor concert raised more than \$3200 for charity. Tickets cost \$5 for adults and \$3.50 for students. 700 tickets were sold.

? How many students could have attended the concert?

A. Could 50 students have attended the concert? Explain. Could 100 students have attended? 150? 200?

B. What does x represent in the equation $5(700 - x) + 3.5x = 3200$? Why doesn't this equation represent the ticket sales?

C. Solve $5(700 - x) + 3.5x = 3200$.

D. Write an inequality that represents ticket sales.

E. How do you know that the inequality $-1.5x > -300$ is equivalent to the inequality you wrote in part D?

F. Test various values for x in the inequality from part E. Explain why the number of student tickets sold must be less than $\frac{-300}{-1.5}$, and not greater than that value.

G. How many students could have attended the concert?

Reflecting

H. Think about your answer to part F. How could you use a number line to explain why $-x > 5$ and $x < -5$ are equivalent?

I. How does solving $3500 - 1.5x = 3200$ help you solve $3500 - 1.5x > 3200$?

WORK WITH the Math

EXAMPLE 1 | Solving an inequality using guess and test

Solve $-5m > 30$.

Zachary's Solution

$-5m > 30$

I know $m = -6$ is the solution to the equation $-5m = 30$. I chose test values to determine the solution to the inequality.

$m = -5$

I chose -5 because it is greater than -6.

$-5(-5) = 25$, which is less than 30

$m = -7$

I chose -7 because it is less than -6.

$-5(-7) = 35$, which is greater than 30

The solution to $-5m > 30$ is $m < -6$

When $m = -7$, the value of $-5m$ is greater than 30. When you multiply by a negative number, you reverse the inequality. I reasoned that values less than -6 would solve the inequality.

Check:

I drew a number line to choose a test value. I assumed that the numbers were rational.

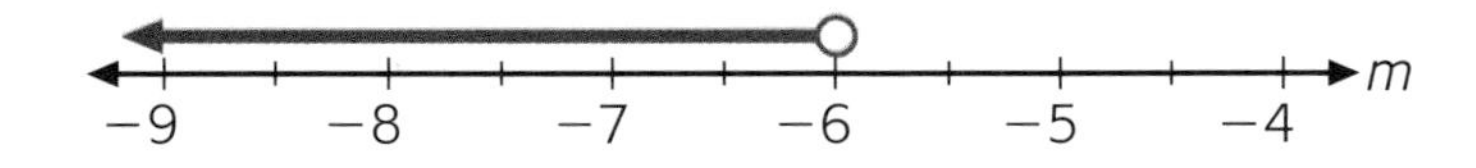

Since $m < -6$, try $m = -6.1$

Left Side	Right Side
$-5m$	30
$\rightarrow -5(-6.1)$	
$= 30.5$	

Since $30.5 > 30$, $m < -6$ is the solution to $-5m > 30$.

To check my solution, I chose -6.1 because it is very close to -6 and less than it.

I substituted 6.1 into the inequality to see if the relationship $-5m > 30$ was true.

Communication | ***Tip***

When there is no context in a problem and no restriction on the numbers in the solution set is stated, assume that the numbers are rational, Q.

EXAMPLE 2 | Solving an inequality

Create a problem that could result in the inequality $\frac{w + 75 + 72 + 80}{4} < 80$. Solve the problem.

Erin's Solution

I shot 75, 72, and 80 over three rounds of golf. What must I shoot to get a mean score less than 80?

The inequality uses <, so I created a problem with a "less than" relation.

$$\frac{w + 75 + 72 + 80}{4} < 80$$

I used w to represent the golf score on the 4th round. I know my score will be a natural number because my score is a count of the number of strokes I take.

$$\frac{w + 227}{4} < 80$$

I simplified the left side of the inequality by adding.

$$\frac{w + 227}{4} < 80$$

$$\frac{w + 227}{4} \times 4 < 80 \times 4$$

$$w + 227 < 320$$

$$w + 227 - 227 < 320 - 227$$

$$w < 93$$

I know that inequalities work just like equations except when I multiply or divide by a negative number. I can use inverse operations to solve an inequality as long as I remember to reverse the inequality when I multiply or divide by a negative number.

Operations on w: add 227, divide by 4.
Inverse Operations to isolate w:
multiply by 4, subtract 227.

I must shoot less than 93 on my next round to achieve a mean score of less than 80.

EXAMPLE 3 | Selecting an inverse operations strategy to solve an inequality

Solve the linear inequality $3x - 1 < 8$.

Francis's Solution

$$3x - 1 < 8$$

$$3x - 1 + 1 < 8 + 1$$

$$3x < 9$$

I treated the inequality like a linear equation and used inverse operations to isolate x.
I added 1 to both sides of the inequality.

$$\frac{3x}{3} < \frac{9}{3}$$

$$x < 3$$

I divided both sides of the inequality by 3.

−1 0 1 2 3 4

A number line helped me visualize the solution.

Check $x = 0$

I chose a value of x that is less than 3 to verify.

Left Side: Right Side:

$3x - 1$ 8

$\rightarrow 3(0) - 1$

$= -1$

LS < RS

The solution set is $x < 3$, where x is a rational number.

There were no restrictions on what the numbers could be, so I assumed the solution set contains rational numbers.

EXAMPLE 4 | Solving a problem involving a single-variable linear inequality

For what integer values of m will the perimeter of the square be greater than the perimeter of the rectangle?

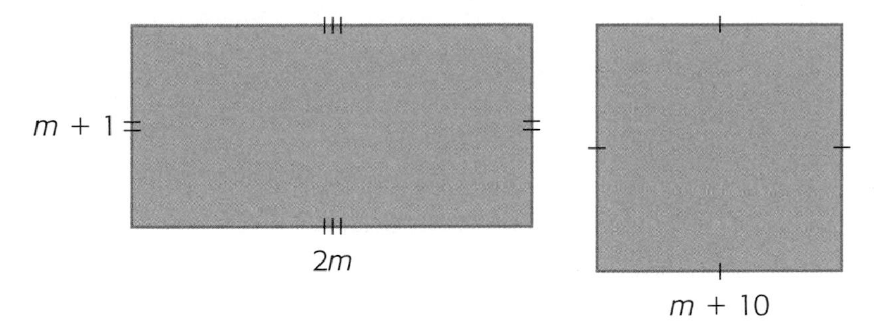

Nola's Solution

Perimeter of square

$= 4(m + 10)$

$= 4m + 40$

Perimeter of rectangle

$= 2(m + 1) + 2(2m)$

$= 2m + 2 + 4m$

$= 6m + 2$

I wrote expressions for the perimeter of each figure, and then I used the distributive property on each expression.
The perimeter of the square is 4 × one side length.
The perimeter of the rectangle is
2 × the length + 2 × the width.

$4m + 40 > 6m + 2$

The problem says the perimeter of the square is greater than the perimeter of the rectangle, so I wrote an inequality using my expressions. The question tells me the values must be integers.

$4m + 40 - 4m > 6m + 2 - 4m$

$40 > 2m + 2$

I subtracted $4m$ from both sides to write an equivalent inequality.

$40 - 2 > 2m + 2 - 2$

$38 > 2m$

$38 \div 2 > 2m \div 2$

$19 > m$

or $m < 19$

I subtracted 2 from both sides to isolate the variable term and divided by 2 to solve the equation.

Check:

$m < 19$, try $m = 18$

The variable m must be less than 19. I chose 18 as a test value since it is close to 19 but still an integer.

Left Side (square)	Right Side (rectangle)
$4(m + 10)$	$2(m + 1) + 2(2m)$
$\rightarrow 4(18 + 10)$	$\rightarrow 2(18 + 1) + 2(2 \times 18)$
$= 112$	$= 110$

Since $112 > 110$, when $m < 19$, this solution is correct.
The perimeter of the square will be greater than the perimeter of the rectangle when $m < 19$.

In Summary

Key Idea

- You can use the same strategies to solve an inequality as an equation.

Need to Know

- You can solve an inequality in several ways.
  - Use the related equation and test values. For example, solve $3m > 18$. The related equation is $3m = 18$ and has a solution of $m = 6$. Test values that are greater than 6 and less than 6. If $m = 5$, then $3(5) = 15$. $15 < 18$ so values less than 6 do not work. If $m = 7$, then $3(7) = 21$. $21 > 18$, so values greater than 6 do work. The solution is $m > 6$.
  - Use inverse operations. For example, solve $2m + 5 > 45$.

$$\begin{aligned} 2m + 5 - 5 &> 45 - 5 \\ 2m &> 40 \\ 2m \div 2 &> 40 \div 2 \\ m &> 20 \end{aligned}$$

- When you divide or multiply by a negative value, reverse the inequality sign.
- Words or phrases give information about relations: greater than: >, greater than or equal to: ≥, less than: <, less than or equal to: ≤
- To verify a solution, test values greater than and less than the solution to the related equation. Substitute to see if the inequality holds true.

Checking

1. Solve and graph each inequality.

a) $x + 5 > 2$, where x is a whole number

b) $-3x \leq -12$

c) $2x + 1 < 0$, where x is an integer

d) $4x \geq -28$

2. How is the graphical solution to $3 + x \leq 10$ related to the solution of $3 + x = 10$?

Practising

3. Solve each inequality and verify your solution.
   a) $2 + 4x > 5$
   b) $-3.5x > 14$
   c) $5 \leq 7 + 4x$
   d) $-4 > 9 - 6x$
   e) $9m + 7 \geq -11$
   f) $2x - 3 < 0$

4. For each solution from question 3, explain whether $-\frac{3}{7}$ is a member of the solution set.

5. When a number is doubled and then decreased by 7, the result is less than 20.
   a) Write an inequality for this situation.
   b) Solve the inequality and verify your solution.

6. Ahmir decides to take up squash. The local racquet club costs \$152 for the season and charges \$5 each time he uses the court. Ahmir has decided not to spend more than \$400.
   a) Write an inequality for the relation between the maximum amount Ahmir wants to spend and the cost to play squash.
   b) Solve the inequality to determine the maximum number of squash games he can play for \$400.
   c) Verify your solution.

7. Solve each inequality and verify your solution.
   a) $-19 \geq 6t - 3$
   b) $2.25x + 1.4 < -3.8$
   c) $15.2 \leq -27.2 + 0.1r$
   d) $11 - 5a > 11$
   e) $-10 \leq -26 - 12p$
   f) $\frac{2}{3}x - \frac{1}{4} > \frac{1}{5}$

8. Andrea solved $-21 > 4 - 5x$ as shown. Her solution was $5 > x$. Correct any errors she made.

$$-21 > 4 - 5x$$
$$-21 - 4 > 4 - 5x - 4$$
$$-25 > -5x$$
$$-25 \div -5 > -5x \div -5$$
$$5 > x$$

9. Solve each inequality and verify your solution.
   a) $2y + 5 - 4y > 15$
   b) $-10a \geq 4a + 2$
   c) $p + 3p - 4 < 0$
   d) $2(q - 8) \leq -5q$
   e) $5(x - 6) > -2(x + 3)$
   f) $-\frac{1}{3}x - 4 < 11 - \frac{1}{6}x$

10. Mike's bull riding times over three attempts were 7.2 s, 5.5 s, and 6.8 s. Jim averaged 7.5 s over four attempts. Jeff averaged 7.0 s over four attempts.

a) Write an inequality for the time Mike needs to have on his fourth ride to have a higher average than Jim's.

b) Write an inequality for the time Mike needs to have on his fourth ride to have a higher average than Jeff's.

11. Anna downloads TV episodes from two online companies. TVTitles charges \$1.50 per download plus a one-time membership fee of \$15. PRionTV charges \$2.25 per download with no membership fee and gives the first 5 downloads free.

a) Write an expression for the cost to download n songs from Music4U.

b) Write an expression for the cost to download n songs from RTunes.

c) Write an inequality to determine when it costs more to download songs from Music4U than from RTunes.

d) Solve the inequality and verify your solution.

e) Which site should Anna use to download music?

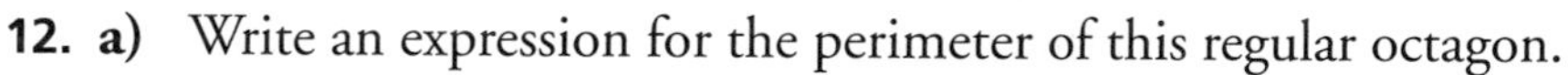

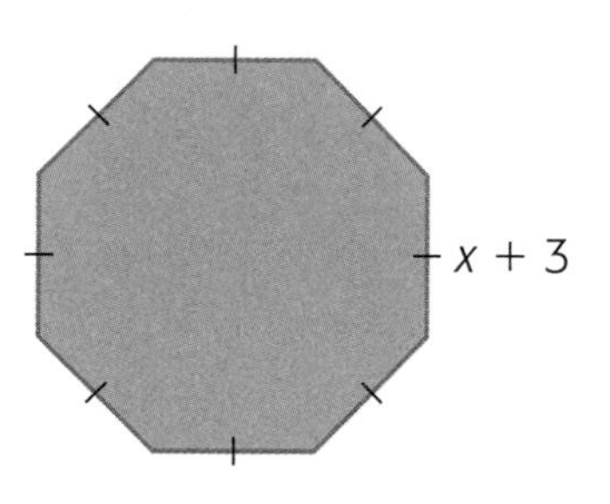

12. a) Write an expression for the perimeter of this regular octagon.

b) The perimeter of this octagon must be less than 52 cm. What inequality would you solve to determine the possible perimeter?

c) Solve the inequality in part b) and verify your solution.

d) What is the length of one side of the polygon?

13. Solve each inequality and graph the solution.

a) $2a + 5 > \frac{1}{2}a$

b) $3 - 2p \leq 5 + p$

c) $2(4 + 3s) \geq -5(2 + s)$

d) $4 - \frac{2}{3}b < 3 - \frac{1}{3}b$

14. Multiple choice. Wilson earns \$7.80 per hour as a bus boy. What is the fewest number of hours he must work to earn more than \$390?

A. 49 **B.** 50 **C.** 51 **D.** 5

15. Nicolas says you can solve an inequality by replacing the inequality sign with an = sign and then putting it back in after solving the equation. Do you agree? Explain.

16. Brendan collects hockey cards. If he triples the number of cards in his collection and then adds 10 more, he will have more than 105 cards.

a) Determine the least number of cards he now has.

b) Determine a reasonable scale to represent this solution on a number line.

c) Represent your solution graphically.

17. This rectangle must have a perimeter less than or equal to 100 cm.

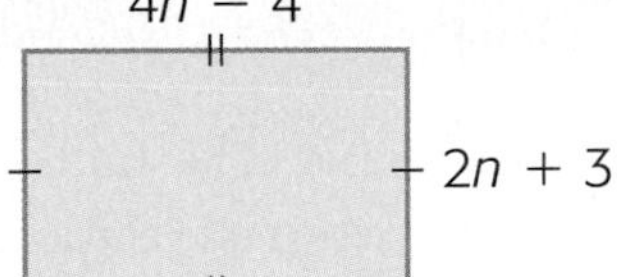

a) Write an inequality for this situation.
b) Solve the inequality.
c) Determine a reasonable scale and number type (integer, whole, or rational) to represent your solution on a number line.
d) Represent your solution graphically.

18. When a number is divided by 3, and then increased by 5, the result is more than 11.

a) Determine three integers for which this is possible.
b) Determine three integers for which this is impossible.
c) Write an inequality for this situation.
d) Solve and graph your solution.

Closing

19. How is solving an inequality similar to solving an equation? How is it different?

Extending

20. During a figure skating competition, Alberta won three times as many medals as Québec. B.C. won 2 more medals than Québec. Suppose n represents the number of medals Québec won.

a) Write an expression for the number of medals B.C. won.
b) Write an expression for the number of medals Alberta won.
c) Write an expression for the number of medals all three provinces won.
d) Fewer than 17 medals were won. What is the greatest number of medals Québec could have won?
e) Represent your solution for each province on a number line.

21. Is $(3, 1)$ a solution to $2x - 3y > 6$? Explain.

22. Solve the following inequalities.

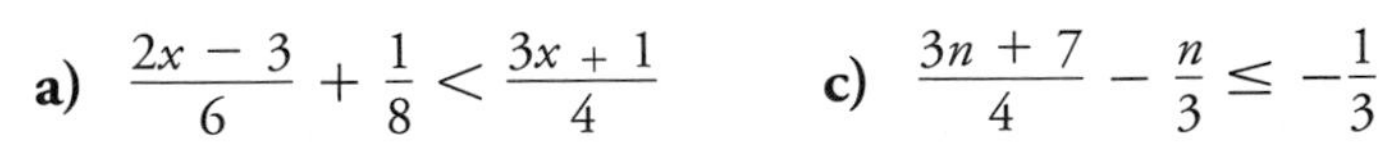

a) $\frac{2x - 3}{6} + \frac{1}{8} < \frac{3x + 1}{4}$

c) $\frac{3n + 7}{4} - \frac{n}{3} \leq -\frac{1}{3}$

b) $\frac{2 - 3a}{4} > \frac{6 - 2a}{5}$

d) $\frac{2d - 3}{6} + \frac{1}{8} \geq \frac{3d + 1}{4}$

Chapter Self-Test

1. A fruit stand sells apples for \$0.25 each.
   a) Describe the relation between cost and number of apples bought using a graph, a table, and an equation.
   b) Create and solve an equation to determine the cost of 150 apples.
2. Gill rented a car for \$45/day plus \$0.15/km. His bill was \$58.50.
   a) How do you know the relation between kilometres and cost is linear?
   b) What relation would you graph to estimate the number of kilometres Gill drove?
   c) What equation would you solve to determine the number of kilometres Gill drove?
3. Identify the relation between Figure n and the number of squares in that figure. Use a table of values, a graph, and an equation to support your answer.

a)

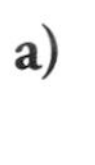

Figure 1

Figure 2

Figure 3

b)

Figure 1

Figure 2

Figure 3

4. Solve each equation and verify your solution.
   a) $-2a + 5 = 3$
   b) $\frac{4}{7} - \frac{2}{3}x = \frac{8}{12}x$
   c) $\frac{5}{6}x - \frac{3}{4} = \frac{1}{4}$
   d) $3(x - 1) + 2(3x + 1) = 2$
5. Justin charges \$21 per linear foot to install a wood fence. It costs him \$19 per linear foot plus \$4000 to buy materials and hire installers each month. How many linear feet of fencing does he need to install each month to make a profit?
6. Solve each inequality and verify your solution.
   a) $3 - 2x > 5$, where x is an integer
   b) $-4x \leq -16$, where x is a rational number
   c) $2(5 + x) \geq \frac{1}{3}x$, where x is a rational number
   d) $\frac{4}{5} - \frac{2}{3}x < \frac{x}{3} + 1$, where x is a whole number
7. Represent your solutions in question 6 on a number line.

WHAT DO You Think Now?

Revisit What Do You Think? on page 199. Have your answers and explanations changed?

Chapter Review

FREQUENTLY ASKED Questions

Q: How do you solve an equation with variables on both sides of the equal sign?

A: Using inverse operations, you can create equivalent equations until the equation is solved. For example,

$$3x + 2 = 5x - 8$$
$$3x + 2 - 3x = 5x - 8 - 3x$$

Collect the variable terms on the right side because $5 > 3$, so the coefficient of the variable term will end up being positive.

$$2 + 8 = 2x - 8 + 8$$
$$10 = 2x$$
$$10 \div 2 = 2x \div 2$$
$$5 = x$$

Adding 8 to both sides collects the constant terms on the left side of the equation.

Study *Aid*

- See Lesson 5.5, Examples 2 and 3.
- Try Chapter Review questions 8, 9, 10, and 11.

Q: How can you graph the solution to a linear inequality?

A: You can use a number line. For integers, whole numbers, and natural numbers, use closed dots and an arrowhead if needed. For rational numbers, use line segments or rays. If the inequality includes the endpoint ($\geq$ or $\leq$) use a closed dot. If it doesn't include the endpoint ($<$ or $>$) use an open dot.

−9 −8 −7 −6 −5 −4 −3 −2 −1 0 1 2 3

Study *Aid*

- See Lesson 5.7, Examples 1, 2, and 3.
- Try Chapter Review questions 13, 14, and 15.

Q: How are an inequality and an equation alike and different?

A: Linear equations and inequalities can both be solved using inverse operations. However, when you multiply or divide an inequality by a negative number, the inequality reverses. This is not true with an equation.

$$-3x - 5 + 5 > 13 + 5$$
$$-3x > 18$$
$$-3x \div -3 < 18 \div -3$$
$$x < -6$$

An inequality has many solutions. A linear equation has only one solution. For example, the solution to $2x = 8$ is $x = 4$. The solution to $2x > 8$ is $x > 4$, and there are many values greater than 4.

Study *Aid*

- See Lesson 5.9, Example 1.
- Try Chapter Review question 16.

Practice

Lesson 5.1

1. Kaycee created this toothpick pattern.

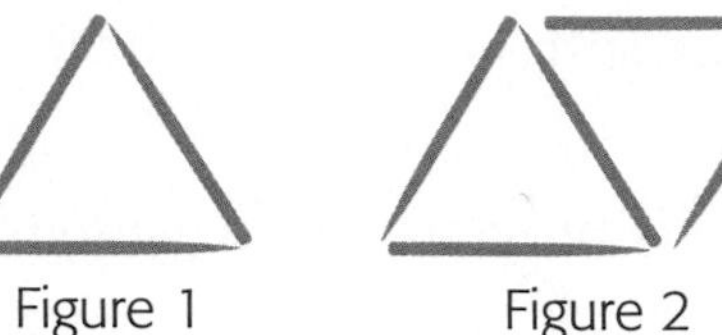

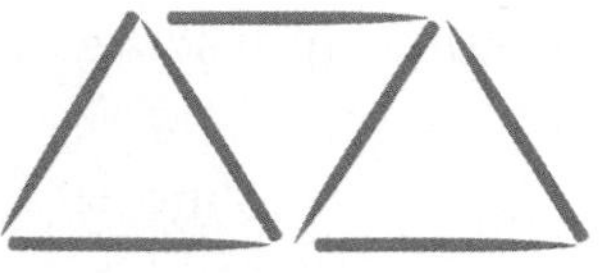

Figure 1 Figure 2 Figure 3

   a) Make a table of values for the number of toothpicks in each figure.
   b) Use your table to determine the rate of change.
   c) Write an equation for the number of toothpicks in Figure n.
   d) Which figure will require 27 toothpicks?

Lesson 5.2

2. a) Create a table of values for the linear relation $y = 3x + 6$ using $x = 0, 5, 10, 15$, and 20.
   b) Use your table of values to graph the relation.
   c) Use your graph to predict the value of y when $x = 4, 18$, and 75.

3. Repeat question 2 for these relations.
   a) $y = 4x - 8$ b) $y = 5 - 2x$ c) $y = -6x + 8$

Lesson 5.3

4. Write the corresponding linear relation for each equation. Estimate the solution graphically.
   a) $4x - 5 = 3$ c) $-2(x - 3) = -4$
   b) $\frac{1}{2}x + 3 = 5$ d) $\frac{1}{4}\left(x + \frac{2}{5}\right) = 0$

5. A promotion company is holding a video dance. Tickets cost \$15 per person, and it has given away 10 free tickets to radio stations.
   a) Write a linear relation for the money the promoter will earn if n people attend.
   b) Graph the linear relation.
   c) Write an equation that you can use to determine the money earned from ticket sales if 100 people attend. Solve the equation using the graph.
   d) Write an equation that you can use to determine how many people attended if ticket sales were \$600. Estimate the solution using the graph.

Lesson 5.4

6. Solve and verify each equation. Justify your choice of method.
   a) $\frac{3}{4}x - \frac{1}{3} = 5$
   b) $4.5 = 0.6(a - 3)$
   c) $-2\frac{1}{3} + 3x = 11$
   d) $-8\left(\frac{f}{5} - 2\right) = \frac{4}{5}$

7. Erynn joined a movie club. The first 10 movies are free, but after that she pays \$15.95 for each movie she orders.
   a) Write an expression for the cost of x movies.
   b) How much would she pay for 15 movies?
   c) Erynn receives her first order of movies with a bill for \$31.90. Write and solve an equation to determine how many she ordered.

Lesson 5.5

8. Solve. Verify each solution.
   a) $9x + 2 = 11x - 10$
   b) $-\frac{4}{5}x + \frac{2}{3} = 1\frac{3}{4}x + 2$
   c) $-3(x + 1) - 2 = 4x - 5(x - 3)$
   d) $\frac{4 + x}{3} + 4 = \frac{x - 6}{2} - 6$

9. To calculate the area of a trapezoid, you can use the expression $\frac{h}{2}(b_1 + b_2)$, where b_1 and b_2 are the two bases. These two trapezoids have the same area. Determine the length of each base.

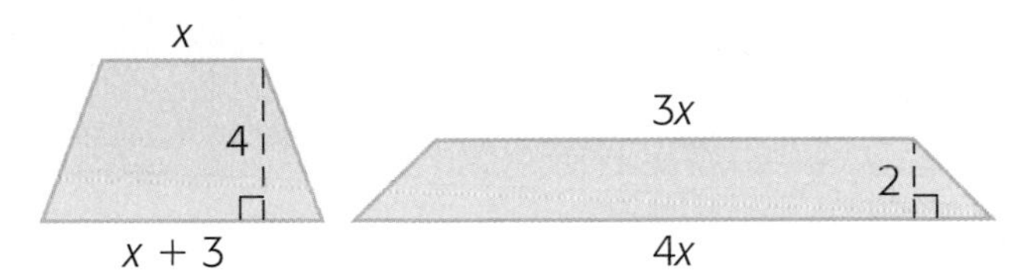

10. Solve. Verify your solution.
   a) $-x + 6 = 2x - 12$
   b) $\frac{2}{3}x - 2 = 4x + \frac{4}{3}$
   c) $4(x - 8) = -2(x - 5)$
   d) $\frac{2}{3}x - \frac{1}{2} = -\frac{1}{2} + \frac{1}{4}x$
   e) $\frac{1}{5}(a + 1) = \frac{1}{3}(2a - 3)$
   f) $\frac{4a - 2}{5} + \frac{1}{2} = \frac{3a + 7}{2} - 1$

11. Write and solve an equation to answer each problem.
   a) The perimeter of a rectangle is 210 m. It is 7 m longer than it is wide. How long is it?
   b) Tom has 117 quarters and dimes worth \$15.75. How many of each coin does he have?
   c) Jamie can paint a house in 10 h and Mario can paint the same house in 12 h. How long does it take if they work together?

Lesson 5.6

12. Two friends left a restaurant in Edmonton and travelled in opposite directions on Highway 16. One drove at 95 km/h and the other at 85 km/h. How long was it before they were 200 km apart?

Lesson 5.7

13. In Whistler Village during June the temperature is typically between 9 °C and 21 °C.

a) Would you use a solid line to represent temperature on a graph or a series of dots? Explain.

b) Represent this temperature range on a number line.

14. Create an inequality for a situation in which the solution is a natural number. Graph the solution.

15. Consider the inequality $c - 3 \geq 2$.

a) Graph a solution in which c is a natural number.

b) Graph a solution in which c is a rational number.

c) How are your answers to part a) and part b) alike and different?

Lesson 5.9

16. Solve and graph each inequality.

a) $3 + 4x < 5$, where x is a rational number

b) $6 \geq 4 - 2x$, where x is a whole number

c) $4 + 6x > 6 - 2x$, where x is a natural number

d) $\frac{1}{3}x \leq \frac{2}{3}x - 4$, where x is an integer

e) $\frac{1}{2}(w + 3) < -2(2w - 1)$, where w is a rational number

f) $2\frac{1}{7}(7a - 8) \geq \frac{1}{5}(2a - 4)$, where a is a rational number

Reducing Your Carbon Footprint

Carbon footprint is the name given to all the greenhouse gases we produce. This "footprint" can have a negative effect on our environment, and one way to reduce it is to plant trees. Every tree takes in about 730 kg of carbon dioxide over its lifetime.

? How many trees should be planted to take in more carbon dioxide than each appliance produces?

A. Estimate the approximate usage on an average day for each appliance in your home. Write an equation to determine the usage for any number of days.

Appliance	Energy per Use (kWh)
microwave oven	0.945
washing machine	0.63
electric dryer	2.5
kettle	0.11
gas oven	1.52
electric oven	1.56
dishwasher at 55 °C	1.07
dishwasher at 65 °C	1.44

B. The amount of electricity, in kilowatt hours (kWh), that each appliance uses is shown in the table. Assume about 0.70 kg of carbon dioxide is produced to generate one kilowatt hour of electricity. Write an equation for the carbon footprint of each appliance for any number of days.

C. Determine the annual carbon footprint of each appliance.

D. How many trees must be planted to more than offset the annual emissions by each appliance in your home?

Task | *Checklist*

- ✔ Did you organize your work?
- ✔ Did you explain your thinking?
- ✔ Did you check that your solutions make sense?

Chapter 6

Polynomials

GOALS

You will be able to

- model, record, and interpret polynomial expressions in a variety of ways
- model, record, and explain polynomial addition and subtraction
- model, record, and explain how to multiply a polynomial by a monomial
- model, record, and explain how to divide a polynomial by a monomial
- solve problems involving polynomials using organized lists

A band has recorded a long version and a short version of a new track. They will sell the long version for 99 cents and the short version for 89 cents. How can you represent their total sales for the track?

Getting Started

Using Algebra to Describe Perimeters

Thomas described the measurements of some shapes he had drawn.

? What are the perimeters of Thomas's shapes?

A. An equilateral triangle has a side s units long.
Write an **algebraic expression** for the **perimeter** of the triangle.

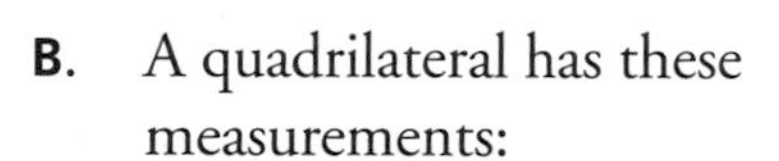

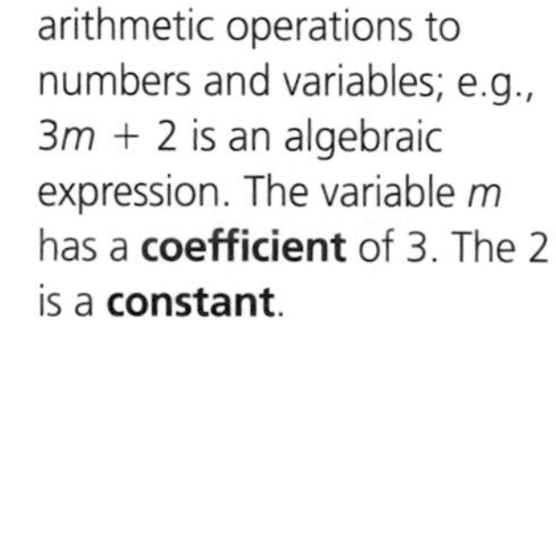

algebraic expression

the result of applying arithmetic operations to numbers and variables; e.g., $3m + 2$ is an algebraic expression. The variable m has a **coefficient** of 3. The 2 is a **constant**.

B. A quadrilateral has these measurements:

- the second side is twice as long as the first side,
- the third side is 1 unit shorter than three times the first side, and
- the fourth side is two units longer than the first side.

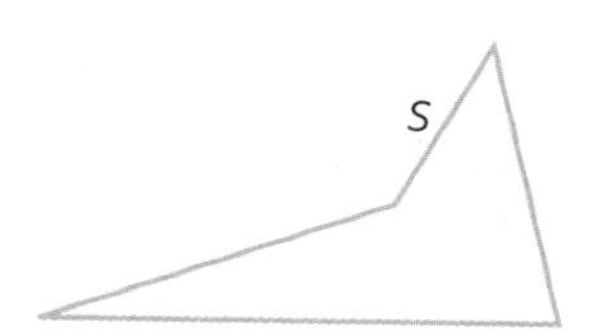

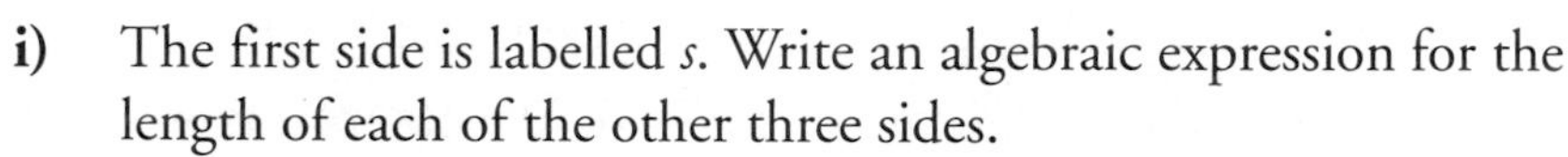

i) The first side is labelled s. Write an algebraic expression for the length of each of the other three sides.
ii) Sketch the shape and label it with those side lengths.
iii) Write the perimeter of the shape as an algebraic expression. Use an expression like this: ■s + ▲.
iv) What is the coefficient of s in your expression?
v) What is the constant?
vi) What is the perimeter of the shape if the value of s is 10 units?
vii) Could the perimeter be 50 units? Explain.
viii) Could the perimeter be 38 units? Explain.

C. A rectangle's width is n units.
Its length is two units longer than three times its width.
i) Write an algebraic expression for the length.
ii) Write the perimeter of the shape as an algebraic expression.
iii) Could the perimeter of the shape be four units? Explain.

D. Thomas said that a triangle has one side n units long.
- A second side is twice as long.
- A third side is four times as long.

i) Describe the lengths of the second and third sides using algebraic expressions.
ii) Is it possible to create this triangle? Explain.

E. Make up your own problem like the ones in parts A to D for a classmate to solve. Trade with a classmate. Each of you can solve the other's problem.

WHAT DO *You Think?*

Decide whether you agree or disagree with each statement. Be ready to explain your decision.

1. x has the same meaning when you write the algebraic expression $3x + 2$ as when you solve the equation $3x + 2 = 17$.
2. When you subtract a negative integer from another negative integer, the answer is usually negative.
3. The area of a rectangle is x, as shown below. It is possible to use shapes like this to represent rectangles of area $3x$, but not rectangles of area $-x$ or area $(3x - 1)$.

x

4. $4x + 2$ is always greater than $3x + 2$.

6.1 Modelling with Polynomials

GOAL

Model and interpret situations involving polynomials.

INVESTIGATE the Math

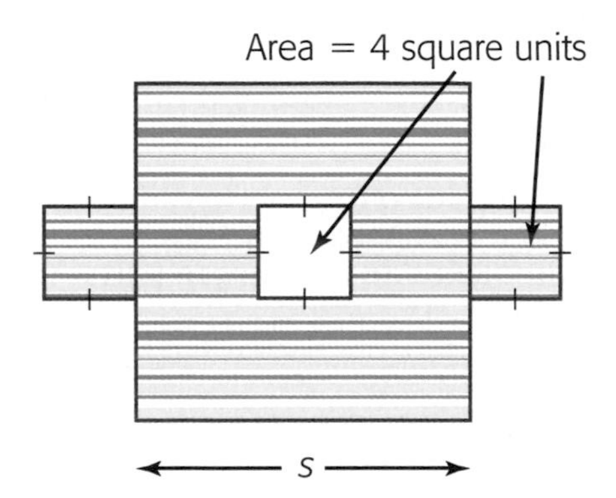

Larissa is designing a fabric wall hanging made from a large square and two identical small squares. A third small square is cut out and removed from the large one. She has not yet decided what size she wants the large square to be.

Larissa plans to use cord to decorate the borders of each part of the design.

polynomial

an algebraic expression that is the sum of numbers and terms involving variables with exponents that are whole numbers; the variables can be multiplied by or divided by any numbers; e.g., $3a^2 + 4ab + 2$ and $bh \div 2$ are polynomials.

term

a part of a polynomial, separated from the other terms by addition signs; e.g., the polynomial $3a^2 + 4ab - 2$ can be written as $3a^2 + 4ab + (-2)$. So its terms are $3a^2$, $4ab$, and -2. It is possible for a polynomial to have only one term. For example, $3a^2$ is a polynomial.

? What expressions could Larissa use to determine the amount of fabric and cord that she needs for her design?

A. Write the algebraic expression that describes the area of the large square with the cut-out removed.

B. The expression in part A is a **polynomial**. How many **terms** does that polynomial have?

C. Which of those terms is a **constant**?

D. What is the **coefficient** of the term involving the variable s?

E. Write the polynomial that describes the area of the whole design.

F. Write the polynomial that describes the length of cord needed for the design. What is the **degree of the term** involving the variable s?

Reflecting

G. Explain why two different people might record the polynomial for part E differently, but still both be right.

H. Does it make sense that the **degree of the polynomial** for part E is 2, but the degree of the polynomial for part F is 1? Explain.

degree of a term

the power to which the variable in a term is raised; if a term contains two variables, its degree is the sum of the exponents of those variables; e.g.,
first degree terms:
$2a$, $-b$
second degree terms:
$4a^2$, $-3b^2$, ab, $-6rs$
The degree of a constant term is 0.

degree of a polynomial

the greatest of the degrees of the polynomial's terms; e.g.,
first degree polynomials:
$-5a + 2$
$8 + 6q$
second degree polynomials:
$3a + 4a^2 - 2$
$2pq - p^2$
$st + 8$

WORK WITH the Math

EXAMPLE 1 Connecting a real-life situation to a polynomial representation using one variable

In January, David used 14 more cellphone minutes than the number he used in December.

He used twice as many minutes in November as he used in December.

a) Record polynomials for January's and for November's minutes.

b) Suppose David used 27 min in December. How many minutes did he use in January? How many minutes did he use in November?

Sam's Solution

a) Let m represent the number of minutes in December.

November and January's minutes are related to the December minutes. So I used the variable m for the December minutes.

January's minutes: $m + 14$

January: 14 more than December's minutes meant I needed to add 14 to m.

November's minutes: $2m$

November: I had to double m.

b) When $m = 27$,

$$m + 14 = 27 + 14$$
$$= 41$$

He used 41 min in January.

To determine the number of minutes in January if he used 27 min in December, I evaluated the polynomial $m + 14$ when $m = 27$.

When $m = 27$

$$2m = 2(27)$$
$$= 54$$

He used 54 min in November.

To determine the number of minutes in November if he used 27 min in December, I evaluated the polynomial $2m$ when $m = 27$.

EXAMPLE 2	Using a polynomial with two variables to represent a measurement

The two bases of a trapezoid are r and $3r$ units long.
The height is h units.

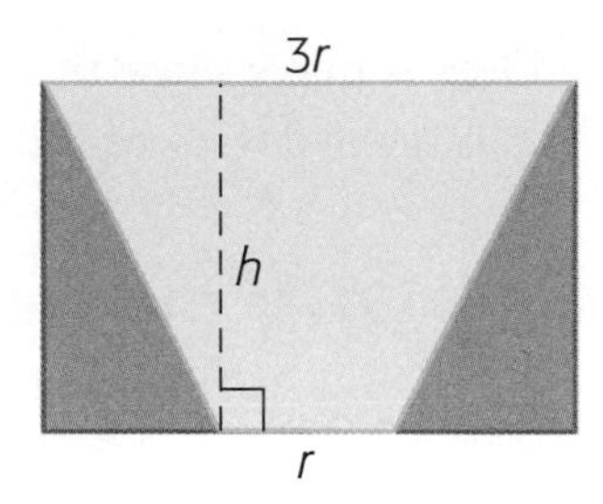

a) Write a polynomial to describe the area of the tan trapezoid.

b) Write a polynomial to describe the purple area outside the trapezoid.

Jia-Wen's Solution

a)

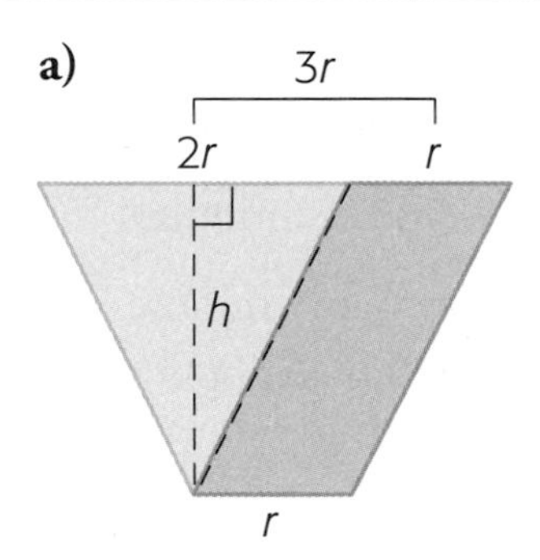

The area of the trapezoid is the sum of the areas of a parallelogram and a triangle.

The area of the parallelogram is the base, r, multiplied by the height, h. The area of the triangle is half the base, $2r$, multiplied by the height, h.

$$A = rh + \frac{1}{2} \times 2rh$$
$$= rh + rh$$
$$= 2rh$$

The polynomial $2rh$ describes the area of the tan trapezoid.

b) $A = 3rh - 2rh$

$$= 1rh$$
$$= rh$$

The area of the rectangle is $3rh$.

The purple area is the difference between the areas of the rectangle and the trapezoid.

The polynomial rh describes the purple area outside the trapezoid.

Communication | *Tip*

You do not need to record a coefficient of 1. For example, you can write $1s^2$ as s^2. Here, you can write $1rh$ as rh, just as you can write 1×5 or 1(5) as 5.

EXAMPLE 3 | Creating a situation represented by a particular polynomial

a) Create a situation that can be represented by the polynomial $4x - 3$.

b) Create a situation that can be represented by the polynomial $3 - 4x$.

Rachel's Solution

a) $4x - 3$

The polynomial has two terms. I needed a situation in which a value is multiplied by 4, and then 3 is taken away.

The cost to download a ring tone is \$4. Jamal already has \$3. The polynomial $4x - 3$ tells how much more money Jamal needs in order to download x ring tones.

I knew you might multiply by 4 if Jamal bought things that cost \$4 each and wanted to know the total price.

For subtracting 3, I thought about how much Jamal would have to add to his \$3 so he could pay for everything.

b) $3 - 4x$

I needed the opposite of the polynomial in part a).

Jamal has \$3. He borrowed money to download x ring tones that cost \$4 each.

The polynomial $3 - 4x$ tells how much debt Jamal has after he downloaded x ring tones.

I thought about how much debt Jamal had instead of how much money Jamal needed.

Communication *Tip*

Polynomials are usually written in order from the highest power to the lowest, going from left to right; e.g., $2p - 3 + 5p^2$ would usually be written as $5p^2 + 2p - 3$.

In Summary

Key Ideas

- A polynomial describing area involves second degree terms (also said as "terms of degree 2").

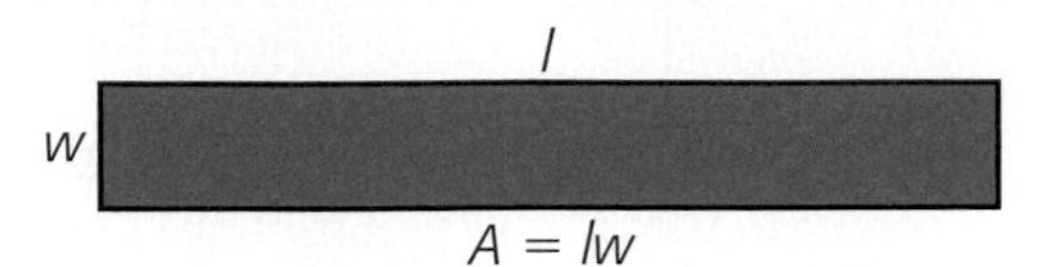

$A = lw$

The polynomial describing the area of the rectangle has degree 2 since l and w each have an exponent of 1.

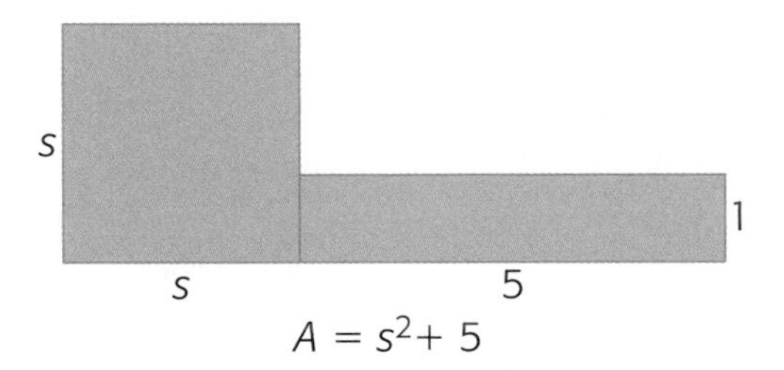

$A = s^2 + 5$

The polynomial describing the area of the L-shape has degree 2 since s has an exponent of 2.

- A polynomial involving linear dimensions only is first degree (or degree 1).

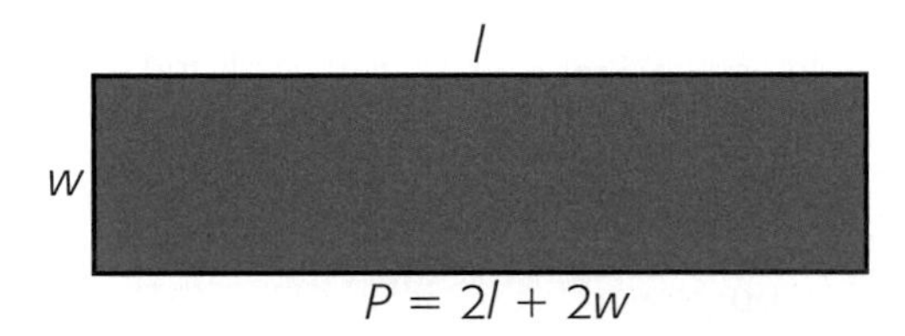

$P = 2l + 2w$

The polynomial describing the perimeter of a rectangle has degree 1 since each term has an exponent of 1.

- Situations that increase or decrease by constant amounts can be represented by first degree polynomials.
  For example, if you have \$50 and earn \$20 a week, the amount of money after w weeks can be described by the first degree polynomial $50 + 20w$.

Need to Know

- You can always think of a polynomial as a sum of terms. If there is a subtraction, think of writing it as adding the opposite.
  For example, $4m - 3$ is the same as $4m + (-3)$.
- A polynomial can have any number of terms.
  For example, the polynomial $2n + 3$ has two terms: $2n$ and 3.
  The polynomial $4m - m^2 + 6$ has three terms: $4m$, $-m^2$, and 6.

Checking

1. For each polynomial, identify its degree, the variables, the coefficients of the variable(s), and the constant term.
   a) $3 - 2k + 4k^2$ b) $-5k^2 - 2$ c) $5 - k + j^2$

2. Which of these are polynomials?
   a) $4k^2$ b) $-\frac{5}{k} - 2$ c) $4 - q$

3. Describe a situation you might represent with the polynomial $8 + 2w$.

Practising

4. For each polynomial, identify its degree, the variables, the coefficients of the variable(s), and the constant term.
   a) $-2p - 7$ b) $4 + 3t$ c) $5ab - 8 + 5b^2$

5. Create polynomials to fit each description.
   a) The degree is 2 and the constant is -9.
   b) The degree is 1 and the coefficient of p is 6.
   c) The variables are m and p, the degree is 2, and there are four terms.

6. Write a polynomial to fit all these clues.
   - It has the same degree as $3a^2 - 2a + 4$.
   - It has the same number of terms as $4bc - 8 + c^2$.
   - It has the same coefficient as j^2 has in $-3m - 2j^2$.
   - It has a different constant than $-4c^2 - 7c - 2$.

7. **Multiple choice.** What is the value of $6 - 8ab + b^2$ when $a = 9$ and $b = 2$?
   A. -142 B. -78 C. -134 D. -146

8. **Multiple choice.** Which is *not* a polynomial?
   A. $w - 2 + p^2$ B. $\frac{1}{x}$ C. $48k$ D. $6x + x^2 - y$

9. **Multiple choice.** Mark had saved \$200. He earns \$45 a week at a part-time job. He saves all the money he earns. Which of the following expressions represents Mark's savings after working for n weeks?
   A. $200 + 45n$ B. $200 - 45n$ C. $245n$ D. $45n - 200$

10. Evaluate each polynomial for $n = 10$.
    a) $3n^2 - 2n + 4 - 10n - 3n^2$ b) $4 - 6n + 2n^2 - 9n$

11. a) A triangle's base and height are equal. Write its area as a polynomial.
    b) What is the area when the base is 10 cm?

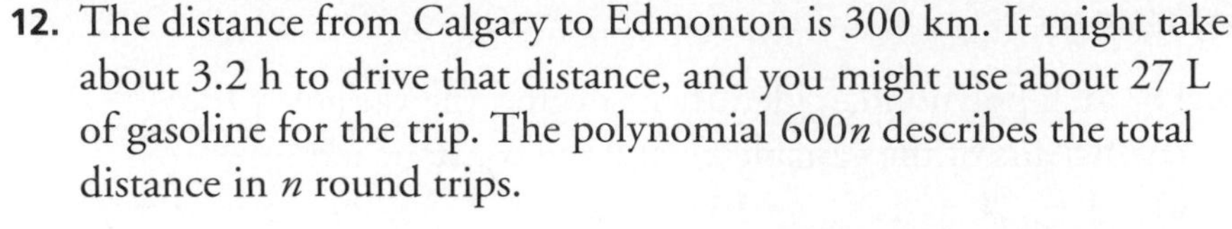

12. The distance from Calgary to Edmonton is 300 km. It might take about 3.2 h to drive that distance, and you might use about 27 L of gasoline for the trip. The polynomial $600n$ describes the total distance in n round trips.

    Record three other polynomials that could describe information related to this trip and describe what each tells about the trip.

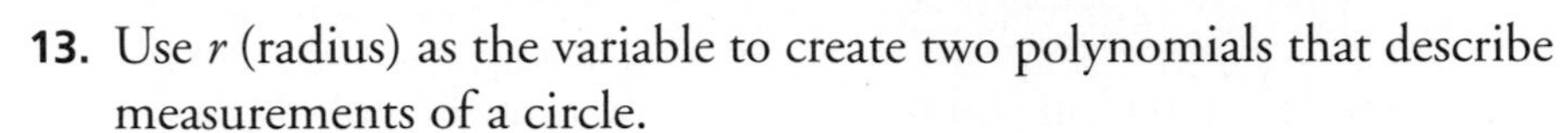

13. Use r (radius) as the variable to create two polynomials that describe measurements of a circle.

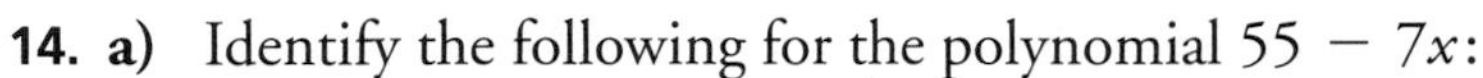

14. **a)** Identify the following for the polynomial $55 - 7x$:
    - its degree
    - the number of terms
    - the variable
    - the coefficient of the variable
    - the constant term

    b) Create a situation that might be described by the polynomial $55 - 7x$.

15. Match equivalent polynomial expressions from List A and List B.

List A	List B
$3x^2 - 2x + 4$	$4 - 2x - 3x^2$
$-3x^2 + 2x - 4$	$-2x + 4 + 3x^2$
$-3x^2 - 2x + 4$	$2x - 4 - 3x^2$
$3x^2 + 2x - 4$	$2x + 3x^2 - 4$

Closing

16. How would a situation that you might describe using the polynomial $50 - 3x$ be different from one you would describe using the polynomial $50 + 3x$?

Extending

17. Jan is a plumber. She charges \$35 to visit a job site. Her hourly rate is \$43.50. Fred repairs furnaces. He charges \$41 for a service call plus \$38.75/h. Let x represent the number of hours they work.

    a) Represent Jan's bill as a polynomial.

    b) Represent Fred's bill as a polynomial.

18. Explain how $3xy + 8$ might describe the area of a shape made up of two rectangles.

6.2 Exploring Models for Polynomials

GOAL

Explore models of polynomials.

YOU WILL NEED

- Algebra Tiles

EXPLORE the Math

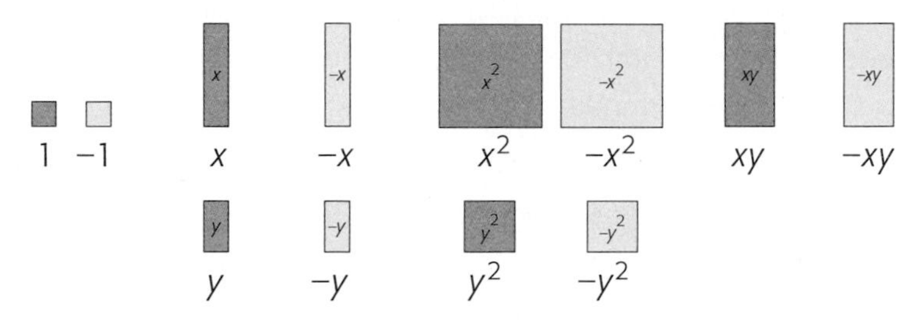

You can represent polynomials using algebra tiles. Notice that the blue tiles are the **opposites** of the red ones. For example, you can represent $-4x^2 - x + 2x + 1$ with 8 tiles. You can use the rules for integer addition and the **zero principle** to see that it can also be modelled with 6 tiles. The zero principle allows you to add or remove pairs of tiles that have the same area but with opposite signs.

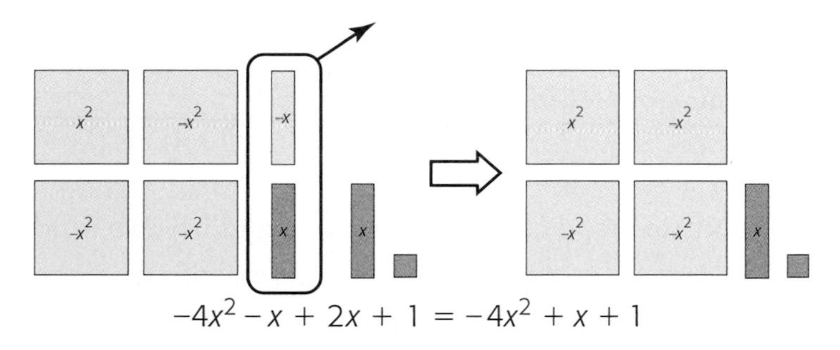

You are going to model a polynomial using three different tile sizes.

- You can use either red or blue tiles.
- You can choose the number of tiles to use. It must be a number from 5 to 10.

? What polynomials can you model with your tiles?

6.3 Gathering Like Terms

YOU WILL NEED

- Algebra Tiles

like terms

terms of a polynomial that are identical (same variable and same exponent) except for their coefficients; like terms are represented by algebra tiles of the same size; e.g., $3x$ and $-2x$ are like terms.

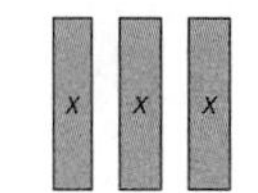

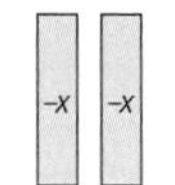

Constants are also like terms.

-3 $+1$

simplify

to combine or gather like terms creating an equivalent polynomial with fewer terms; e.g., $2x - 3x + 8 + 9$ can be simplified to $-x + 17$.

GOAL

Simplify polynomials.

INVESTIGATE the Math

Jia-Wen, her mother, father, and two 6-year-old brothers are planning a skiing holiday. The ski lodge charges \$77 a day for an adult ticket, \$55 for a teen ticket, and \$24 a day for a ticket for a 6-year-old. They need \$60 a day for a room and food for each person.

They have a discount coupon for \$21 for each adult lift ticket and \$10 for each teen or child lift ticket that they will use on the first day.

? What polynomial describes the cost for the family for *d* days?

A. What algebraic expression describes each?

- **i)** the ticket charges for both of Jia-Wen's parents for *d* days before the discount
- **ii)** the room and food charges for both of Jia-Wen's parents for *d* days
- **iii)** the total discount for the parents

B. What algebraic expression describes each?

- **i)** the ticket charges for Jia-Wen and her two brothers for *d* days before the discount
- **ii)** the room and food charges for Jia-Wen and her two brothers for *d* days
- **iii)** the total discount for Jia-Wen and her brothers

C. Create an algebraic expression for the total cost for *d* days. Make sure to add **like terms** to **simplify.**

Reflecting

D. Why are the terms for the room charges and the terms for the discounts not like terms?

E. Explain why it might be useful to simplify a polynomial to evaluate it for a particular value of the variable.

WORK WITH the Math

EXAMPLE 1 | Gathering like terms to simplify

Simplify $2x - 3x^2 + 5 - 4x + 6x^2$

Rachel's Solution: Using algebra tiles

$2x + (-3x^2) + 5 + (-4x) + 6x^2$

I thought of the polynomial as a sum by thinking of subtraction as adding the opposite.

I represented each term of the polynomial with algebra tiles.

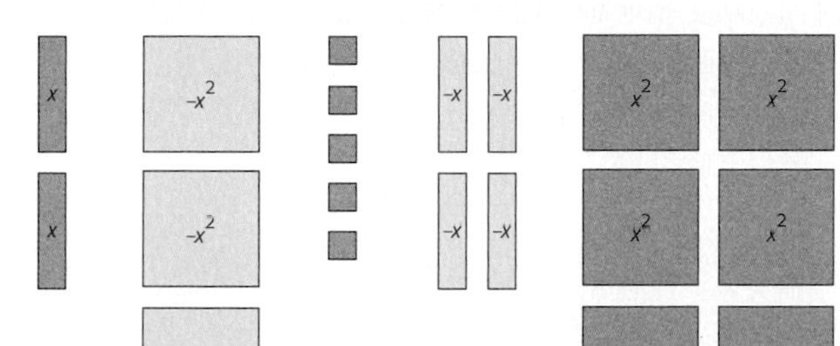

I grouped like terms together by grouping all the tiles with the same shape. Then I used the zero principle to simplify.

$2x + (-4x) = -2x$

$6x^2 + (-3x^2) = 3x^2$

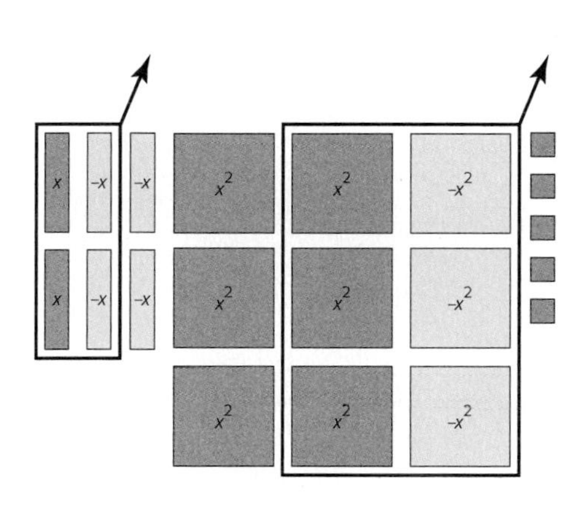

$= -2x + 3x^2 + 5$

I wrote a polynomial that is equivalent to the original one. My polynomial is in a simpler form since it has fewer terms.

Check

Let $x = 2$ in $2x - 3x^2 + 5 - 4x + 6x^2$:

$\rightarrow 2(2) - 3(2)^2 + 5 - 4(2) + 6(2)^2$

$= 4 - 12 + 5 - 8 + 24$

$= 13$

Let $x = 2$ in $-2x + 3x^2 + 5$

$\rightarrow -2(2) + 3(2)^2 + 5$

$= -4 + 12 + 5$

$= 13$

$2x - 3x^2 + 5 - 4x + 6x^2$

$= -2x + 3x^2 + 5$

I decided to check my answer to see if it gave me the same value as the original polynomial by evaluating both expressions for a value for x. I could use any number, but decided to use $x = 2$.

Since both polynomials give the same value when evaluated for $x = 2$, I know my answer is correct.

David's Solution: Using symbols

$2x - 3x^2 + 5 - 4x + 6x^2$
$= 2x + (-3x^2) + 5 + (-4x) + 6x^2$

I rewrote the polynomial to be the sum of its terms.

Like terms: $2x$ and $-4x$
$-3x^2$ and $6x^2$

The like terms are the ones with exactly the same variables and exponents.

$= 2x + (-3x^2) + 5 + (-4x) + 6x^2$
$= [2x + (-4x)] + [6x^2 + (-3x^2)] + 5$
$= -2x + 3x^2 + 5$

I grouped the like terms together and added the coefficients just as I would add integers.

EXAMPLE 2 | Identifying equivalent polynomials

Which two of the polynomials below are equivalent? Explain.

Polynomial 1:

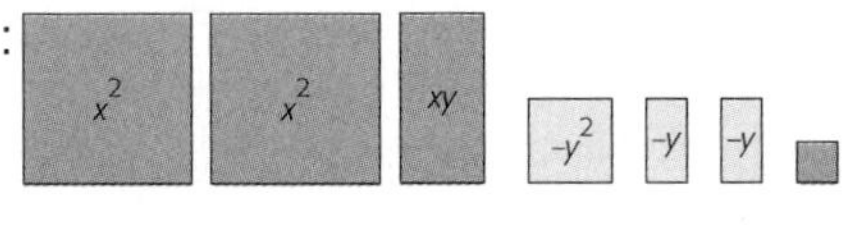

Polynomial 2:

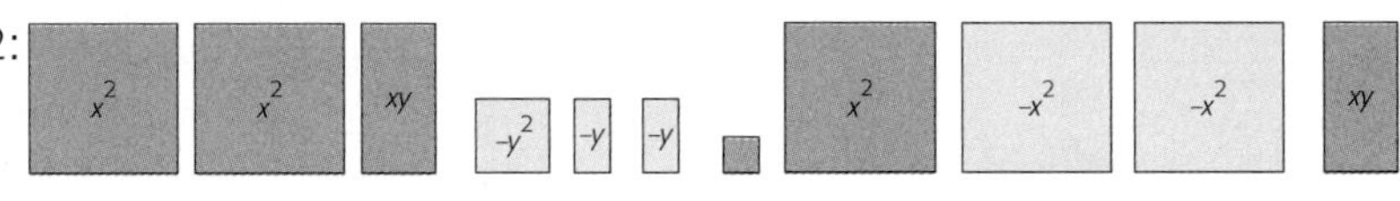

Polynomial 3:

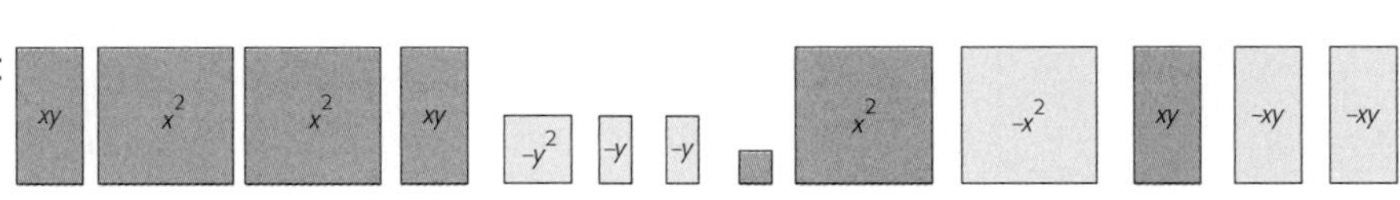

Larissa's Solution: Using algebra tiles

All three polynomials include the tiles for Polynomial 1: two x^2-tiles, an xy-tile, a $(-y^2)$-tile, two $(-y)$-tiles, and a 1-tile.

To compare the polynomials, I noticed what tiles all three polynomials had in common.

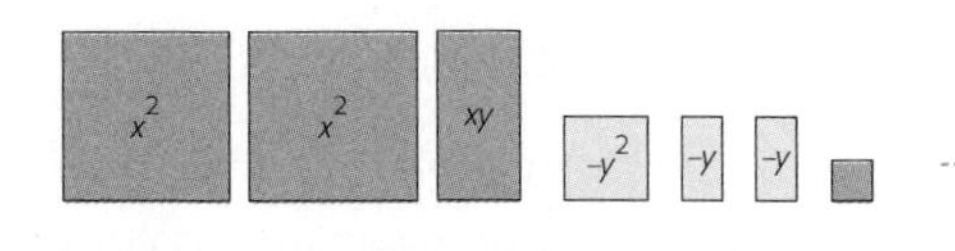

They were the tiles for Polynomial 1.

The leftover tiles for Polynomial 2 are

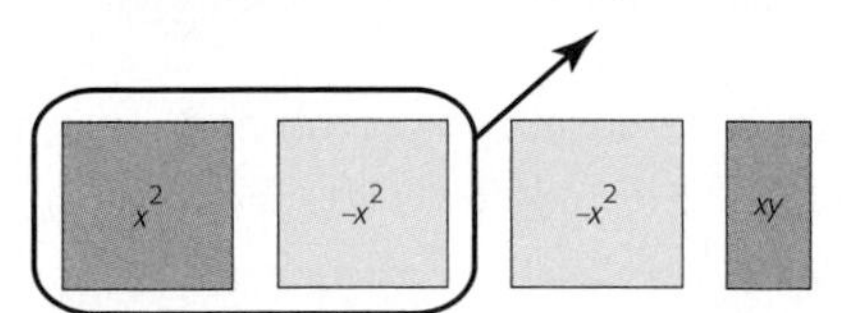

Then I checked to see if the extra tiles for Polynomial 2 or Polynomial 3 made 0.

The first two tiles are x^2 and $-x^2$, which makes a 0, but the other two tiles are not the same shape and size. One is $-x^2$ and the other is xy.

Polynomial 2 is not equivalent to Polynomial 1.

The leftover tiles for Polynomial 3 are

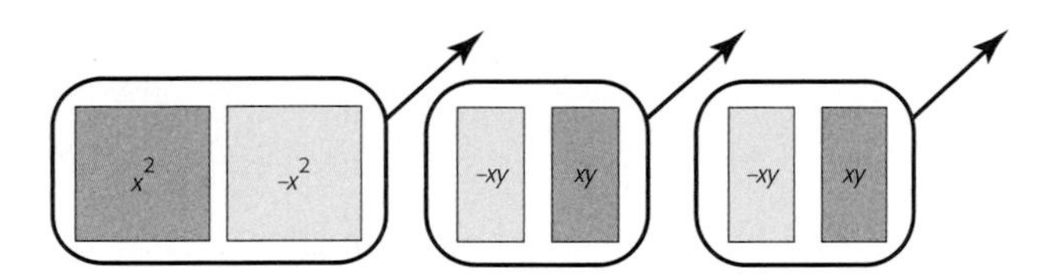

The extra tiles make 0, so Polynomial 3 is equivalent to Polynomial 1.

EXAMPLE 3 | Identifying equivalent polynomials

Which two polynomials below are equivalent?

Polynomial 1: $3y^2 - 4xy + 8 - 2x^2$
Polynomial 2: $y^2 - 3xy + 8 + 2y^2 - 2x^2 - xy$
Polynomial 3: $3y^2 + 4xy + 8 - x^2 + x^2$

Thomas's Solution: Using symbols

Polynomial 1:
$3y^2 - 4xy + 8 - 2x^2$

I noticed that Polynomial 1 could not be simplified because there were no like terms.

Polynomial 2:
$y^2 - 3xy + 8 + 2y^2 - 2x^2 - xy$
$= 1y^2 + (-3)xy + 8 + 2y^2 + (-2)x^2 + (-1)xy$
$= 3y^2 - 4xy + 8 - 2x^2$

I simplified Polynomials 2 and 3 by adding the coefficients of like terms.

Polynomial 3:
$3y^2 + 4xy + 8 - x^2 + x^2$
$= 3y^2 + 4xy + 8 + (-1)x^2 + 1x^2$
$= 3y^2 + 4xy + 8$

Polynomial 2 is equivalent to Polynomial 1.

In Summary

Key Ideas

- When two polynomials are simplified, only like terms are combined. For example, when simplifying $-5x^2 + x + 3x^2 - x + 4$, you add $-5x^2$ to $3x^2$ and x to $-x$.
$$\begin{aligned}-5x^2 + x + 3x^2 - x + 4 &= (-5x^2 + 3x^2) + [x + (-x)] + 4\\ &= (-2x^2) + 0 + 4\\ &= -2x^2 + 4\end{aligned}$$
- The rules that apply to adding integers apply to adding like terms of polynomials. For example,
$$\begin{aligned}-5x^2 + 3x^2 &= (-5 + 3)x^2\\ &= -2x^2\end{aligned}$$

Checking

1. Write a simplified polynomial for each set of algebra tiles.

a) 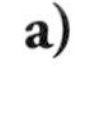 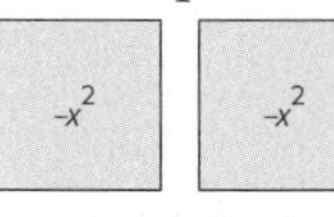  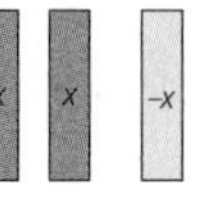 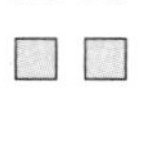

b) 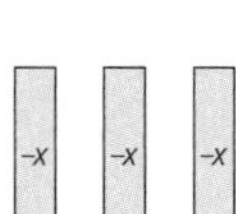 

2. Copy the polynomials and gather the like terms.

a) $4x + 2 - 2x^2 - 3x + 6$

b) $5 - 2x^2 + 4y - 2y + x^2 + 7$

Practising

3. Write a polynomial expression for each algebra tile model. Identify which expressions are equivalent.

a)  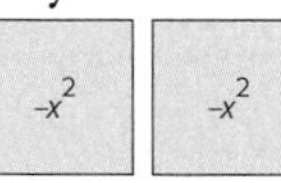 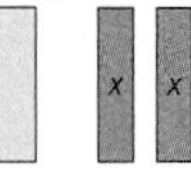

c) 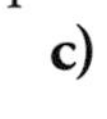 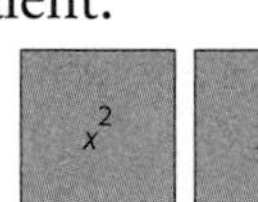 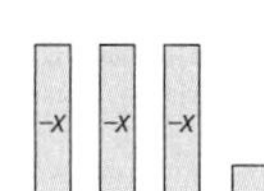

b) 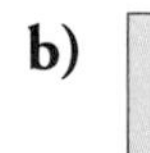 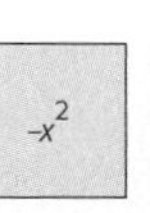 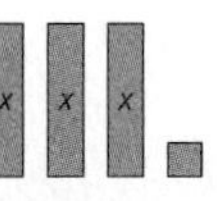 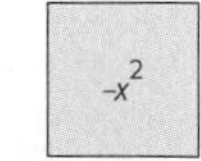

d) 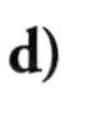 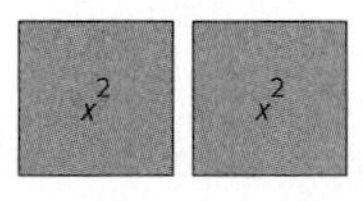 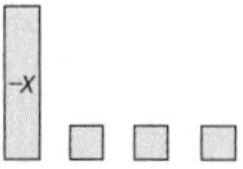

4. Write a simplified polynomial for each set of algebra tiles.

a) 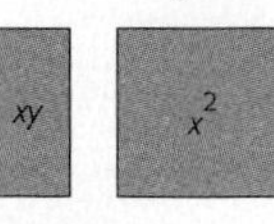 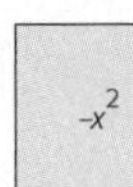 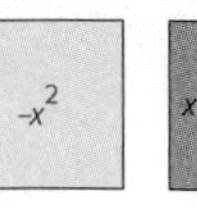 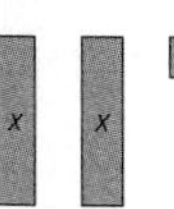 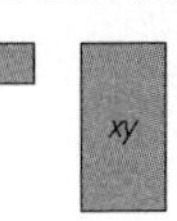  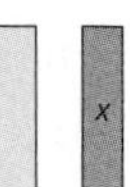

b) 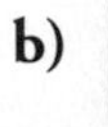 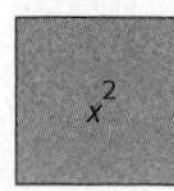 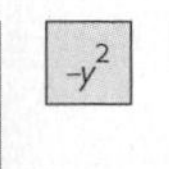 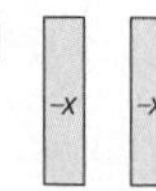 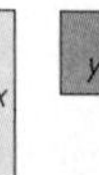 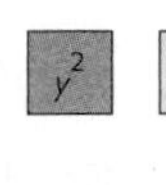 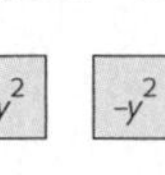

5. List the like terms. Then simplify.
   a) $4x^2 + 2x - 4x^2 - 3$
   b) $-6xy + 2x^2 - y^2 + 9 + (-5) + 2xy$
   c) $15 + 3y + 6x^2 + 4y - 2y$
   d) $4x - 2xy + 8x^2 - 5xy + 3y + 7x - 5x^2$

6. **Multiple choice.** What is the simplified form of $4x^2 + 2x - 3x^2 - 3x - y$?
   A. $x^2 + x - y$
   B. $x^2 - x - y$
   C. $-x^2 - x - y$
   D. $6x - y$

7. **Multiple choice.** How many terms are there when you simplify $-6y^2 + 2x^2 - y^2 + 9 + (-5) + 2xy$?
   A. two
   B. three
   C. four
   D. five

8. **Multiple choice.** Which shows an error?
   A. $2x^2 - 3xy + y^2 - 2y + 4x$ is simplified to $2x^2 - xy + y^2$
   B. $3x^2 + xy - x^2 - y^2 - 3$ is simplified to $2x^2 + xy - y^2 - 3$
   C. $15 - 3x + 4y + 2y$ is simplified to $15 - 3x + 6y$
   D. $4y + 3y^2 - xy + 6xy$ is simplified to $3y^2 + 5xy + 4y$

9. Write the missing values in each pair of polynomials so that the polynomials are equivalent. Explain one of your solutions.
   a) $2y^2 - 5xy + \blacksquare xy + 9y^2$ and $\blacksquare y^2 - 12xy$
   b) $3x^2 - 4xy - 9 + \blacksquare + \blacksquare xy - 9x^2$ and $\blacksquare x^2 + 12xy - 12$
   c) $\blacksquare x + 2x^2 - 5xy + 8 + 7x - \blacksquare x^2 + \blacksquare$ and $-5x - 9x^2 - 5xy - 9 + 5x$
   d) $10x - 7xy + \blacksquare y^2 + 9y^2 + \blacksquare xy$ and $\blacksquare x + xy + 12y^2$

10. Create a polynomial with three pairs of like terms. Simplify it.

11. A polynomial is represented with 15 algebra tiles. After simplifying it by gathering like terms, it can be represented with nine tiles. What could the original polynomial be? Explain.

12. Express the perimeter of each figure as a polynomial. Simplify.

a)

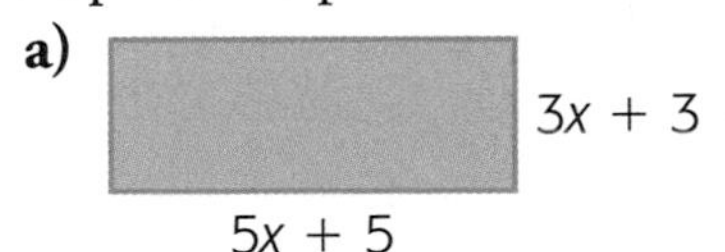

b)

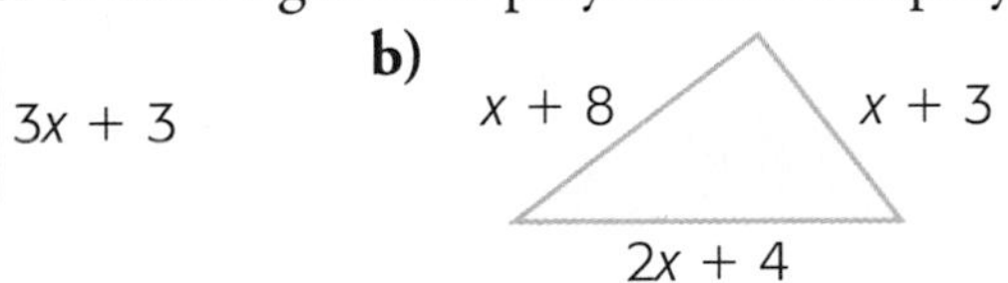

Closing

13. Sam said that y and y^2 are like terms since they both use a y. Do you agree? Explain.

Reading Strategy

Visualizing

Use algebra tiles to model and support your answer.

Extending

14. Sketch two different shapes to fit each description.
   a) The perimeter is $8x + 10$.
   b) The area is $4x^2 - 2x - 9$.

6.4 Adding Polynomials

YOU WILL NEED

- Algebra Tiles

GOAL

Simplify polynomial sums.

INVESTIGATE the Math

Sam adds two polynomials and the sum is $-x^2 - 2y + 4$.

? What two polynomials might Sam have added?

A. 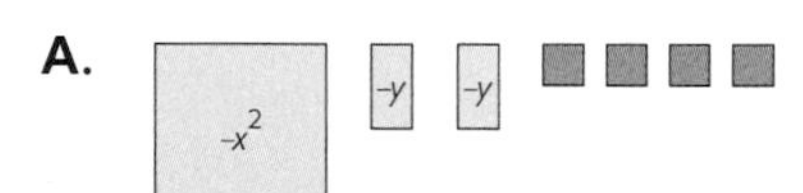

Could Sam have represented the two polynomials with blue tiles only? Could he have represented them with red tiles only? Explain.

B. Suppose $2x^2$ was a term of one of the polynomials. What do you know about the other polynomial? Explain.

C. Suppose $3y$ was a term of one of the polynomials. What do you know about the other polynomial?

D. List three different pairs of polynomials Sam might have added.

Reflecting

E. How did knowing how to add integers help you solve the problem?

F. Why can only like terms be added when you add polynomials?

G. Why might you say that adding polynomials is really the same as simplifying?

WORK WITH the Math

EXAMPLE 1 | Identifying an error in simplifying a polynomial by visualizing

Rachel simplified $(-2x^2 + 4x - 3) + (2x^2 - 4x - 1)$ and got $-4x^2 - 2$.

Describe Rachel's mistake. How would you help her correct it?

Jia-Wen's Solution: Using algebra tiles

I would suggest using algebra tiles.

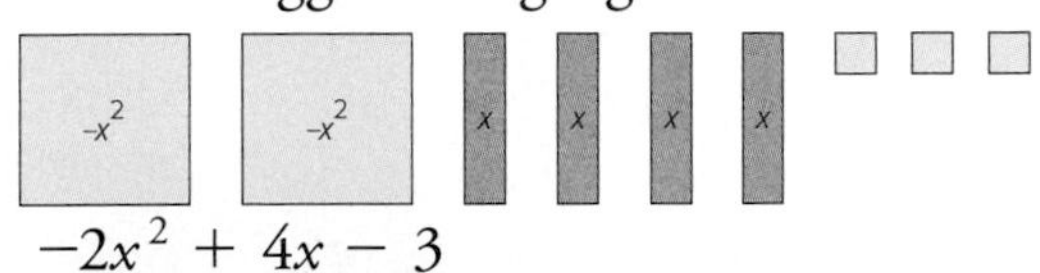

$-2x^2 + 4x - 3$

$2x^2 - 4x - 1$

I think Rachel added the x^2 terms and the constants incorrectly.

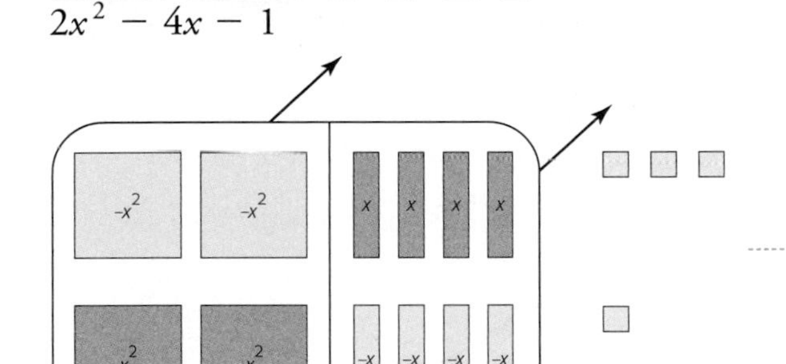

I used the zero principle to add red and blue tiles that were alike. When they added to 0, I removed them.

Four (-1)-tiles were left, so the sum should be -4 and not $-4x^2 - 2$.

Larissa's Solution: Using symbols

I would add the coefficients of like terms.

$$(-2x^2 + 4x - 3) + (2x^2 - 4x - 1)$$

I noticed that the coefficients of x^2 were opposites and so were the coefficients of x. That means they add to 0.

The constant terms are -3 and -1, so they add to -4.

$$= 0x^2 + 0x - 4$$

$$= -4$$

I noticed that I began with second degree polynomials but ended with a 0 degree polynomial.

EXAMPLE 2 | Using the zero principle to simplify polynomial sums

Add $(4x^2 + 2xy - 8)$ to $(-6x^2 - 4xy)$.

Sam's Solution: Using algebra tiles

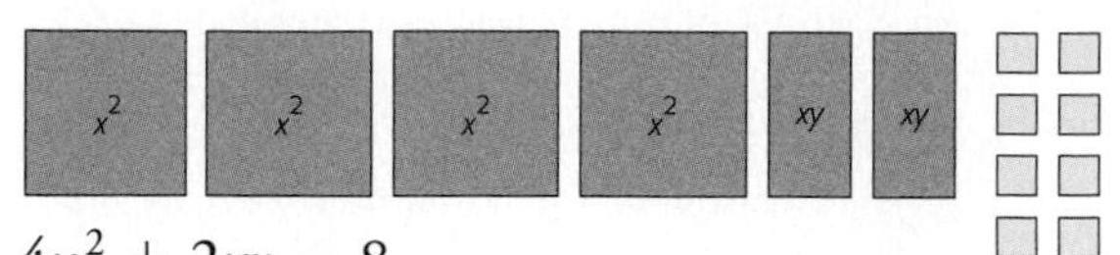

I represented each polynomial with algebra tiles.

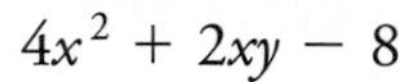

$4x^2 + 2xy - 8$

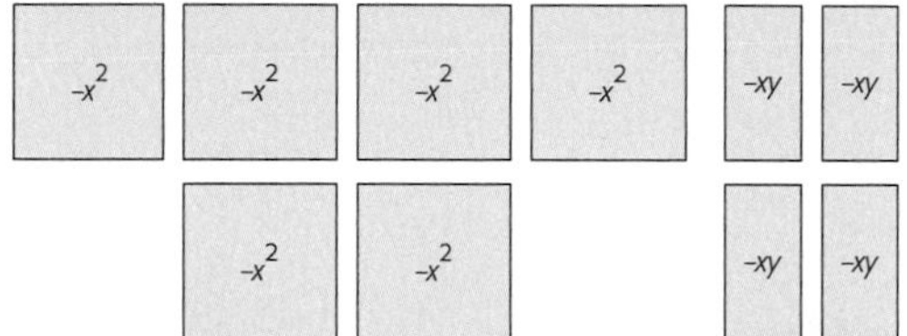

$-6x^2 - 4xy$

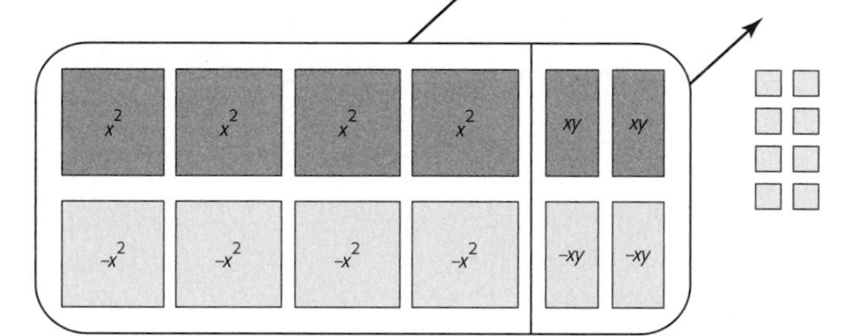

I combined like terms.
I used the zero principle.
Whenever there were identical numbers of red and blue tiles, the sum is 0, so they could be removed.

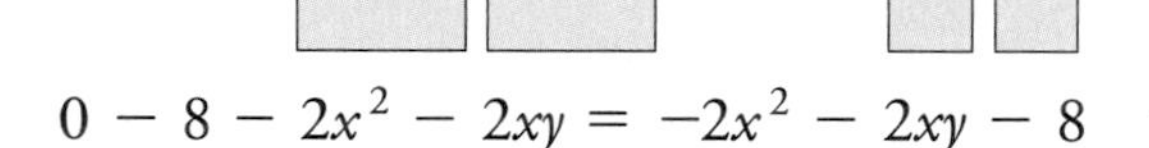

$0 - 8 - 2x^2 - 2xy = -2x^2 - 2xy - 8$

Then I recorded the expression for the tiles that were left.

$(4x^2 + 2xy - 8) + (-6x^2 - 4xy) = -2x^2 - 2xy - 8$

Rachel's Solution: Using symbols

$(4x^2 + 2xy - 8) + (-6x^2 - 4xy)$
$= [4x^2 + (-6x^2)] + [2xy + (-4xy)] - 8$

I knew I could regroup then combine like terms: $4x^2$ and $-6x^2$ as well as $2xy$ and $-4xy$.

$= [4x^2 + (-4x^2) + (-2x^2)] + [2xy + (-2xy) + (-2xy)] - 8$

I thought about it the same way I think about adding integers.

$= 0 + (-2x^2) + 0 + (-2xy) - 8$
$= -2x^2 - 2xy - 8$

I used the zero principle to combine numbers and their opposites, and then figured out how much was left over.

EXAMPLE 3 | Using polynomials to represent and solve problems

Joan and Chris both have jobs. They work the same number of hours per week. Their pay rates and expenses are shown.

	Pay per Hour	Weekly Expenses
Joan	\$15	\$40 transportation
Chris	\$14	\$35 cafeteria charge

a) Use a polynomial to describe their combined income.
b) Determine their combined weekly income if they both work 40 h in a week.

Thomas's Solution

a) Let h be the number of hours worked.
Joan's income per week $= 15h - 40$
Chris's income per week $= 14h - 35$

I used h as the variable. It represents how many hours they worked. I had to multiply h by their pay rate and subtract their expenses since they have to pay for these costs out of the money they earn.

$$(15h - 40) + (14h - 35)$$
$$= 15h + 14h + (-40) + (-35)$$
$$= 29h - 75$$

I added the polynomials to get the combined income. I regrouped then added like terms.

b) $29h - 75 \rightarrow 29(40) - 75$
$= 1160 - 75$
$= 1085$

Their combined income is \$1085 if they both work 40 h in a week.

I substituted 40 for h in the polynomial I created, then evaluated the expression.

In Summary

Key Idea

- The sum of two polynomials is always a polynomial.

Need to Know

- Two polynomials can be added by
  - representing each using algebra tiles and simplifying by using the zero principle
  - grouping the like terms together from both polynomials and adding their coefficients
    For example, when adding $(-5x^2 + x)$ to $(3x^2 - x + 4)$, you add $-5x^2$ to $3x^2$, x to $-x$, and 0 (the constant in the first polynomial) to 4.
- The rules that apply to adding integers apply to adding like terms of polynomials. For example, $-5x^2 + 3x^2$ is equivalent to $(-5 + 3)x^2$.

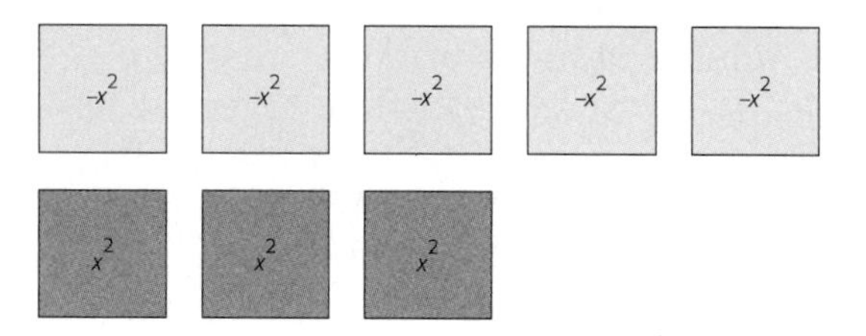

- The degree of the sum of two polynomials is equal to or less than the degree of each polynomial being added.
  For example,
  $(2y^2 - xy + 4) + (2x^2 + 2xy + 3) = 2x^2 + 2y^2 + xy + 7$
  second degree   second degree   second degree
  $(2y^2 - xy + 4) + (-2y^2 + xy + 3 + x) = 7 + x$
  second degree   second degree   first degree

Checking

1. Draw algebra tiles to represent each sum.
   Use a simplified polynomial to describe the sum.
   a) $(2x^2 + 5xy) + (-4x^2 + 1)$
   b) $[-x^2 + (-3xy)] + (6xy - 4)$
   c) $(-4y^2 - 2) + (8y^2 + xy + 7)$

2. Add by grouping like terms and adding the coefficients.
   a) $(-4xy + 2x + 7) + (3xy - 7x + y - 9)$
   b) $(3x^2 - 2x - 3y) + (-5x^2 + 4y - 7x)$

Practising

3. You are going to add $(2x^2 - 8)$ to $(3x^2 + 5x + 2)$. Which like terms will you add?

4. Use algebraic expressions to describe the polynomials modelled. Then determine the sum.

a)

b)

c)

d)

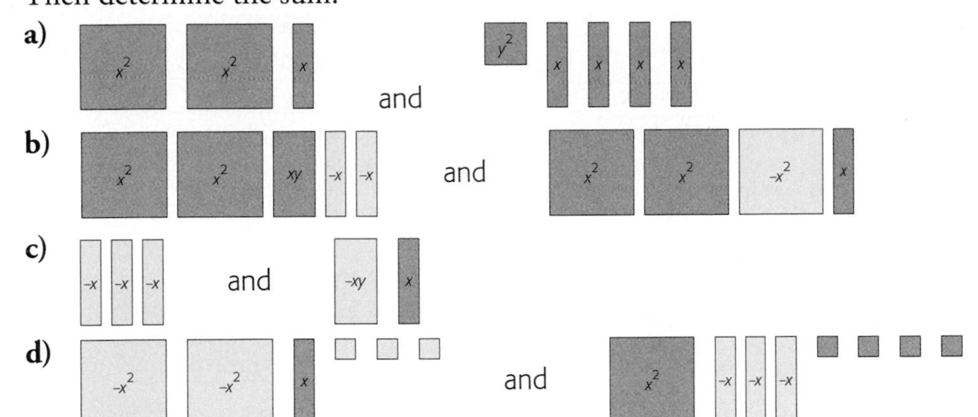

5. Draw algebra tiles to represent each sum. Use a simplified polynomial to describe the sum.
   a) $(-8y^2 - 4xy) + (-4y^2 + 2xy - 7)$
   b) $[-3x^2 + (-5y)] + [8y - 8 + (-5x^2)]$
   c) $(-6x^2 - 2x) + (8x^2 + 3xy - 8x - 2)$

6. Model each sum. Then write a simplified polynomial for the sum.
   a) $(2x + 8) + (-x + 7)$
   b) $(x^2 - 3xy + 2) + (2x^2 + 7xy - 4)$
   c) $(-x^2 + 3y + 2) + (3x^2 - y - 4)$
   d) $(4y^2 - 2xy - 1) + (-6y^2 + 5xy + 6)$

7. **Multiple choice.** What expression represents the perimeter of this rectangle?

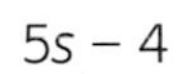

   A. $16t - 4s + 6$ **C.** $3s - t - 3$
   B. $6t + 6s - 6$ **D.** $3t + 3s - 3$

8. **Multiple choice.** What is the coefficient of xy when you simplify $5x^2 - 3xy - y^2 + 12xy - 3x^2$?
   A. 2 **B.** 8 **C.** -9 **D.** 9

9. **Multiple choice.** What is the sum of $2x^2 + 5x + 3xy - 2$ and $-6xy - 5x^2 + 7$?
   A. $-4x^2 + 3xy + 5$ **C.** $-3x^2 + 5x + 3xy + 5$
   B. $-3x^2 + 5x - 3xy + 5$ **D.** $-4x^2 - 3xy + 5$

10. Which two pairs of polynomials have the same sum?

a) $(-7x^2 - 4x - 2) + (3x^2 - 6x + 8)$
b) $(6x^2 - 7x + 5) + (-10x^2 - 3x - 6)$
c) $(8x + 5) + (-4x^2 - 18x + 1)$
d) $(-x^2 - 2x + 4) + (5x^2 - 8x + 2)$

11. Add each pair of polynomials. Explain your strategy. Use an algebra tile model for at least one pair.

a) $(2x^2 + 7x - 9) + (3x^2 + 8x - 2)$
b) $(-2x^2 + 7xy - 9) + (3x^2 - 8xy - 2)$
c) $(2y^2 + 7x) + (-y^2 - 3x - 2)$
d) $(-8x^2 + 2xy - 3) + (3x^2 - 2)$

12. Describe how the zero principle can help you add $(-2x^2 + 7xy - 3)$ to $(2x^2 - 3xy + 5)$.

13. Express the total area of each design as a polynomial.

a)

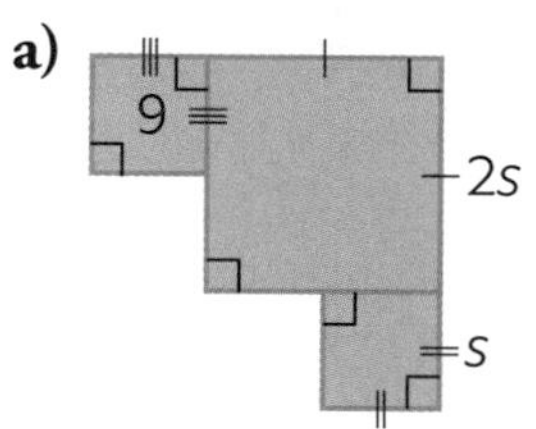

b)

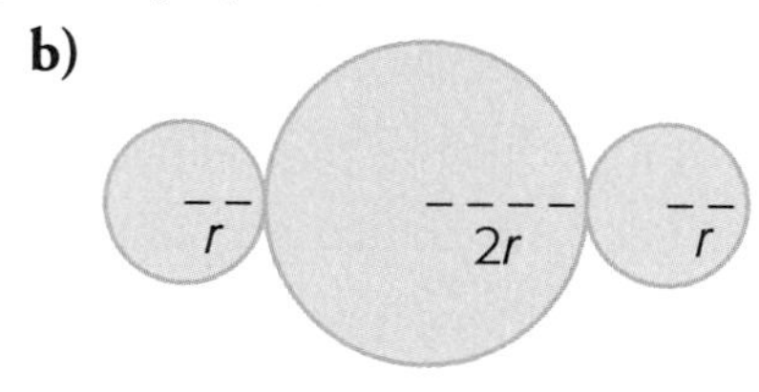

14. Jeff had \$42 and bought some T-shirts that cost \$8 each. Alistair had \$80 and bought the same number of shirts, but the ones he bought cost \$9 each. What polynomial describes how much money Jeff and Alistair have left altogether?

15. David added $(3x^2 - 2x + 4) + (5x^2 - 6)$ and got $8x^2 - 8x + 4$. Discuss with a partner how you could convince David that he made an error.

Closing

16. Why can any polynomial be considered a sum of other polynomials?

Extending

17. Two simplified polynomials are added. The coefficients of x are four apart.

a) Can the coefficient of x in the sum be negative?
b) Can it be positive?
c) Can it be zero?

18. Create two 3-term polynomials so that the sum has each of the following numbers of terms:

a) 2 terms **b)** 1 term

Mid-Chapter Review

FREQUENTLY ASKED Questions

Q: How might polynomials be alike and how might they be different?

A: Polynomials are alike since they are all expressions that are the sums of numbers (constants) and terms that involve variables raised to positive integer powers. Their degrees, the variables used, the number of terms, the coefficients, and the constants can be different.

For example, $3x^2 - 2x + 4$ is a polynomial with three terms using the variable x. It is second degree since there is an x^2 term. The coefficients for x^2 and x are 3 and -2. The constant is 4.

The polynomial $-2x + 4$ is first degree since there is only an x^1 term and there are only two terms, but it has the same variable, the same coefficient for x, and the same constant term as the first polynomial.

Study | *Aid*

- See Lesson 6.3, Examples 1, 2, and 3.
- Try Mid-Chapter Review questions 1, 2, and 8.

Q: When and how might you use a polynomial to model a real-life situation?

A: You can sometimes use a polynomial to represent a situation in which there is a variable representing an unknown amount.

For example, the total green area below could be represented as $x^2 - 4$.

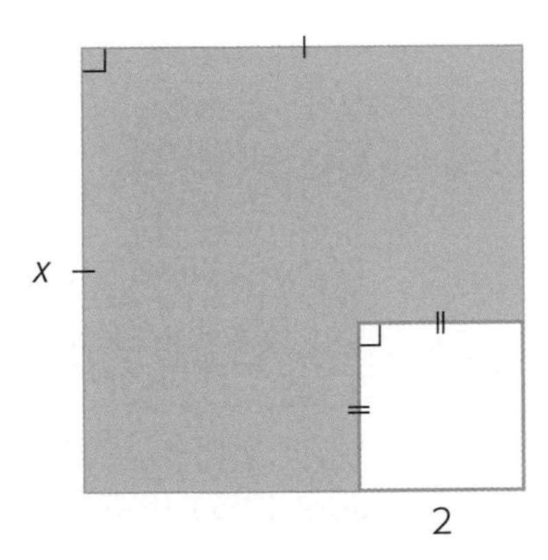

For example, the total cost of n items that cost $6 each, if there is a final discount of $5, is $6n - 5$.

Study | *Aid*

- See Lesson 6.1, Examples 1, 2, and 3.
- Try Mid-Chapter Review questions 3 and 4.

Study | *Aid*

- See Lesson 6.3, Examples 1 and 2.
- Try Mid-Chapter Review questions 5, 6, and 8.

Q: How can you represent polynomials with models?

A: You can use algebra tiles to represent polynomials. You can represent opposites using a different colour.

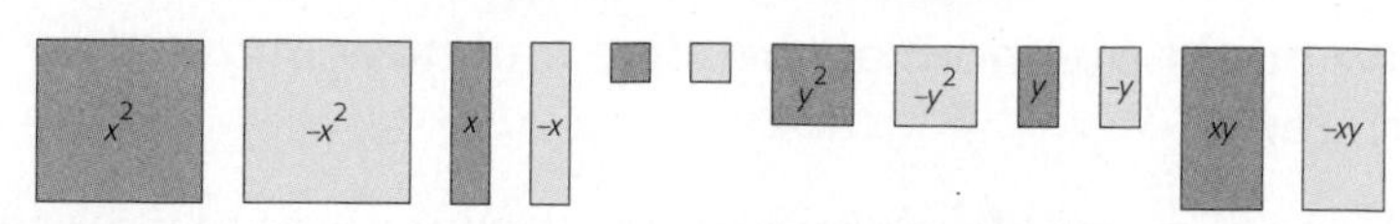

Study | *Aid*

- See Lesson 6.4, Examples 1, 2, and 3.
- Try Mid-Chapter Review questions 6, 7, 8, and 9.

Q: How do you recognize equivalent polynomials?

A: You might check to see if the terms are the same but just in a different order. You might also simplify a polynomial by gathering like terms.

For example, the polynomial $2x + 5 - 3 - 4x$ could be simplified to $-2x + 2$ using the zero principle, since $2x + (-4x) = -2x$ and $5 + (-3) = 2$.

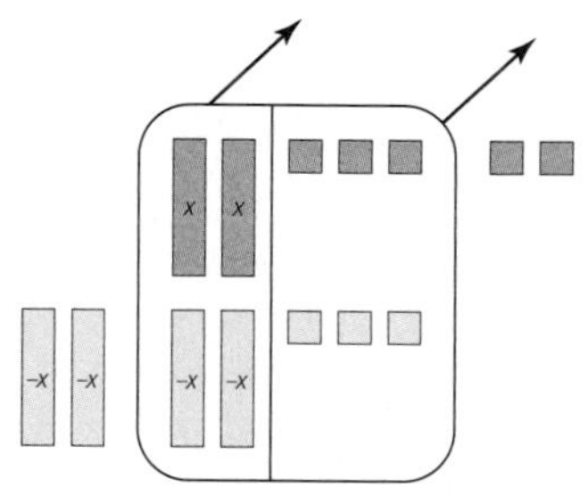

Study | *Aid*

- See Lesson 6.4, Examples 1, 2, and 3.
- Try Mid-Chapter Review questions 11, 12, 13, and 15.

Q: How can you add polynomials?

A: You add polynomials by gathering like terms. Sometimes you have to use the zero principle to simplify the sum.

For example, to add $(-2x^2 - 5xy + 3) + (3x^2 + 6xy - 2)$, you combine the x^2 terms, the xy terms, and the constants.

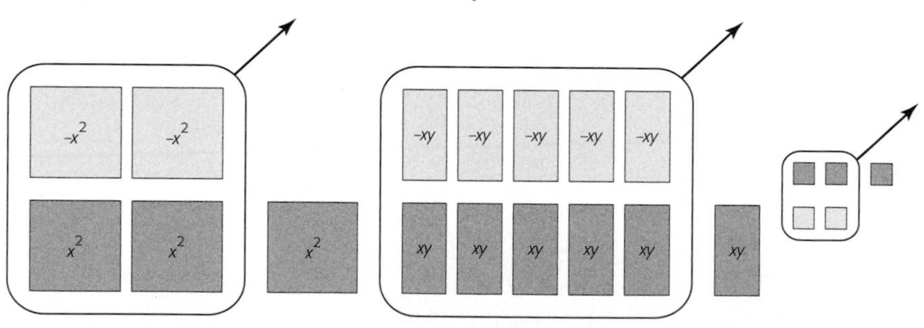

$-2x^2 + 3x^2 = x^2$ since $(-2) + 3 = 1$

$-5xy + 6xy = xy$ since $(-5) + 6 = 1$

$3 + (-2) = 1$

So $(-2x^2 - 5xy + 3) + (3x^2 + 6xy - 2) = x^2 + xy + 1$

You can add using the rules for adding integers. For example,

$$(2xy - 3x + 8) + (-7xy + 5x - 12)$$
$$= [2xy + (-7xy)] + (-3x + 5x) + (8 - 12)$$
$$= -5xy + 2x - 4$$

Practice

Lesson 6.1

1. For each polynomial, identify its degree, the variable(s), the coefficient of x^2, and the constant term.

a) $-6x^2 - 2xy + 5$ **b)** $4x^2 - 3$ **c)** $-3y - 4$

2. Write a polynomial to match each description.

a) the same degree as $-t^2 + 4$

b) the same number of terms as $4t^2 - 8st + 7$

c) the same coefficient of x as $-2x^2 + 5x$

d) a different constant than $-2m^2 + 7m - 3$

3. Evan bought 4 composters at one price, p, and another 2 composters that cost \$2 more. Record a polynomial to describe the total price.

4. Describe a situation to fit each polynomial.

a) $4x + 16$ **b)** $20 - 2c$ **c)** $-16n + 52$

Lesson 6.3

5. What polynomial does each algebra tile model represent?

a)

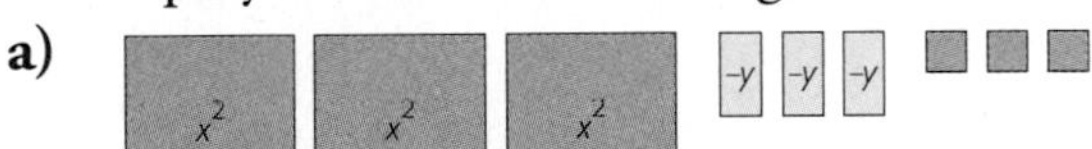

b)

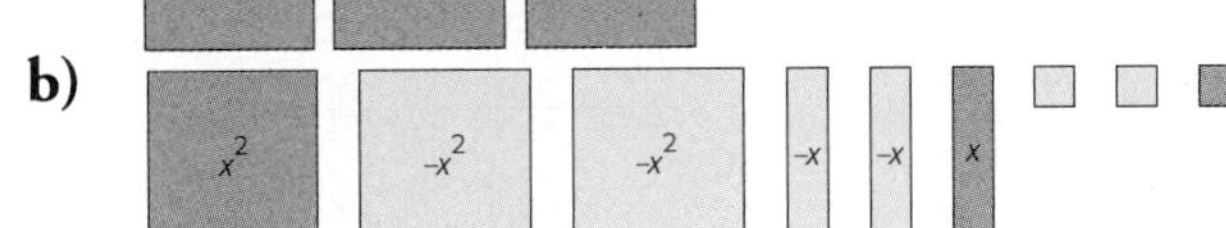

c)

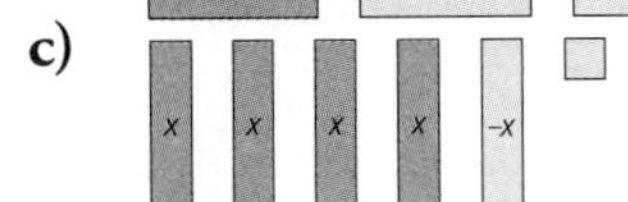

6. Model each polynomial. Gather like terms and simplify.

a) $-2x^2 - 4xy + 7 + 2xy$

b) $-4x^2 - 9 + 8x^2 + 2y$

c) $3x^2 + 2x - 4x - 8$

d) $-3y^2 - 4 - 5x - 2x + 5y^2 + 2$

7. Simplify each.

a) $4m - 3m$ **c)** $-7x + 6 + 2x - 8$

b) $-k^2 - 2k^2 + 4k$ **d)** $6x + 3x^2 + 2 - 8x^2$

8. a) Show that the polynomial $4x^2 - 2x - 3$ can be modelled with nine algebra tiles.

b) Create three other polynomials that can also be modelled with nine algebra tiles.

9. Liam gathered like terms for the polynomial $2j^2 - 5k + 7j$. His result is $9j - 5k$. Is he correct? Explain.

10. Express the perimeter of each polygon as a polynomial.

a)

$x + 2$

$3x - 4$

b)

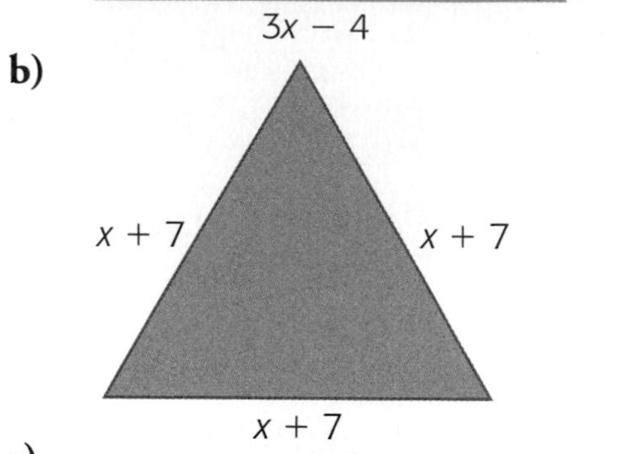

c)

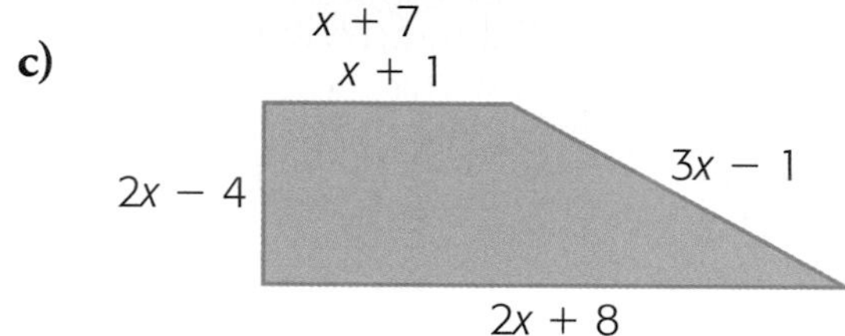

Lesson 6.4

11. Name the polynomials modelled. Then determine the sum.

a) **b)**

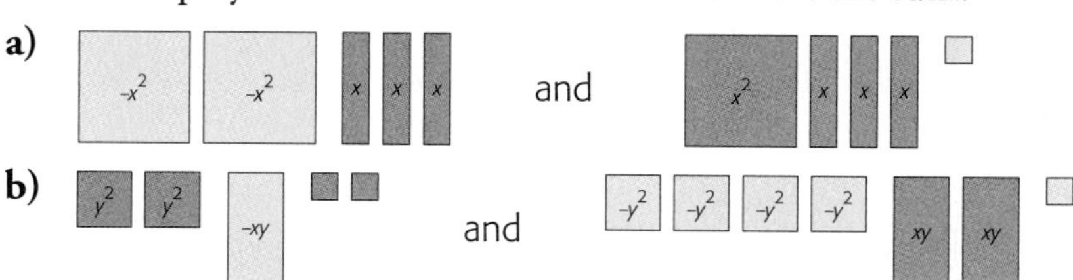

12. Model the sums. Then write a simplified polynomial for the sum.

a) $(-x + 2) + (-4x + 1)$

b) $(2y^2 - 5x + 1) + (-4y^2 + 6x - 3)$

c) $(-3x^2 + 2xy + 5) + (3x^2 - 4xy - 7)$

d) $(-4x^2 - 3x - 4) + (-2x^2 + 2x + 4)$

13. The sum of two polynomials is given. For each, list three pairs of second degree polynomials that might have been added to get that sum.

a) $-6x^2 - 5xy + 1$ **b)** $10x^2 - 7x + 6$

14. You add two simplified second degree polynomials with one variable, x. The first has two negative coefficients and a positive constant. The second has one negative coefficient, a constant of 0, and one positive coefficient. What could the signs of the coefficients and the constant for the sum be? Show your thinking.

15. Create and solve a problem that can be modelled by adding $(100 - 5w)$ to $(200 - 4w)$.

6.5 Subtracting Polynomials

YOU WILL NEED

- Algebra Tiles

GOAL

Subtract like terms using different strategies.

LEARN ABOUT the Math

A class is playing a game with algebra tiles. Each player gets two pouches that contain tiles. The player draws some tiles from each pouch and must subtract the contents of one pouch from the other.

What are some strategies you can use to determine the difference between two polynomials?

EXAMPLE 1 Using a take-away strategy

From the first pouch, the tiles drawn represent $3x^2 - 2x + 2$.
From the second pouch, the tiles drawn represent $2x^2 - 2x + 1$.
Determine the difference.

Erin's Solution

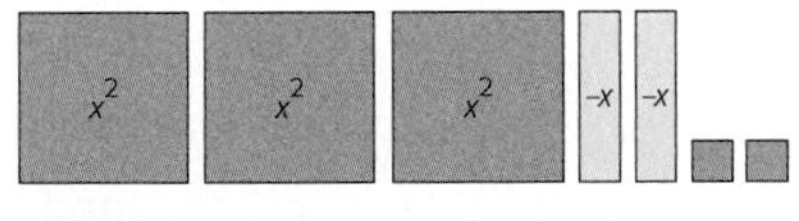

$3x^2 - 2x + 2$

I modelled the first polynomial with tiles.
I thought about subtraction as the process of taking away. In this case, I need to take away two x^2-tiles, two $(-x)$-tiles and one 1-tile. I can do this by removing these tiles.

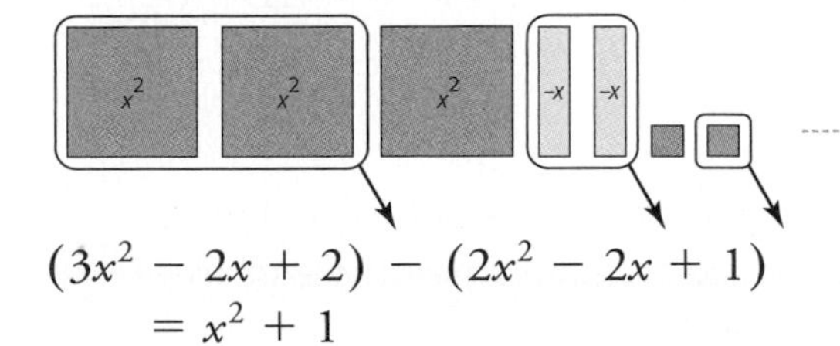

$(3x^2 - 2x + 2) - (2x^2 - 2x + 1)$
$= x^2 + 1$

I subtracted by removing the tiles that represented the second polynomial. I was left with one x^2-tile and one 1-tile. This is the difference.

Example 2 | Using a take-away strategy with the zero principle

From the first pouch, the tiles drawn represent $3x^2 - 2x + 1$.
From the second pouch, the tiles drawn represent $2x^2 - 2x - 2$.
Determine the difference.

David's Solution

To subtract, I can model the first polynomial and take away tiles for the second polynomial.

I started with the tiles for $3x^2 - 2x + 1$. I took away two x^2-tiles and two $(-x)$-tiles. I needed to take away two (-1)-tiles, but I didn't have any.

I used the zero principle to add two 1-tiles and two (-1)-tiles first.

Then I took away the two (-1)-tiles.

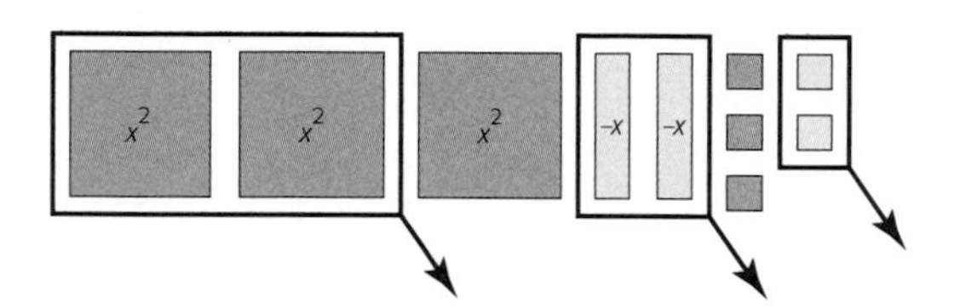

$(3x^2 - 2x + 1) - (2x^2 - 2x - 2) = x^2 + 3$
$x^2 + 3$ uses only 4 tiles.
You should subtract to have the fewest tiles.

I counted the leftover tiles. I realized that I had subtracted like terms.

$$3x^2 - 2x^2 = x^2$$
$$-2x - (-2x) = 0$$
$$1 - (-2) = 3$$

EXAMPLE 3 | Visualizing a comparison to subtract

From the first pouch, the tiles drawn represent $-4x^2 + xy + 1$.
From the second pouch, the tiles drawn represent $-2x^2 + 3xy + 1$.
Determine the difference.

Larissa's Solution

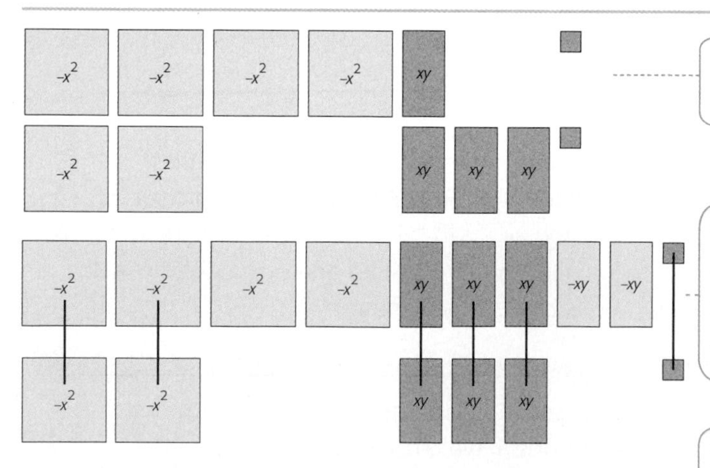

I modelled both polynomials. To subtract, I can compare like terms.

The first polynomial had two more $(-x^2)$-tiles and the same number of 1-tiles. It had fewer xy-tiles, so I added two xy-tiles and two $(-xy)$-tiles to the first polynomial.

$(-4x^2 + xy + 1) - (-2x^2 + 3xy + 1)$
$= -2x^2 - 2xy$

By matching like terms, I could see exactly what was extra in the first polynomial. The extra tiles are the difference.

EXAMPLE 4 | Reasoning about adding the opposite

From the first pouch, the tiles drawn represent $2y^2 - 2x - 2$.
From the second pouch, the tiles drawn represent $-y^2 - x + 4$.
Determine the difference.

Jia-Wen's Solution

$$(2y^2 - 2x - 2) - (-y^2 - x + 4)$$
$$= (2y^2 - 2x - 2) + (y^2 + x - 4)$$

I know that, with integers, a strategy you can use to subtract is to "add the opposite." I reasoned that this might work with polynomials, since a polynomial becomes a number when the variables are replaced with numbers. I changed the subtraction sign to addition then wrote the opposite of the second polynomial.

$$= (2y^2 + y^2) + (-2x + x) + [(-2) + (-4)]$$
$$= 3y^2 - x - 6$$

I grouped the like terms, then simplified.

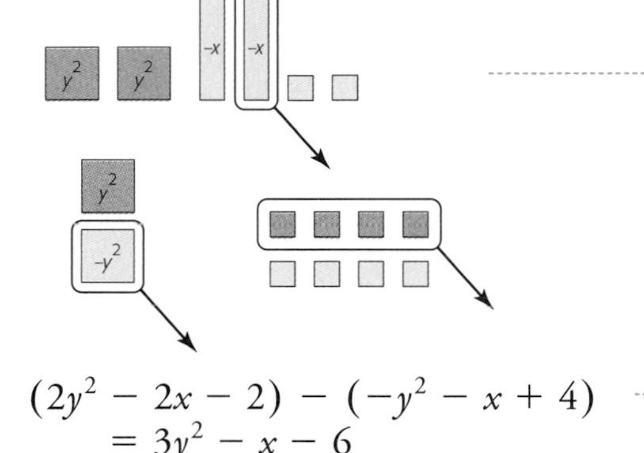

To verify my conjecture I used tiles to see if I would get the same result. I started with the tiles for $2y^2 - 2x - 2$ and took away one $(-x)$-tile. I needed to take away one $(-y^2)$-tile and four 1-tiles, but didn't have any.

I used the zero principle to allow me to take away one $(-y^2)$-tile and four 1-tiles.

$$(2y^2 - 2x - 2) - (-y^2 - x + 4)$$
$$= 3y^2 - x - 6$$

I counted the leftover tiles to determine the difference. My answer was the same. Adding the opposite worked.

Reflecting

A. Why did Erin, David, Larissa, and Jia-Wen subtract only like terms?

B. When is the zero principle important for subtracting polynomials? Explain.

C. Why is it useful to be able to add polynomials in order to subtract?

D. Do you think "adding the opposite" is a strategy that will always work to subtract two polynomials? Explain.

WORK WITH the Math

EXAMPLE 5 | Subtracting polynomials symbolically.

Simplify $(3x^2 - 7x + 12) - (-4x^2 - 3x + 13)$

Sam's Solution

$$\begin{aligned}&(3x^2 - 7x + 12) - (-4x^2 - 3x + 13)\\ &\quad = (3x^2 - 7x + 12) + (4x^2 + 3x - 13)\end{aligned}$$

To do this subtraction with algebra tiles would require 42 tiles. I decided it would be easier to add the opposite instead. I changed the subtraction sign to addition then wrote the opposite of the second polynomial.

$$\begin{aligned}&\quad = (3x^2 + 4x^2) + (-7x + 3x) + (12 - 13)\\ &\quad = 7x^2 - 4x - 1\end{aligned}$$

I grouped the like terms together, then simplified.

EXAMPLE 6 | Representing and solving a problem using polynomials

At a track meet, there were 7 competitors from each school as well as 28 other top-ranked competitors. The number of competitors at a second event was 8 from each school and 14 other top-ranked competitors. Use a polynomial to describe how many more students were at the second meet than the first one.

Rachel's Solution

Let s represent the number of schools.

I used s as the variable to represent the number of schools since it was an unknown.

Event 1

Total number of competitors $= 28 + 7s$

Event 2

Number of competitors $= 14 + 8s$

$$\begin{aligned}&(14 + 8s) - (28 + 7s)\\ &\quad = (14 - 28) + (8s - 7s)\\ &\quad = -14 + s\end{aligned}$$

I subtracted to tell how many more were at the second meet.

There were $s - 14$ more competitors in Event 2.

Check: $(s - 14) + (28 + 7s) = 14 + 8s$

I checked by adding the difference to the number of competitors in Event 1.

In Summary

Key Idea

- When you subtract one polynomial from another, the result is always a polynomial.

Need to Know

- You can interpret subtraction of polynomials using a *take away*, *comparison*, or *adding the opposite* strategy. To calculate the result, you may need to use the zero principle. For example, for $(-4x^2 + 5x + 3) - [-2x + (-3x^2) - 8]$, you could:
  - take away $-3x^2$ from $-4x^2$, leaving $-x^2$
  - add $(-2x)$ and $2x$ using the zero principle and then take away $(-2x)$
  - add $+8 + (-8)$ using the zero principle and then take away the -8,

  so $(-4x^2 + 5x + 3) - [-2x + (-3x^2) - 8] = -x^2 + 7x + 11$.

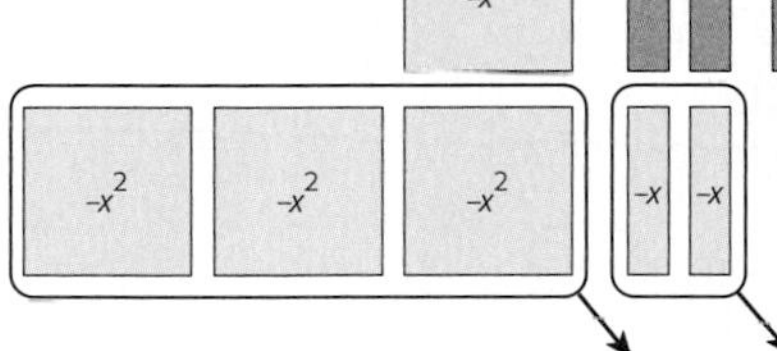

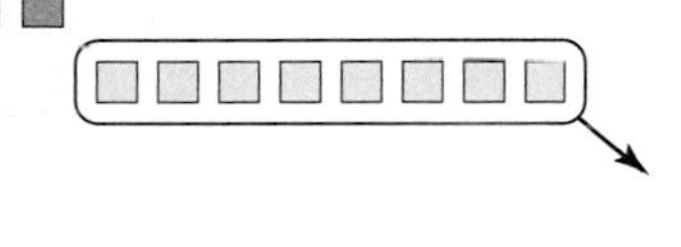

  You can check by adding the difference $[-x^2 + 7x + 11]$ to $[-2x + (-3x^2) - 8]$. The sum is $(-4x^2 + 5x + 3)$.
- You can subtract polynomials by subtracting like terms. For example, to calculate $(-2x^2 + 7x - 3) - (5x^2 + 4x + 1)$, you subtract $5x^2$ from $-2x^2$, $4x$ from $7x$, and 1 from -3, and then add the three resulting terms: $-7x^2 + 3x - 4$.
- When you subtract like terms, you can apply the rules for subtracting integers. For example, $-2x^2 - 5x^2 = -7x^2$, since $-2 - 5 = -7$.
- The difference of two polynomials has a degree equal to or less than that of the polynomial with the greater degree.

Checking

1. What is the polynomial subtraction that is modelled? The circled blocks are being removed.

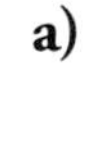

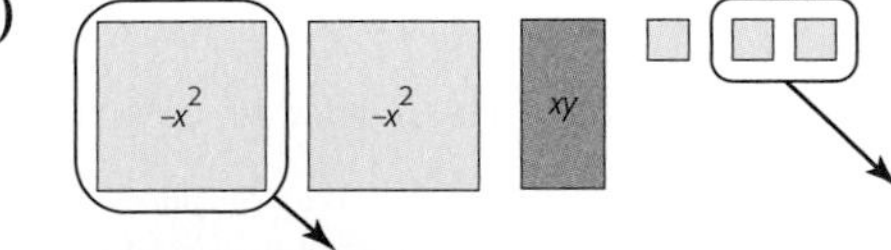

b)

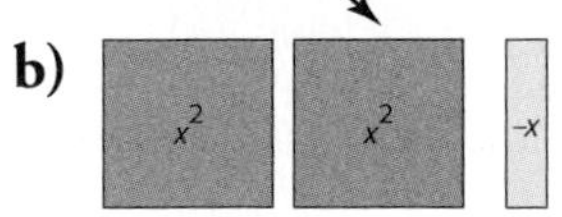

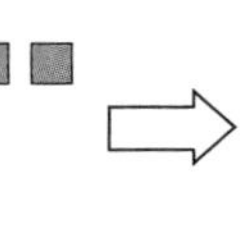

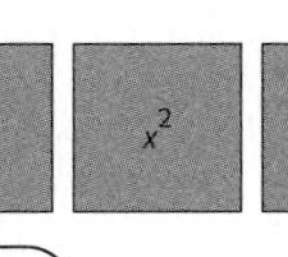

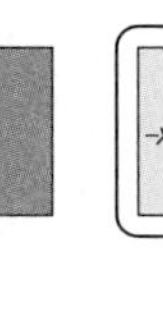

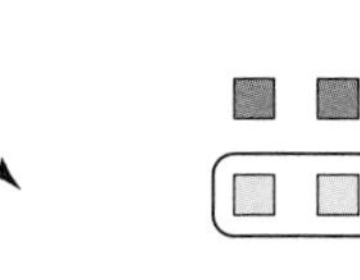

2. Subtract.
   a) $(4y^2 - 2xy - 8) - (-2y^2 + xy - 7)$
   b) $(3x^2 - 7) - (-4x + 9)$

3. Use a polynomial to describe how much more money Angela has left than Bryce. Angela had \$182 and bought hockey tickets for \$23. Bryce had \$157 and bought the same number of tickets for \$22.

Practising

4. What is the polynomial subtraction that is modelled?
   a)

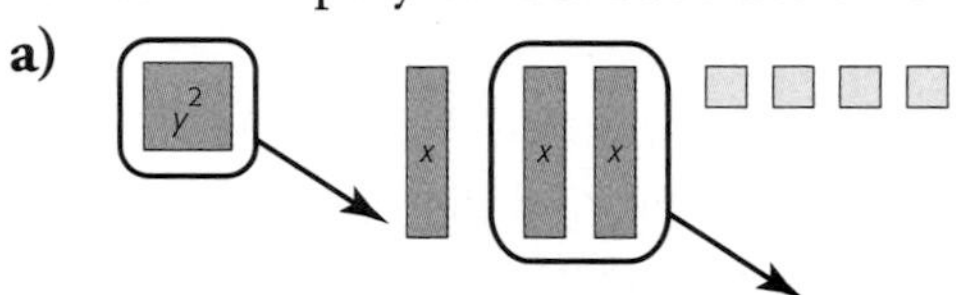

   b)

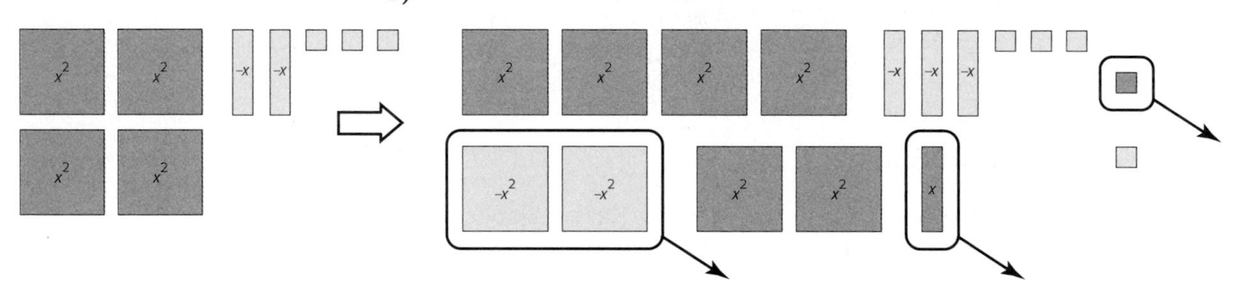

5. What integer subtractions must you perform to subtract $(4y^2 - 3x)$ from $(-6y^2 + 5x)$?

6. Write algebraic expressions for each model then simplify.
   a)
   b)

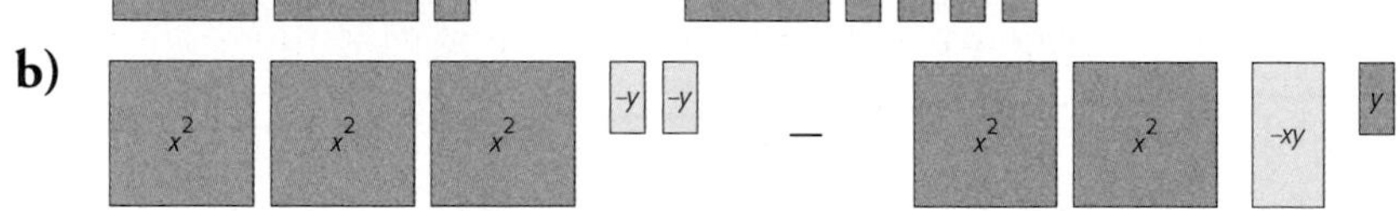

   c)

7. Model the differences using algebra tiles. Then record a simplified polynomial for the difference.
   a) $(2y + 8) - (-y + 7)$
   b) $(x^2 - 3x + 2) - (2x^2 + 7x - 4)$
   c) $(-x^2 + 3xy + 2) - (3x^2 - xy - 4)$

8. **Multiple choice.** Which expression represents the difference between the length and the width of the rectangle?

A. $9r - 2s$ **C.** $16r - s$
B. $s + 8r$ **D.** $8r - s$

9. **Multiple choice.** What is the coefficient of xy when you subtract $-12xy - 3x^2$ from $5x^2 - 3xy - y^2$?

A. -9 **B.** 9 **C.** -15 **D.** 15

10. **Multiple choice.** Which expression is equivalent to $[12x^2 + 5x - 3xy - 2] - [-6xy - 6x^2 + 2]$?

A. $18x^2 - 9xy + 5x - 4$ **C.** $6x^2 - 3xy + 5x - 4$
B. $6x^2 - 3xy + 5x$ **D.** $18x^2 + 3xy + 5x - 4$

11. Subtract. Explain your strategy for each to a partner. Model at least one subtraction using algebra tiles.

a) $(2x^2 + 7x - 9) - (3x^2 + 8x - 2)$
b) $(-2y^2 + 7x - 9) - (3y^2 - 8x - 2)$
c) $(2x^2 + 7xy) - (-x^2 - 3xy - 2)$
d) $(-8y^2 + 2y - 3) - (3y^2 - 2)$

12. Which two pairs of polynomials have the same difference? What is the difference? Show your work.

A. $(3x^2 - 4x + 8) - (-x^2 - 6x + 2)$
B. $(-6x^2 - x + 5) - (-10x^2 + 3x - 6)$
C. $(8x + 2x) - (-4x^2 - 4x + 6)$
D. $(-x^2 - 2x + 4) - (-5x^2 - 4x - 2)$

13. How would you help Rachel understand that her subtraction is incorrect?

$(-2p^2 - 4q + 8) - (5p^2 + 8q - 2) = 3p^2 - 12q + 6$

14. How can you use an algebra tile model to subtract $(-2x^2 + 5y + 2)$ from $(-3x^2 - 4y + 8)$?

15. What must you add to each polynomial to reach a sum of $-4x^2 - 2xy + 7$?

a) $-2x^2 - 8$ **b)** $6x^2 - 8xy + 2$ **c)** $-10x^2 + 2xy - 9$

16. The difference of two polynomials is given. List three pairs of second degree polynomials that might have been subtracted to get that difference for each.

a) $(-2x^2 - 4x + 3)$ **c)** $(5y^2 - xy + 7)$
b) $(3x^2 + y - 8)$ **d)** $(-6x^2 - 4x - 7)$

17. Jeff had \$42 and bought some movie tickets that cost \$8 each. Alistair had \$80 and bought the same number of tickets, but the ones he bought cost \$9 each. What polynomial describes how much more money Alistair has left than Jeff?

18. Create and solve a problem that could be modelled by the polynomial subtraction $(48w - 2) - (18w + 10)$.

19. In a magic square, the rows, columns, and diagonals have the same sum. Complete this magic square.

$8x^2 - 5x + 6$		
	$5x^2 - 4x + 15$	
	$9x^2 - 2x + 3$	$2x^2 - 3x + 24$

Closing

20. Thomas said that to subtract one polynomial from another, "you take away like terms and record what's left." Use an example to show why it might be difficult for someone to follow those instructions.

Extending

21. Two simplified polynomials are subtracted. The coefficients of t^2 in the two polynomials are two apart.

a) Can the coefficient of t^2 in the difference be negative?

b) Can it be positive?

c) Can it be zero?

22. Create two 3-term polynomials so that the difference has each of the following numbers of terms:

a) 2 terms **b)** 1 term

6.6 Solve Problems Using an Organized List

YOU WILL NEED

- Algebra Tiles

GOAL

Solve problems involving polynomials using organized lists.

LEARN ABOUT the Math

Thomas subtracted a polynomial from $3x^2 - 2x - 1$.
The difference required eight algebra tiles to represent it.

? What polynomials could Thomas have subtracted?

EXAMPLE 1 | Using an organized list and the zero principle to determine which polynomial to subtract

The polynomial Thomas subtracted did not use the xy-tiles, y-tiles, or y^2-tiles. What polynomial might he have subtracted?

David's Solution

1. Understand the Problem
I can represent $3x^2 - 2x - 1$ with six tiles.

$3x^2 - 2x - 1$

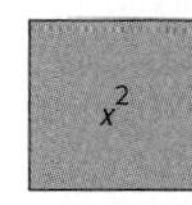
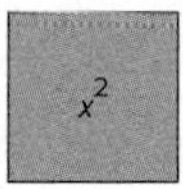
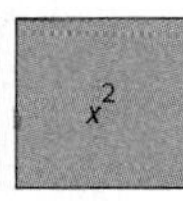
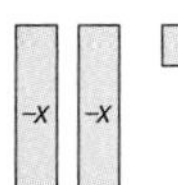

To subtract and end up with more than six tiles, I have to add in extra tiles.

2. Make a Plan
I have to end up with two extra tiles after I take some tiles away, so I have to add three or more extra tiles.

To do that without changing the polynomial, I need to use the zero principle.

3. Carry Out the Plan
Add in tiles that are equivalent to zero, and take away tiles that are a different colour than the tiles you started with.

To use the zero principle, you always add tiles in pairs, so I decided the least number of tiles I could add is four tiles, two red and two blue.

I could add:
$2x^2 + (-2x^2)$
$2x + (-2x)$
$2 + (-2)$
$x^2 + (-x^2)$ and $x + (-x)$
$x^2 + (-x^2)$ and $1 + (-1)$
$x + (-x)$ and $1 + (-1)$

I decided to be organized and think about possible combinations for adding four tiles in the form of zero. First, I imagined adding and subtracting only one kind of tile, and then more than one kind.

So the polynomial subtraction could have been
$(3x^2 - 2x - 1) - (-2x^2)$
$(3x^2 - 2x - 1) - (2x)$
$(3x^2 - 2x - 1) - (2)$
$(3x^2 - 2x - 1) - (-x^2 + x)$
$(3x^2 - 2x - 1) - (-x^2 + 1)$
$(3x^2 - 2x - 1) - (x + 1)$

Then I would subtract two of the new tiles.

4. Look Back
There are many more possibilities if I add more pairs of zero tiles. For example, I could add $2x^2 + (-2x^2)$ and x and $-x$, and then subtract $-2x^2$, x, and -1:
$(3x^2 - 2x - 1) - (-2x^2 + x - 1)$
$= 5x^2 - 3x$

Reflecting

A. How do you know there are more possibilities if you add other pairs of zero tiles?

B. Did David find all the ways to solve the problem by adding four tiles? How do you know?

C. How did using an organized list help David?

WORK WITH the Math

EXAMPLE 2 | **Using an organized list to determine a missing addend**

You add a polynomial to $(-2x^2 - x + 4)$ and the sum requires five algebra tiles.

What could you have added? Show five possible answers.

Thomas's Solution

1. Understand the Problem
I know that I started with seven tiles and ended with five tiles, so I had to get rid of two tiles even though I was adding.

2. Make a Plan
I need to add two tiles that are opposites of tiles in the original polynomial.

First, I'll add only x^2-tiles, then only x-tiles, then only 1-tiles, and then combinations.

3. Carry Out the Plan
There are two $(-x^2)$-tiles, so add two x^2-tiles.
$(-2x^2 - x + 4) + 2x^2 = -x + 4$.
That can be represented with five tiles.

I cannot get five tiles by adding only x-tiles or $(-x)$-tiles.

There was a single $(-x)$-tile. If I added an x tile, I would still have six tiles. If I added two x-tiles, there would still be a single tile, but it would be an x-tile.

$(-2x^2 - x + 4) + 2x = -2x^2 + x + 4$

There are four 1-tiles.
If I add -2, the result is $+2$.
$(-2x^2 - x + 4) + (-2) = -2x^2 - x + 2$
That can be represented with five tiles.

$(-2x^2 - x + 4) + (x^2 + x) = -x^2 + 4$
$(-2x^2 - x + 4) + [x^2 + (-1)] = -x^2 - x + 3$
$(-2x^2 - x + 4) + [x + (-1)] = -2x^2 + 3$

I used two tiles, each time a combination of x^2-tiles, x-tiles, and (-1)-tiles, to get rid of two of the $(-x^2)$-tiles, $(-x)$-tiles, and 1-tiles.

Each can be represented with five tiles.

Five possible polynomials to add are
$2x^2$, -2, $x^2 + x$, $x^2 + (-1)$, and $x + (-1)$.

4. Look Back
There are other possibilities with combinations of three terms. For example,
$(-2x^2 - x + 4) + (2x^2 + x + 1) = 5$.

In Summary

Key Idea

- To use an organized list to solve problems, you need to consider and analyze all the possible situations that could occur. You must account for each situation in your solution.

Need to Know

- Using the zero principle when adding polynomials can reduce the number of tiles needed to model the sum. For example, if you start with $-x^2 + 2$ and add $x^2 + 3$, you would represent the two polynomials you are adding with three tiles and four tiles, for a total of seven tiles.

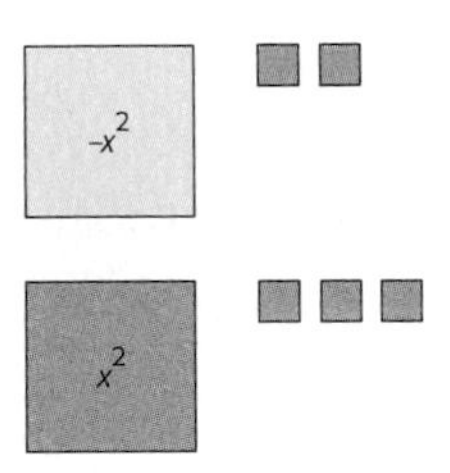

But when you add them, the $(-x^2)$-tiles and x^2-tiles are removed, since their sum is zero, and you are left with only five tiles, not seven.

- Using the zero principle when subtracting polynomials can increase the number of tiles needed to model the difference. For example, if you start with $-x^2 + 2$, you will start with only three tiles. If you want to subtract $x^2 + 4$, you need to add $x^2 + (-x^2)$ so you can subtract the x^2. You must also add $2 + (-2)$ so you can subtract the 4.

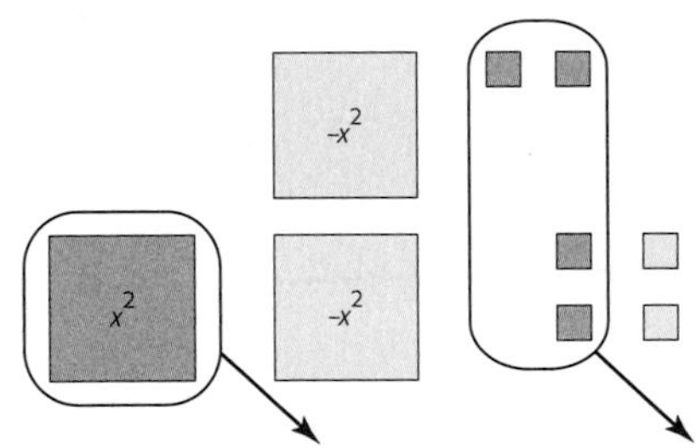

You started with three tiles and ended up with four tiles.

Checking

1. You subtract a polynomial from $2x^2 - 8$. The difference requires three tiles to model it. What might you have subtracted? List three possibilities.

Practising

2. The coefficients of a second degree polynomial where the only variable is x are 3 and -4. The constant term is -2. Work with a partner to list all possible polynomials and calculate the sum of two of them.

3. When you add a polynomial to itself, the sum requires 12 algebra tiles to represent it. What could the polynomial be? Work with a partner to list six possibilities.

4. You add a polynomial to $5x^2 + 3x - 2$. The sum requires only two tiles to model it. What might you have added? List six possibilities. Explain your strategy.

5. List four simplified second degree polynomials you can model with three algebra tiles.

6. The sum of the integer coefficients and constant of a simplified polynomial with three terms is 3. The product of the coefficients and the constant is -12. What could the polynomial be? List five possibilities. Explain your strategy.

7. A rectangle has a perimeter of $4x + 28$.
List eight possible sets of dimensions.

8. The perimeter of the six-sided shape at right is $22x + 4$.
List four possible sets of side lengths.

Closing

9. You are asked to indicate how many simplified polynomials you can model using exactly four algebra tiles. How would an organized list help you solve this problem?

Extending

10. You add two polynomials. Each can be modelled using four algebra tiles. Show that modelling the sum could require 0, 2, 4, 6, or 8 tiles.

11. You subtract two polynomials. Each can be modelled using four algebra tiles. Show that the difference could require 4, 6, or 8 tiles to model it.

12. You add a polynomial that is represented with three algebra tiles to one that is represented with four algebra tiles.
    a) How many tiles could be needed to represent the sum?
    b) How do you know you have all the possibilities?

Math GAME

Target 10

Number of players: 2 to 4

YOU WILL NEED
- Polynomial Game Cards
- Algebra Tiles

How to play

1. Choose two polynomial game cards.
2. Choose a pair of like terms to add or subtract.
3. The player with the coefficient closest to 10 gets a point.
4. The first player with 10 points wins.

David's Turn

$3x^2 - 2y + 5$

$-4x^2 + 6y - 2$

I'll subtract $6y - (-2y)$ to get a coefficient of 8.

Rachel's Turn

$3x^2 - 2y + 5$

$4x^2 - 7x + 8$

$-4x^2 + 6y - 2$

$5x^2 + 12x - 6$

I'll add $5x^2$ and $4x^2$ to get a coefficient of 9.
I get the point.

6.7 Multiplying or Dividing a Polynomial by a Monomial

GOAL

Multiply and divide with a monomial.

YOU WILL NEED

- Algebra Tiles

INVESTIGATE the Math

Rachel has three sets of algebra tiles. Each set is made up of two x^2-tiles, four $(-x)$-tiles, and eight 1-tiles.

She has to share all of the tiles fairly with Jia-Wen.

? What polynomial describes how many tiles are in each share?

A. Why can you write $3(2x^2 - 4x + 8)$ to describe the total number of tiles?

B. What polynomial describes that total? Use tiles to show your thinking.

C. What must you divide the polynomial from part B by to describe each person's share? Explain.

D. What polynomial describes each share? Use tiles to show your work.

Reflecting

E. In which part or parts above did you show that the **distributive property** applies when you multiply a **monomial** by another polynomial? Explain.

monomial

a polynomial with only one term; e.g., $3x$, $4xy$, and (-5) are monomials.

WORK WITH the Math

EXAMPLE 1 Multiplying and dividing monomials

Simplify

a) $(4x)(2x)$ **b)** $10xy \div 5y$

David's Solution

a) $(4x)(2x) = (4)(x)(2)(x)$
$= (4)(2)(x)(x)$

I knew that $4x$ means $(4)(x)$ and $2x$ means $(2)(x)$, so I wrote the expression as a product placing the coefficients together and the variables together. I knew I could do this because you can multiply in any order and get the same answer.

$= (8)(x^{1+1})$
$= 8x^2$

I simplified by adding the exponents on the variable x and by multiplying the coefficients.

b) $10xy \div 5y = \dfrac{(10)(x)(y)}{(5)(y)}$
$= \left(\dfrac{10}{5}\right)(x)(y^{1-1})$

Since division is the inverse operation of multiplication, I reasoned that I could use a similar process for division. I divided the coefficients and subtracted the exponents of the variables that had the same base.

$= 2xy^0$
$= 2x$

I simplified using the fact that $y^0 = 1$.

$(2x)(5y) = (2)(5)(x)(y)$
$= 10xy$

I checked by multiplying. My answer was correct.

EXAMPLE 2 Representing a product

Determine the product $-4(5 - 2x)$.

Jia-Wen's Solution: Using repeated addition

$4(5 - 2x)$
$= (5 - 2x) + (5 - 2x) + (5 - 2x) + (5 - 2x)$
$= 20 - 8x$

First I calculated $4(5 - 2x)$ by adding $5 - 2x$ four times, since multiplication is repeated addition. I added like terms.

$-4(5 - 2x) = -20 + 8x$

Then I took the opposite since I was multiplying by -4, not 4.

$-4(5 - 2x) = -4(5) - (-4)(2x)$
$= -20 + 8x$

I noticed that multiplying each term inside the brackets by -4 resulted in the same product.

Rachel's Solution: Using an area model

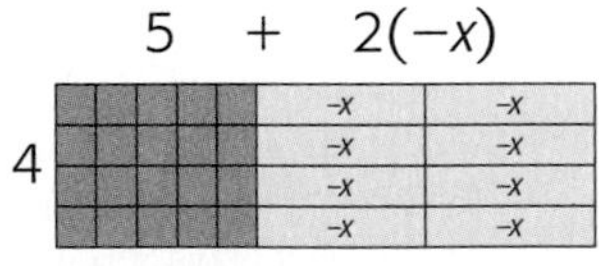

$4(5 - 2x) = 20 - 8x$

I knew that to multiply, you can calculate the area of a rectangle whose length and width are the dimensions being multiplied.

I used a length of $5 - 2x$ and a width of 4. I thought of $5 - 2x$ as $5 + 2(-x)$.

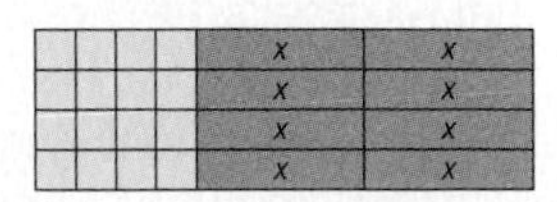

$-4(5 - 2x) = -20 + 8x$

I still had to take the opposite since I was multiplying by -4, not 4.

To get the opposite, I switched red tiles to blue, and blue tiles to red.

EXAMPLE 3 | Multiplying polynomials

Parm is an artist who works in metal and ceramics. He is building a sculpture in the shape of a large trapezoid. The sculpture's proportions are shown in the diagram. To order materials, he needs to calculate the trapezoid's area.

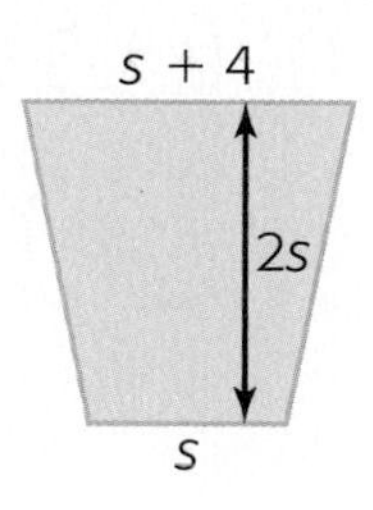

Sam's Solution

$$A = \frac{1}{2}h(a + b)$$
$$= \frac{1}{2}(2s)[s + (s + 4)]$$

I looked up the formula for the area of a trapezoid. It is the height multiplied by the average length of the bases.

I used $2s$ for the height, s for the length of one base, and $s + 4$ for the length of the other base.

$$= \frac{1}{2}(2s)(2s + 4)$$
$$= s(2s + 4)$$

I simplified by collecting like terms inside the square brackets then multiplying $\frac{1}{2}$ and $2s$.

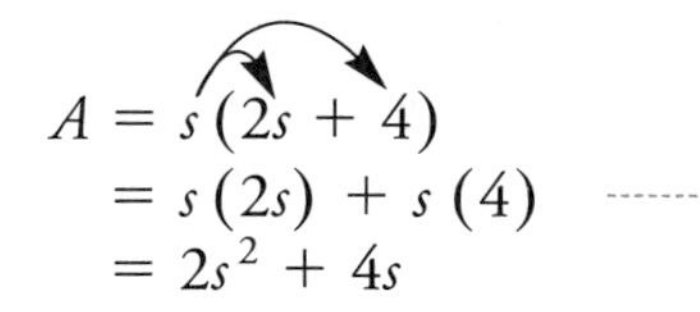

$$A = s(2s + 4)$$
$$= s(2s) + s(4)$$
$$= 2s^2 + 4s$$

I knew that I could use the distributive property to multiply each term inside the brackets by the term outside the bracket(s).

EXAMPLE 4 | Using reasoning and the distributive property to divide

Complete and verify this equation: ■ $(2x - 5) = 8x^2 - 20x$.

Thomas's Solution

■ $(2x - 5) = 8x^2 - 20x$

Using the distributive property, I knew that whatever factor was represented by the blank box would be multiplied by $2x$ and result in $8x^2$.

■ $\times (2x) = 8x^2$

$4x \times (2x) = 8x^2$

$4x$ multiplied by $2x$ gave me $8x^2$.

Check:

$4x(2x - 5) = 8x^2 - 20x$

To verify my answer, I replaced the box with the factor $4x$ and multiplied to make sure the other term would be $-20x$, and it was.

Communication Tip

The words *expand*, *use the distributive property*, and *remove brackets* all mean to multiply a polynomial by a factor.

EXAMPLE 5 | Dividing by a monomial

Divide $(4x^2 + 8x)$ by $2x$.

David's Solution: Using the relationship between multiplication and division

$2x(\blacksquare + \blacksquare) = 4x^2 + 8x$

The quotient is what I have to multiply $2x$ by to get $4x^2 + 8x$.

$4x^2 \div 2x = 2x$ since $(2x)(2x) = 4x^2$
$4(2x) = 8x$

so $2x(2x + 4) = 4x^2 + 8x$
and $(4x^2 + 8x) \div 2x = (2x + 4)$

First, I figured out what to multiply $2x$ by to get $4x^2$. Then I made sure that the value multiplied by 4 gave $8x$.

Larissa's Solution: Using an area model

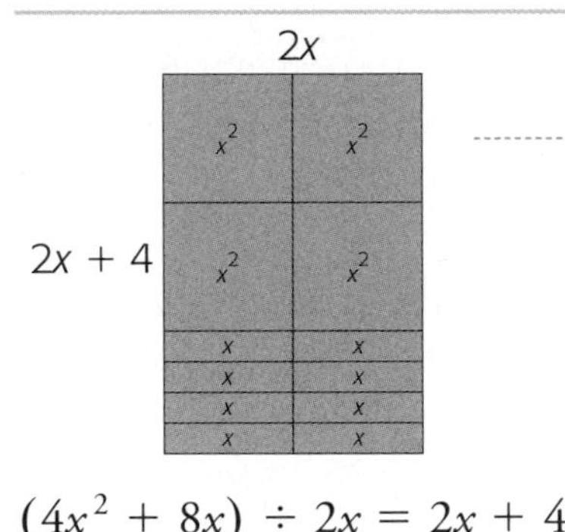

$(4x^2 + 8x) \div 2x = 2x + 4$

You can think of division by thinking about $4x^2 + 8x$ as the area of a rectangle and $2x$ as one of the dimensions.

I arranged the tiles for $4x^2 + 8x$ into a rectangle so that the width was $2x$. The quotient is the length.

I knew I needed a length of $2x$ to multiply by $2x$ to get an area of $4x^2$ and a length of 4 to multiply by $2x$ to get an area of $8x$.

Jia-Wen's Solution: Using the exponent laws

$(4x^2 + 8x) \div 2x = \frac{4x^2}{2x} + \frac{8x}{2x}$

You can divide each part of the polynomial by $2x$.

$= 2x + 4$

When you divide x^2 by x^1, you can subtract exponents to get x^1.
When you divide 4 by 2, you get 2.
When you divide x by x, you get 1.
When you divide 8 by 2, you get 4.

$(4x^2 + 8x) \div 2x = 2x + 4$

In Summary

Key Ideas

- You can multiply or divide two monomials by applying the appropriate operation to the coefficients of the terms and corresponding exponent law to the variables that have the same base. For example, $(-3y)(4y) = -12y^2$ and $-16x^2 \div (-8x) = 2x$
- You can determine the product of a monomial and a polynomial by applying the distributive property—multiplying each term of the polynomial by the monomial. For example,

$$\begin{aligned} 3(2x^2 - 5x + 4) &= 3(2x^2) + 3(-5x) + 3(4) \\ &= 6x^2 - 15x + 12 \end{aligned}$$

- You can determine the quotient of a polynomial divided by a monomial by applying the distributive property—dividing each term of the polynomial by the monomial. For example,

$$\begin{aligned} (9x^2 - 6x) \div 3 &= \frac{9x^2}{3} - \frac{6x}{3} \\ &= 3x^2 - 2x \end{aligned}$$

Need to Know

- You can use repeated addition to represent the product of a constant and a polynomial.
- You can use an area model to represent the product of a constant and a linear polynomial. For example, for $3(2x - 5)$, use a rectangle with length $2x - 5$, or $2x + (-5)$ and width 3.

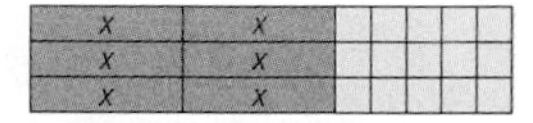

The area of the rectangle is $6x - 15$, which is the product.
- You can use a sharing model to interpret the quotient of a polynomial divided by a constant. For example, for $(6x - 4) \div 2$, you can model $6x - 4$ and put it into two equal groups. The quotient is the size of each group: $3x - 2$.

Checking

1. What multiplication does each represent?
   a) $(3x^2 + 2) + (3x^2 + 2) + (3x^2 + 2) + (3x^2 + 2)$
   b)
2. What division does the model represent?

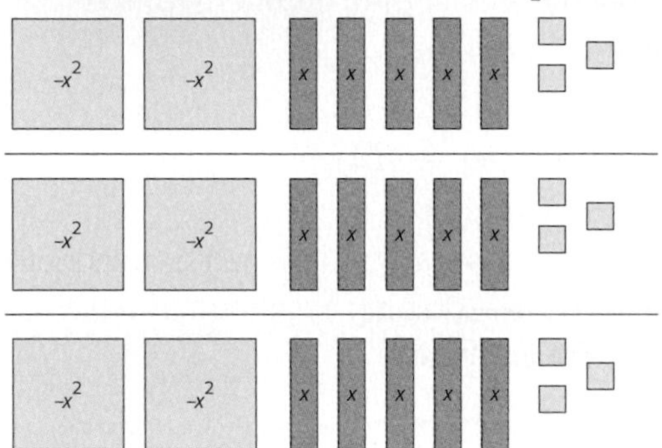

3. Calculate.
   a) $(4x)(-5x)$
   b) $-4(5 - 3s)$
   c) $2y(5y - 4)$
   d) $20y^2 \div (-5y)$
   e) $(12x^2 - 15x + 27) \div 3$
   f) $(12x^2y + 6xy) \div 3x$

Practising

4. What multiplication and what repeated addition does each model represent?
   a)
   b)
   c)
   d)
5. What division does each model represent?
   a)

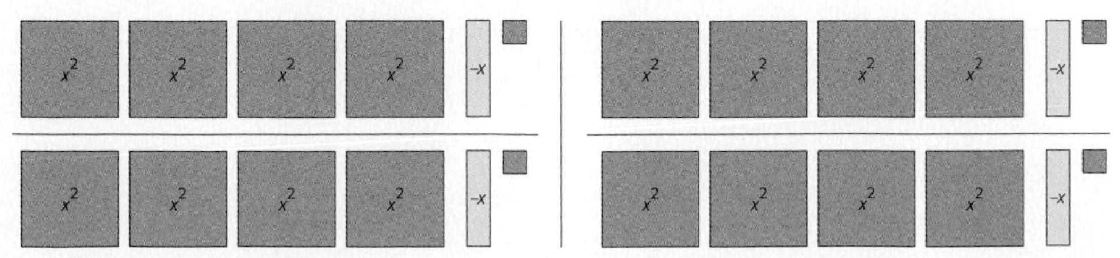

b)

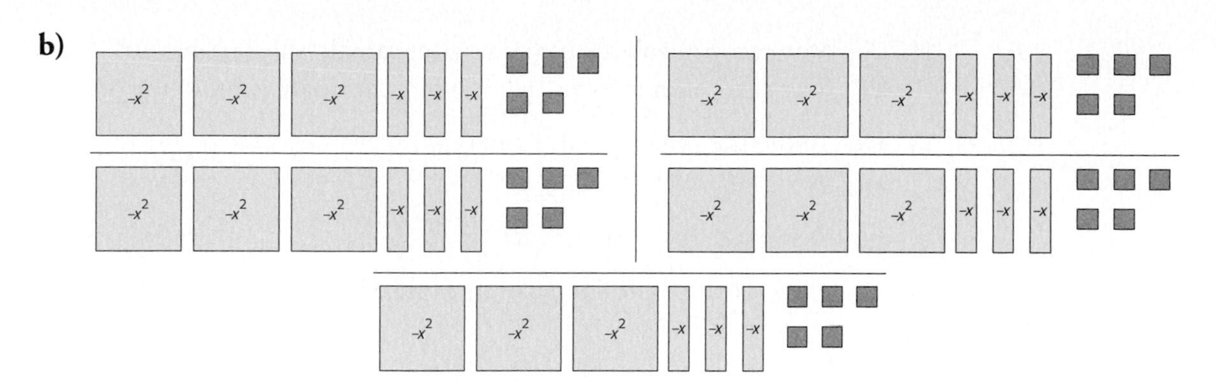

6. Simplify

a) $(-3)(6y)$
b) $(2x)(6y)$
c) $(5y)(6y)$
d) $15y \div (-3)$
e) $15xy \div (-3x)$
f) $15y^2 \div (5y)$

7. Multiply. Use a model for at least one part.

a) $3(2xy + 5)$
b) $8(5x^2 - 2y + 2)$
c) $3x(2y - 1)$
d) $-4(-y^2 - 2x + 3)$
e) $-2x(x + 1)$
f) $-2(2x^2 + 3xy - 2)$

8. Divide. Use a model for at least one part.

a) $(16x^2 - 4x + 8) \div 4$
b) $(25x^2 + 5x) \div 5x$
c) $(-8x + 64) \div (-8)$
d) $(3x^2 + 2x) \div x$
e) $(-12x^2 + 27x - 3xy) \div (-3)$
f) $(-15x^2 + 25xy - 30x) \div (5x)$

9. Explain why the number of terms after you divide a polynomial by a monomial is the same as the number of terms you started with.

10. Multiple choice. Determine the missing polynomial if ■ $\div 5 = 10x + 20$.

A. $2x + 4$ B. $50x + 100$ C. $2x + 100$ D. $50x + 4$

11. Multiple choice. What product does the model at right show?

A. $2x(x - 1)$
B. $-2x(1 - x)$
C. $-2x(x + 1)$
D. $-2x(x - 1)$

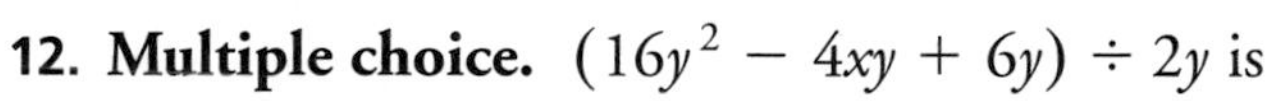

12. Multiple choice. $(16y^2 - 4xy + 6y) \div 2y$ is

A. $3 + 8y - 2x$
B. $8y - 4x + 3$
C. $16y - 4xy + 3$
D. $8 - 2xy + 3$

13. Multiply or divide each. Represent two results using algebra tiles.

a) $5(3y + 1)$
b) $-2(5x - 3)$
c) $x(4x + 2)$
d) $-2(3x^2 + x - 5)$
e) $(4t^2 - 2t + 8) \div 2$
f) $(6s^2 - 15) \div (-3)$
g) $(5y^2 + 2y) \div y$
h) $(8x^2 - 6x + 4) \div 2$

14. a) Why can you solve $16x \div 2x$ by repeatedly subtracting $2x$?
b) Why can you not solve $16x \div 4$ by repeatedly subtracting 4?

15. Determine the missing polynomial.

a) $■ \div 5 = 2x + 3$

b) $■ \div 3x = 5x - 6$

c) $■ \div (-2) = -2x^2 - 4x + 1$

d) $\dfrac{4x^2 + 10x - 8}{■} = 2x^2 + 5x - 4$

16. a) Which of these products are equivalent?

A. $4(3x^2 - 2x - 1)$

B. $2(6x^2 - x - 2)$

C. $4x(3x - 2 - 1)$

D. $2(6x^2 - 4x - 2)$

b) Write another polynomial product equivalent to $6(2x^2 - 4)$.

17. Write simplified algebraic expressions for the perimeter, P, and area, A, of the following figures.

a)

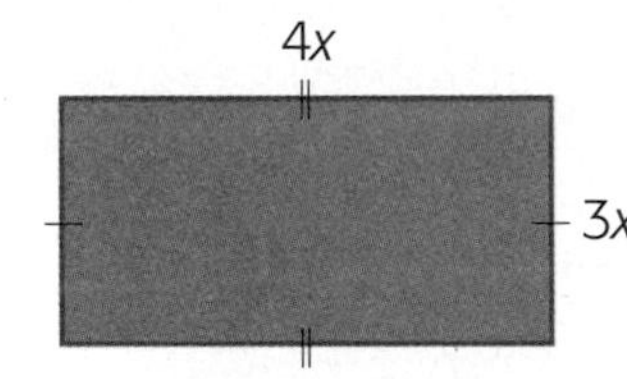

c)

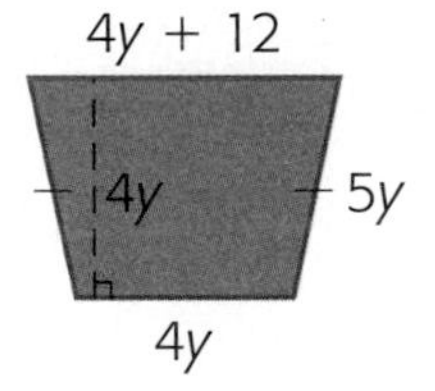

b)

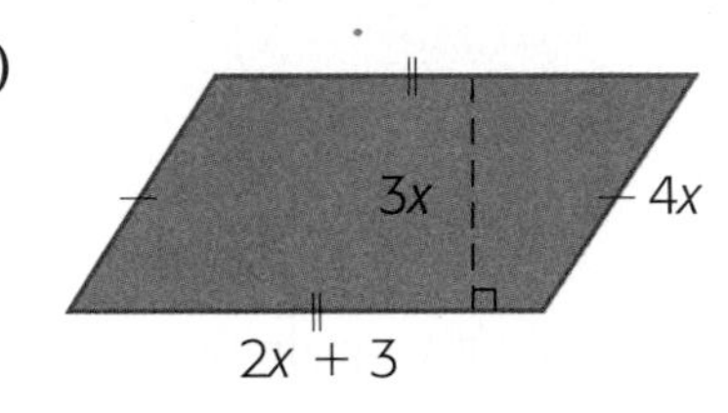

d)

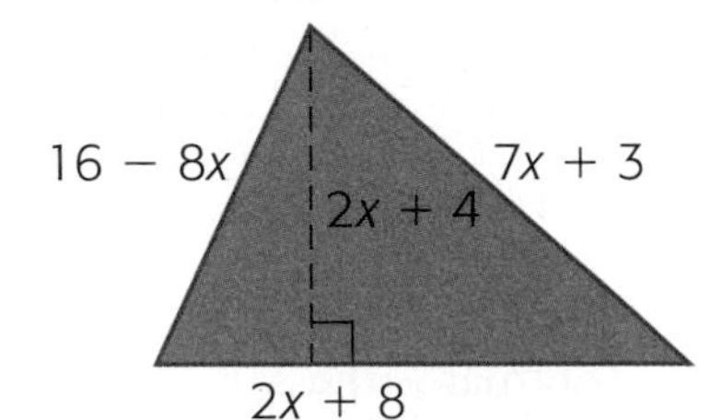

e) Evaluate the perimeter and the area of the rectangle in part a) when $x = 4$ cm.

18. Draw and label dimensions for each rectangle.
a) The area of a rectangle is $4s + 20$.
b) The height of a rectangle is $(40 - 12m) \div 4$.

19. Jeremy said that $(8p^2 - 4p + 12) \div 4 = 2p^2 - 4p + 12$. Do you agree or disagree? Explain.

Closing

20. a) Why does the degree of a polynomial using the variable x not change when you multiply or divide it by a constant?
b) Why does the degree change if you multiply or divide it by x and the result is still a polynomial?

Extending

21. How do you know that $5x(3 - x)$ is not $15x - x = 14x$?

Curious MATH

Pythagorean Polynomials

Choose a whole number from 1 to 10. Call it n.
Form two other numbers as follows:
Number 1: Double n and add 1.
Number 2: Add n^2 to n. Then double the sum.
Form a third number as follows:
Number 3: Determine the square of Number 1 and the square of Number 2.
Add the two new numbers.
Take the square root of the sum.
The three numbers are always whole numbers that form the sides of a right triangle, a **Pythagorean triple**.

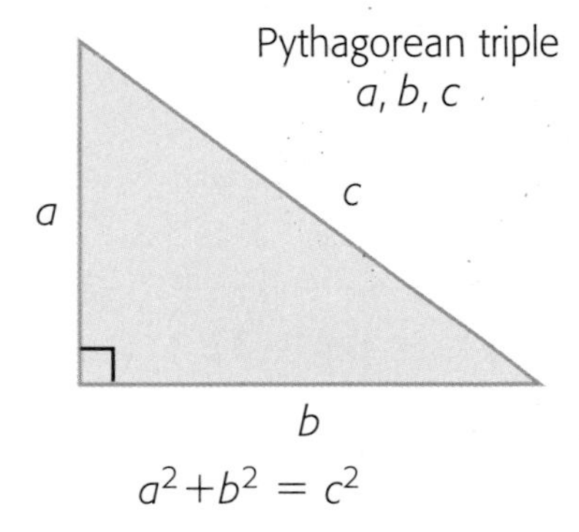

$a^2+b^2 = c^2$

For example, if $n = 2$:

Number 1 $= 2 \times 2 + 1 = 5$

Number 2 $= (2^2 + 2) \times 2 = 12$

Number 3 $= \sqrt{5^2 + 12^2} = \sqrt{25 + 144} = \sqrt{169} = 13$

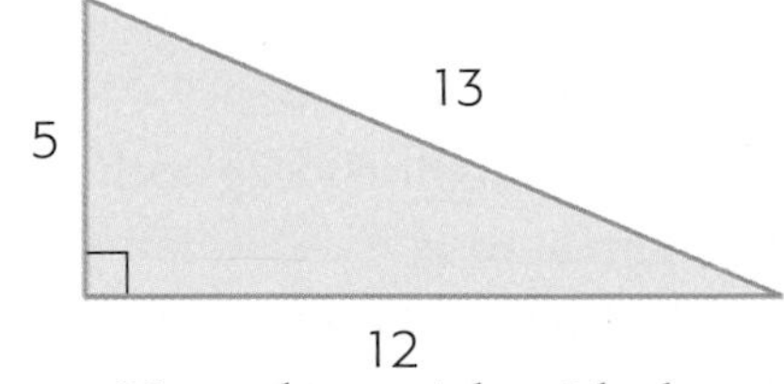

n	Number 1	Number 2	Number 3
	a	b	$\sqrt{a^2 + b^2}$

1. Use polynomials with the variable n to describe Numbers 1 and 2.
2. Test this method for calculating Pythagorean triples using at least four different values for n.
3. What do you notice about the third number each time?
4. How could you write the third number as a polynomial in terms of n?

Chapter Self-Test

Reading Strategy

Summarizing

List three facts you know about polynomials. Share these facts with a partner.

1. Create a polynomial to fit each description.
   a) second degree; variable j; four terms; constant of (-3)
   b) second degree; variable m; not simplified
   c) five terms including two pairs of like terms

2. a) Use a polynomial to represent this situation and explain why the polynomial works. A field has a length 300 m longer than twice its width. What is its perimeter?
   b) Describe a situation that might be represented by the polynomial $180 - 3m$.

3. What polynomials are represented?
   a)
   b)

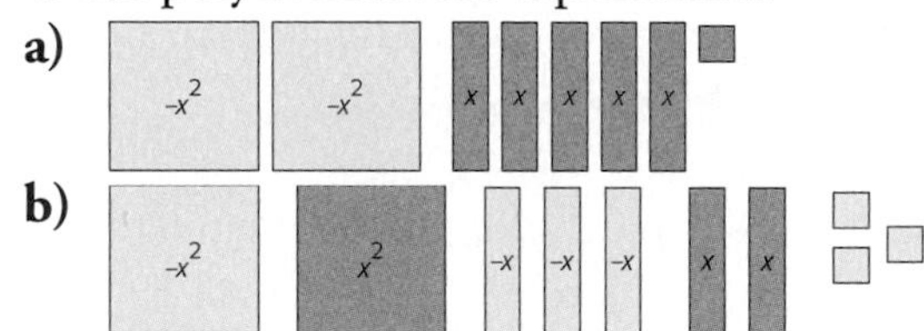

4. Simplify. Represent parts b) and d) using a model.
   a) $(5s^2 - 4t + 3) - (2s^2 - t + 2)$
   b) $(5x^2 - 4x + 3) + (-2x^2 + x - 7)$
   c) $(5y^2 - 4xy + 3) + (-3xy - 5)$
   d) $(5x^2 - 4y + 3) - (-2x^2 + y - 7)$

5. Simplify. Represent a multiplication and a division using a model.
   a) $(4x)(-7x)$
   b) $-4(3k^2 - 6)$
   c) $2t(-3t + 5)$
   d) $12xy \div (-4y)$
   e) $(-36j^2 - 12j + 18) \div (-6)$
   f) $(15r^2 - 3r) \div r$

6. Explain why you combine only like terms when you add or subtract polynomials.

7. a) Represent a polynomial with seven algebra tiles.
   b) Describe a situation in which you might end up with fewer tiles when you add another polynomial to it.
   c) Describe a situation in which you might end up with more tiles when you subtract another polynomial from it.

8. a) Draw a picture that shows why $x(2x + 1) = 2x^2 + x$.
   b) Explain how your picture shows why $(2x^2 + x) \div x = 2x + 1$

WHAT DO You Think Now?

Revisit What Do You Think? on page 275. How have your answers and explanations changed?

Chapter Review

FREQUENTLY ASKED Questions

Q: How do you subtract polynomials?

A: You can think of subtracting as any of the following:
- taking away
- comparing
- adding the opposite

For example, for $(2x^2 - 3x + 4) - (5x^2 + 1)$, you could model the first polynomial and add $3x^2 + (-3x^2)$, which is zero, in order to take away $5x^2$ tiles.

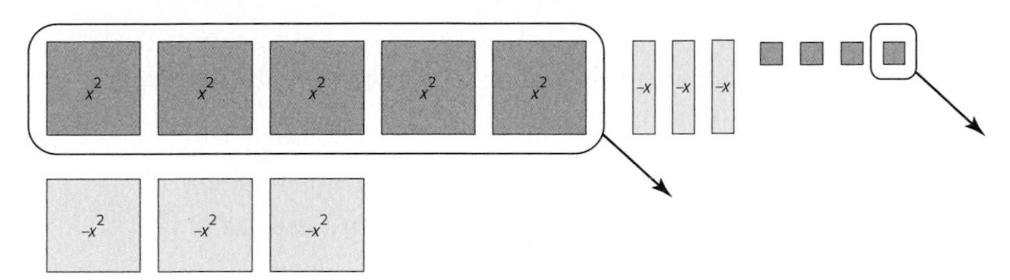

Once the additional tiles are added, it is possible to remove both $5x^2$ and 1, and you are left with $-3x^2 - 3x + 3$.

You get the same result by adding the opposite:

$$\begin{aligned}(2x^2 - 3x + 4) - (5x^2 + 1) &= (2x^2 - 3x + 4) + (-5x^2 - 1)\\ &= -3x^2 - 3x + 3\end{aligned}$$

Study *Aid*
- See Lesson 6.5, Examples 1, 2, 3, and 4.
- Try Chapter Review questions 11 and 13.

Q: How do you multiply a polynomial by a monomial?

A1: You multiply each term of the polynomial by the monomial.

For example, $5x(2x - 4) = (5x)(2x) - (5x)(4) = 10x^2 - 20x$

A2: You use repeated addition if the monomial is a constant, taking the opposite if necessary.

For example, $-3(4x + 2)$ is the opposite of combining three groups of $4x + 2$.

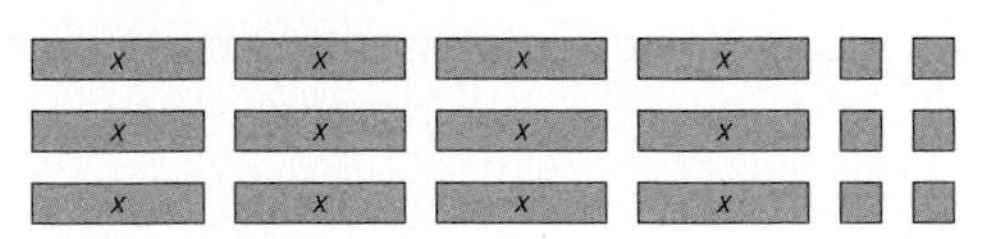

The opposite of $12x + 6$ is $-12x - 6$.

Study *Aid*
- See Lesson 6.7, Examples 1 and 2.
- Try Chapter Review question 15.

A3: You create a rectangle with dimensions representing the values of the monomial and the polynomial and determine its area.

For example, $4(2x - 3) = 8x - 12$.

Q: How do you divide a polynomial by a constant?

Study | *Aid*

- See Lesson 6.7, Examples 3 and 4.
- Try Chapter Review questions 15 and 16.

A1: You divide each term of the polynomial by the constant.

For example,

$$(8x^2 - 2x + 6) \div 2 = \frac{8x^2}{2} - \frac{2x}{2} + \frac{6}{2}$$
$$= 4x^2 - x + 3.$$

A2: Think of it as a sharing situation. If the constant is negative, remember to use the opposite.

For example, $(8x^2 - 2x + 6) \div (-2)$ means to share $(8x^2 - 2x + 6)$ into two equal groups, and then take the opposite of the share size.

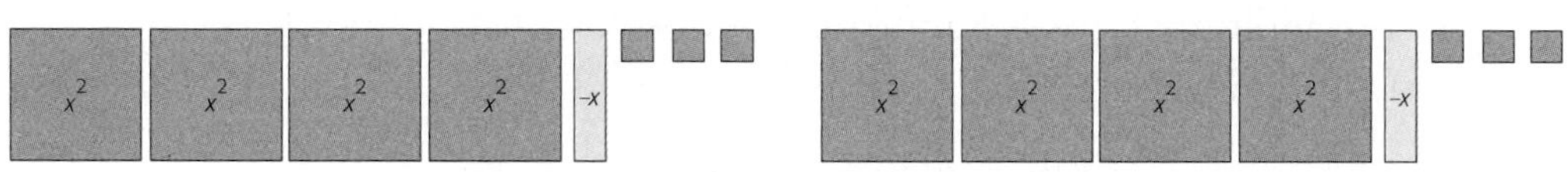

The opposite is $-4x^2 + x - 3$, so

$(8x^2 - 2x + 6) \div (-2) = -4x^2 + x - 3$.

Q: How do you divide a polynomial by a monomial involving a variable?

Study | *Aid*

- See Lesson 6.7, Examples 3 and 4.
- Try Chapter Review questions 15, 16, and 17.

A1: You divide each term of the polynomial by the monomial.

For example,

$$(16x^2 - 14x) \div 2x = \frac{16x^2}{2x} - \frac{4x}{2x}$$
$$= 8x - 7$$

A2: You can represent the polynomial using algebra tiles as the area of a rectangle. You use the divisor to be one dimension. The quotient is the other dimension.

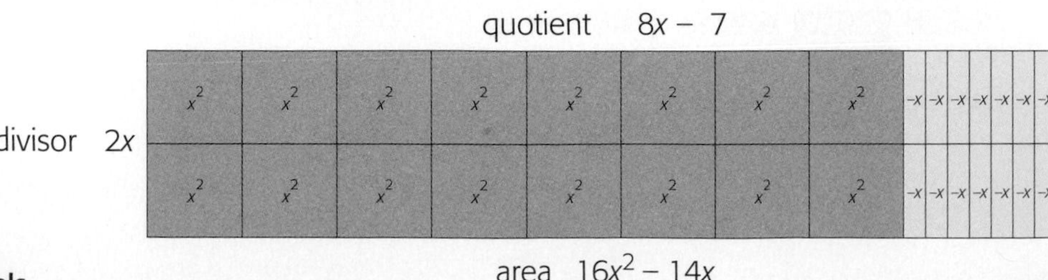

Practice

Lesson 6.1

1. For each polynomial, state its degree, the coefficient of the x term, the constant, and the number of terms.
   a) $3x^2 - 4x + 7$ b) $8 - 5x$ c) $-3xy - 2$

2. Describe this situation using a polynomial. Aaron puts \$15 in the bank every week. He started with \$48. How much money does he have after w weeks?

Lesson 6.3

3. Represent each polynomial using algebra tiles.
   a) $-3x^2 - 4 + 5x^2$
   b) $5x^2 + 3x - 4x - 7$
   c) $-5x - 2 + 8 + 5x$
   d) $3x^2 - xy + 5x - 2xy - x^2$

4. Simplify the polynomials in question 3.

5. Write a simplified polynomial for each set of tiles.
   a)

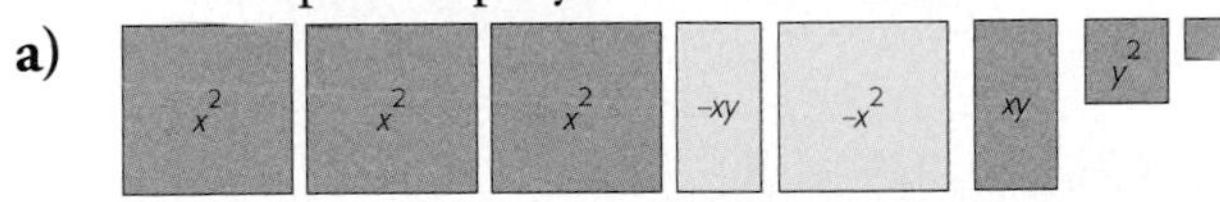

   b)

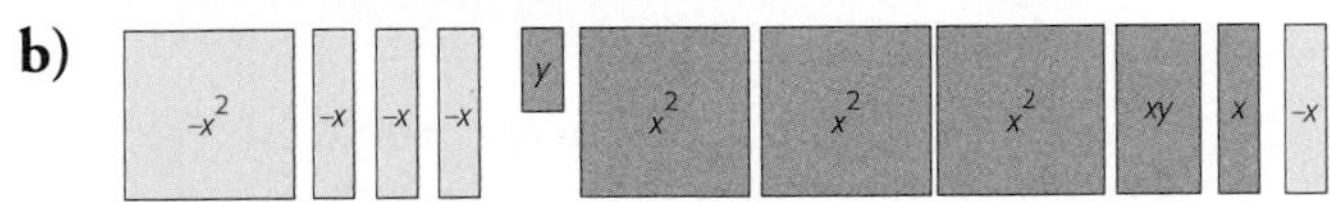

6. List the like terms.
   a) $3s - 4t + 4t^2 + 7t$
   b) $6j + 5 - 8$
   c) $-8t + 4t^2 + 7 - 3 + 9t$
   d) $12j + 5jk - 3k - 8jk$

7. Simplify each polynomial in question 6.

Lesson 6.4

8. **Multiple choice.** Which sum will have a coefficient of x^2 that is 2 less than the coefficient of x?
   A. $(3x^2 - 4x + 2) + (2x^2 + 3x - 7)$
   B. $(3x^2 - 2x + 2) + (2x^2 - 2x - 7)$
   C. $(-3x^2 - 4x + 2) + (5x^2 + 2x - 1)$
   D. $(3x^2 - 4x + 2) + (-3x^2 + 6x + 3)$

9. Describe the total area of this figure using a polynomial.

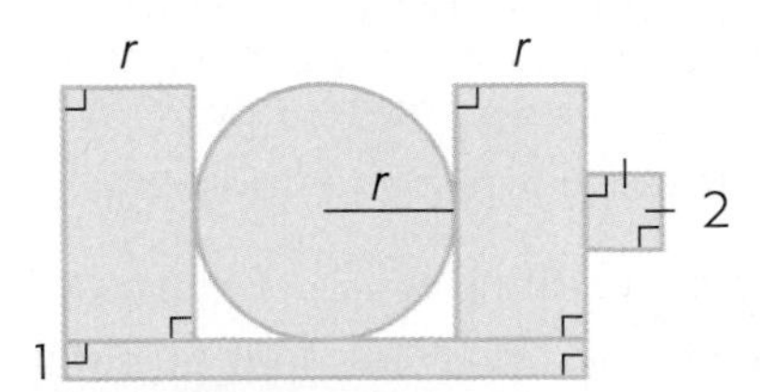

10. Use models to represent two polynomials with a sum of $-3x^2 - 4x + 1$.

Lesson 6.5

11. Which of the following will not contain an x^2 term in the difference? Explain.

a) $(-4x^2 + 2x^2 + 6) - (2x^2 - 2x - 4)$
b) $(4x + 2x^2 + 6) + (-2x^2 - 6x - 4)$
c) $(-7x + 2x^2 + 6) + (7x - 4)$
d) $(-4x + 2x^2 + 6) - (-2x^2 - 2x - 4)$

12. How much greater is the perimeter of the shape on the left than the one on the right? Explain.

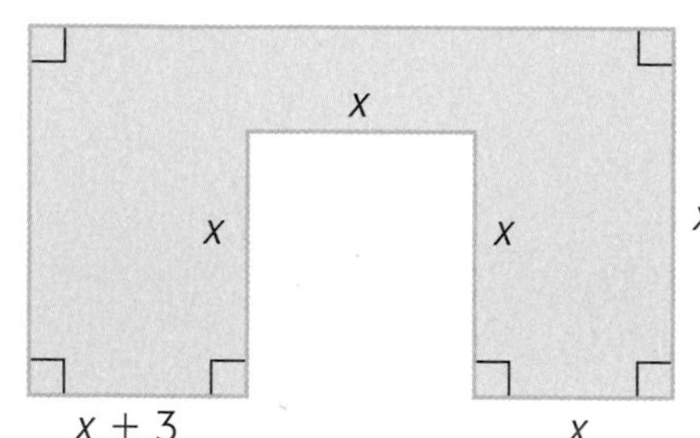

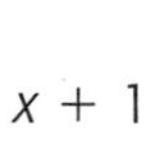

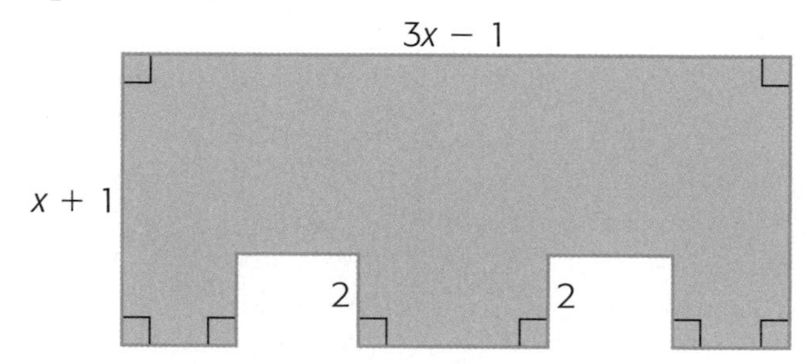

13. David simplified $(2x^2 - 3xy + 5) - (-4x^2 + x - 2)$ to $6x^2 - 4xy + 7$.
Is he correct? If so, explain why. If not, correct the difference.

Lesson 6.6

14. Two polynomials are subtracted.
The result can be modelled as shown.
List two possible pairs of polynomials that could have been subtracted.

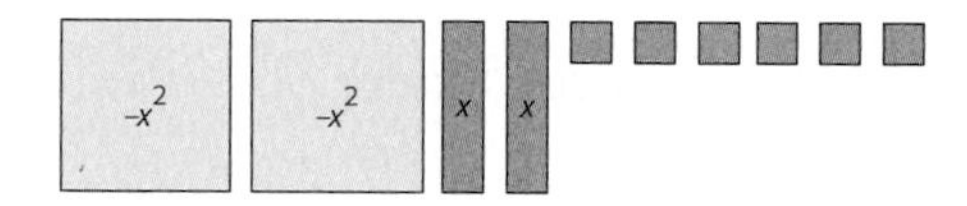

Lesson 6.7

15. Simplify.

a) $3y(-8y)$
b) $72ab \div 9b$
c) $-2x(3x - 6)$
d) $(10x^2 - 5x - 5) \div 5$
e) $4(-2x^2 - 3x - 7)$
f) $(-27x^2 + 18x) \div (-3x)$

16. Larissa divided $(4y^2 + 2x - 2xy)$ by 2 and got $4y + x - xy$.
Is she correct? If so, explain why. If not, correct the quotient.

17. The product of a monomial and a polynomial is $12x^2 - 8x$. What could the monomial and polynomial have been? List four possibilities.

18. Can the product of a polynomial and monomial be the same as the quotient of the same polynomial and monomial? Explain.

Chapter Task

Algebra Tile Puzzles

Larissa gave her friend Rachel some algebra tile puzzles to solve.

? How can you model each situation Larissa gave Rachel?

Part 1

For each question, use at least five positive and five negative tiles. Sketch your model, describe your thinking, and write an algebraic equation to describe your calculation.

A. Model and complete an addition.

B. Model and complete a subtraction.

C. Model and complete a multiplication of $3x + 2$ by a monomial.

D. Model and complete a division by 3.

Part 2

For each question, the answer must be $2x^2 + x - 1$. Each time, describe your thinking, sketch a model, and write an algebraic equation to describe your calculation.

E. Add two polynomials that are modelled with 12 tiles altogether, before simplifying.

F. Subtract two polynomials that are modelled with at least 10 tiles altogether, before simplifying.

G. Divide a polynomial that can be modelled with 12 tiles by a monomial.

Task ***Checklist***

- ✔ Did you correctly model the polynomials you used?
- ✔ Did you verify that the answer was $2x^2 + x - 1$ in part 2?
- ✔ Did you clearly describe your thinking?

23

Chapter 7

Probability

GOALS

You will be able to

- recognize situations involving probability
- state the assumptions used to determine a probability
- use probabilities in different ways to support conclusions
- communicate about probability situations

What probabilities might affect which pitcher the manager chooses to put in as a substitute?

Getting Started

Fair or Unfair Game?

In a particular game, each of two players puts out 1, 2, or 3 fingers at the same time.

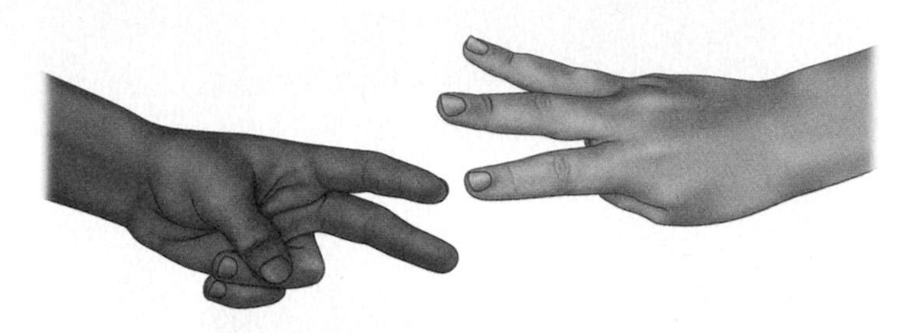

If both players put out the same number of fingers, player A gets a point.

If the players put out a different number of fingers, player B gets a point.

How can you decide whether the game is fair?

A. A two-player game is fair if each player has an equal probability of winning $\left(50\% \text{ or } \frac{1}{2}\right)$. Predict whether you think this game is fair.

B. Play the game three times and determine the **experimental probability** of each player winning. Would you change your prediction about whether the game is fair? Explain.

C. Are the three **trials** considered **independent events**? Explain.

D. Copy and complete this tree diagram to show the possible outcomes for each **event**. Explain how you can use the tree diagram to determine if the game is fair.

Possible Outcomes for the Game

A's number	B's number	Winner
1	1	A
	2	B
	3	B
2	1	B
	?	?
	?	?

E. How could you have used addition, subtraction, multiplication, or division to calculate the **theoretical probability** of each player winning in part D? Explain your thinking.

F. How do your conclusions in parts D and E depend on believing that the number of fingers each player puts out is **equally likely**?

G. Would you use the experimental probability from part B or the theoretical probability from part D to convince someone else whether the game is fair? Explain your choice.

WHAT DO *You Think?*

Decide whether you agree or disagree with each statement. Explain your decision.

1. The experimental probability is very close to the theoretical probability when you repeat an experiment 10 times.
2. There is only one number that correctly describes the theoretical probability for a given outcome or event.
3. Probability is useful mostly when describing someone's chance to win in a game or contest.

4. Since the probability of rolling two dice and getting a sum of 7 is $\frac{6}{36}$, if you roll a pair of dice 36 times, you will get a sum of 7 six times.

7.1 Recognizing Probability Situations

GOAL

Identify situations where probability is used.

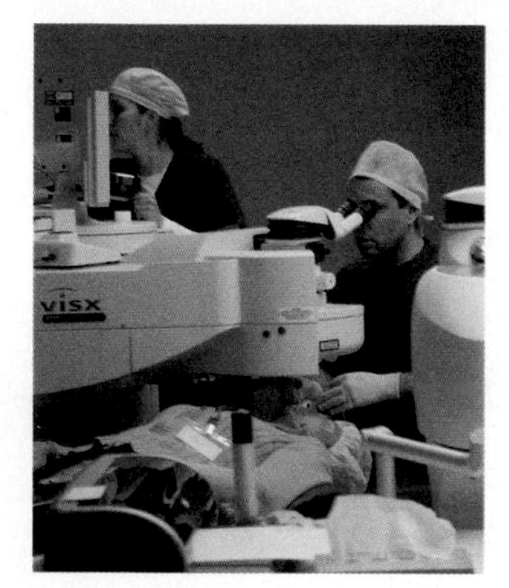

INVESTIGATE the Math

Marta is considering whether to have laser eye surgery so that she won't need glasses anymore.

? What probabilities might influence Marta's decision to go ahead with the laser eye surgery?

A. The doctor tells Marta that, based on **first-hand data** from his own patients, 95% of people with mild nearsightedness achieve normal vision from this surgery. Why might this number be considered a probability?

B. The doctor tells Marta that **second-hand data** shows that 10% of patients experience significant eye discomfort as a result of the surgery. Why might this number be considered a probability?

C. The doctor tells her that in some studies, about 3 out of every 100 patients actually end up with poorer vision than they began with. Why might this number be considered a probability?

D. What other probabilities might influence a patient's decision to go ahead with laser eye surgery?

Reflecting

E. Why is it important to consider probabilities in making medical decisions?

F. Which of the probabilities do you think might matter most to Marta in making her decision? Explain your choice.

G. How do you know if a given percent is a probability?

WORK WITH the Math

EXAMPLE 1 | Recognizing probabilities in consumer situations

Nicole's family was investigating the safety of vehicles before purchasing one. They found a report that showed the chance of rollovers for different kinds of vehicles in crash tests.

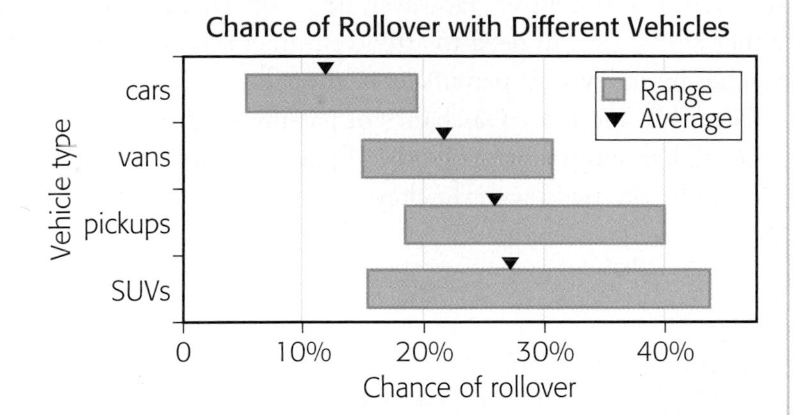

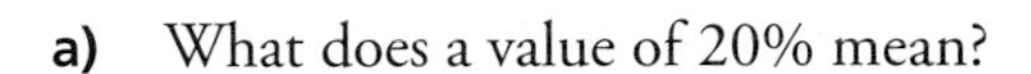

a) What does a value of 20% mean?

b) Why is there a range for each type of vehicle?

c) Why might these percentages be considered probabilities?

Nicole's Solution

a) A 20% chance of rollover probably means that in 20 out of 100 crash tests, that type of vehicle rolled over.

The report doesn't tell clearly how the values were calculated, so I have to make some assumptions.

b) There are probably a lot of different cars in each category, so the rollover rates might be different for different cars in the category.
Or
There might have been different rates depending on the type of crash situation.

I couldn't tell from the given information if the ranges had to do with crash tests of many different models, tests in many different years, or tests under different types of crash conditions.

c) The percent is the number of rollovers divided by the number of crash tests. If you think of favourable outcomes as rollovers and the possible outcomes as the number of crash tests that were performed, the percent is a probability.

Probabilities are the ratio of favourable outcomes to possible outcomes.

Communication | ***Tip***

The term "favourable outcome" is used to describe the numerator of a fractional probability. That does not mean that the outcome is actually a "happy" one. For example, in Example 1, a favourable outcome is a rollover. A favourable outcome is an outcome in which you are interested.

EXAMPLE 2 | Relating risk to probability considerations

Derek wants to pre-register for a week of hockey school during July. To do so, he must make a $200 non-refundable deposit. However, he is concerned about his grades in English and Math. If he fails either course he will need to attend summer school in July, and would lose his deposit. At parent-teacher interviews his parents learn the following:

- Derek has about a 70% chance of passing English.
- Derek has about a 60% chance of passing Math.

Should he pre-register for hockey school?

Derek's Solution

$$P(\text{pass English}) = 0.7$$
$$P(\text{fail English}) = 1 - 0.7 = 0.3$$
$$P(\text{pass Math}) = 0.6$$
$$P(\text{fail Math}) = 1 - 0.6 = 0.4$$

I listed the likelihood of passing and failing each course. I knew that the probability of an event and its complement must add to one.

$$P(\text{pass Math and English}) = 0.7 \times 0.6 = 0.42$$
$$P(\text{pass Math and fail English}) = 0.6 \times 0.3 = 0.18$$
$$P(\text{fail Math and pass English}) = 0.4 \times 0.7 = 0.28$$
$$P(\text{fail Math and English}) = 0.4 \times 0.3 = 0.12$$

I made the assumption that passing English and passing Math are independent events. This means that I can multiply probabilities to determine the likelihood that two events will occur.

I need to determine the likelihood that I will fail at least one of these courses, so I highlighted the cases where I fail one or both courses.

$$\begin{aligned} P(\text{summer school}) &= P(\text{pass Math and fail English}) + \\ &\quad P(\text{fail Math and pass English}) + \\ &\quad P(\text{fail Math and English}) \\ &= 0.18 + 0.28 + 0.12 \\ &= 0.58 \end{aligned}$$

To determine the probability that I will go to summer school, I added the probabilities where I fail Math, English, or both.

$$\begin{aligned} P(\text{summer school}) &= 1 - P(\text{pass Math and English}) \\ &= 1 - 0.42 \\ &= 0.58 \end{aligned}$$

I realized that I could have also calculated this probability using the complement of passing both courses.

There is a 58% chance that I will have to go to summer school. Based on my teachers' estimates, I should not pre-register.

There is only a 42% chance that I won't have to go to summer school, but a 58% chance that I will. However, this probability can change if I work hard to improve my grades.

In Summary

Key Ideas

- Probabilities are sometimes used formally, but they are frequently used informally in everyday life.
- Probabilities are involved whenever there is some uncertainty about what could occur, often when an associated risk is being evaluated. For example, a teenager might use data about the percent of bicycles that are stolen in a particular area to decide whether to risk leaving her bike there.

Need to Know

- The experimental probability of event E is $\frac{\text{number of occurrences of E}}{\text{total number of trials}}$.
- The theoretical probability of event E is $\frac{\text{number of outcomes for E}}{\text{total number of outcomes}}$.

Checking

1. Which of these situations involve probabilities? What information might you use to determine whether the probabilities are high or low?
   a) Whether a new car will last 7 years
   b) The age at which a teenager is allowed to drive
   c) The value of a tile in a Scrabble game
   d) The languages in which government forms are made available

Practising

2. Which of these situations involve probabilities? Explain how you would evaluate the probability.
   a) Whether you should buy a dress now or wait for a sale
   b) Whether a basketball player is likely to make a free throw
   c) Your mark in a course
   d) How much rain we will get on July 15 next year

3. **Multiple choice.** Which of these is the probability that a particular brand of pain medication will help your headache?
   A. the number of bottles of the medication sold in the last year
   B. $\frac{\text{number of people who said it helped their headache}}{\text{number of people participating in the survey}}$
   C. the number of people who have said that this medication helped them with a headache
   D. $\frac{\text{number of people who said it helped their headache}}{\text{number who said it did not}}$

4. **Multiple choice.** Which of these everyday probabilities is most likely to be high?
   A. the probability that the fruit you buy in a large grocery store will be of reasonable quality
   B. the probability that it will snow if the probability of precipitation is 20%
   C. the probability that someone who uses solar power will have a higher heating bill than someone who does not
   D. the probability that a teenage boy driving a car will frequently have car accidents
5. Think of a TV game show where players consider probabilities when deciding how to proceed. Explain the extent to which probability is involved.
6. What information and what probabilities would you use to evaluate the risk in each situation?
   a) Should you leave your bike on a bike rack near a store?
   b) Should your family drive to your grandmother's if the weather forecast calls for snow?
7. What probabilities might be involved in each of these situations? Explain your thinking.
   a) deciding which patient will get a heart that's available for transplant
   b) deciding which stock is a better one to buy
   c) deciding whether a plane is likely to land on time
   d) deciding which candidate is going to win an election

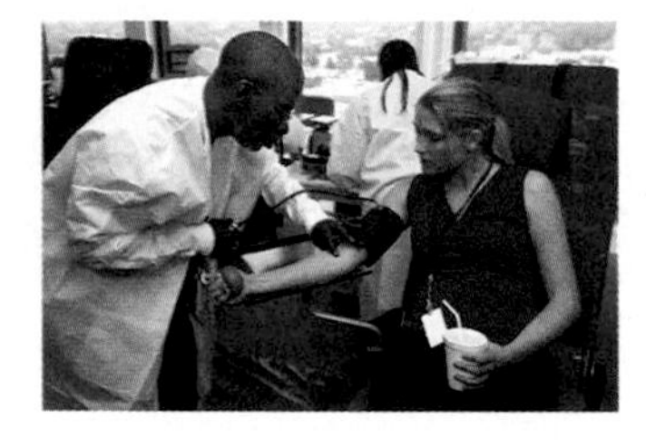

8. **a)** Use print materials or the Internet to research the probability that a person who arrives in the emergency room has a particular blood type.
   b) How might a hospital use this information?
9. **a)** How do random drug tests for athletes involve probability?
   b) Look up the term "false positives" in a reference or on the Internet. How are probabilities related to the report of false positives?
10. Look through print media and on the Internet to find an example in each case. Describe how the probabilities were involved.
    a) at least one situation where decisions affecting your community were made that might have been based on probabilities
    b) at least one situation where an Internet company uses probabilities
    c) at least one situation where a medical organization might make a decision based on probabilities

11. A farmer tells you that his horses are almost always calm, but they get jumpy right before a storm.
    a) How might the farmer use this fact to state a probability?
    b) Explain why this is a probability.

12. Does each game situation involve probability? If so, explain how.
    a) In an Aboriginal game called Pa-tol, three wooden prisms with diagonal markings called "sticks" are tossed. The score is based upon the faces that turn up.

Front faces

Reverse faces

Pa-tol Scoring

Outcome	Points
	2 points
	3 points
	5 points
	10 points
	15 points

    b) In the board game Scrabble, the letter Z is worth 10 points, but the letter E is worth only 1 point.

13. How might you use probabilities to decide what time you need to get to the bus stop to catch a bus?

14. How might road engineers use probabilities involving animal migration patterns to decide where to put a road in the North?

Closing

15. Describe a situation in the past week where you used a probability to make a decision.

Extending

16. Explore the research on how using blister packs rather than bottles for pills might affect the likelihood that medication is used correctly by the patient. Describe how probabilities are involved.

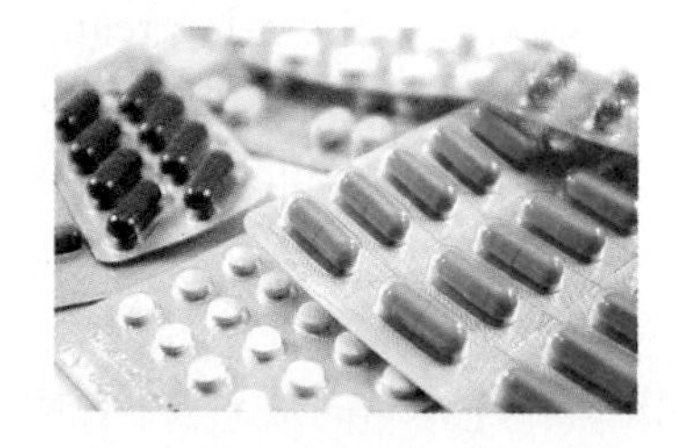

17. Explore the research on the need for follow-up testing for appendicitis if a patient comes to a doctor with suspected appendictis. Describe how probability might be involved in the doctor's decision to perform an ultrasound.

7.2 Using Probabilities to Make Decisions

GOAL

Identify the assumptions associated with a probability.

LEARN ABOUT the Math

A junior hockey league team, the Eagles, is down 2–0 to the Vipers in a best-of-five, first-round playoff series.

Martine is a big fan of the Eagles.

She has a ticket to game 5 but she also has an opportunity to go on a trip that leaves on the same day that game 5 is scheduled for. Before she knows the results of game 3, Martine has to decide whether to pay for the trip. She can't get her money back.

Should Martine pay for the trip?

Bay's Solution: Using previous data to calculate an experimental probability

I looked up statistics for previous playoffs for the past 10 years. I learned that if a team won the first two games, the series only went to five games 10% of the time.

I decided to look up statistics for other best-of-five playoff series in this league where one team was up 2–0.

If I assume that this series would be just like previous ones where the other team was up 2–0, I would advise Martine to pay for the trip since the probability of the game happening is very low, only 10%.

It seemed very unlikely that the series would go to five games.

It is hard to know whether to assume this series is special and not like the others, but if you don't assume that, there is no way to use previous information.

Shelby's Solution: Using a simulation to calculate an experimental probability

I used a coin to simulate the outcomes of the next two games. I let heads represent a win for the Eagles, and tails represent a win for the Vipers.

I can't know what's going to happen, but I can use a **simulation** to model what might happen.

I decided to use a coin to help me calculate the experimental probability for a game 5.

For a game 5 to occur, the Eagles must win games 3 and 4.

The series ends once a team has won three games. I know the series does not go to game 5 if the Vipers win either game 3 or game 4.

I tossed the coin twice.
I repeated the experiment 20 times.

The outcomes of the first and second toss represent the results of games 3 and 4, respectively.

HH	HT	TT	TH
HT	HH	TT	TH
TH	TT	HT	HT
HT	HH	HT	TH
TT	TT	HT	HH

There is a game 5 if the results are HH since that means the Eagles won both games and so neither team had won three games.

That happened $\frac{4}{20}$ of the time.

That means that $\frac{16}{20}$, or 80%, of the time, the series ended before game 5.

To use this model, I assumed that each team has an equal chance of winning each game. I did that to make the calculations simpler.

Even though I assumed each team was equally likely to win, I knew that there might be some home-ice advantage or momentum that would make the probability a bit higher for the Vipers.

I thought it was okay to assume an equal probability since the Eagles might be really motivated, so their probability could be the one that is higher too.

I think Martine should pay for the trip since it's not very likely there will be a game 5.

Amanda's Solution: Using theoretical probability

To calculate the theoretical probability, I made some assumptions:

- that what happens in one game has nothing to do with what happened previously, so the events are independent, and
- that each team is equally likely to win each game.

I decided to calculate the theoretical probability that the series would go to five games.

Even though I assumed the games were independent and each team was equally likely to win, I knew that this might not be true.

I made those assumptions so that I could use a tree diagram to analyze the possible outcomes.

This tree diagram shows possible results after the Vipers have won the first two games. I used the letter of the team if that team won, E for Eagles and V for Vipers.

I know the series is over when a team has won three games.

I made a tree diagram to show possible results.

The series ends before game 5 if the first three or four results are
V V V or
V V E V

The series continues to game 5 if the first four results are
V V E E

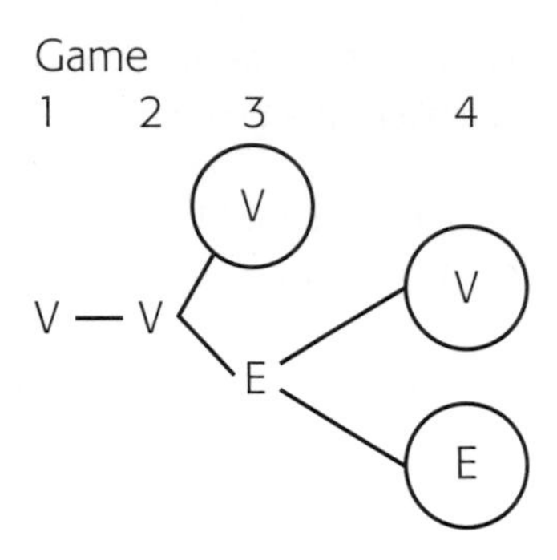

From the diagram, there is a game 5 only $\frac{1}{3}$ of the time.

The tree diagram I drew did not look right since the branches did not all end at the same place. I drew another diagram where they did.

Game
1 2 3 4
V — V
V
E
V
E
V
E

VVV
(three-game series)

VVEV
(four-game series)

VVEE
(five-game series)

When I showed the full tree for the results of the first four games, I could see that the theoretical probability was actually lower than $\frac{1}{3}$ for a game 5.

Because the whole tree is shown, all the probabilities are equally likely. In the other tree, not all of the branches were equally likely.
For example, V V V is actually a combination of 2 outcomes (V V V V and V V V E) so there are really four possible outcomes, and only one of them results in a five-game series.

The probability of a game 5 is really only $\frac{1}{4}$.
I would advise Martine to pay for the trip. But if she is a huge Eagles fan, she might decide to take the risk of waiting around, even though the chance for the game is not very likely.

Reflecting

A. Why are Amanda's assumptions necessary to calculate a theoretical probability in this situation?

B. Do you think Shelby's or Bay's solution is a better way to use experimental probability? Why?

C. Which of the assumptions made in the three solutions do you think are valid?

D. How do the assumptions made in each solution affect the conclusions each student can actually make?

WORK WITH the Math

EXAMPLE 1 | Assumptions in a mathematical calculation

Decide if this game for two players is fair.
A player rolls two dice on his or her turn.
Player A wins a point if consecutive numbers are rolled.
Player B wins a point if doubles are rolled.

Derek's Solution: Using theoretical probability

I decided to use theoretical probability. I have to think about all the possible outcomes.

First, I listed the assumptions I made:

- Each number on each die has an equally likely chance of being rolled.
- The events are independent; that is, the number on one die has nothing to do with what number turns up on the other die.

Outcome Table for Game

I made an outcome table to show all of the possible outcomes.

	Roll on 1st Die						
		1	**2**	**3**	**4**	**5**	**6**
Roll on 2nd Die	**1**	1, 1	2, 1	3, 1	4, 1	5, 1	6, 1
	2	1, 2	2, 2	3, 2	4, 2	5, 2	6, 2
	3	1, 3	2, 3	3, 3	4, 3	5, 3	6, 3
	4	1, 4	2, 4	3, 4	4, 4	5, 4	6, 4
	5	1, 5	2, 5	3, 5	4, 5	5, 5	6, 5
	6	1, 6	2, 6	3, 6	4, 6	5, 6	6, 6

For the outcomes with green highlight, A wins a point.
For the outcomes with yellow highlight, B wins a point.
For the outcomes with no highlight, nobody gets a point.

From the table, the probability that player A will win is $\frac{10}{36}$ and the probability that player B will win is only $\frac{6}{36}$.

The game is not fair if you assume that the events are independent and the dice are fair.

Yvonne's Solution: Using experimental probability

I used a random dice roller on the Internet that rolls two virtual dice. I recorded the values and then decided who won each time.

To find a random dice roller, I did an Internet search for virtual dice.

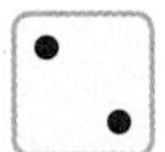

A random dice roller assumes each number is equally likely on each die.

I rolled the virtual dice 20 times.

Rolls and Winners

Game Number	1	2	3	4	5	6	7	8	9	10
Rolls	1,1	2,4	4,4	1,6	2,4	6,4	1,6	5,2	3,4	6 3

Game Number	11	12	13	14	15	16	17	18	19	20
Rolls	4,3	6,2	2,6	5,6	4,5	2,5	5,2	1,1	6,6	3,5

Sometimes nobody wins a point.

To compare the points for player A and player B, I counted how many times each won in 20 trials.

Blue means that Player A wins a point.
Red means that Player B wins a point.

Player A won 3 times.
Player B won 4 times.
The game appears to be fair.

3 out of 20 is pretty close to 4 out of 20.

To determine that the game is fair, I have to assume that 20 is enough trials. I am not sure it really is.

EXAMPLE 2 | Assumptions in a real-world situation

Austin and his friends are planning a camping trip.

Austin doesn't mind some rain, but doesn't like camping in thunderstorms. One of his friends is very afraid of thunderstorms. The long-range weather forecast predicts a 60% chance of rain, with a 20% chance of thunderstorms.

The spot must be reserved a week ahead of time. Should they go ahead with the trip? If they reserve and don't go, they will lose the reservation fee.

Austin's Solution

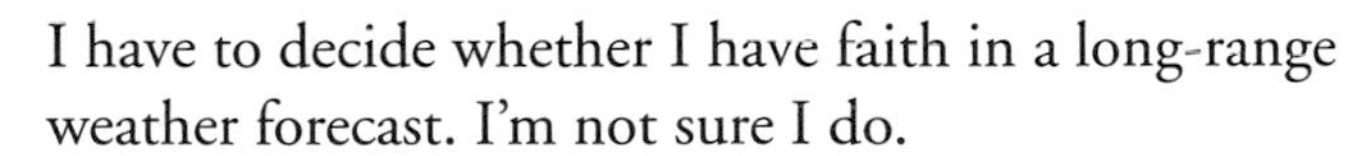

I have to decide whether I have faith in a long-range weather forecast. I'm not sure I do.

Environment Canada only forecasts 5 days in advance since they don't believe they can reliably predict weather beyond that time.

If I assume that the forecast is not reliable, then I shouldn't use the probabilities at all.

If I believe the forecast, I have to decide whether the small risk of thunderstorms is worth missing the trip. The risk is worth it for me, but I'm not sure it is for my friend, who is afraid of thunderstorms.

My friend might look at the same probabilities and come up with a different conclusion. It has a lot to do with how you each view the consequences of a result you don't want.

I think we should go ahead with the trip.

In Summary

Key Idea

- Calculations of probability are always based on assumptions. If you examine the assumptions, you can determine whether the calculated probability is useful when making a decision.

Need to Know

- You can sometimes calculate the probability of the same event either experimentally or theoretically.
- You have to consider whether events are independent when you calculate their combined theoretical probability.
- You have to consider whether events are equally likely when you calculate their probabilities.

Checking

1. A game involves rolling a die. You win if you roll a 1. Aaron says that the probability of winning is $\frac{1}{6}$. What assumptions is Aaron making?

Practising

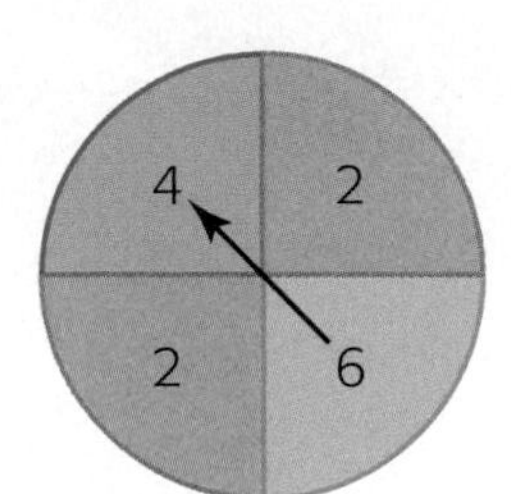

2. In a game, two players take turns spinning this spinner twice. Player A gets a point if the sum of the spins is 8 or more. Player B gets a point if the sum of the spins is less than 8.
   a) Is this game fair? How do you know?
   b) Would you play this game? How would you explain your decision to someone who wants you to play? Include your assumptions.

3. Zac's bus has been on time 90% of the time in October. He has an appointment that he can't be late for. It's January. Is it reasonable to assume that the bus has a 90% chance of being on time? Explain.

4. Kate played a game 20 times and won 8 times. What assumptions would you make to decide whether the game is or is not fair?

5. **Multiple choice.** Which of these assumptions must you make when you say that the probability of rolling an even sum on two 6-sided dice is $\frac{1}{2}$?
   A. The dice each have 3 even and 3 odd numbers on them.
   B. The dice are the same size.
   C. The dice have to have the numbers from 1 to 6 on them.
   D. The dice have the same numbers on them.

6. **Multiple choice.** You are spinning a spinner with a red, a blue, and a green section. Which is most likely NOT to be an assumption you make when you say the probability for spinning a red is $\frac{1}{3}$?
   A. The sections are of equal area.
   B. The spinner spins freely.
   C. You do not interfere with the spin.
   D. You have to spin at least 20 times.

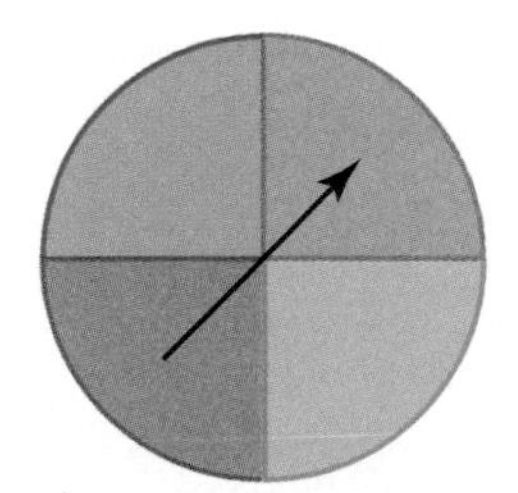

7. Four players are playing a board game that involves both skill and luck. To decide how likely it is that each player will win, they spin an on-line spinner 40 times. They each chose a different colour on the spinner, and then calculated the experimental probability each player would win. What assumptions are being made in calculating these probabilities? How valid are those assumptions?

8. What assumptions do you make when you say that the chance of flipping a head and a tail in two coin tosses is $\frac{1}{2}$?

9. Alyssa says that a best-of-seven Stanley Cup final will be over in 4 games about 40% of the time, so in the next 10 years, this will happen 4 times. What assumptions is Alyssa making?

10. An airline reports that its probability of on-time arrival is 78%. Suppose you need to make a connecting flight on this airline. What other probabilities would you want to consider?

Reading Strategy

Inferring

Use probability data and experience to draw inferences that will influence your decision.

11. A weather reporter indicates that the probability of snow on a particular day is 40%.
    a) What assumptions might be made in determining this probability?
    b) What other factors would your family consider in deciding whether to drive 200 km that day to visit relatives?

12. What probabilities might city planners use in deciding on a snow removal budget for the next year? What assumptions might they make?

13. Campbell says that he is lucky. He says that if you think of a number between 1 and 10, he can guess it correctly 80% of the time. You perform the experiment 12 times, and he guesses your number correctly 75% of the time. Is it reasonable to conclude that Campbell is lucky? Explain.

Closing

14. Are there always assumptions involved in making a probability statement or only sometimes? Explain your choice.

Extending

15. Government officials are trying to decide whether to grant a scientist's alternative-energy funding request by considering the probability her research will succeed. What factors might they consider in making that decision?

16. Rob's little sister is collecting prizes from boxes of cereal. She is trying to collect all four prizes.
    a) Use a model to estimate the probability that Rob's sister will collect all four prizes if she has eight boxes of cereal.
    b) What assumptions were you making when you decided that your model was appropriate?

Curious MATH

That's So Random!

What many people identify as random and what is actually random are often very different things.

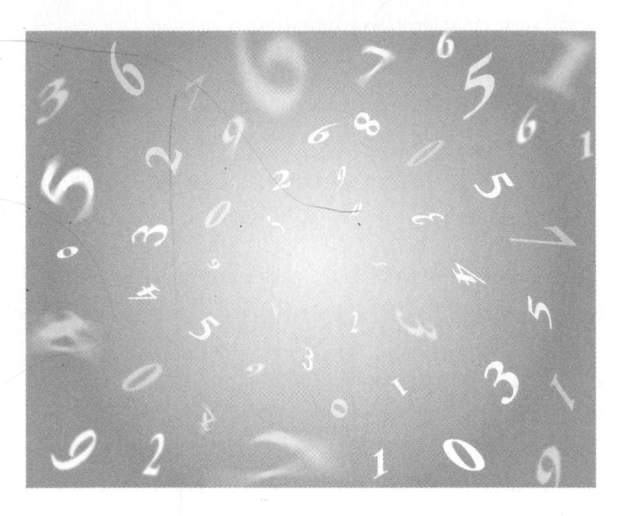

1. Suppose you ask a group of 100 people to pick a natural number from 1 to 10. (Go ahead and pick your own number before reading on, just for fun.) What would you expect to happen? What assumption are you making?
2. Research has shown that more people pick 3 or 7 than any other numbers. Explain why this might happen.
3. Suggest a process that you could use to ensure that picking the numbers from 1 to 10 in a group of 100 people truly occurs in a random manner.

   Another common mistake people make with probability is to judge some results as less likely to occur because they don't look random enough. However, patterns can and do occur over the long term, just by chance.

4. Suppose that you flip a coin 10 times and get the following result:

   HTHTTTTTTH.

   Your friend repeats the experiment and gets:

   THTHHTHTHT

   Is your result less likely than your friend's? Explain.

7.3 Communicate about Probability

GOAL

Communicate clearly about how probability information leads to particular decisions.

INVESTIGATE the Math

A bank employee is explaining to a customer why the bank closes at 5 p.m. on most days of the week instead of staying open later.

The bank employee says that a national survey showed that the probability a Canadian Internet user would bank online is about $\frac{1}{3}$ and the probability that a person who had banked online once would continue to do so was close to 100%. He also mentioned that ATMs are open 24 hours.

How could you help the bank employee convince the customer that the bank's position is reasonable?

A. In what way is the $\frac{1}{3}$ a probability?

B. What assumptions is the bank employee making?

C. Do you think the bank employee's assumptions are reasonable? Explain.

D. If you were the customer, how might you use probabilities to respond to the bank employee's explanation?

E. Use the Communication Checklist to suggest to the bank employee how he might make a more convincing explanation that takes into account your answer to part D.

Communication | ***Checklist***

- ✔ Did you explain why the values involved represented probabilities?
- ✔ Did you explain your assumptions?
- ✔ Did you explain how your probabilities were estimated or calculated?
- ✔ Was your explanation clear and persuasive?

Reflecting

F. In what ways is your response in part E more effective than the original explanation?

WORK WITH the Math

EXAMPLE 1 | Recognizing probabilities

Explain how a local food store manager might use probabilities to consider whether to stock locally grown produce.

Austin's Solution

The manager should consider these probabilities:
- the probability that local suppliers can deliver all the produce the store needs
- the probability that local suppliers can supply produce better than or equal in quality to imported produce
- the probability that the cost of using local suppliers is competitive with the cost of using big wholesalers
- the probability that customers will value the fact that the store sells locally grown produce

I have to think about what a food store manager might be concerned about.

He has to think about both customer satisfaction and costs.

These are all probabilities since you can't be sure of the answers. You can only predict based on experimental or historical data.

I explained how probabilities were involved.

The manager should consider previous experiences with local producers to predict the size and quality of their deliveries.

He also has to consider the probability that the weather will result in a good crop.

He has to consider the probability that his customers would appreciate locally grown produce.

The manager might base this probability on conversations he had with customers. He might even conduct a survey. He could also look over past sales records.

In Summary

Key Idea

- Clear communication, including stating assumptions, and explaining them, is helpful in describing probability situations.

Need to Know

- Probabilities are involved whenever there is some uncertainty about what could occur.

Checking

1. Suppose you flip a coin 10 times. Which is more likely to occur?
   - 9 out of 10 tosses are heads
   - 4 out of 10 tosses are tails

   Explain how you know. State any assumptions you have made.

Practising

2. Describe the probabilities a recording company executive might consider in deciding whether to sign a particular artist looking for a new agency and how she might estimate those probabilities.

3. Logan asked a friend to choose a number between 1 and 50. Describe the assumptions you make when you say that the probability his friend selects the number 36 is $\frac{1}{50}$.
4. Suppose a family plans to have four children. Describe how to use a model to estimate the likelihood that the family will have three girls in a row and then a boy. What assumptions are you making in the use of that model?
5. Avery's mother has an important presentation to make tomorrow morning at a conference that is 200 km away. She has an evening meeting at work tonight. There is a reported 50% probability of snow in the morning. The company would pay for her hotel overnight. What are all the probabilities Avery's mother has to consider when deciding whether to make the drive tonight or tomorrow morning? Which probability do you think would have the most impact on her decision? Explain.
6. Car insurance companies charge different amounts depending on the age of the insured driver, the type of car, and the driving record of the person they are insuring. Explain how probabilities might be used to determine fair car insurance rates.

7. What probabilities might your family consider when deciding on where to go camping on a long holiday weekend in the summer?

8. How might Noreen use probabilities to decide whether to fly, take the train, or take the bus to visit her grandmother in Ontario?

9. Describe how a baseball coach might use probabilities to decide which player to use as a pinch hitter if there are runners in scoring position with one out, in a tie game in the bottom of the 9th inning.

10. Tell how a football quarterback might use probabilities to decide what to do on the next play.

11. Describe a situation where intuition or beliefs might have more effect on a person's decision than a calculated probability. Why might personal beliefs be viewed as more important in this case?

Reading Strategy

Synthesizing

How do you draw conclusions from information or data?

12. Some people say probabilities are often hidden. They are there in situations even when the word is not used. Do you agree or disagree? Explain.

Closing

13. Why might communicating clearly about probability be even more critical than communicating clearly in other mathematical situations?

Extending

14. Describe how a game manufacturer might use probabilities to create scoring rules for a video game.

Math GAME

Which Is Which?

Number of players: 3

In this game, players match picture cards to cards with descriptions of spinners.

YOU WILL NEED

- 2 sets of Which Is Which? Picture Cards
- 2 sets of Which Is Which? Description Cards

How to play

1. One player is chosen as the "referee." Each of the other players gets one set of picture cards and one set of description cards. Shuffle the cards in each set. Place each set face down in a pile.
2. When the referee says "Go," both players turn over one card from each pile at the same time. If the cards match, the player puts the pair aside. If they do not match, the player continues to turn over one card from each pile until a match can be made.
3. The first player who can correctly match the picture cards with the description cards wins the game.

Bay's Turn

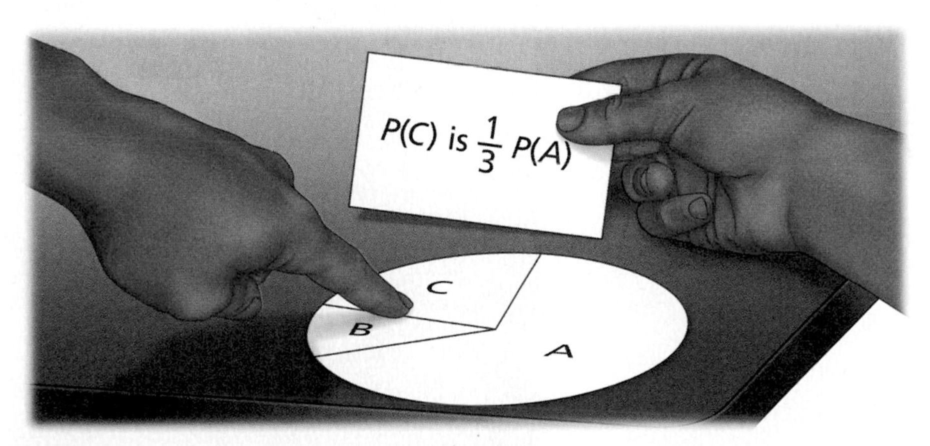

The "P(C) is $\frac{1}{3}$ P(A)" description card matches this spinner card.

I could see that sector A was about $\frac{2}{3}$ of the circle. That left $\frac{1}{3}$ of the circle for sectors B and C. Sector C looked like $\frac{1}{3}$ of sector A, so that made it $\frac{2}{9}$, and $\frac{2}{9}$ is $\frac{1}{3}$ of $\frac{2}{3}$.

7.4 Using a Probability to Reach Alternative Conclusions

GOAL

Recognize the differences possible in arriving at probability conclusions.

EXPLORE the Math

Nicole and Simon are looking forward to Friday's dance. The poster advertising the dance is shown below.

Simon says he plans to be at the dance early to get in line because he has a good chance of getting a CD he likes. Nicole says she won't be going early to line up because the chances of getting a CD she likes are not very good.

? How can both students make different decisions based on probability, and both be right?

Chapter Self-Test

1. Which of these situations involve probabilities? Explain.
   a) The time slot a TV network uses for a new show
   b) The admission fee for a concert supporting your local SPCA
   c) The percent of protein in a protein bar
2. Describe a situation at your school where probabilities might be involved.
3. Suppose that you want to know the likelihood that the next two babies born in your area will be boys. To model the situation you flip a coin two times, then repeat the experiment a total of 20 times. What assumptions do you make when you use this model and use the probability that you get two heads to represent the probability of two boys? Are these assumptions valid?
4. Your teacher assigns homework 80% of the time. What assumptions do you make when you decide the probability that she will assign homework tomorrow night?
5. A tutoring service says that 70% of students who use their service improve their marks. You say that this means that if you go for tutoring, there is a probability of $\frac{7}{10}$ that your marks will improve. What assumptions are you making?
6. Life insurance companies charge different amounts for life insurance policies depending on the age of the people they insure, their gender, their family health history, and whether they are smokers or non-smokers. Explain how probabilities might be used to determine fair life insurance rates.
7. Describe the probabilities that a boater might consider before heading out onto the water for a day of sailing.

WHAT DO You Think Now?

Revisit What Do You Think? on page 333. How have your answers and explanations changed?

Chapter Review

FREQUENTLY ASKED Questions

Study | *Aid*

- See Lesson 7.1, Examples 1 and 2.
- Try Chapter Review questions 1, 2, and 3.

Q: What situations in your everyday life involve probabilities?

A: You might use probabilities to decide which product to buy, whether an activity or location is safe, or how likely it is that you will win a door prize at an event. For example, if there are 200 students at an event and there are 5 door prizes, your chance of winning a prize is $\frac{1}{40}$.

Sometimes data about a group can be interpreted as a probability. For example, if you know that 10% of the students in a certain age group play organized sports, then the probability that the first person you meet in that age group plays organized sports is 10%.

Study | *Aid*

- See Lesson 7.2, Examples 1 and 2.
- See Lesson 7.3, Example 1.
- Try Chapter Review questions 4 to 10.

Q: What kinds of assumptions might you make when estimating or calculating probabilities?

A: When you are estimating or calculating a probability, you might assume

- that the experiment you use to calculate the experimental probability has a lot of trials
- that you have clearly described and counted the possible outcomes and the favourable outcomes to calculate a theoretical probability
- that you have considered the "fairness" or independence of the events you are describing
- that you have thought of any non-mathematical issues that might influence the result

For example, if you know that 2 out of 10 students who try out for a varsity team make it onto the team, you might assume that your probability of getting on the team is 20%. But if you know that your ability is much better than average, the probability you will make the team is actually higher. You might also be assuming that there will be a similar number of players trying out this year as in previous years and that may not be true. You might also be assuming that the coach has a similar number of places available as in previous years, and that also may not be true.

Q: Why might you come to different probability conclusions when using the same information?

A: Probabilities can be based on experimental data or an analysis of theoretical outcomes, but they also involve assumptions and personal decisions about risks. Confidence in those assumptions and personal decisions can vary. For example, in deciding whether to buy an item now or wait for a sale, there are some probabilities to consider.

Study *Aid*

- See Lesson 7.4.
- Try Chapter Review question 11.

Probability to Consider	Possible Decisions
probability that there will be a sale	Wait for a sale: • sales usually happen in this month Buy now: • there might not be a sale this year
probability that the item will be available	Wait for a sale: • I don't care that much about the item, so I can wait for a lower price Buy now: • I really want the item, and it might be sold out if I wait

Practice

Lesson 7.1

1. What probability might be involved in each of these situations?
   a) whether a musical artist gets a standing ovation
   b) whether a car will have difficulty starting when you turn it on
   c) whether you will wake up before your alarm goes off

2. a) Use a print reference or the Internet to estimate the probability that an average 15-year-old is concerned about climate change.
   b) How might that probability have been calculated?

3. How might a patient use a probability to decide whether to allow doctors to use a local or general anesthetic during surgery?

Lesson 7.2

4. a) In a game, two dice are rolled. Player A scores a point if the difference of the numbers on the dice is 1. Determine the probability that player A scores a point on his next turn. Show your work.
   b) List the assumptions you made in your answer to part a).

5. The cafeteria has served broccoli with lunch every Wednesday for two years.
   a) What is the probability that broccoli will be served next Wednesday?
   b) What assumptions are you making in drawing that conclusion?

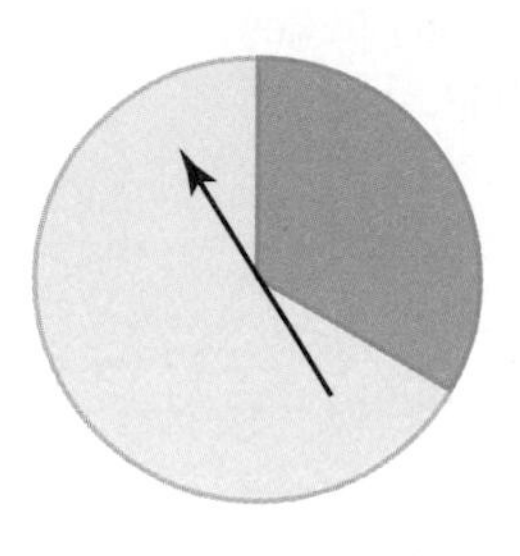

6. a) What is the probability that you will spin green on the spinner to the left?
   b) What assumptions did you make when calculating the probability in part a)?

7. Suppose that in the last 10 years, a Western team has won the Grey Cup 70% of the time.
   a) What is the probability that a Western team will win the Grey Cup next time?
   b) What assumptions did you make in your answer to part a)?

Lesson 7.3

8. Sharyn says that a good way to model the performance of a baseball player who gets a hit 1 time in 4 is to use a spinner with 4 sections. What assumptions is she making? Are her assumptions valid?

9. Tomasz heard that the probability of finding a prize in a milk container during the company's "big giveaway" campaign is 5%.
   a) How might he collect data to confirm this claim?
   b) What assumptions would he be making using the method in part a)?

10. A patient who suffers from serious migraine headaches is told that a new drug has a 30% chance of being successful, and there is a 5% chance of serious side effects and a 50% chance of mild side effects. Explain how the patient might use these probabilities to help him decide about taking the drug. What other probabilities might the patient want to know about before making his decision?

Lesson 7.4

11. The table shows the number of days with at least one scheduled event at the Jubilee auditorium in Edmonton for the next 6 months.

Month	1	2	3	4	5	6
Number of days with scheduled events	28	14	9	3	2	5

   a) Why might Lili determine that the probability that there will be more than 10 days with at least one scheduled event in month 7 is very low?
   b) Why might she come to a different conclusion?

Chapter Task

Choosing a Menu

A new restaurant is opening in the neighbourhood.

They are looking to appeal to teenagers.

They are committed to serving only healthy food.

They want to have a specialty menu of about 5 items that would draw in their target customers.

? How can a specialty menu be created that is likely to draw in the restaurant's target customers?

A. What probabilities might be relevant to the success of the specialty menu?

B. How might you estimate each of those probabilities? Consider both strategies that use **first-hand data** and strategies that use **second-hand data**, using, for example, the Internet.

C. What assumptions are you making in calculating those probabilities?

D. What specialty menu items would you suggest and how could you convince the restaurant owners that these are good choices?

Task | *Checklist*

- ✔ Did you consider as many relevant probabilities as you could?
- ✔ Did you consider different ways to estimate the required probabilities?
- ✔ Did you consider all the assumptions you were making?
- ✔ Were your arguments convincing?

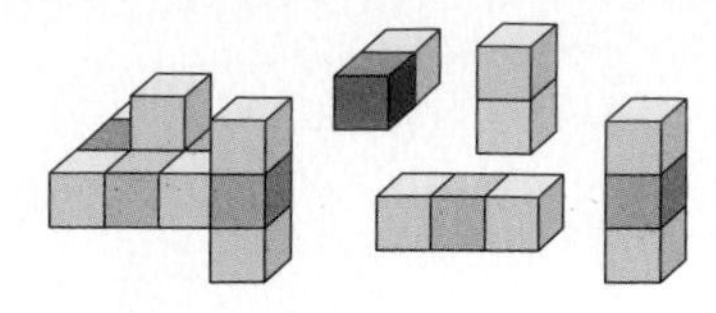

1. Colin decomposed the cube structure as shown. Each side of each cube is 2.5 cm long. What is the total area of overlap?
   A. 20 cm^2
   B. 18.75 cm^2
   C. 25.0 cm^2
   D. 12.5 cm^2

12 cm
5.6 cm
8 cm
44 cm
10.5 cm

2. What is the surface area of the object at left?
   A. 1531.1 cm^2
   B. 4329.3 cm^2
   C. 2007.1 cm^2
   D. 2429.3 cm^2

3. A linear relation passes through (0, 5) and (15, 35). What is the rate of change?
   A. 0.5 B. 2 C. −2 D. −0.5

4. Predict the value of y when $x = 12$ for the linear relation in question 3.
   A. 29 B. 3.5 C. 35 D. 5

5. Predict the value of y when $x = 35$ for the linear relation in question 3.
   A. 70 B. 15 C. 75 D. 12.5

6. Select the correct graph for the relation $y = 7 - 2x$.

A.

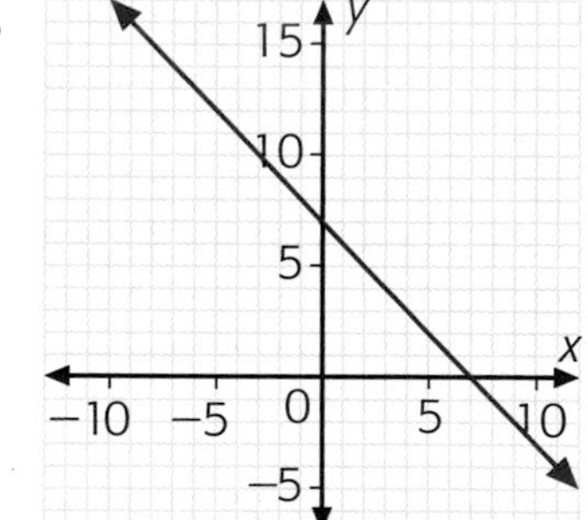

C.

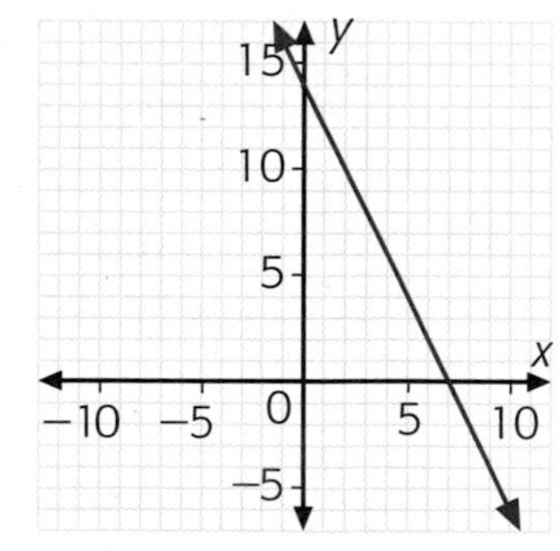

B.

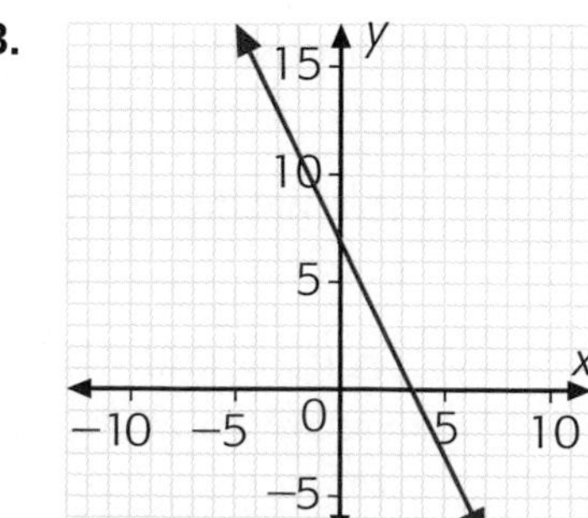

D.

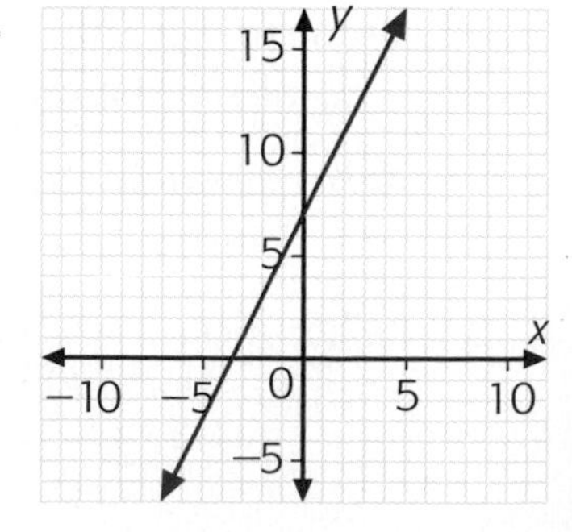

7. According to the ad at right, how much will 25 DVDs cost?
A. \$150.00 **B.** \$194.85 **C.** \$324.75 **D.** \$129.90

8. A first order cost \$64.95. How many DVDs were ordered?
A. 5 **B.** 10 **C.** 15 **D.** 20

9. The solution to $7x + 7 = 14x - 11$ is
A. $x = 2\frac{4}{7}$ **B.** $x = \frac{4}{7}$ **C.** $x = -\frac{4}{7}$ **D.** $x = -\frac{4}{21}$

10. Solve $-\frac{1}{4}x + 8 = \frac{1}{8}x + 5$.
A. $x = 4$ **B.** $x = 6$ **C.** $x = -8$ **D.** $x = 8$

11. Which graph represents the solution to the inequality $2 + 4x \leq 7$, where x is rational?

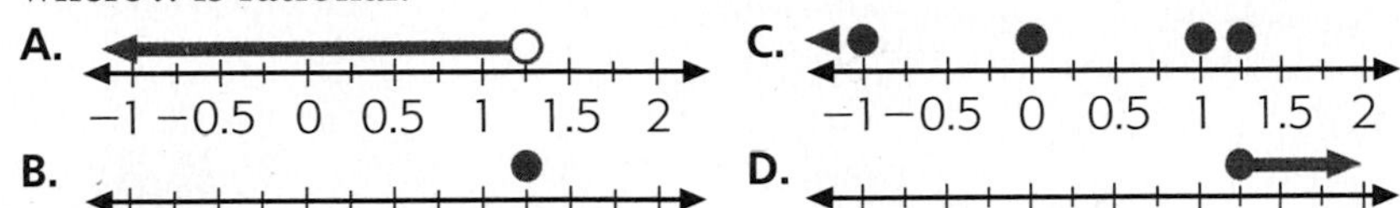
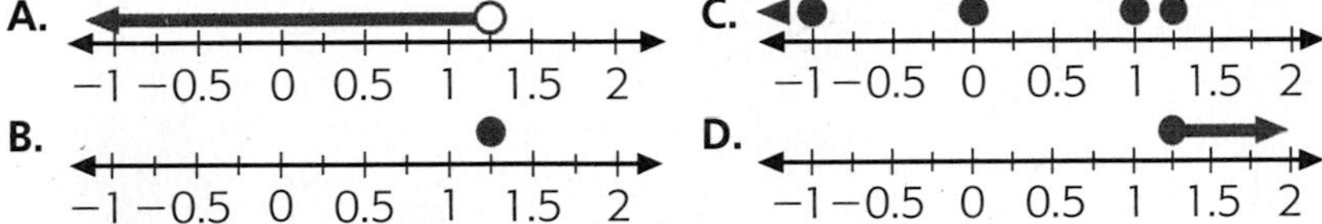

12. Select the simplified representation for
$6 - 2x^2 + 6xy - 3y + x^2 + 7xy - 11$.
A. $x^2 + 13xy - 3y + 17$ **C.** $-x^2 - xy - 3y - 5$
B. $13xy - x^2 - 3y + 17$ **D.** $13xy - x^2 - 3y - 5$

13. When you subtract a polynomial from $-2x^2 + 6$, you need three tiles to model the difference. Which polynomial below *cannot* be the one that was subtracted?
A. $-5x^2 + 6$ **B.** $-2x^2 + 9$ **C.** $6x^2 + 9$ **D.** $-2x^2 + 3x + 6$

14. The solution to $(6x^2 + 12x)$ divided by $6x$ is
A. $6x + 2$ **B.** $x^2 + 2x$ **C.** $x^2 + 2$ **D.** $x + 2$

15. Players roll two dice in a game. Player A scores a point if the difference of the numbers is 3. Player B scores a point if the sum of the numbers is greater than 10. Which statement describes the game?
A. The game is fair. Each player has three winning outcomes.
B. The game is fair. Only one player can score a point on a turn.
C. The game is unfair. Player A has more winning outcomes than Player B.
D. The game is unfair. Player B has more winning outcomes than Player A.

16. A college advertises that 75% of graduating students find a job they rate as desirable within 6 months. To consider this a good college to attend as a student, which of the following would you need to assume?
A. A desirable job pays well and is related to your field of study.
B. A high percentage of graduating students look for work.
C. A high percentage of students at the college graduate and look for work related to their field of study.
D. Other colleges advertise lower percentages.

Chapter 8

Symmetry

GOALS

You will be able to

- identify and apply line symmetry
- identify and apply rotation symmetry
- relate symmetry to transformations
- solve problems by using diagrams

Symmetry is often seen in art. What symmetry do you see in this art?

Getting Started

YOU WILL NEED
- cardboard
- scissors
- a ruler

Square Symmetry

Zachary said, if you rotate a square, you can only make four-sided and eight-sided shapes with **lines of symmetry**.

Can you make shapes with other numbers of sides by rotating a square?

A. Cut out a square.

B. Rotate the square about its centre point 180° **clockwise**. What shape do you get?

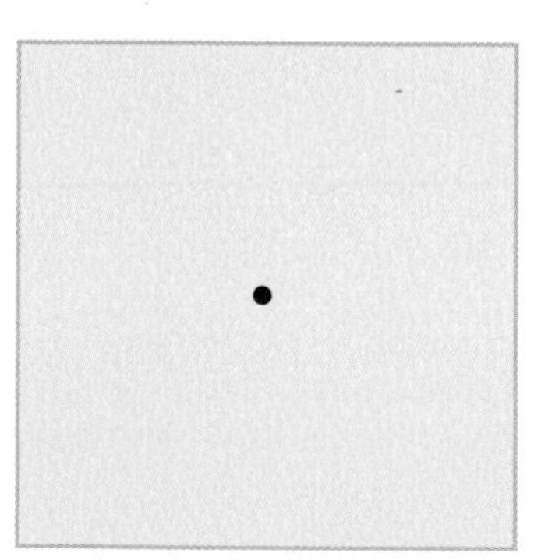

C. Rotate the original square about the bottom right vertex 90° cw. What shape do you get if you combine the new shape with the original one to make one large shape?

D. How do you know your combined shape from part C has a line of symmetry?

E. Try rotating the square around different points, using different numbers of degrees. How many sides do your combined shapes have?

F. Can you make shapes that do not have four sides or eight sides or do not have lines of symmetry? Explain.

WHAT DO You Think?

Decide whether you agree or disagree with each statement. Explain your decision.

1. A parallelogram is not symmetrical.
2. A line that separates a 2-D figure into two equal parts is a line of symmetry.
3. Shapes with more sides have more lines of symmetry.
4. If a shape has symmetry, it will fit in the same outline after you rotate it.

8.1 Line Symmetry

YOU WILL NEED
- coloured pencils
- a ruler
- scissors
- square dot paper
- triangle dot paper

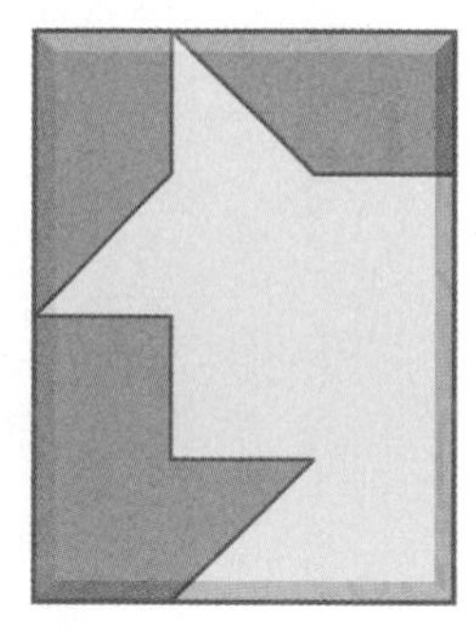

GOAL

Use line symmetry to classify polygons and complete shapes.

INVESTIGATE the Math

Zachary has a quarter of a piece of tile left from his grandmother's tiled floor. He wants to see what the whole tile looked like. He decides that the original tile probably had symmetry.

? What did the original tile probably look like?

A. Draw the shape on square dot paper, as shown.

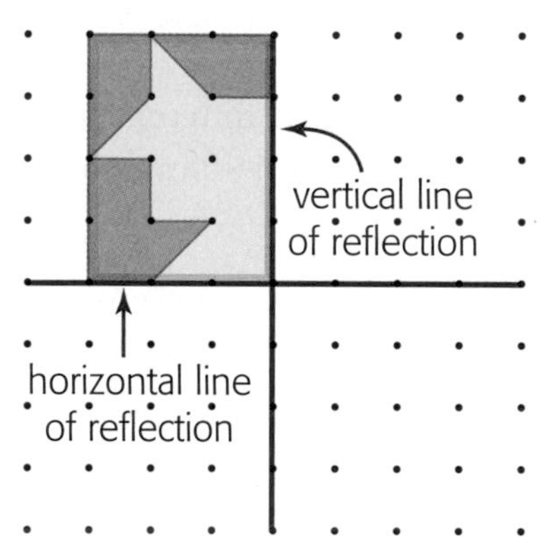

B. Reflect the shape from part A across the vertical line of reflection shown. Measure the distance of each point from the line to check your drawing.

C. Reflect the combined shape from part B across the horizontal line of reflection shown. Measure the distance of each point from the line to check your drawing.

Reflecting

D. How did drawing the shape on the dot paper help you complete it?

WORK WITH the Math

EXAMPLE 1 | Completing a shape using a line of symmetry

Zachary drew half of the pattern for his stained glass window as shown. He asked Francis to finish it. What will the complete pattern look like?

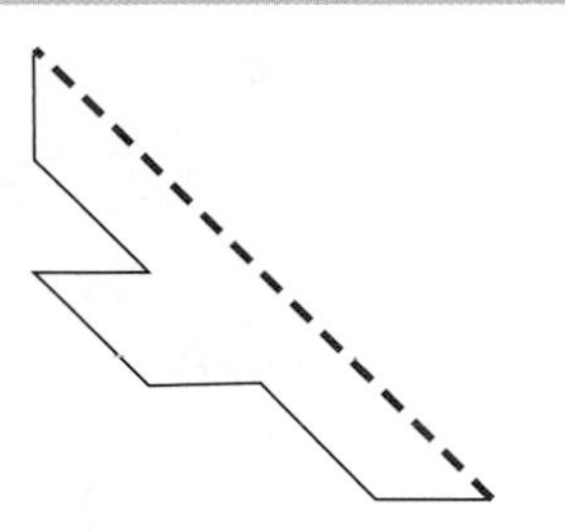

Francis's Solution

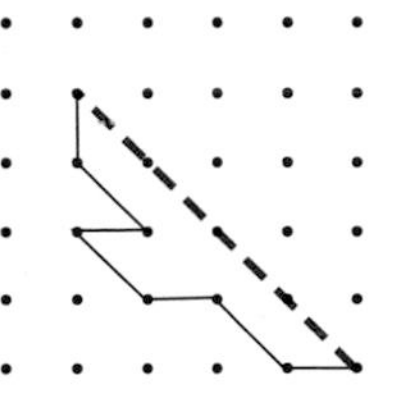

I drew the half of the pattern on dot paper. The red line is the line of symmetry.

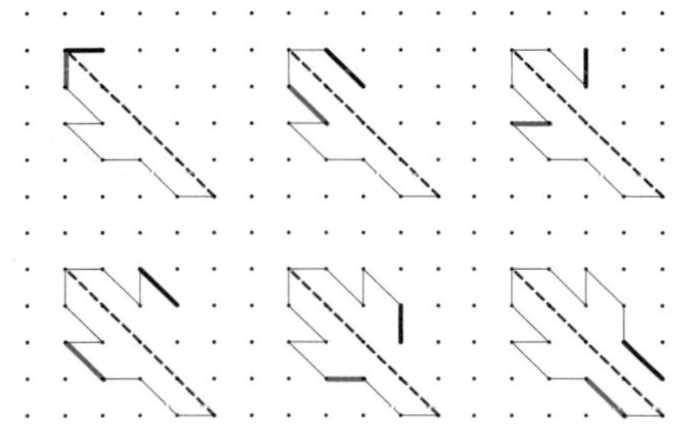

I drew each point of the image to be the same perpendicular distance from the line of symmetry as the original point.

The stained glass window will look like this.

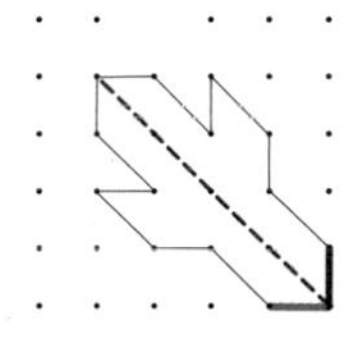

EXAMPLE 2 | Determining if a line is a line of symmetry

Is *DB* a line of symmetry?

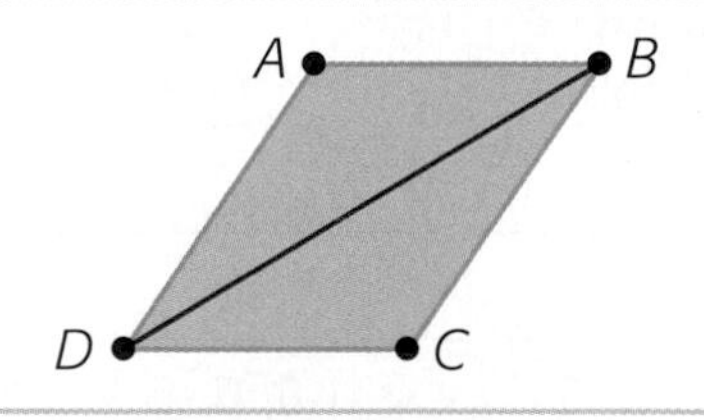

Viktor's Solution

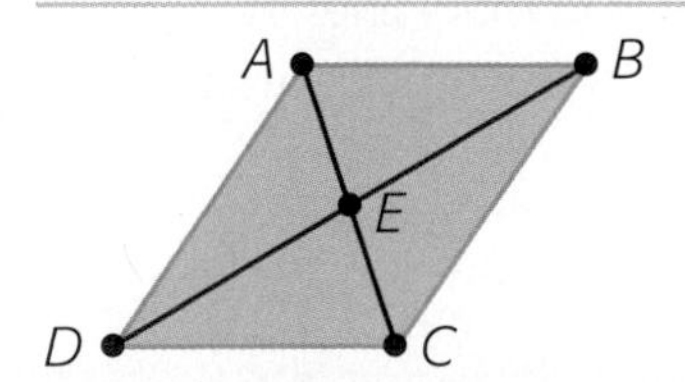

I drew the line *AC*. If *DB* were a line of symmetry, then *AC* would be its perpendicular bisector. *AE* and *EC* would have equal lengths and $\angle AEB$ would be a right angle.
I measured with a ruler. *AE* and *EC* are not equal.
I measured $\angle AEB$ with a protractor. It is not 90°.

DB is not a line of symmetry.

EXAMPLE 3 | Classifying designs by number of lines of symmetry

Sort these designs according to the number of lines of symmetry they have.

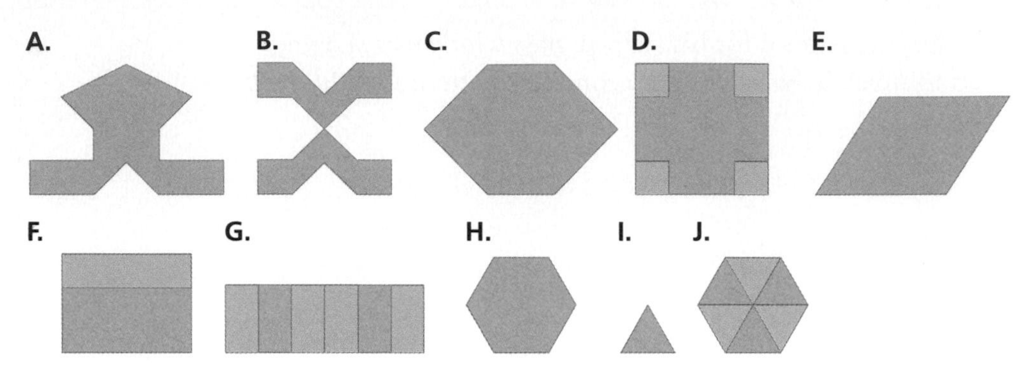

Rani's Solution

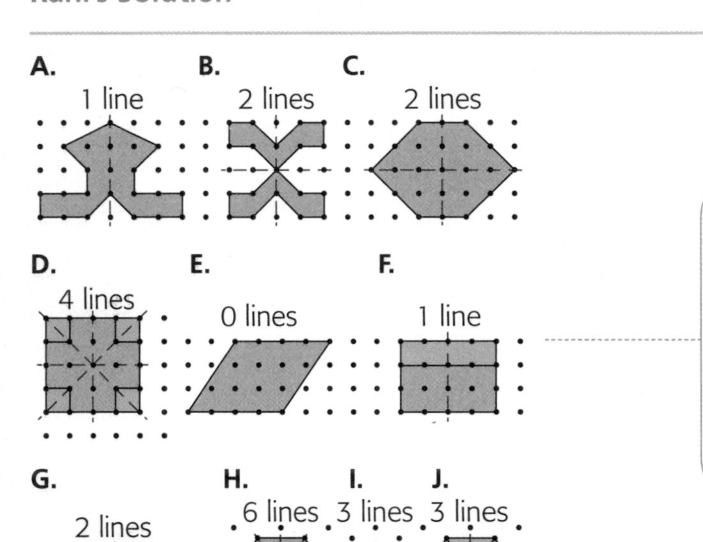

I drew each design on dot paper.
I located lines of symmetry by measuring, and then I drew them. I knew that a point on one side of a line of symmetry would be the same perpendicular distance from the line as the corresponding point on the other side.
I decided to consider both colour and shape to decide whether there really was a line of symmetry.

Number of Lines of Symmetry	Shape
0	E
1	A, F
2	B, C, G
3	I, J
4	D
6	H

I sorted the designs according to the number of lines of symmetry they had.
Some shapes would have had more lines of symmetry if they hadn't had coloured sections.

EXAMPLE 4 | Identifying reflection symmetry in a tessellation

Identify lines of symmetry in this **tessellation**.

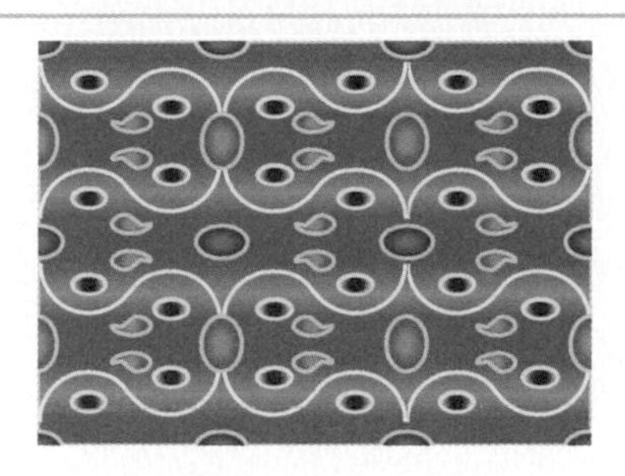

Luc's Solution

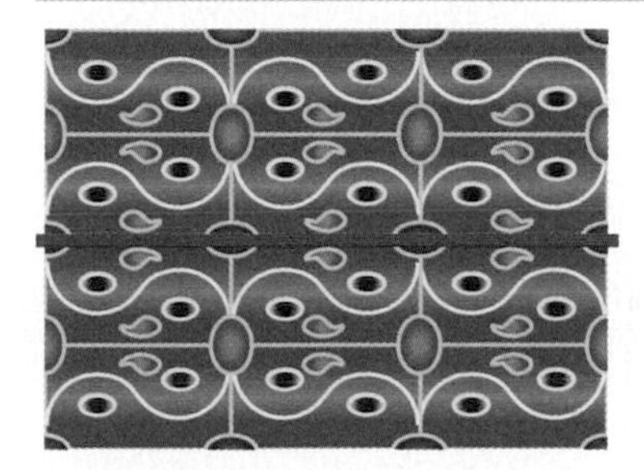

I thought about the design in columns and rows. I drew a horizontal line between rows. The design above the line was reflected below the line. That means the line is a line of symmetry.

I drew a vertical line between columns. I could see that the column of design on the left of the line was reflected on the right.

When I drew a second line between columns, I could see that the columns of design on left and right were again reflected.

Because tessellations go on forever, any line I draw between columns in this design will be a line of reflection.

I can draw horizontal and vertical lines of symmetry in this tessellation.

In Summary

Key Ideas

- A line of symmetry is a line that separates a figure or a shape into two congruent halves so that each point of one half is at the same perpendicular distance from the line of symmetry as the corresponding point in the other half.
- In a design, each corresponding point must be the same colour.

Need to Know

- You can classify a polygon by the number of lines of symmetry it has.
- You can complete a symmetrical design if you are given half of it and the line of symmetry.
- If you can identify line symmetry in one part of a tessellation, you will be able to find the same symmetry elsewhere in the tessellation.

Checking

1. Complete each shape using the red line of symmetry.

a) 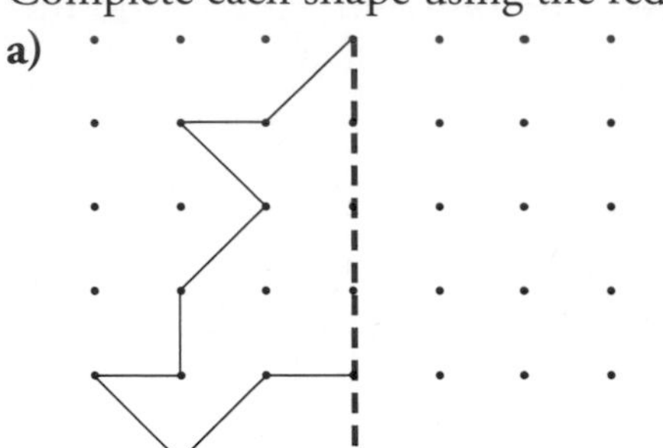

b) 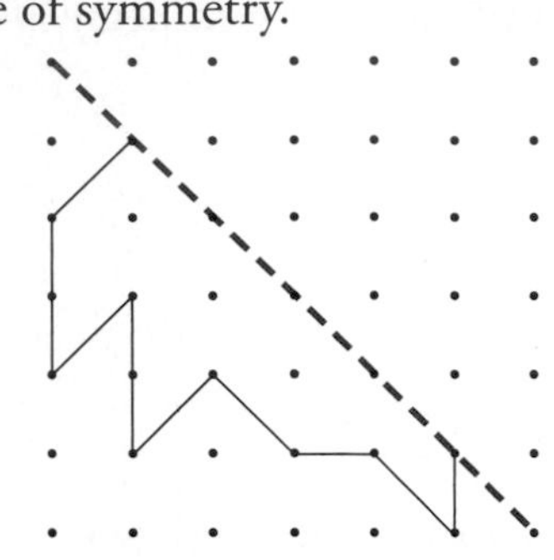

2. Sort the shapes into two groups: those with fewer than six lines of symmetry and those with six or more lines of symmetry.

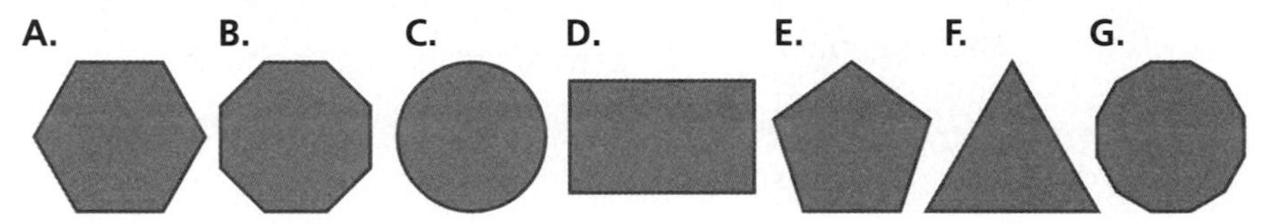

Practising

3. Sort the designs into two groups: those with fewer than six lines of symmetry and those with six or more lines of symmetry.

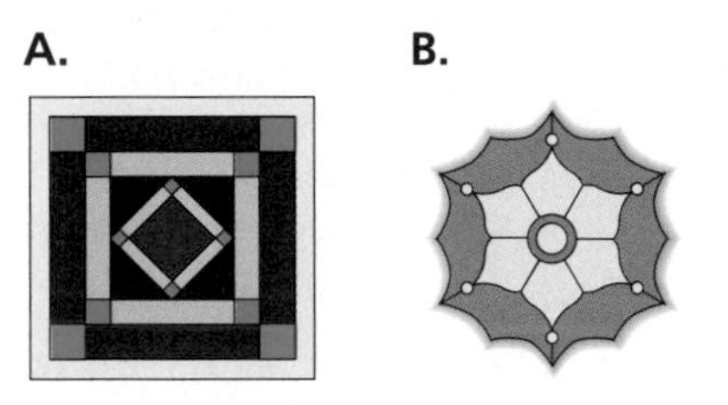

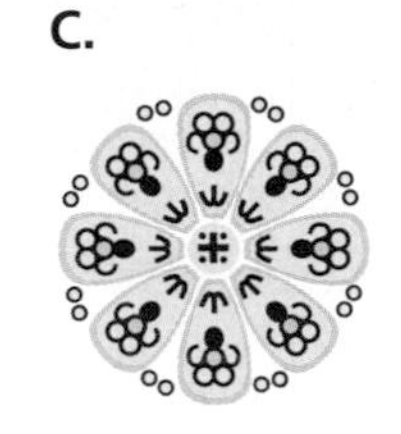

4. **Multiple choice.** Which of these tiles has line symmetry?

A. 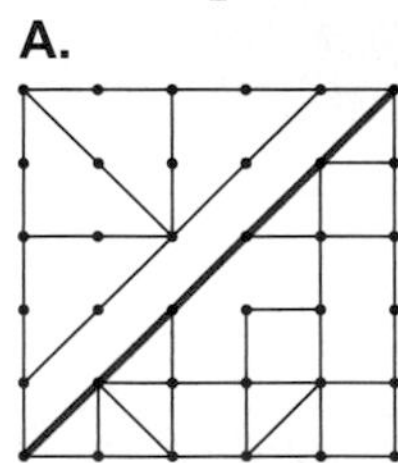

B. 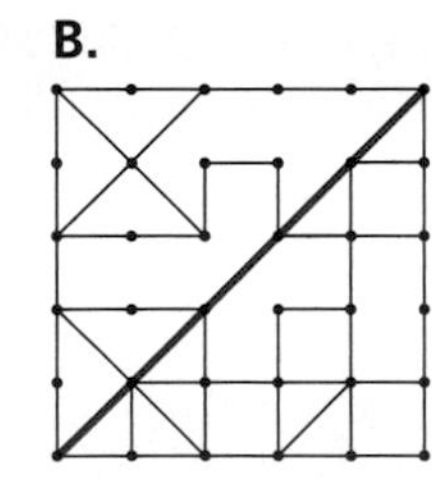

C. 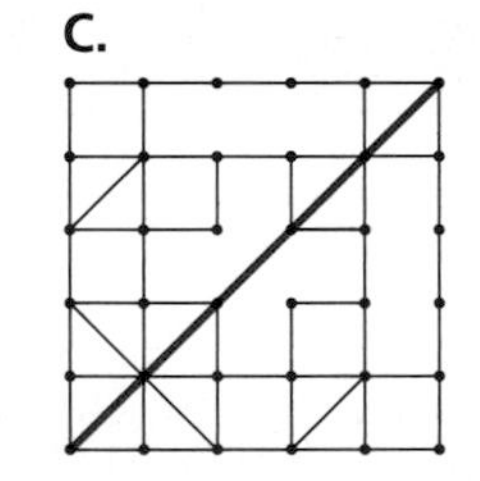

D. 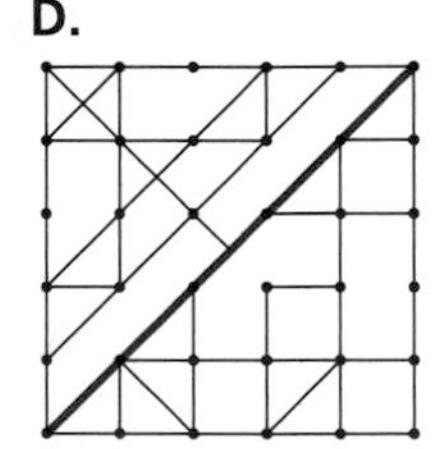

5. **Multiple choice.** Which line in this tessellation is a line of reflection?

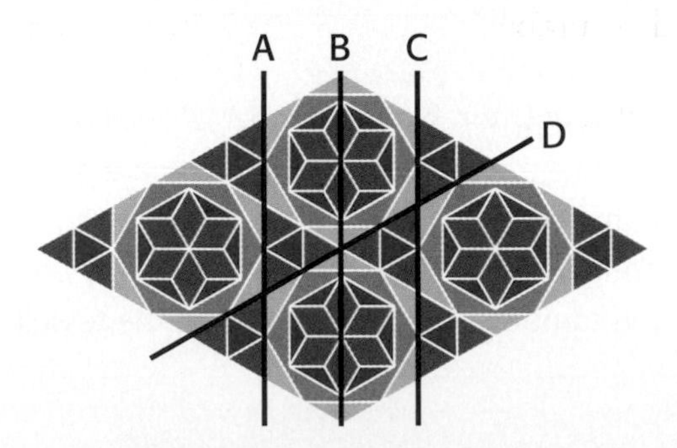

6. **Multiple choice.** Which line in this tessellation is not a line of reflection?

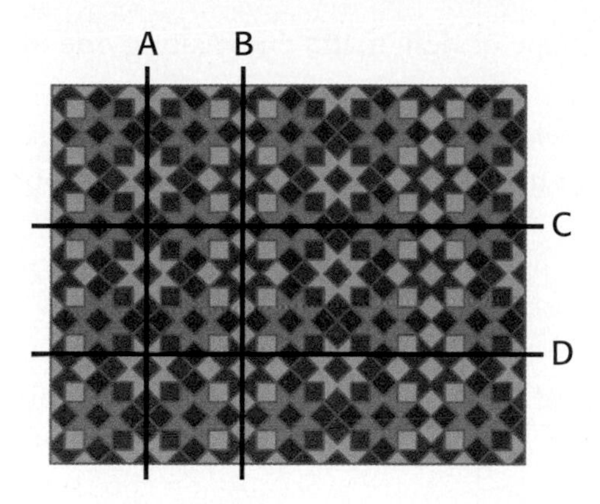

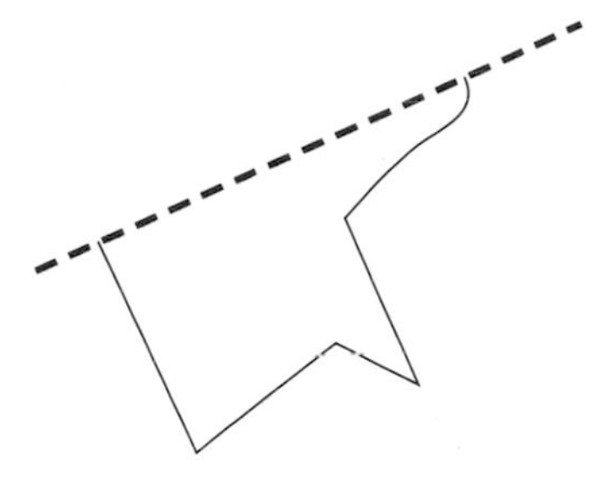

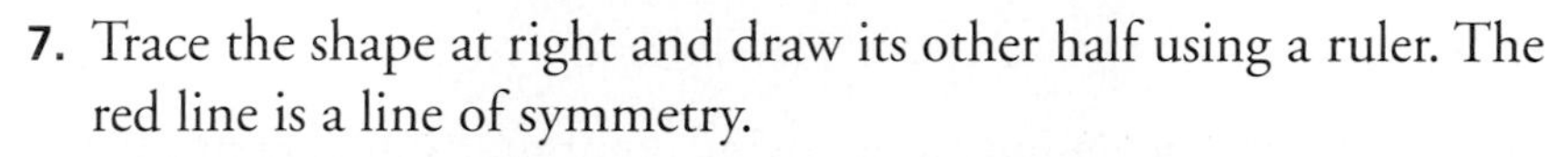
7. Trace the shape at right and draw its other half using a ruler. The red line is a line of symmetry.

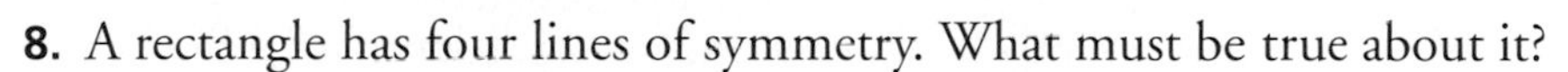
8. A rectangle has four lines of symmetry. What must be true about it?

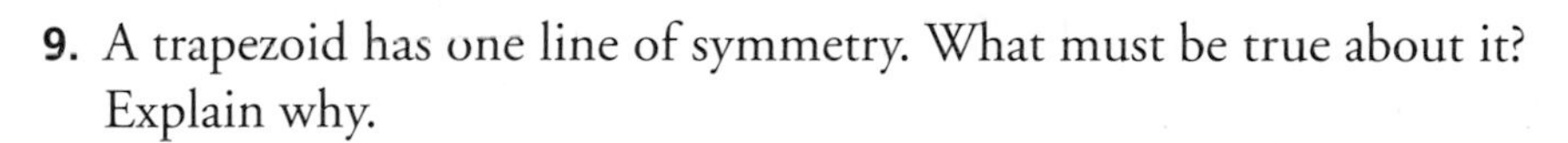
9. A trapezoid has one line of symmetry. What must be true about it? Explain why.

10. Can a trapezoid have two lines of symmetry? Explain.

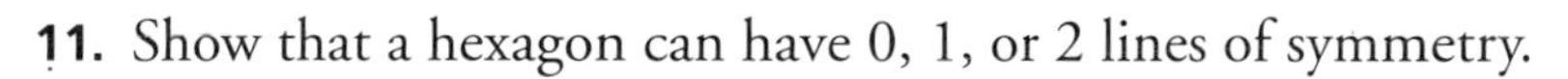
11. Show that a hexagon can have 0, 1, or 2 lines of symmetry.

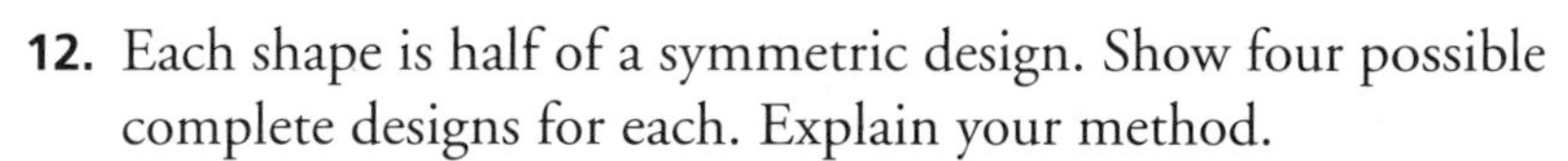
12. Each shape is half of a symmetric design. Show four possible complete designs for each. Explain your method.

a)

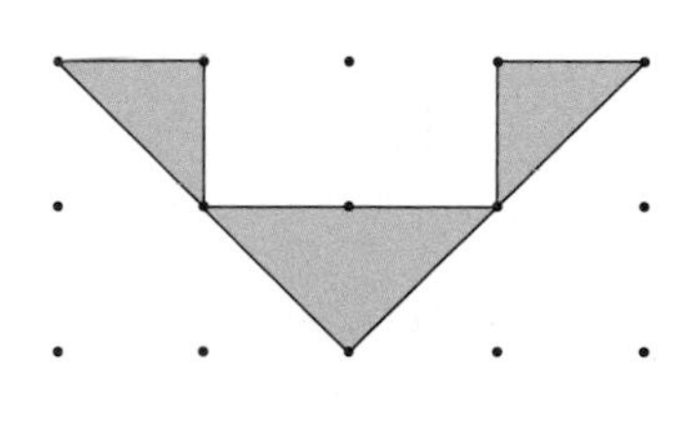

b)

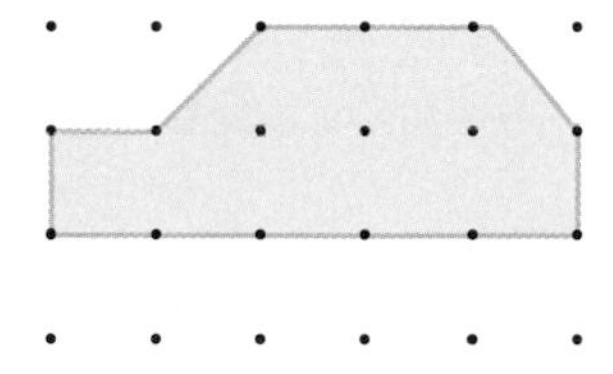

13. Explain how the number of lines of symmetry of a **regular** polygon relates to the number of sides it has.

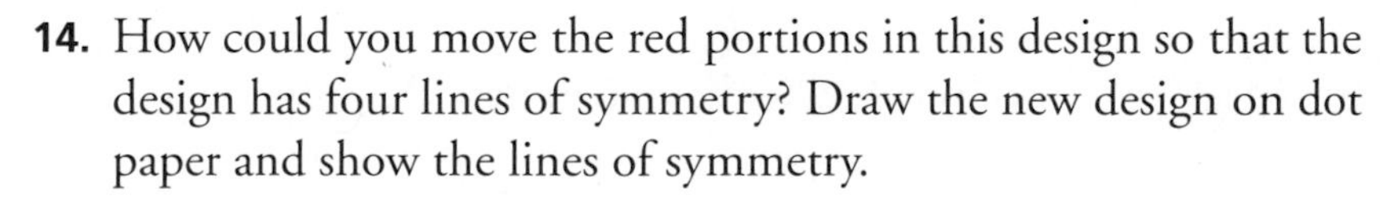
14. How could you move the red portions in this design so that the design has four lines of symmetry? Draw the new design on dot paper and show the lines of symmetry.

15. How do you know that a shape with two lines of symmetry has at least four sides?

16. **a)** Draw a shape or design and cut it along one of the lines of symmetry.

b) Ask another student to complete the design using one of the cut pieces and to explain how he or she figured out the complete pattern.

Closing

17. How is a line of reflection related to a line of symmetry? Give an example.

Extending

18. Create an artistic design, either using computer software or by hand, that has exactly six lines of symmetry. Identify the lines of symmetry in your design.

19. This shape is $\frac{1}{8}$ of a shape that has four lines of symmetry. What might the shape look like?

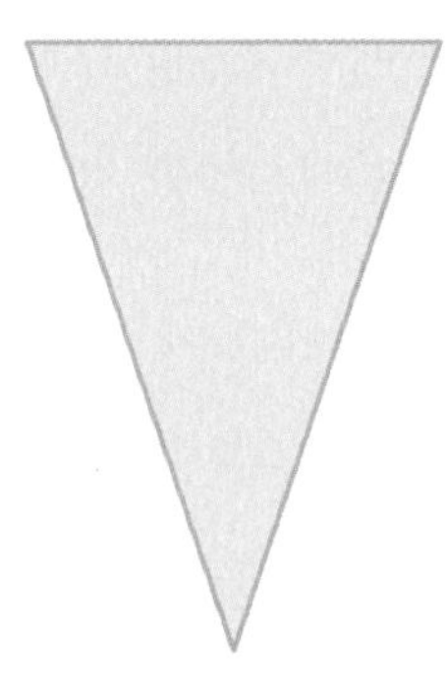

20. **a)** Trace these shapes. Put them together to make a shape with line symmetry.

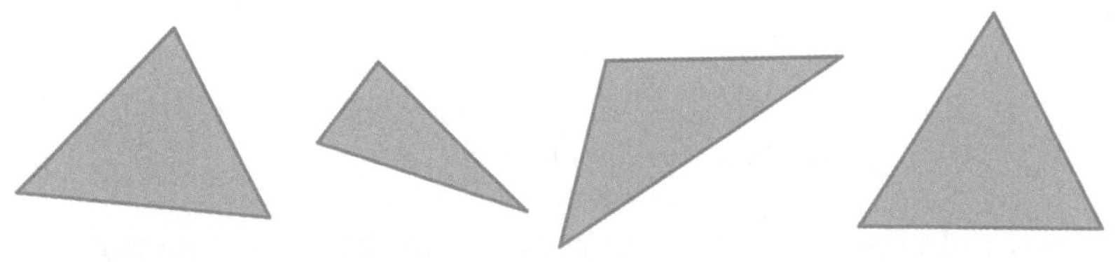

b) Make your own puzzle like the one in part a).

8.2 Rotation Symmetry

GOAL

Determine whether and how a shape can be turned to fit onto itself.

YOU WILL NEED

- cardboard or Bristol board
- scissors
- a protractor

INVESTIGATE the Math

Francis is designing candy boxes for an assembly line. Each box will be filled with candy and covered with a lid. Francis has to choose one of these three designs for the boxes. For the process to go as quickly as possible, he should choose the design whose lid can be attached the most quickly.

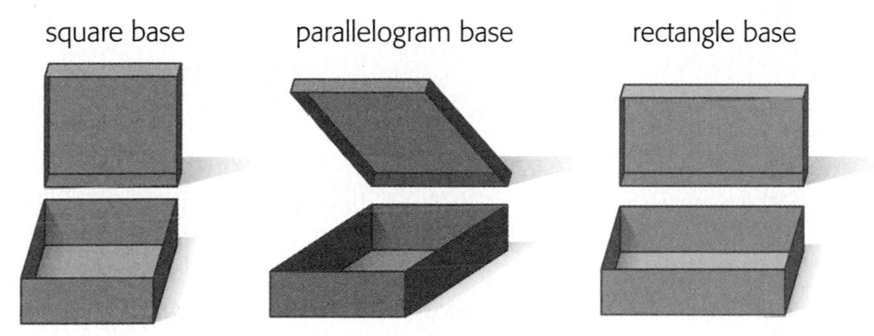

? Which design should Francis choose?

A. Draw a square on a piece of cardboard. Mark one corner with an X. Draw the lines of symmetry of the square and extend them past the edges.

B. Determine the centre of the square. Describe how you located it and how you know it is the centre.

C. Draw an outline of the square on paper. Rotate the square clockwise about the centre until it fits into its outline again. Draw the image.

D. Through what angle was the square rotated? How can you tell?

E. Continue to rotate the square clockwise, stopping when it fits in its outline. Measure the angle of rotation each time. When the square is back in its original position, record the number of times you rotated the square and the number of degrees that you rotated it each time.

F. Repeat parts A, B, and E for the rectangle and then for the other parallelogram.

G. Which of these lids has **rotation symmetry**? Which lid has the greatest **order of rotation symmetry**?

H. Which design should Francis choose for the box? Why?

rotation symmetry

When a rotating shape fits exactly over its original position with a turn of less than 360°, the shape has rotation symmetry.

order of rotation symmetry

the number of times, within a 360° rotation about an internal point, that a shape will coincide with its original position; for example, this shape has rotation symmetry of order 2 because, during a 360° rotation, it coincides with its original position twice.

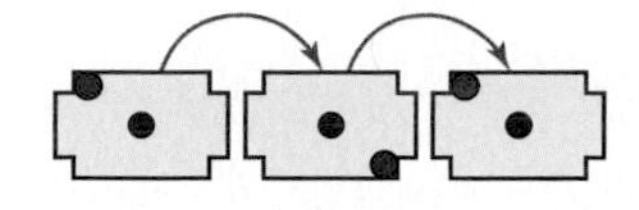

Reflecting

I. How did you locate all three shapes' centres of rotation?

J. Can a shape with line symmetry also have rotation symmetry? Explain with an example.

K. Can a shape have rotation symmetry but not have line symmetry? Explain with an example.

WORK WITH the Math

EXAMPLE 1 | Determining order of rotation symmetry

What is the order of rotation symmetry about the centre of a yield sign? What is its angle of rotation?

Francis's Solution

The yield sign is an equilateral triangle. I drew the triangle and marked one vertex with a black dot. I drew the three lines of symmetry. The point where they intersect is the centre of rotation.

I traced the triangle and rotated it about the centre clockwise until it fit into the tracing. I measured the angle of rotation to be 120°. The shape looked the same, but now the marked vertex was on the opposite side.

I rotated it 120° again to fit into the tracing. Now the marked vertex was on the bottom.

I rotated the triangle again to fit in the tracing. Again, the angle of rotation was 120°. This time the marked vertex returned to the original position.

I rotated the yield sign three times to return it to its original position. So, it has rotation symmetry of order 3. Each turn was 120°, so the angle of rotation is 120°.

EXAMPLE 2 | Rotating a shape about a vertex

Rotate this kite about a vertex to create a shape with rotation symmetry.

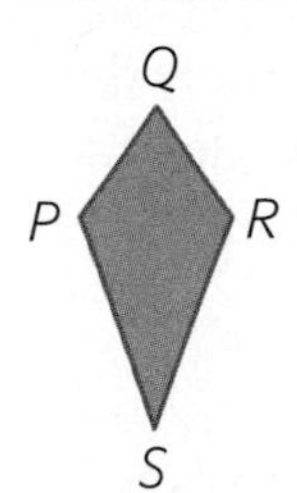

Erin's Solution

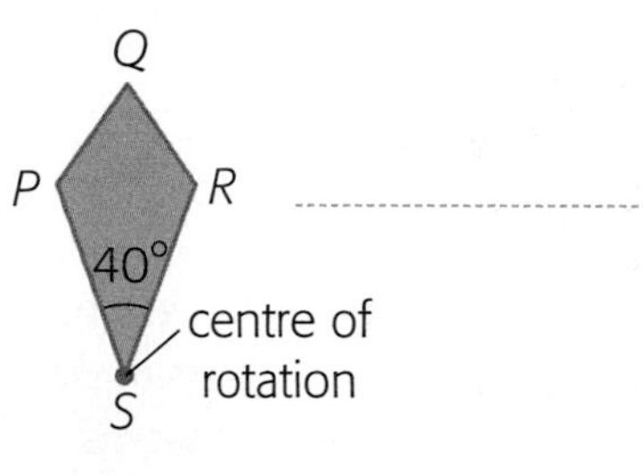

I cut out the kite and drew its outline. I decided to rotate it about the vertex *S*. I measured with a protractor, and the internal angle of *S* is 40°. I decided to rotate the kite by this amount so that there wouldn't be any spaces.

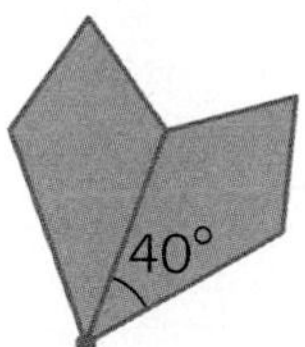

I rotated the cut-out kite 40° and drew its outline.

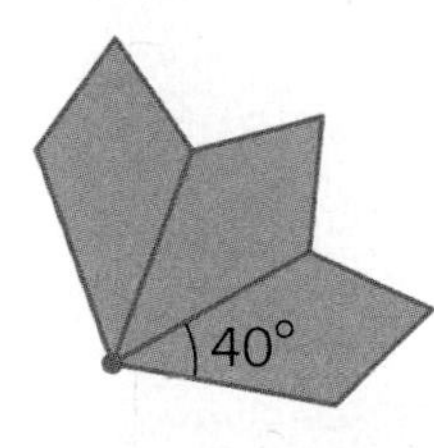

I rotated the cut-out kite a second time by 40°. I drew the outline of the shape.

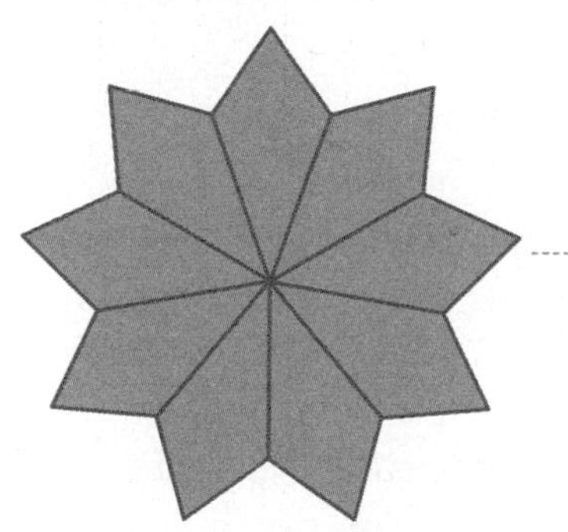

I rotated the cut-out kite by 40° six more times, eight times in all. There were now nine copies of the kite. By drawing each image, I got a design with rotation symmetry.

This is my shape. It has rotation symmetry of order 9.

The angle of rotation is 40°.

I noticed that $9 \times 40 = 360$. I think I could have predicted the order of rotation symmetry by dividing 360 by the measure of the angle S at the centre of rotation.

EXAMPLE 3 | Identifying rotation symmetry in a tessellation

Determine the order of rotation symmetry and angle of rotation of the shape upon which this tessellation is based.

Zachary's Solution

I thought the angle of rotation should be 60°, because I thought I saw six equilateral triangles making a hexagon in the design. I rotated the design 60°. The flowers in the design matched one another, so it seems that I was right.

I continued to rotate the design by 60°. It returned to its original position after six turns.

There are six flowers around the central flower, so the basic shape, hexagon, was rotated six times. The complete circle is 360°. Since the pattern has a rotation symmetry of order 6, each angle will be 60°.

The order of rotation symmetry is 6.
The angle of rotation is 60°.

In Summary

Key Ideas

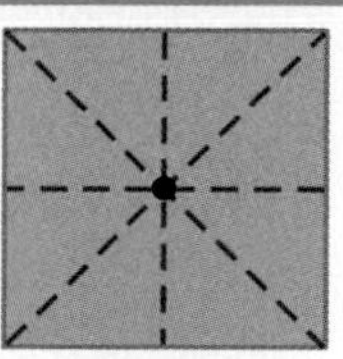

- A shape may have rotation symmetry and line symmetry:
  lines of symmetry: 4
  order of rotation symmetry: 4

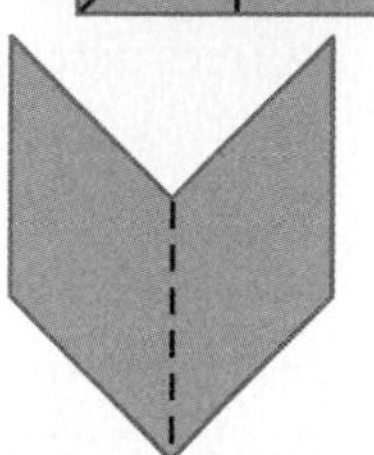

- It may have line symmetry but not rotation symmetry:
  lines of symmetry: 1
  order of rotation symmetry: 1

- It may have rotation symmetry but not line symmetry:
  lines of symmetry: 0
  order of rotation symmetry: 2

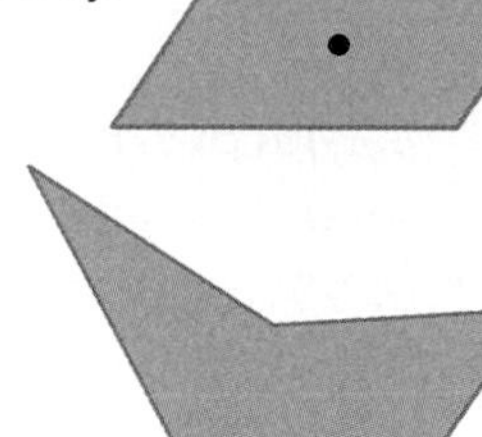

- It may have neither type of symmetry:
  lines of symmetry: 0
  order of rotation symmetry: 1

Need to Know

- A shape with rotation symmetry of order 1 has no rotation symmetry.
- The order of rotation symmetry and the angle of rotation for that symmetry are factors of 360. For example, the square above has rotation symmetry of order 4, so the angle of rotation for that symmetry must be $360 \div 4 = 90°$.
- If a shape has more than one line of symmetry, then its centre of rotation is located where those lines intersect.
- If you identify rotation symmetry around one point in a tessellation, you will be able to identify the same rotation symmetry around every like point.

Checking

1. For each shape, determine the number of lines of symmetry, its order of rotation symmetry, and the angle of rotation.

a)

b)

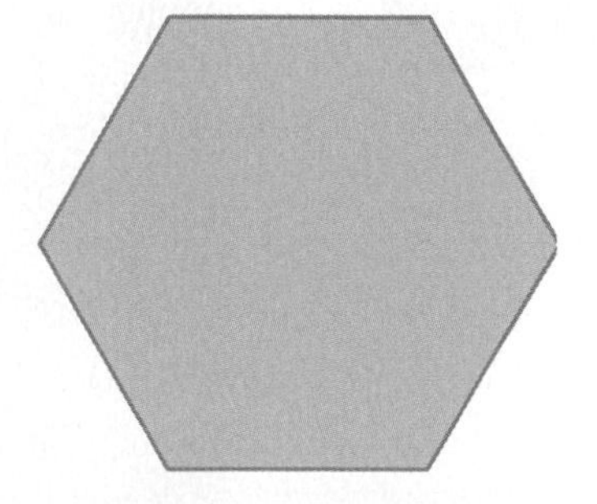

c)

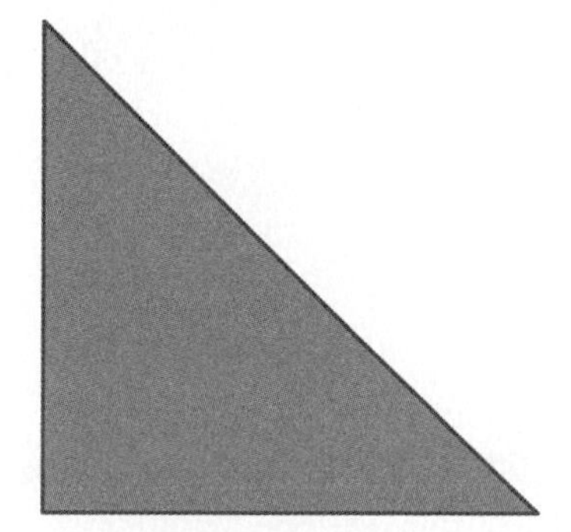

Practising

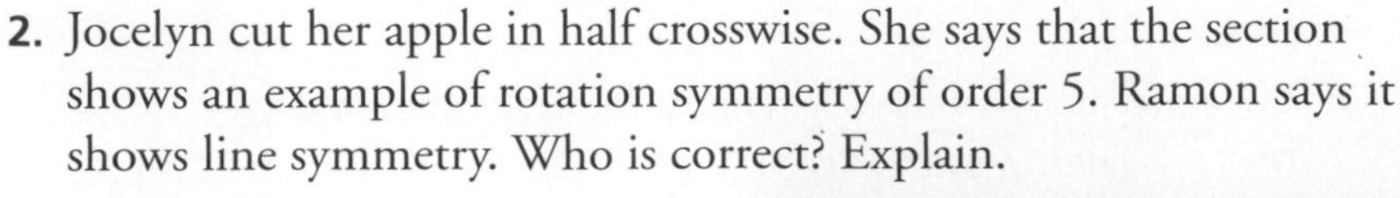

2. Jocelyn cut her apple in half crosswise. She says that the section shows an example of rotation symmetry of order 5. Ramon says it shows line symmetry. Who is correct? Explain.

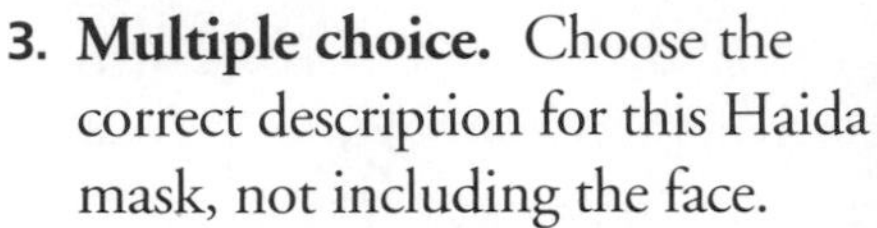

3. **Multiple choice.** Choose the correct description for this Haida mask, not including the face.

   A. 1 line of symmetry, rotation symmetry of order 1, no angle of rotation
   B. 2 lines of symmetry, rotation symmetry of order 2, 180° angle of rotation
   C. 4 lines of symmetry, rotation symmetry of order 4, 90° angle of rotation
   D. 8 lines of symmetry, rotation symmetry of order 8, 45° angle of rotation

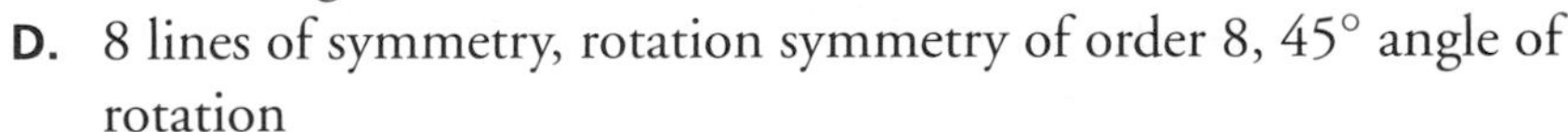

4. **Multiple choice.** Which statement is false?

   A. An octagon can have rotation symmetry of order 2.
   B. An isosceles triangle has rotation symmetry of order 2.
   C. A shape can have an order of symmetry that is 4 less than its number of sides.
   D. A parallelogram can have rotation symmetry of order 4.

5. For each object, determine the number of lines of symmetry the design has, its order of rotation symmetry, and the angle of rotation.

a)

b)

c)

6. Does this portion of a tessellation have rotation symmetry? If so, what are the angle and order of rotation symmetry?

7. Complete the other half of each shape using the indicated line of symmetry. What is the order of rotation symmetry of the full shape?

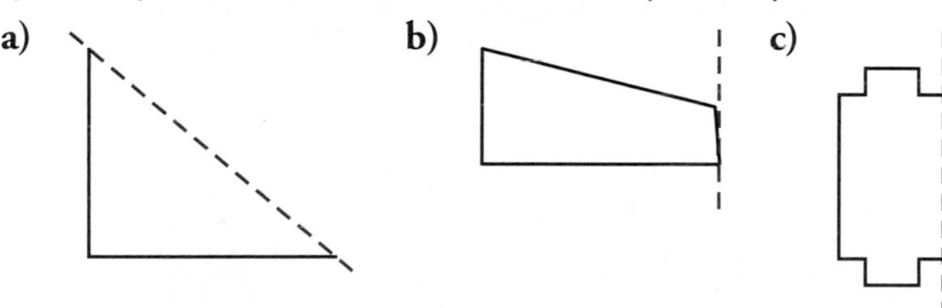

8. a) Which of these items have rotation symmetry but not line symmetry?

b) Identify the order of rotation symmetry of each item.

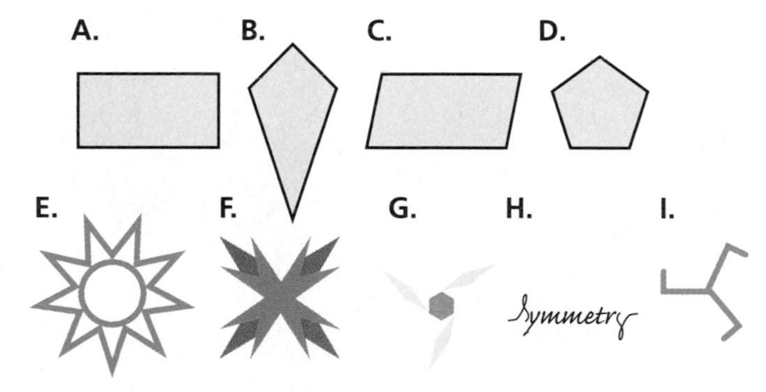

9. Which parallelogram has a higher order of rotation symmetry? Explain your answer.

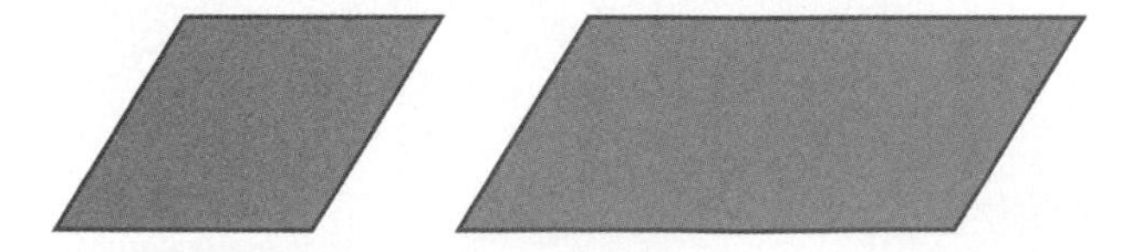

Reading Strategy

Monitoring Comprehension

How can you apply what you know about polygons and interior angles?

10. a) For each regular polygon, determine its order of rotation symmetry and its angle of rotation.

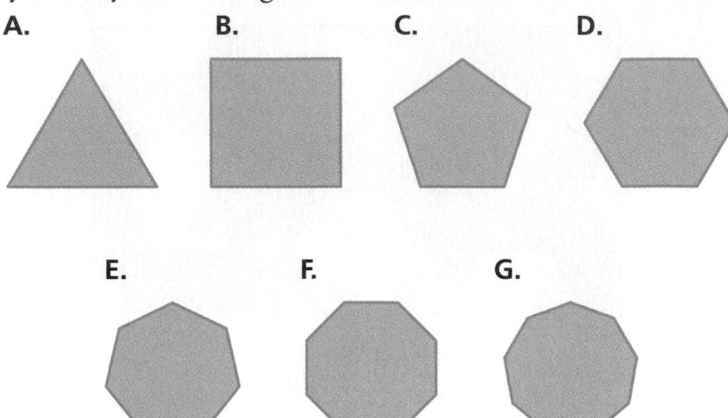

b) Look at your answers to part a). Explain how a regular polygon's order of rotation symmetry relates to the number of sides it has and why that makes sense.

11. Which of these screw heads have the same order of rotation symmetry? Explain.

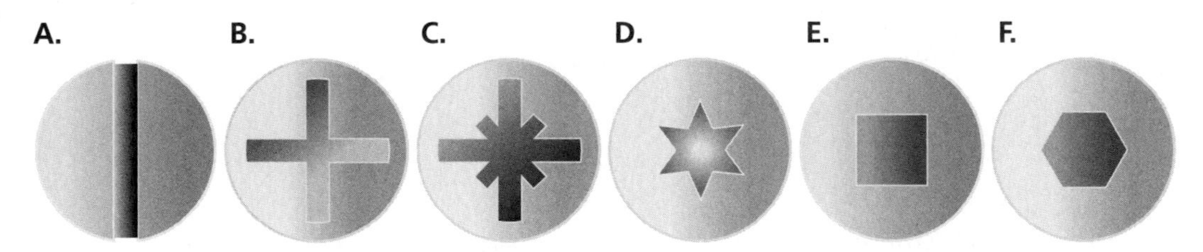

12. What is the order of rotation symmetry for each washer?

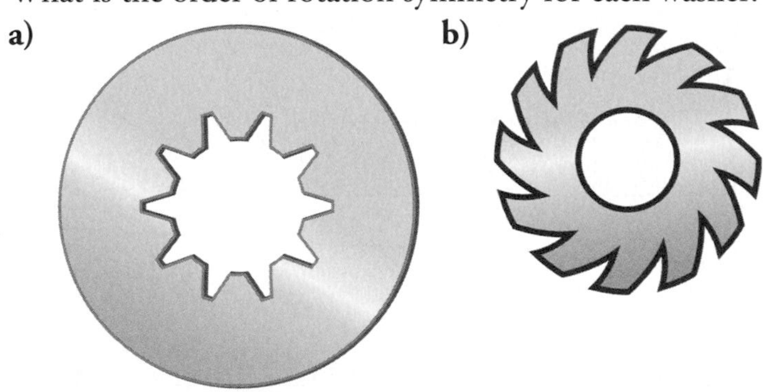

13. Alexandra drew a square that was 4 cm on each side. Then, she lengthened each side by 2 cm. Will the new shape still have rotation symmetry? Explain.

14. a) These polygons have no equal sides. Do they have rotation symmetry about their centres? Explain.

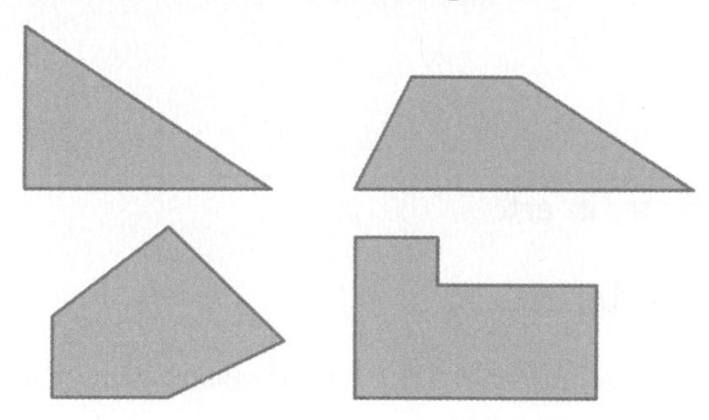

b) Each of these polygons has at least two equal sides. Do they have rotation symmetry about their centres? Explain.

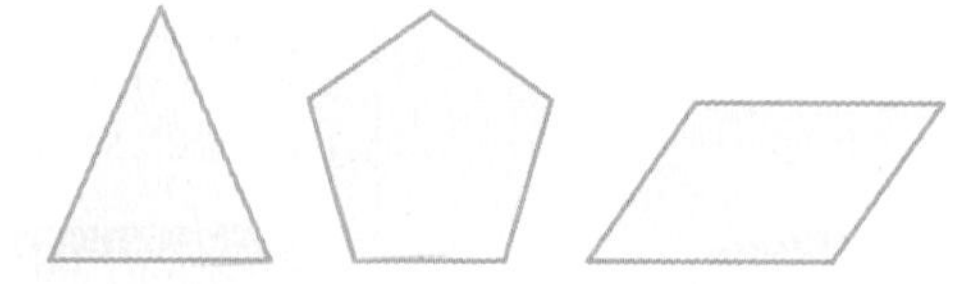

15. Show that the purple shape has rotation symmetry.

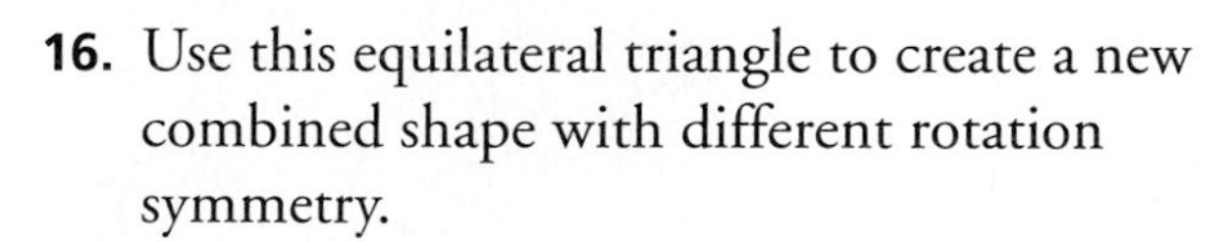

16. Use this equilateral triangle to create a new combined shape with different rotation symmetry.

17. Find a photograph or drawing of each item.

a) a 2-D shape with line symmetry and rotation symmetry

b) a 2-D shape with line symmetry but without rotation symmetry

c) a 2-D shape with rotation symmetry but without line symmetry

18. A shape has rotation symmetry of order "infinity." What is the shape and what does that mean?

Closing

19. In what ways is rotation symmetry like line symmetry? In what ways is it different?

Extending

20. Tape two mirrors together and set them up as shown. Draw a straight line on a piece of paper. Set the mirror on top of the paper so that the line extends from the bottom edge of one mirror to the bottom edge of the other. Look in. Explain why the shape you see has rotation symmetry.

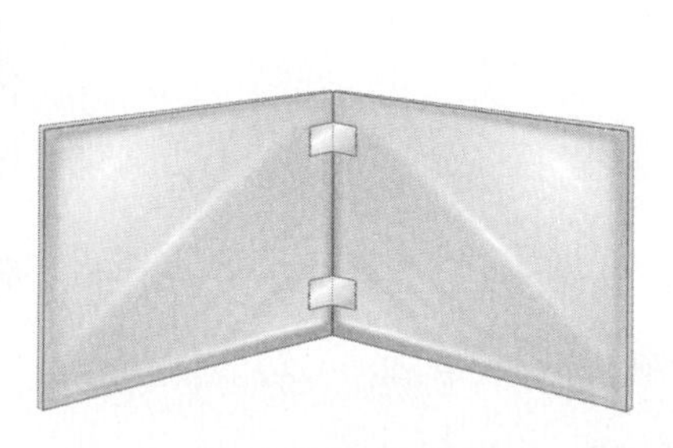

8.3 Symmetry in Art

YOU WILL NEED

- art from a number of sources

GOAL

Identify symmetry in art.

EXPLORE the Math

Nola, Viktor, and Luc showed their friends examples of art forms from their cultures that use symmetry.

Inuit art: pendant carving	Ukrainian art: egg decoration	French-Canadian art: ceinture fléchée (a woven sash worn around the waist to keep a jacket closed)
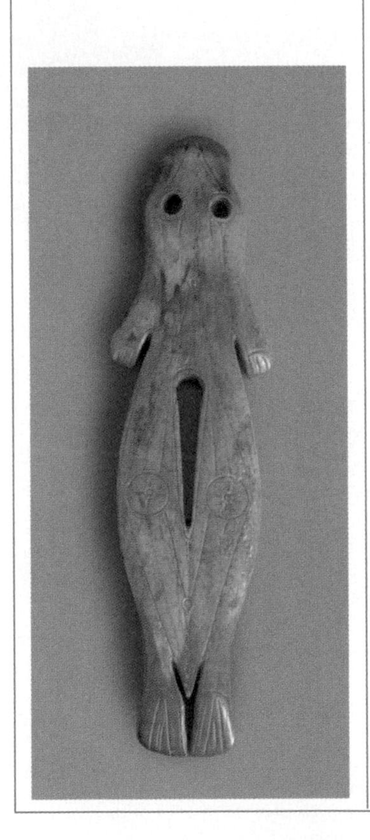		

Explore different types of art such as paintings, jewellery, quilts, tiles, murals, and cultural artwork.

? How do artists use symmetry in their art?

Curious MATH

Kaleidoscopes

Kaleidoscopes were invented in 1816. With a kaleidoscope, you can look at things in a new way.

These beautiful images are all from kaleidoscopes.

YOU WILL NEED

- two mirrors
- a protractor
- adhesive tape
- a small, flat object such as a heart-shaped sticker

Make your own kaleidoscope images.

1. Tape two mirrors together so that they stand up on the table at an angle of 90°.
2. Put a small flat object on the table between them.
3. Look at the image. How many images, including the object, do you see?

4. Change the angle of the mirrors to 72°, 60°, 45°, and 30°. How many images do you see, including the object, at each angle?
5. Suppose you could draw a line to connect the images in questions 3 and 4. What geometric shapes would you create?
6. Identify the order of rotation symmetry and the angle of rotation in those shapes.
7. Explain how changing the angle in the kaleidoscope changes the resulting rotation symmetry.

Mid-Chapter Review

FREQUENTLY ASKED Questions

Study | *Aid*

- See Lesson 8.1, Examples 1, 2, and 3.
- Try Mid-Chapter Review questions 1, 2, and 3.

Q: How can you tell that a 2-D object has line symmetry?

A: A 2-D object has line symmetry if you can draw a line through it that creates two halves, so that every point in one half is the same perpendicular distance from the line as the mirror image of the point.

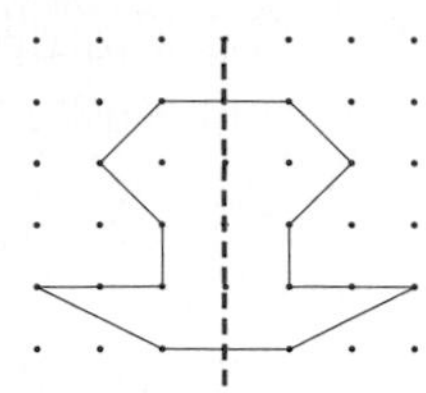

Study | *Aid*

- See Lesson 8.2, Examples 1, 2, and 3.
- Try Mid-Chapter Review questions 4, 5, 6, and 7.

Q: What is the order of rotation symmetry of a shape?

A: This is the number of times that you can turn a shape about its centre to fit into its outline.

- All shapes have rotation symmetry of order at least 1.
- All regular polygons have rotation symmetry of order greater than 1.
- All shapes with two or more lines of symmetry, such as this pentagon, have rotation symmetry.
- Shapes can have rotation symmetry, but no line of symmetry, such as this parallelogram.

Practice

Lesson 8.1

1. Sort these pictures of instruments into those that have more than one line of symmetry and those that do not. Explain your answer.

A.

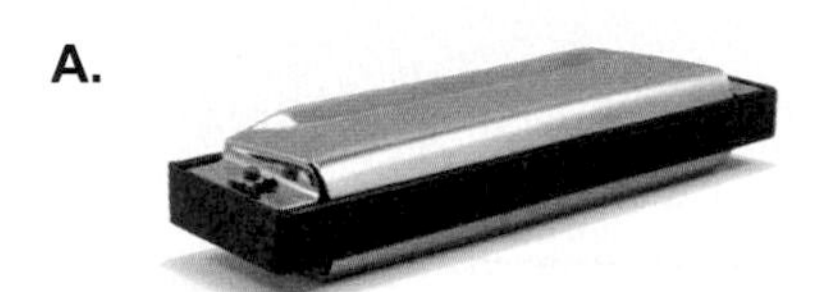

B.

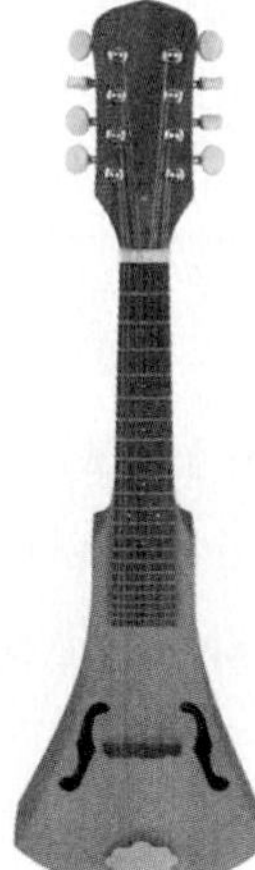

C.

2. A shape has more lines of symmetry than another, but fewer sides. What could the two shapes be?

3. Complete each shape using the red line of symmetry.

a) b)

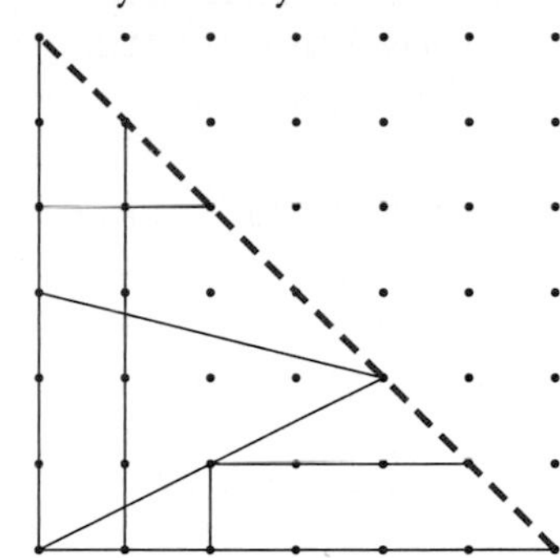

Lesson 8.2

4. a) Determine the order of rotation symmetry and the angle of rotation of this snowflake by tracing and rotating the shape.

b) How can you fold a square piece of paper to make a shape with the same order of rotation symmetry? Check by making a paper snowflake of the same order of rotation symmetry.

5. Louise says the kings, queens, and jacks in a pack of cards are an example of designs with rotation symmetry. Do you agree or disagree? Explain.

6. Draw two shapes or designs that do have rotation symmetry but do not have lines of symmetry. Do not draw parallelograms.

7. Show that a shape with six sides can have a greater order of rotation symmetry than a shape with eight sides.

8.4 Symmetry on the Coordinate Plane

YOU WILL NEED

- grid paper
- a protractor
- a ruler
- a transparent mirror

GOAL

Recognize how transformations relate to line symmetry and rotation symmetry.

LEARN ABOUT the Math

Rani says that you can translate, reflect, or rotate $\triangle ABC$ to create a design with symmetry. Nola says that you can't.

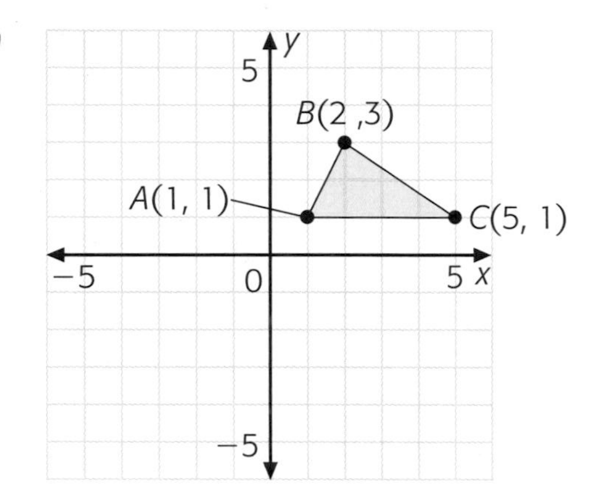

Do you agree with Rani or Nola?

EXAMPLE 1 Determining how transformations result in shapes or designs with symmetry

Use $\triangle ABC$ to create a shape with symmetry.

Rani's Solution: Reflecting, rotating, and translating to create symmetry

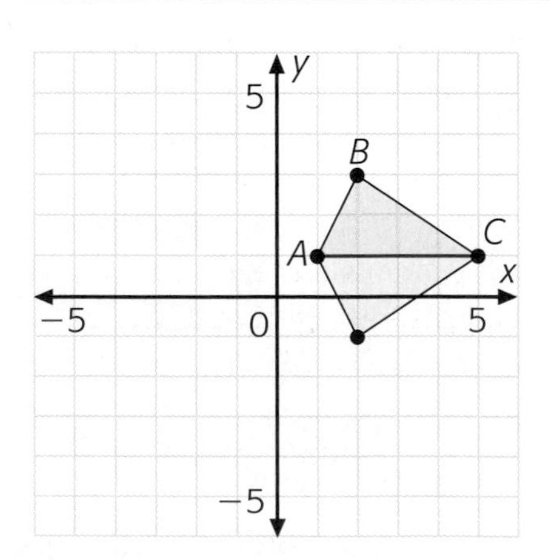

I reflected $\triangle ABC$ along side AC. I ended up with a shape with four sides. The vertices are at (1, 1), (2, 3), (5, 1), and (2, −1). The shape has a line of symmetry along side AC.
It makes sense that reflections result in shapes with lines of symmetry since the two halves match, but are opposite, when there is a line of symmetry.

The two shapes are related by line symmetry.

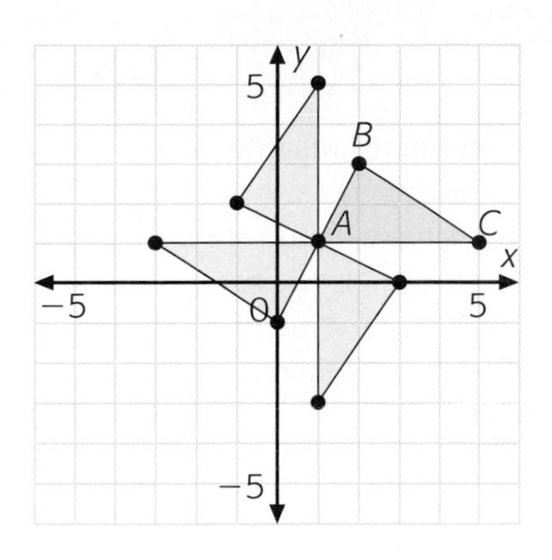

I noticed that $\triangle ABC$ looked like $\frac{1}{4}$ of a pinwheel. If I rotate the triangle 90° over and over, with point A as the centre of rotation, I knew I would end up with a design with rotation symmetry. The resulting shape had 9 vertices: (1, 1), (2, 3), (5, 1), (1, 5), (−1, 2), (−3, 1), (0, −1), (1, −3), and (3, 0).

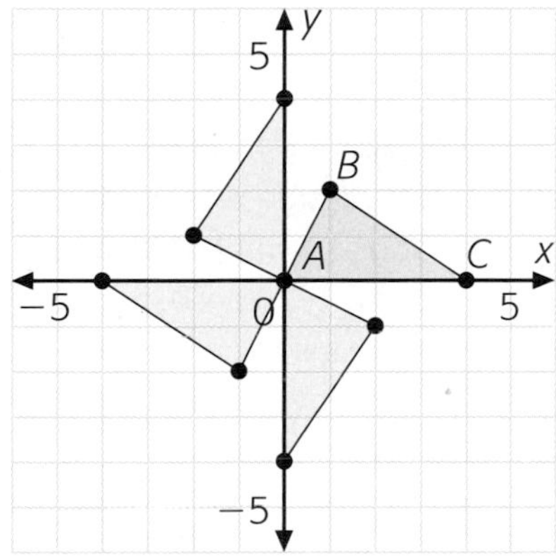

I translated the shape so its centre was at the origin. The shape still had rotation symmetry. The new vertices were (0, 0), (1, 2), (4, 0), (0, 4), (−2, 1), (−4, 0), (−1, −2), (0, −4), and (2, −1).

I reflected to make a shape with line symmetry. I rotated and translated to make a shape with rotation symmetry of order 4.
These shapes are related by rotation symmetry.

Communication Tip

Two shapes are said to be related by line symmetry if they form a shape with line symmetry when they are combined.

Two shapes are said to be related by rotation symmetry if one shape can be rotated over the other.

Nola's Solution: Translating to create symmetry

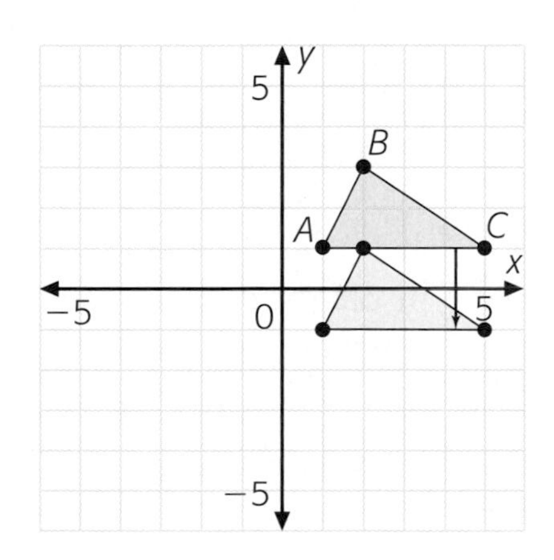

I saw what Rani did, but wondered if you could do just a translation to make a shape that had symmetry.
I tried a vertical translation (D2).
This design was made up of two triangles, with coordinates (1, 1), (2, 3), (5, 1), (1, −1), (2, 1), and (5, −1). It did not have any reflection or rotation symmetry.

Communication Tip

Translations are often described by abbreviations like D2, which means down 2, and L4, which means left 4.

The letters U and R can also be used, to describe up and right.

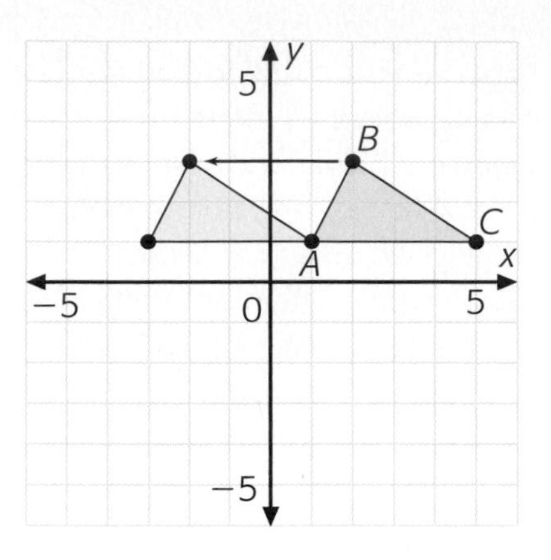

I tried a horizontal translation (L4). This design was also made up of two triangles, with coordinates (1, 1), (2, 3), (5, 1), (−3, 1), and (−2, 3). It did not have any reflection or rotation symmetry either.

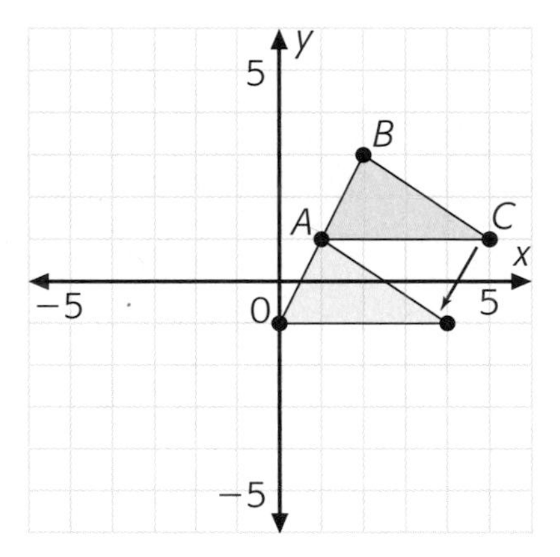

I tried a diagonal translation (L1, D2). This design was made up of two triangles, with coordinates (1, 1), (2, 3), (5, 1), (0, −1), and (4, −1). Like my other designs, it did not have reflection or rotation symmetry.

I think that you won't get a shape with symmetry if you just translate the triangle. I think we are both right, but in different ways.

There was no line of symmetry or rotation point since each point on the plane moves when it is translated. One point has to stay put when you rotate and a whole line of points has to stay put when you reflect.

Reflecting

A. Why does a reflection result in a design with line symmetry?

B. Rani rotated the triangle 90° each time. Why did she need to rotate the triangle four times to end up with a design with rotational symmetry?

C. How might the coordinates of the design after you rotated or reflected help you decide if the design has symmetry?

WORK WITH the Math

EXAMPLE 2 | Examining coordinate changes for specific transformations

Determine what happens to the coordinates of a shape as a result of each transformation:

- reflection across the x-axis
- reflection across the y-axis
- reflection across the line $y = x$
- $180°$ rotation about $(0, 0)$

Zachary's Solution

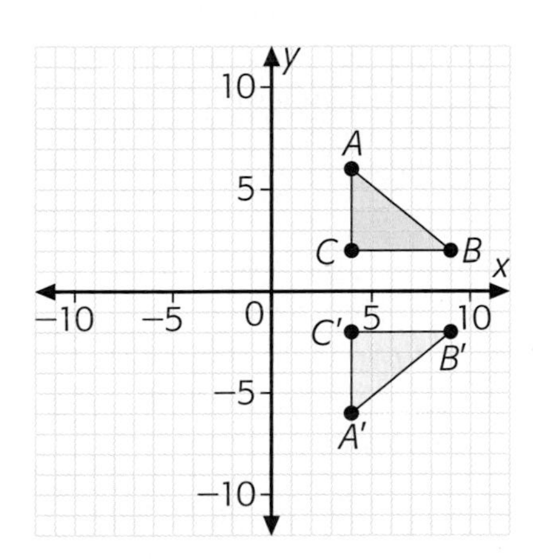

I drew a right triangle on a grid to see what happened with each motion.
When you reflect across the x-axis, points above the axis move below the axis, and vice versa.

When you reflect across the x-axis, the x-coordinates stay the same and the y-coordinates become opposites.

$A(4, 6)$ becomes $A'(4, -6)$
$B(9, 2)$ becomes $B'(9, -2)$
$C(4, 2)$ becomes $C'(4, -2)$

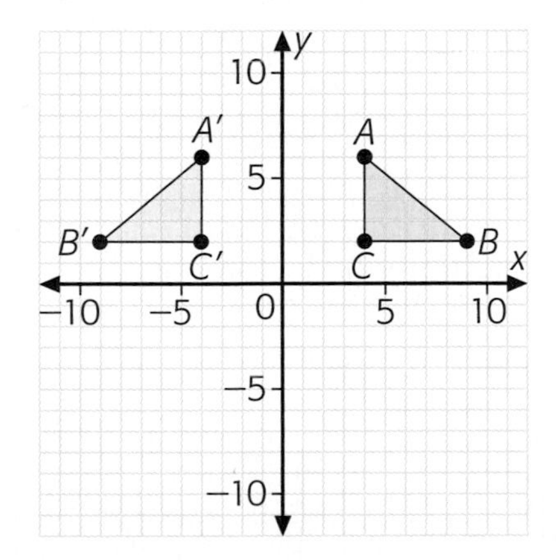

When you reflect across the y-axis, points to the right of the axis move to the left, and vice versa.

When you reflect across the y-axis, the y-coordinates stay the same and the x-coordinates become opposites.

$A(4, 6)$ becomes $A'(-4, 6)$
$B(9, 2)$ becomes $B'(-9, 2)$
$C(4, 2)$ becomes $C'(-4, 2)$

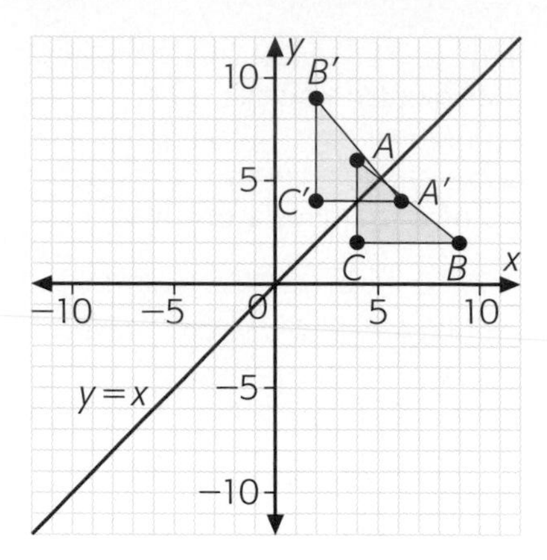

When you reflect across the line $y = x$, both coordinates change.

When you reflect across the line $y = x$, the y-coordinates and x-coordinates switch.

$A(4, 6)$ becomes $A'(6, 4)$
$B(9, 2)$ becomes $B'(2, 9)$
$C(4, 2)$ becomes $C'(2, 4)$

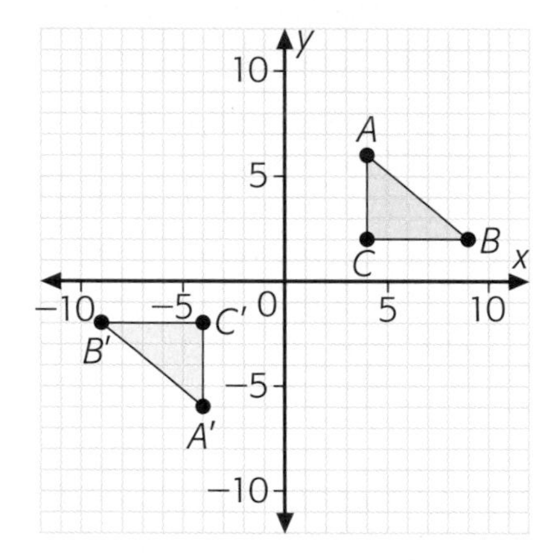

When you rotate 180° about $(0, 0)$, the shape ends up in the diagonally opposite quadrant.

When you rotate 180° about $(0, 0)$, the image coordinates are both opposites of the original coordinates.

$A(4, 6)$ becomes $A'(-4, -6)$
$B(9, 2)$ becomes $B'(-9, -2)$
$C(4, 2)$ becomes $C'(-4, -2)$

EXAMPLE 3 | **Determining a transformation using coordinates**

Francis transformed a shape, and the combined shape that resulted was this square. What was the original shape and what was the transformation? How could you use the coordinates to determine the transformation?

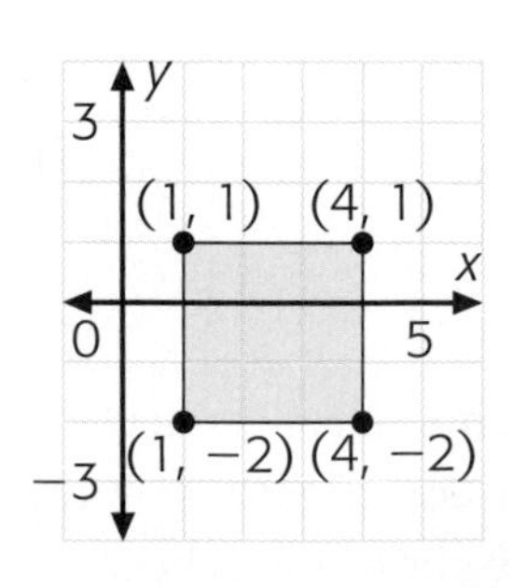

Luc's Solution

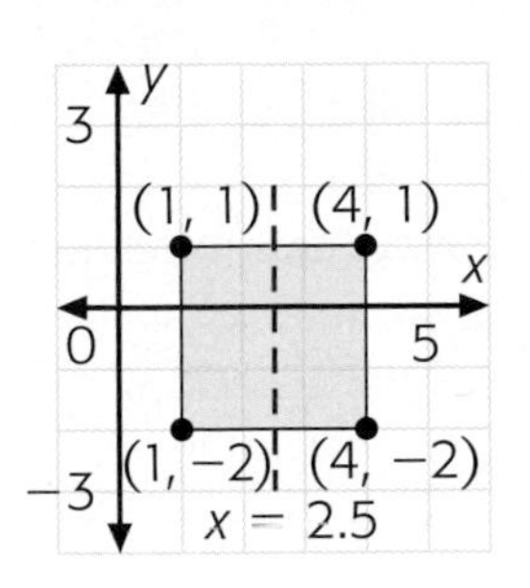

I imagined a vertical line of symmetry through the centre of the shape. I saw that one way to think of the shape was as the result of reflecting the left half of it across a vertical line down the centre and looking at the combined shape.

$$\text{Length of square} = 4 - 1 = 3$$

I subtracted the x-coordinates of $(1, 1)$ and $(4, 1)$ to determine the side length of the square.

$$3 \div 2 = 1.5$$

I know that the line of symmetry goes through the centre of the side.

$$1 + 1.5 = 2.5$$

I had to add half the side length to 1 or subtract it from 4 to get the x-coordinate for the reflection line.

The original shape could be a rectangle with vertices at $(1, 1)$, $(2.5, 1)$, $(1, -2)$, and $(2.5, -2)$ and the line of reflection was the line $x = 2.5$.

Erin's Solution

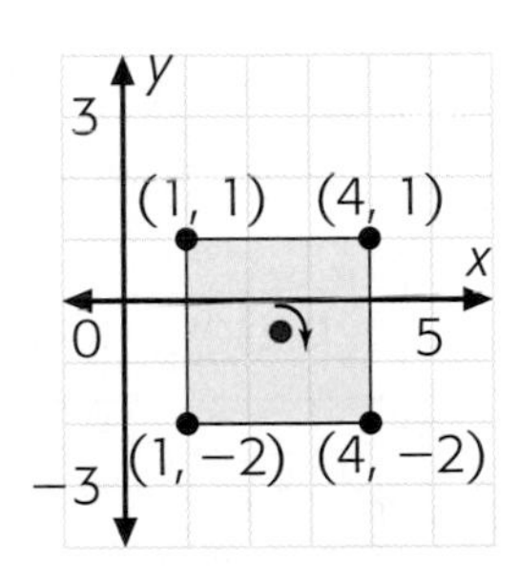

I know that a square has rotation symmetry of order 4 about its centre.

$$\text{Length of square} = 4 - 1 = 3$$

I determined the centre by dividing the side length in half.

$$3 \div 2 = 1.5$$

$$1 + 1.5 = 2.5$$

I added half the side length to the x-coordinate of $(1, 1)$

$$1 - 1.5 = -0.5$$

I subtracted that half from the y-coordinate of $(1, 1)$.

The square could be the result of a rotation of itself about the centre, $(2.5, -0.5)$.

In Summary

Key Ideas

- The combined figure created when a figure is reflected will have line symmetry. It may or may not have rotation symmetry.
- The combined figure created when a figure is rotated may have rotation symmetry, but not always. It may or may not have line symmetry.
- The combined shape or design created when a figure is translated will not usually have symmetry.

Need to Know

- If a shape is reflected across the x-axis, its x-coordinates remain the same, and its y-coordinates become the opposite.
  $P(a, b) \rightarrow P'(a, -b)$
- If a shape is reflected across the y-axis, its y-coordinates remain the same, and its x-coordinates become the opposite.
  $P(a, b) \rightarrow P'(-a, b)$
- If a shape is reflected across the line $y = x$, its x-coordinates and y-coordinates switch.
  $P(a, b) \rightarrow P'(b, a)$
- If a shape is rotated 180° about the origin, its x-coordinates and y-coordinates are the opposites of the original.
  $P(a, b) \rightarrow P'(-a, -b)$.

Checking

1. a) Reflect $\triangle ABC$ across the y-axis and the x-axis.

b) Rotate $\triangle ABC$ 180° about the origin.

c) Write the coordinates of the three images.

d) What type of symmetry will the completed design have? Explain.

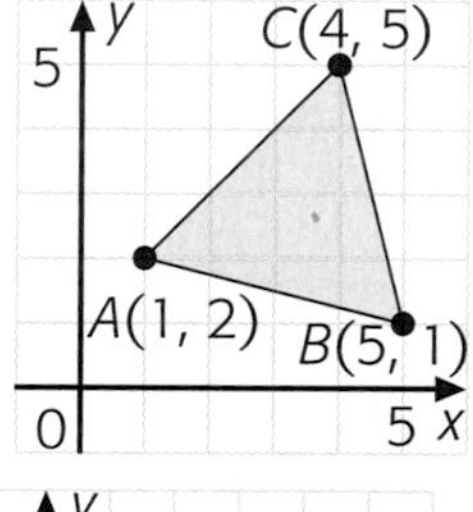

2. a) Reflect figure $ABCDE$ to create a design with symmetry. Write the coordinates of A', B', C', D', and E'.

b) Rotate $ABCDE$ about the vertex E to create a design with symmetry. Write the coordinates of A', B', C', D', and E'.

c) Translate $ABCDE$ using the rule (L1, D1). Write the coordinates of A', B', C', D', and E'. Does the combined design have symmetry?

Practising

3. a) What type(s) of symmetry does the combined shape have? Describe the line of reflection or the centre of rotation.

b) Explain how figure $ABCD$ was transformed to create $A'B'C'D'$.

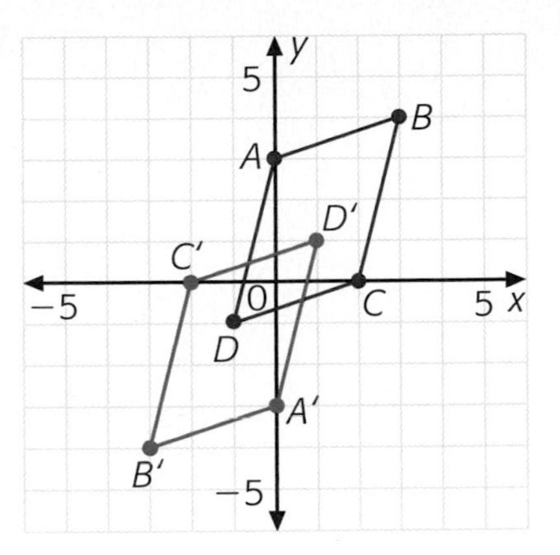

4. Jonathan reflected figure $EFGH$ to create this design. He says that it has line symmetry. Do you agree or disagree? Explain.

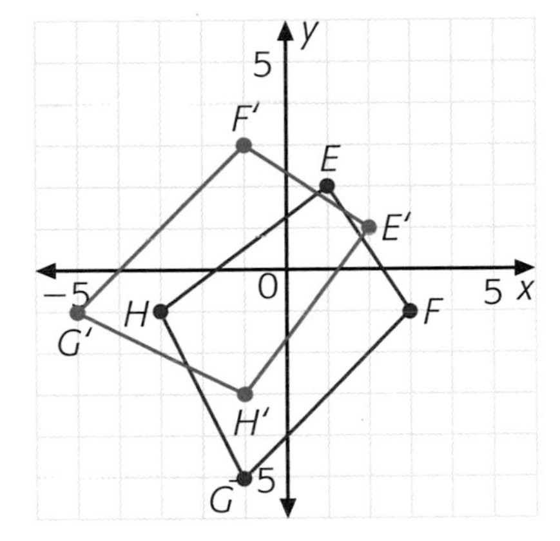

5. Multiple choice.

a) Which two shapes are not related by line symmetry?

A. P and Q **C.** Q and R
B. P and R **D.** Q and S

b) Which two shapes are related by rotation symmetry about the origin?

A. R and S **C.** Q and R
B. P and R **D.** Q and S

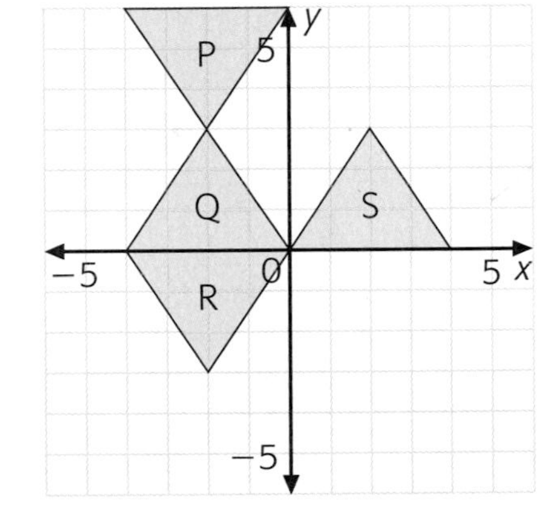

6. Multiple choice. Choose the correct description of this design.

A. It has no line symmetry and no rotation symmetry.
B. It has line symmetry, but no rotation symmetry.
C. It has no line symmetry, but does have rotation symmetry.
D. It has line symmetry and rotation symmetry.

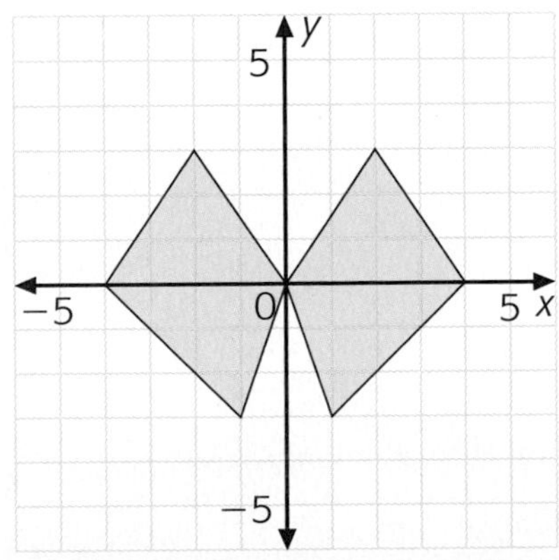

7. In each case, figure $ABCD$ has been transformed. Write the coordinates of each image. Describe the transformations that may have been used and how you know. Describe the symmetry of the design.

a)

b)

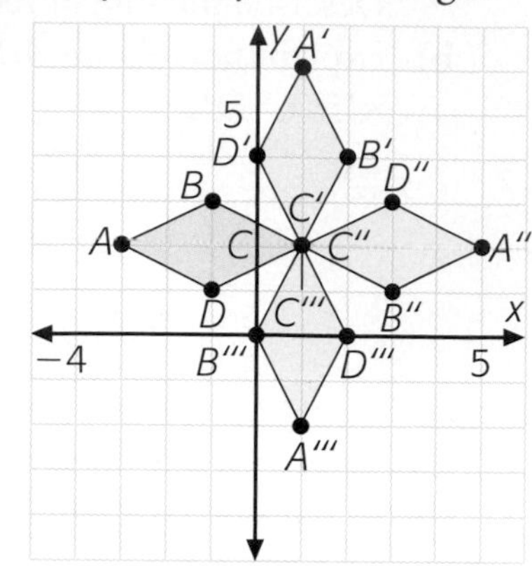

8. a) Draw a polygon that has line symmetry on a coordinate grid.
   b) Show that you can reflect that shape on its line of symmetry and end up with the same shape by describing the image of each original vertex.
   c) Show that you can reflect the shape across a different line and end up with a different design with line symmetry. Identify the new line of symmetry.
   d) Show that you can rotate the original shape 180° about a vertex to get a shape with rotation symmetry of order 2.
   e) Show that sometimes you can rotate a shape and end up with a combined shape with line symmetry.

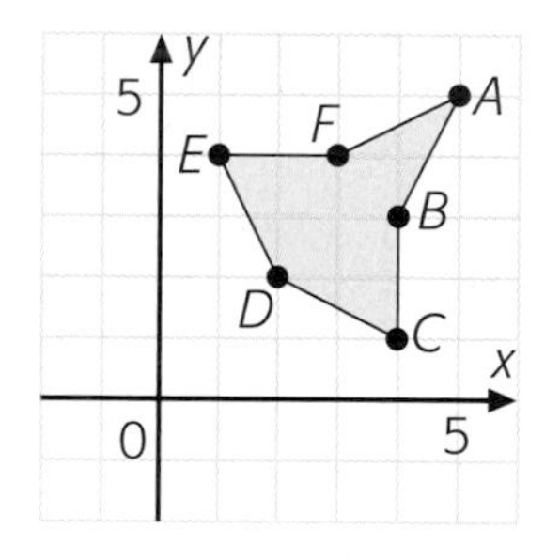

9. This shape is a quarter of a tile pattern. The entire pattern has four lines of symmetry and a rotational symmetry of order 4 with an angle of rotation of 90°. Use transformations to complete the pattern.

10. Show that any rectangle on a coordinate grid can be created by reflecting a different rectangle.

Closing

11. Show that it is possible to translate a shape and end up with a combined shape with both line symmetry and rotation symmetry.

Extending

12. A transformation moves the vertex of a shape from $A(1, 2)$ to the point $A'(-1, 2)$.
    a) What kind of transformation might it be?
    b) Could the resulting design have symmetry? If so, what kind?

13. A shape is rotated 90° ccw about the point $(0, 0)$. What happens to the coordinates of the original vertices?

Math GAME

What's the Message?

Number of players: 2 to 4

YOU WILL NEED
- Word Search Sheet for each player
- a timer

How to play

1. There are ten words in the Word Search Sheet. The words have been reflected or rotated. Take turns looking for the words. Allow one minute for each turn.

И T F J L N D A K ꓘ H T R U Q M W ∩ C E ∩ G
I N F G C E A O Y Я T Ǝ M M Y S И V P < C A
D O K G O F R Q V O Ɔ T Q M Z A I X O Я X ꓘ
U Q O K W W T Ɔ P R N X L E W N L D И A A Ǝ
S H U > N O H C S Γ T R F Z L A D D P V E W
L P G P B ∩ I Γ D I И C S Z O T P F Ǝ Y I M
A W D N B U 1 B G I T J K Γ X U L K W O U Q
M O S Z U I L B A E T D I I R R A K F I И L
I X I И V H G X U E S K M U T E H Ǝ Y Q S B
M Z B O D ∩ M T Y S N W D S Ǝ Z I A C G R U
A G C X P F O C V R E U Y Ǝ S A N A Ɔ ∩ K X

2. Score one point for each letter in the word that has line symmetry and one point for each letter in the word that has rotation symmetry of order 2 or more.
3. When all ten words have been found, take turns trying to form a sentence. Allow one minute for each turn. Score 10 points for forming a sentence.
4. The player with the higher score wins.

Luc's Turn

I found "SEE." It has two letters with line symmetry (E), and one letter with rotation symmetry of order 2 (S). I score 3 points.

8.5 Solve Problems Using Diagrams

YOU WILL NEED

- grid paper
- a ruler

GOAL

Solve problems involving symmetry by using diagrams.

LEARN ABOUT the Math

Francis wrote these instructions for a design, but some of the paper was torn. Viktor has to complete the design.

Francis's Design

I drew rectangle *ABCD* with one vertex in each quadrant of the Cartesian plane. I rotated *ABCD* to form its image, *A'B'C'D'*. The combined shape has rotation symmetry of order 4. The vertices of the original rectangle are *A*(4, 5),

How can Viktor complete the design?

EXAMPLE 1 | Rotating rectangles to create a shape

I decided to draw a diagram to solve the problem.

Viktor's Solution

1. Understand the Problem
   I need to rotate a rectangle with one vertex in each quadrant to form a shape with an order of rotation symmetry of 4.
2. Make a Plan
   I'll plot point $A(4, 5)$ and draw $ABCD$ using the x-axis and the y-axis as lines of symmetry. I think that if I rotate $ABCD$ 90° cw, the rectangle will fit over itself 4 times in a full turn, so the shape I create will have rotation symmetry of order 4. That's because $4 \times 90 = 360$.

3. Carry Out the Plan

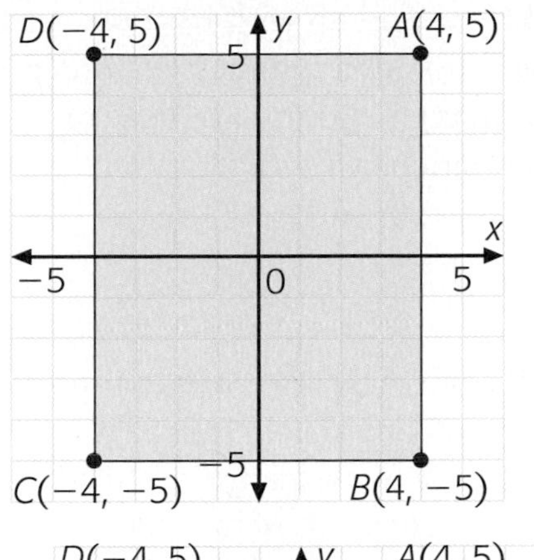

With the x-axis as a line of symmetry, B must be at $(4, -5)$. With the y-axis as a line of symmetry, D must be at $(-4, 5)$. Vertex C is at $(-4, -5)$. I joined the vertices.

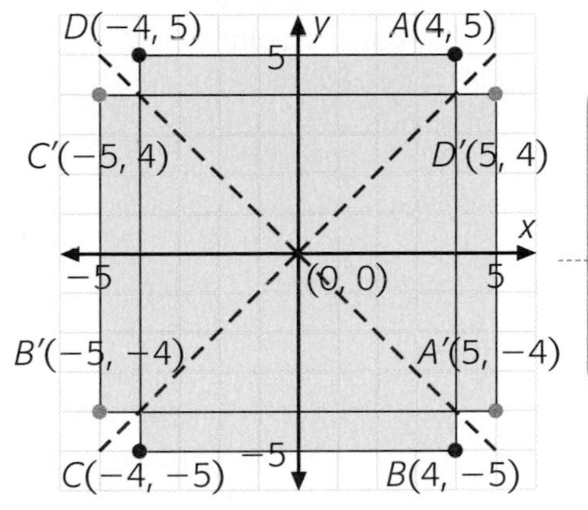

I rotated $ABCD$ 90° cw about the origin to create $A'B'C'D'$. The combined shape has rotation symmetry of order 4. I figured it out by rotating the shape in my head with the centre of rotation at (0, 0).

This design has rotation symmetry of order 4.
I think it is Francis's design.

Reflecting

A. Can Viktor be sure he drew Francis's design? Explain.

B. How did Viktor's diagrams help him solve the problem?

WORK WITH the Math

EXAMPLE 2 | Solving a problem using rotation symmetry

Rotate a triangle once to create a star with six lines of symmetry and rotation symmetry of order 6.

Rani's Solution

1. Understand the Problem
   I need to determine which kind of triangle to choose and which point to rotate it about, so that the original triangle and the image will form a star.

2. Make a Plan
I figured that I would be more likely to end up with rotation symmetry of order 6 if I started with rotation symmetry of order 3. So, I decided to use an equilateral triangle and not a scalene or isosceles one; they don't have any rotation symmetry.

3. Carry Out the Plan

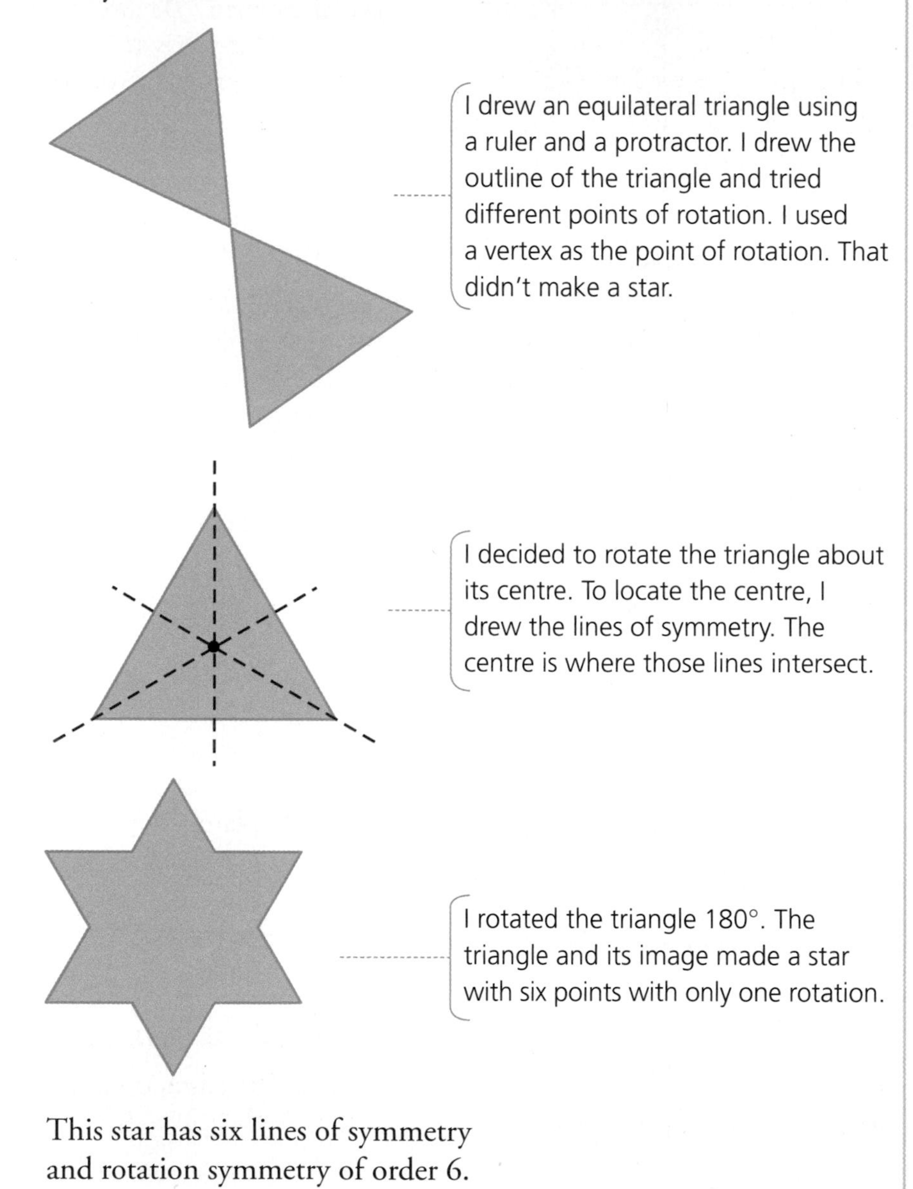

This star has six lines of symmetry and rotation symmetry of order 6.

EXAMPLE 3 | Locating coordinates using rotation symmetry

Part of a design has the vertices $A(0, 8)$, $B(4, 6)$, $C(3, 5)$, $D(5, 2)$, and $E(0, 0)$. The entire design has rotation symmetry of order 4 about the origin. What are the other vertices?

Nola's Solution

1. Understand the Problem
   The entire design has rotation symmetry of order 4. So, to see the entire design, I need to rotate the part that I know three times, by 90° each time.

2. Make a Plan
   I will trace the part I know and rotate the tracing 90° cw. Then, I will draw the figure and locate its coordinates. I will do the same for rotations of 180° cw and 90° ccw.

3. Carry Out the Plan

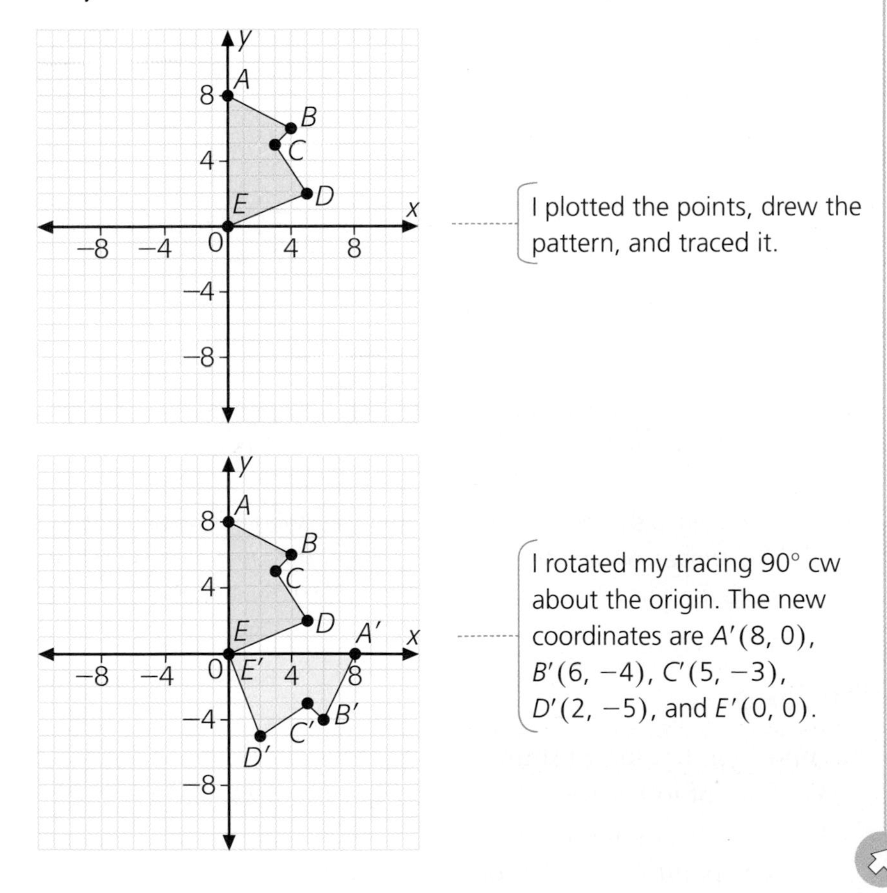

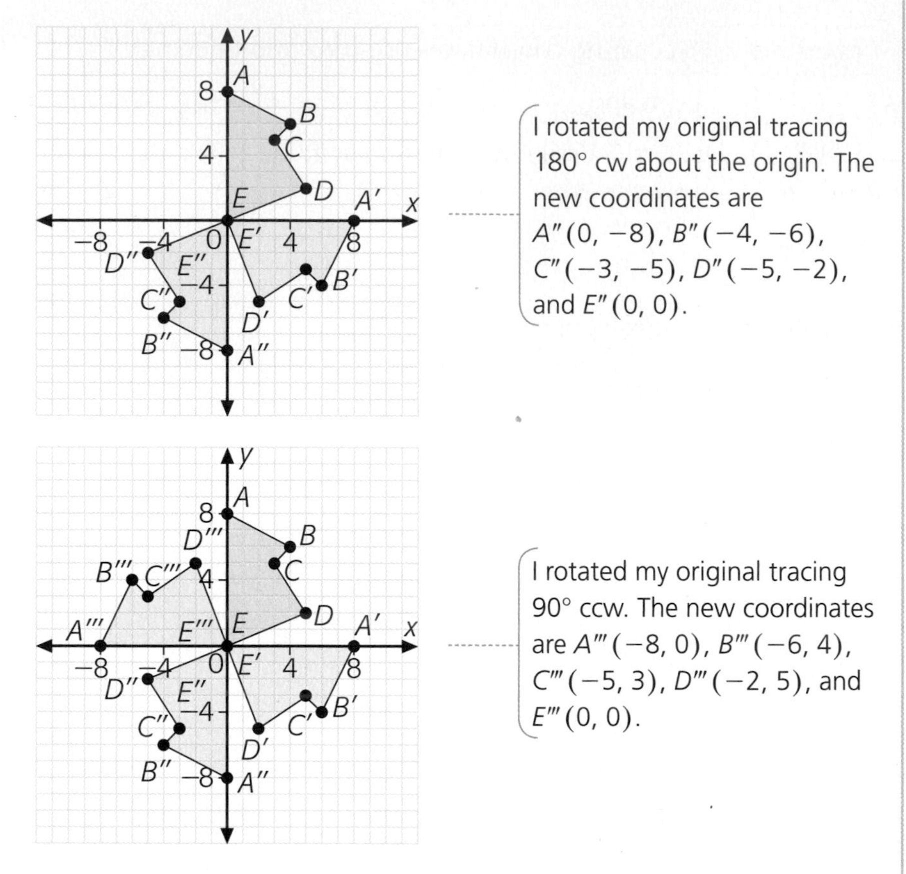

This is the combined shape when the images rotated and the original drawing are all drawn. This shape has rotation symmetry of order 4 when rotated 90° about the origin.

In Summary

Key Idea

- Many combined shapes and designs can be analyzed by drawing a diagram on the Cartesian plane. The diagram can suggest how to solve a problem regarding the type of transformations required to create that shape.

Checking

1. A polygon has these features:
- Four of its vertices are $(0, 4)$, $(4, 4)$, $(6, 2)$, and $(-2, 2)$.
- It has four lines of symmetry.
- The point at $(2, 4)$ is on one line of symmetry.
- The point at $(-2, 0)$ is on another line of symmetry.

Determine the coordinates of the other vertices.

Practising

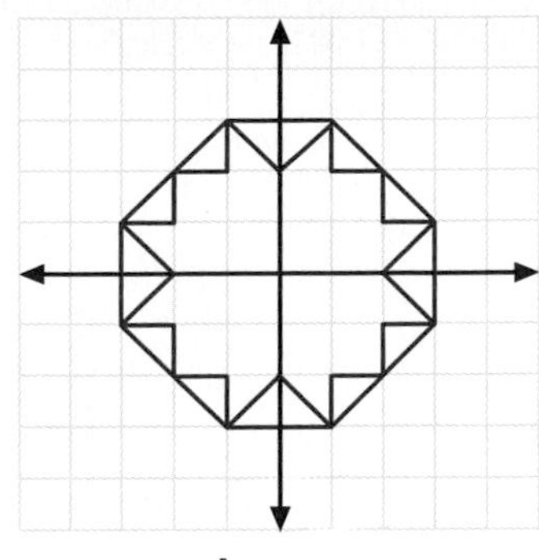

2. Copy this design and colour the grid so that the design has two lines of symmetry and rotation symmetry of order 2.
3. a) $\triangle ABC$ has vertices $A(2, 1)$, $B(5, 4)$, and $C(5, 1)$. Transform $\triangle ABC$ to create a design with four lines of symmetry and rotation symmetry of order 4.
   b) Transform $\triangle ABC$ to create a design with no line of symmetry but rotation symmetry of order 4.
4. Complete this design. The red and blue lines are both lines of symmetry.

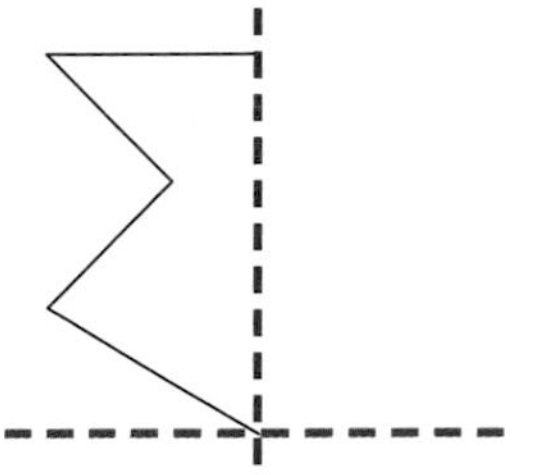

5. a) Draw a shape on a coordinate grid that has rotation symmetry of order 8.
   b) Reflect it so that the resulting combined shape also has rotation symmetry of order 8.
6. Matthew is creating a stained glass window that will have rotation symmetry of order 6. This green and white triangle is one part of the window. Complete the pattern for the window.

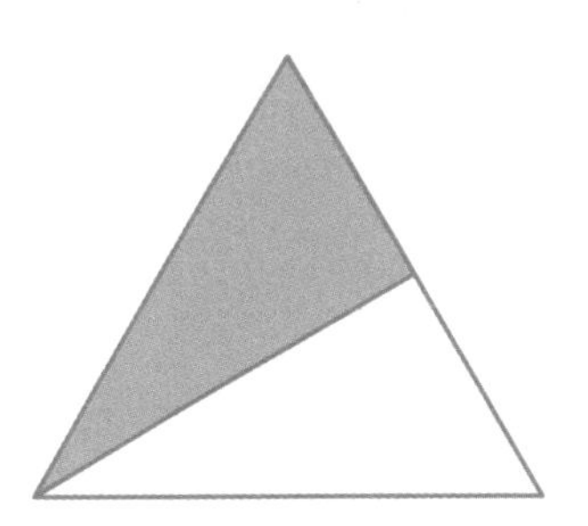

7. Matthew is creating another stained glass window. It will have the same shape as the window in question 6, but will have two lines of symmetry and rotation symmetry of order 2. Using the same piece as in question 6, complete the pattern for the window.
8. a) Draw a triangle with the vertices $(5, 1)$, $(5, -2)$, and $(1, 0)$.
   b) Reflect the shape in three ways so that each design has line symmetry. Describe each line of reflection.
   c) Rotate the shape in two ways so that each design has rotation symmetry. Describe the order of rotation and the centre of rotation.
9. You translate a hexagon and the combined shape has a line of symmetry. Show what shape it could have been and what the translation was.

Reading Strategy

Questioning

What clarifying questions can you ask yourself as you work through the solution to questions 6 and 7?

Closing

10. Create and solve a problem about transformations and symmetry that would be more easily solved by using a diagram.

Extending

11. You draw two perpendicular lines on a coordinate grid. Show that, if you reflect a shape first across one line, then the other, then the first again, you get a shape with rotation symmetry of order 2.

Chapter Self-Test

1. Sort these tiles according to the number of lines of symmetry their designs have.

2. Complete the other side of this puzzle piece using the red line of symmetry.

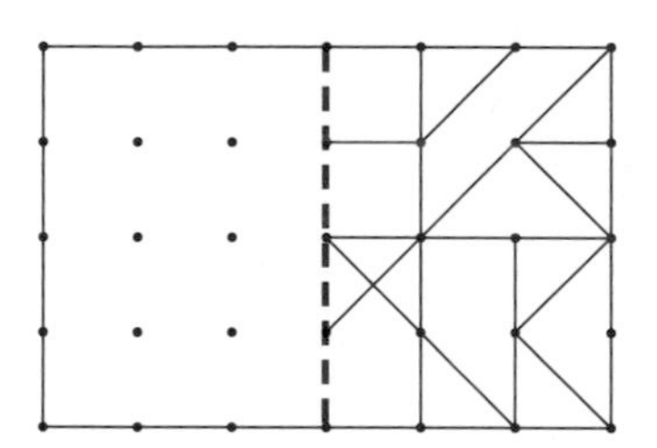

3. Determine whether each shape has rotation symmetry, and if it does, state the order and angle of rotation.

a) 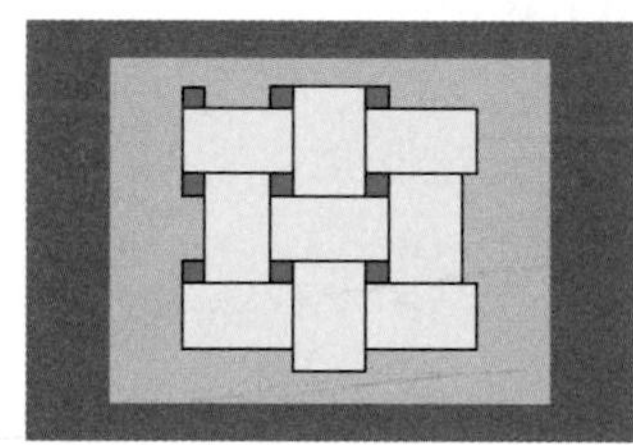

b) 

c) 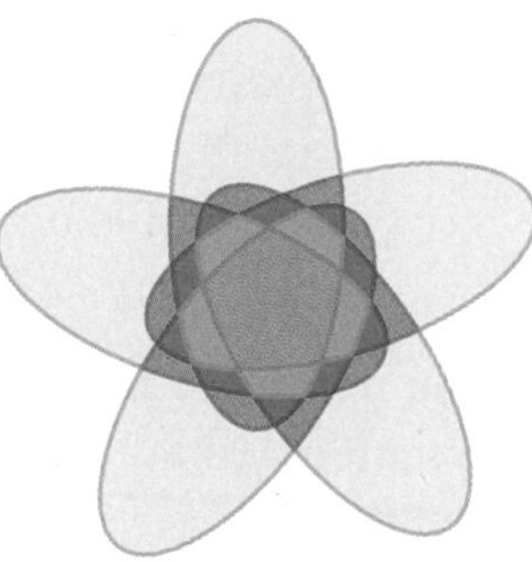

4. Which of these shapes have rotation symmetry of order 5 about the centre?

A. 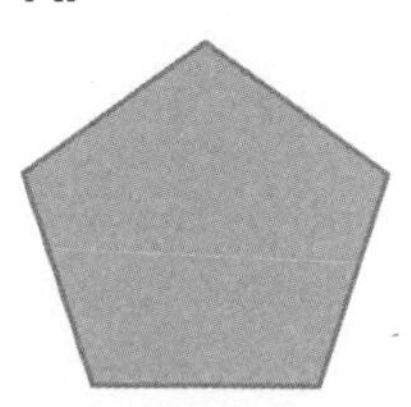

B. 

C. 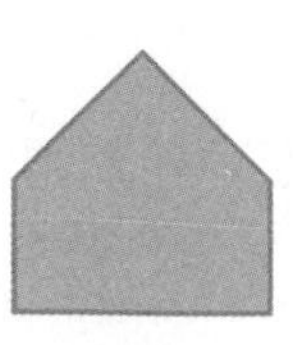

D. 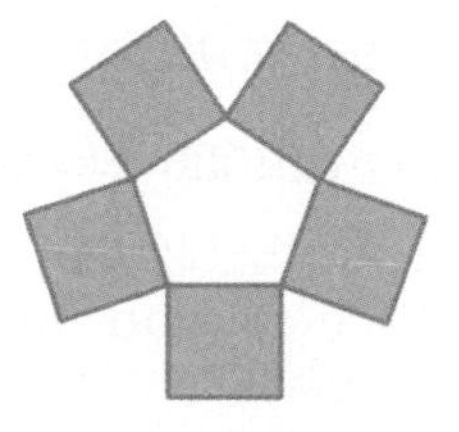

5. Determine whether each tessellation has line symmetry or rotation symmetry. If it has rotation symmetry, identify the order of rotation symmetry and the angle of rotation.

a)

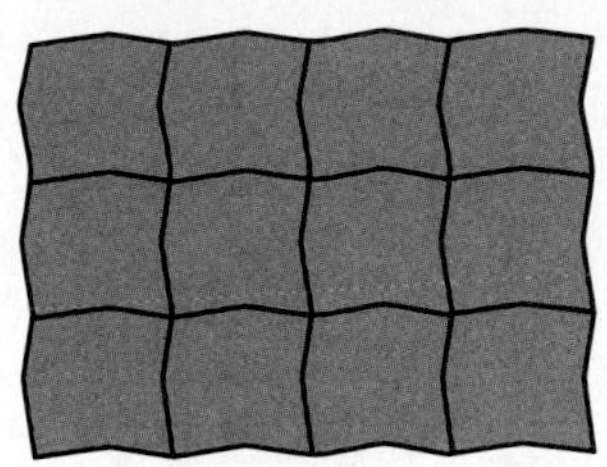

b)

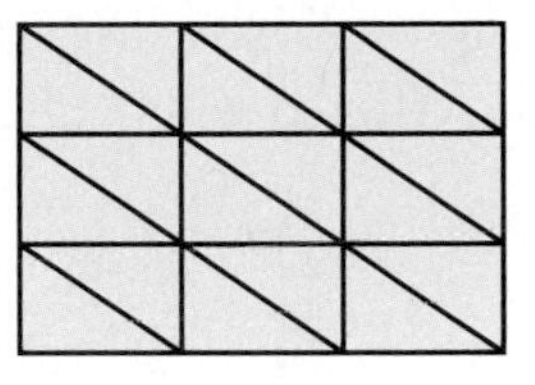

c)

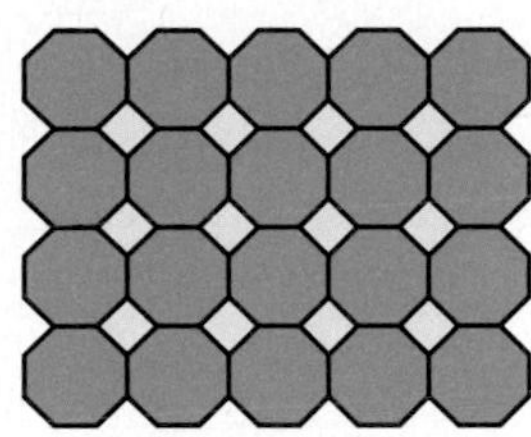

6. Dimitri says *ABCD* and *A′B′C′D′* together make a design that has line symmetry and rotation symmetry. Milos says it only has rotation symmetry. Who is right? Explain.

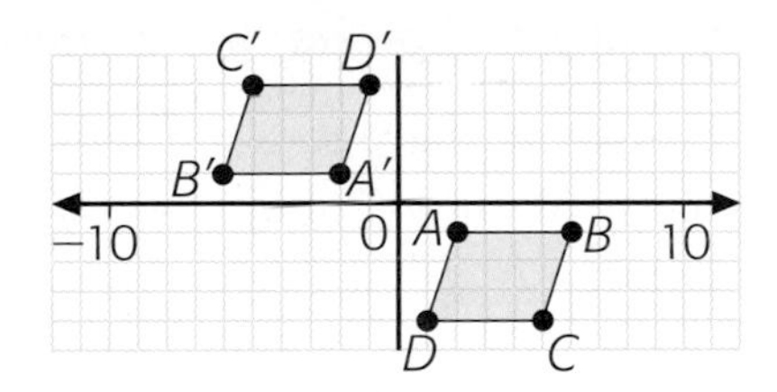

7. a) Create a design with rotation symmetry by rotating quadrilateral *ABCD* about *A*.

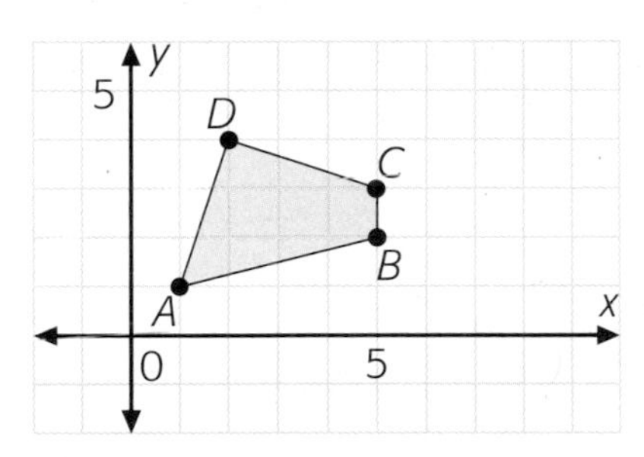

b) Record the coordinates of *A′*, *B′*, *C′*, and *D′*.

8. a) Create a design with line symmetry by reflecting quadrilateral *ABCD* from question 7 across the *x*-axis.

b) Record the coordinates of *A′*, *B′*, *C′*, and *D′*.

***WHAT DO** You Think Now?*

Revisit What Do You Think? on page 365. How have your answers and explanations changed?

Chapter Review

FREQUENTLY ASKED Questions

Study Aid

- See Lesson 8.4, Examples 1 and 2.
- Try Chapter Review questions 4 and 9.

Q: What symmetry will a design have if a shape is reflected?

A: The design will have line symmetry. The line across which the shape is reflected will be the line of symmetry.

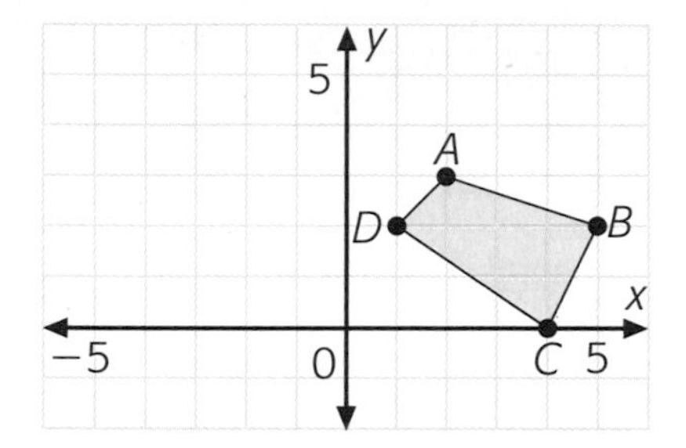

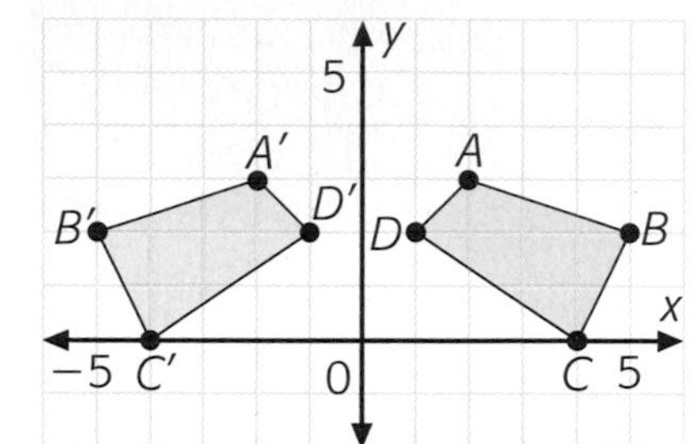

Study Aid

- See Lesson 8.4, Examples 1 and 2.
- Try Chapter Review questions 5 and 9.

Q: What symmetry will a design have if a shape is rotated?

A: The design may or may not have rotation symmetry. This design has rotation symmetry of order 2 about $(0, 0)$, since it was rotated $180°$ about that point.

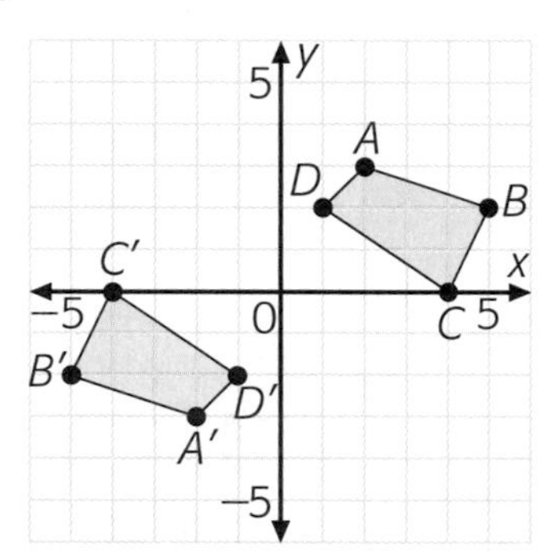

Study Aid

- See Lesson 8.4, Examples 1 and 2.
- Try Chapter Review question 6.

Q: What symmetry will a design have if a shape is translated?

A: The symmetry depends on the translation and also on the original shape's symmetry. The design on the left has neither line nor rotation symmetry, but the design on the right has line symmetry.

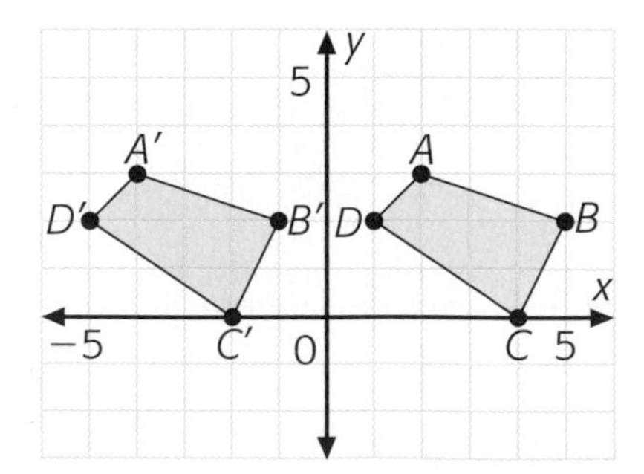

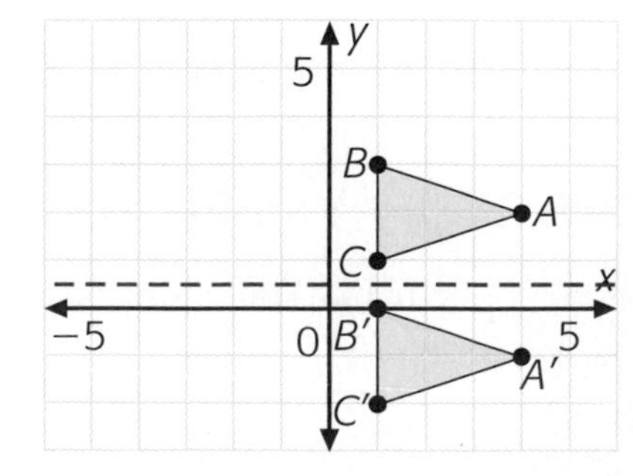

Practice

Lesson 8.1

1. Complete each shape using the red line of symmetry.

   a)

   b)

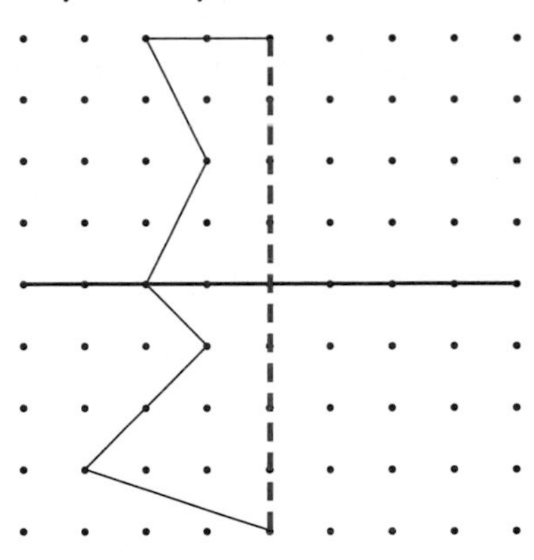

Lesson 8.2

2. Sketch each wheel. Determine if each sketch has rotation symmetry, and if it does, state the order and angle of rotation.

   a)

   b)

   c)

   d)

Lesson 8.3

3. Identify and describe the types of symmetry in each rug.

   a)

   b)

Lesson 8.4

4. a) Reflect quadrilateral $ABCD$ across the y-axis to create a new design.
b) Write the coordinates of A', B', C', and D'.
c) Describe what symmetry the new design has, if any.

5. a) Rotate quadrilateral $ABCD$ $180°$ ccw about D to create a new design.
b) Write the coordinates of A', B', C', and D'.
c) Describe what symmetry the new design has, if any.

6. a) Translate quadrilateral $ABCD$ by the translation rule (L6, D3) to create a new design.
b) Write the coordinates of A', B', C', and D'.
c) Tell why the new shape does not have symmetry.

Lesson 8.5

7. Colour the squares of this mosaic to have four lines of symmetry and rotation symmetry of order 4.

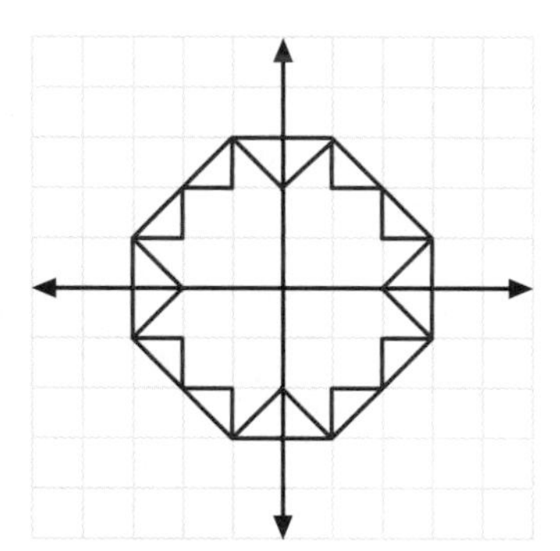

8. Determine whether each tessellation has line symmetry or rotation symmetry. If it does have rotation symmetry, identify the order of rotation symmetry and the angle of rotation.

a)

b)

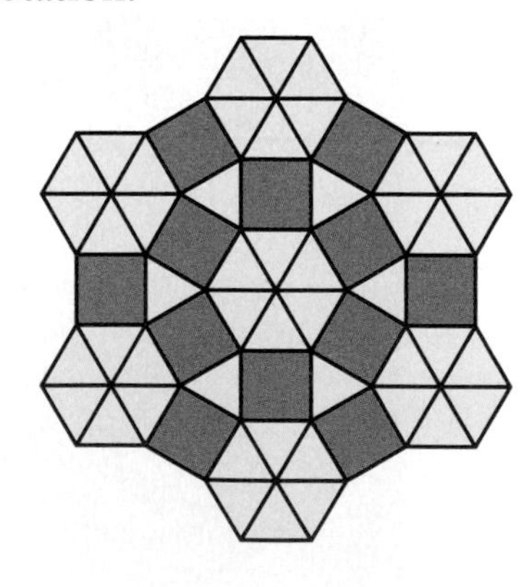

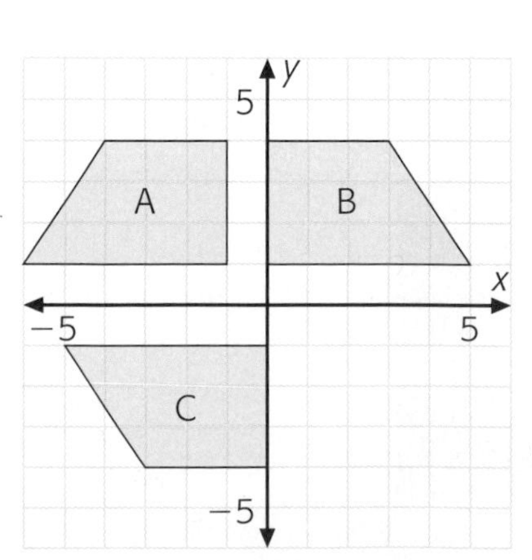

9. a) Which two shapes shown at left are related by line symmetry?
b) Which two shapes shown at left are related by rotation symmetry?

Chapter Task

Symmetrical T-shirt Designs

You will make three designs to put on T-shirts. The theme is symmetry.

YOU WILL NEED

- grid paper

? How can you make symmetrical designs?

A. Draw three different designs on grid paper.

B. Each design must include
- the coordinates of vertices
- a combination of line symmetry and rotation symmetry
- a different order of rotation symmetry than your other two designs
- a different number of lines of symmetry than your other two designs
- symmetry of colour as well as shape

C. For each design, explain
- how your design meets the conditions given in part B
- why your design represents the theme of symmetry well

Task | *Checklist*

✔ Did you include all of the drawings needed?

✔ Did you include all of the types of symmetries needed?

✔ Did you use the appropriate math language?

Chapter

9

Circle Geometry

GOALS

You will be able to

- identify and apply the relationships between inscribed angles and central angles
- use properties of chords to solve problems
- identify properties of tangents to circles
- solve problems involving circle properties using an experiment

The circle is an important symbol in many cultures. To this dancer, from the Alexander First Nation near Edmonton, the circle symbolizes life. Why do you think the circle is an important symbol to so many people?

Getting Started

YOU WILL NEED

- a compass
- a protractor
- a ruler

  or
- geometry software

Designing Jewellery

Erin is designing jewellery. Her design consists of a circle placed inside a triangle as shown.

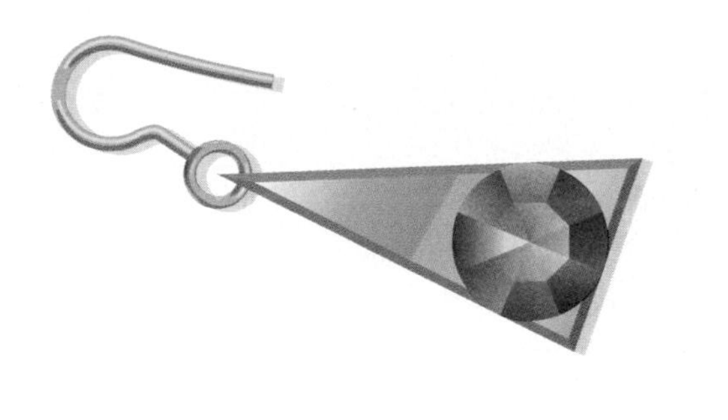

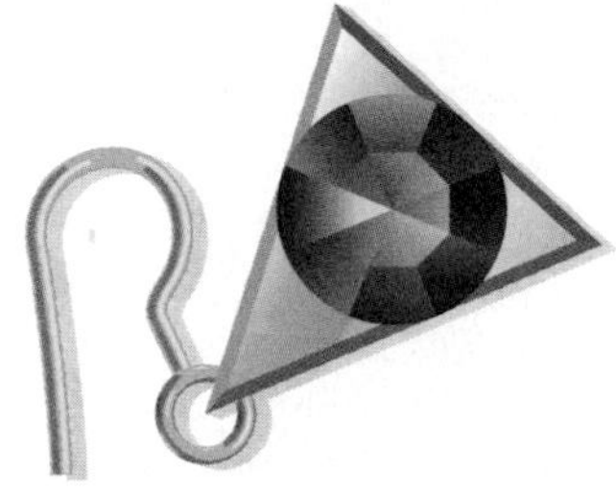

How can Erin ensure that each circle touches all three sides of the triangle?

A. Draw a triangle, and construct the **angle bisectors** for two angles.

B. Label the intersection of the angle bisectors as *P*.

C. Construct the angle bisector for the third angle. What do you notice?

angle bisector

a line that divides an angle in half to form two equal angles

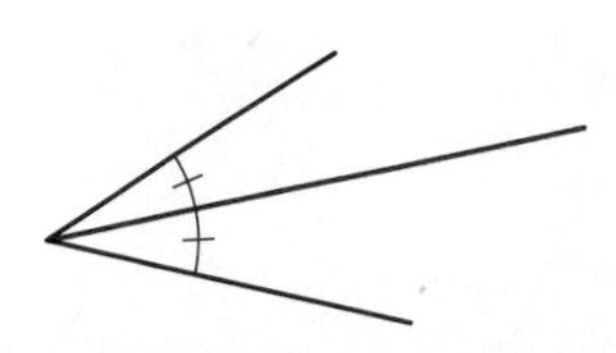

D. Construct line segments from P that are perpendicular to each side of the triangle. What do you notice?

E. Construct a circle with centre P, and a radius equal to the length of one of the perpendicular segments from step D. What do you notice about the circle in relation to the triangle?

F. Move the vertices of your triangle to create a triangle of a different shape. Does your observation from step E still hold?

G. Describe how Erin can ensure that each circle touches all three sides of the triangle using the fewest number of steps.

WHAT DO You Think?

Decide whether you agree or disagree with each statement.
Be ready to explain your decision.

1. It is possible to draw a right angle in a circle using only a ruler.
2. It is possible to draw a circle that touches all the vertices of any polygon.
3. In a circle of diameter 10 cm, it is possible to connect two points on the circle using a line segment 5 cm long.
4. A line can intersect a circle at one, two, or three points.

9.1 Relating the Central Angle to an Inscribed Angle

YOU WILL NEED

- geometry software
  or
- a compass
- a protractor
- a ruler

chord

a line segment joining two points on a circle

GOAL

Relate the measure of a central angle to an inscribed angle in a circle.

INVESTIGATE the Math

Rani designs hoop earrings made of silver wire. For one design, she uses **chords** to create a coloured insert in the hoop as shown.

central angle

an angle whose vertex is at the centre of a circle

inscribed angle

an angle formed by two chords whose vertex lies on the circle

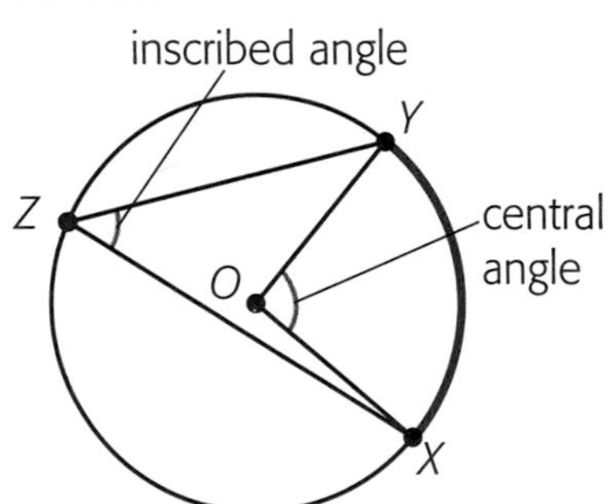

Chords XZ and YZ form inscribed $\angle XZY$.

? How is the central angle related to the inscribed angle?

A. Draw a circle with centre C. Place points X, Y, and Z on the circle.

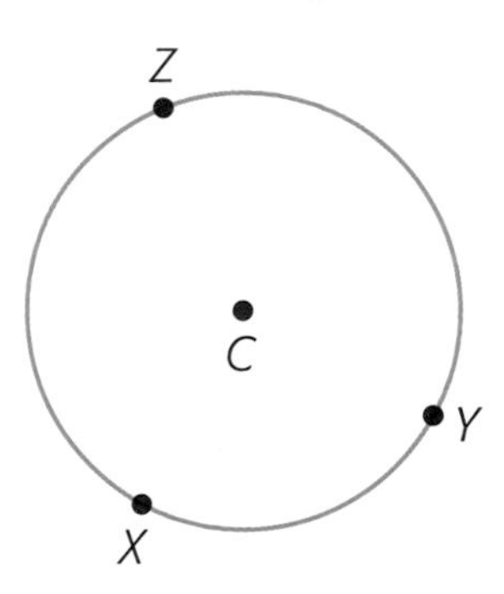

B. Draw radii CX and CY. Measure central $\angle XCY$.

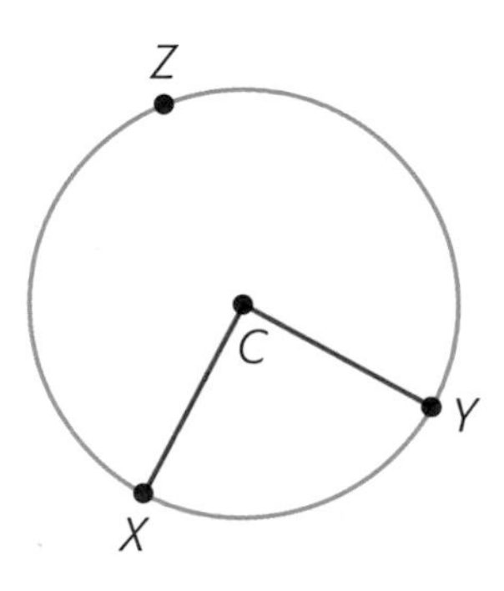

C. Draw chords XZ and YZ to form $\angle XZY$. Predict the measure of this inscribed angle. Check your prediction by measuring.

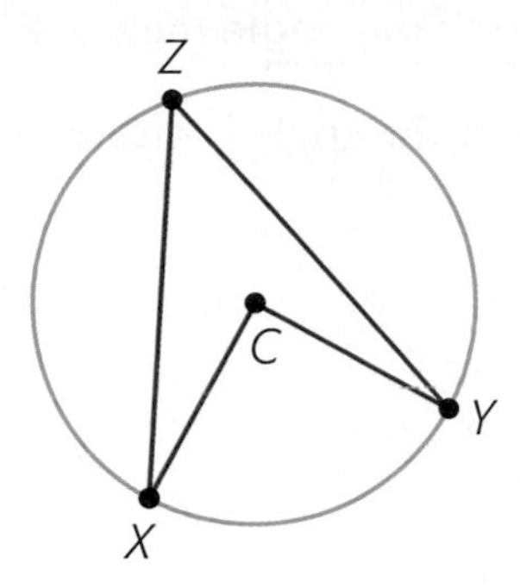

D. Move point X to a different location on the circle, but not between points Y and Z. How do the measures of $\angle XCY$ and $\angle XZY$ compare?

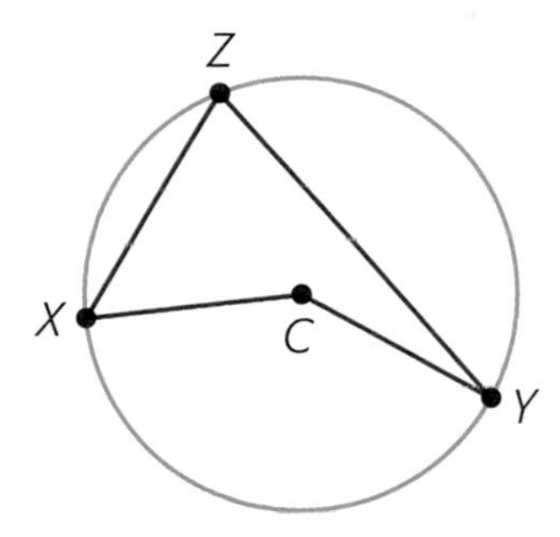

E. Continue moving point X to different locations on the circle, but not between points Y and Z. Each time, record the measurements of the inscribed angle and the central angle.

Reflecting

F. What conclusion can you draw about any inscribed angle and central angle **subtended** by the same **arc**?

G. Compare your results to those of others. Does this relationship change if the radius of the circle changes?

subtend

to define or limit; an arc that subtends an angle defines where the arms of the angle are placed.

arc

part of the circumference of a circle; a **major arc** is greater than a semicircle, and a **minor arc** is less than a semicircle.

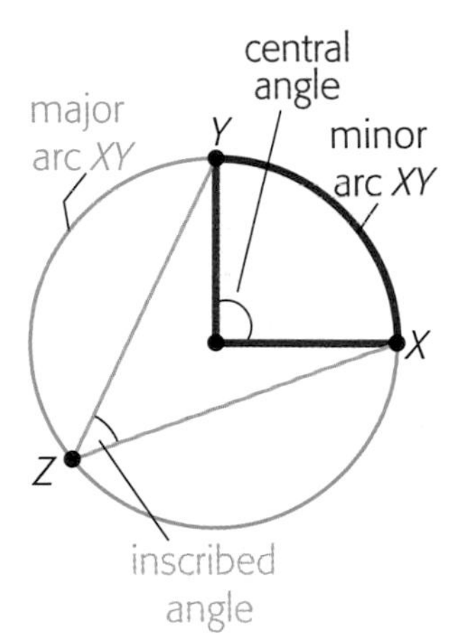

WORK WITH the Math

EXAMPLE 1 | Determining angle measures in circles

Determine the measure of the angle indicated by x. O is the centre of each circle.

Communication | Tip

The letter O is often used to indicate that a point is the centre of a circle. When this letter is used, you can assume that the point is the centre of the circle.

a)

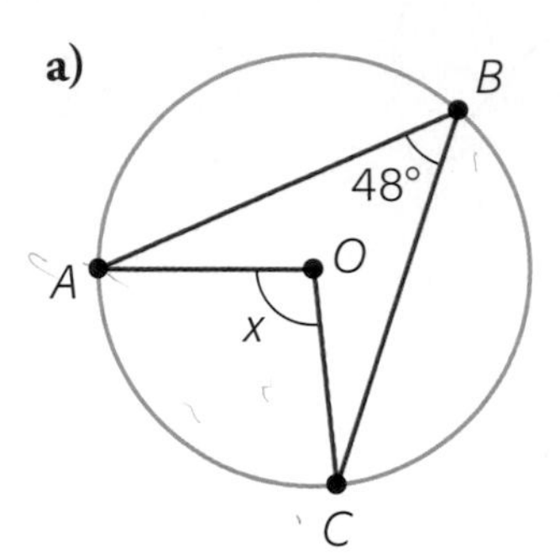

b)

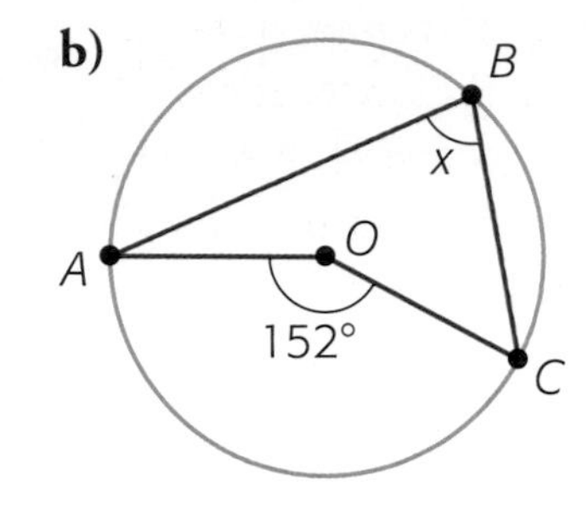

Luc's Solution

a) $\angle AOC = 2\angle ABC$

Since O is the centre of the circle, $\angle AOC$ is a central angle subtended by arc AC. $\angle ABC$ is an inscribed angle subtended by the same arc AC. The central angle is twice the measure of an inscribed angle subtended by the same arc.

$$x = 2(48)$$
$$= 96°$$
$\angle AOC$ is 96°

I substituted the measure for $\angle ABC$ and solved for x.

b) $\angle AOC = 2\angle ABC$

Since O is the centre of the circle, $\angle AOC$ is a central angle subtended by arc AC. $\angle ABC$ is an inscribed angle subtended by the same arc AC. The central angle is twice the measure of an inscribed angle subtended by the same arc.

$$152 = 2x$$
$$152 \div 2 = 2x \div 2$$
$$76 = x$$
$$\angle ABC = 76°$$

I substituted the measure of $\angle AOC$ and solved for x.

EXAMPLE 2 | **Relating an inscribed angle to a semi-circle arc that subtends it**

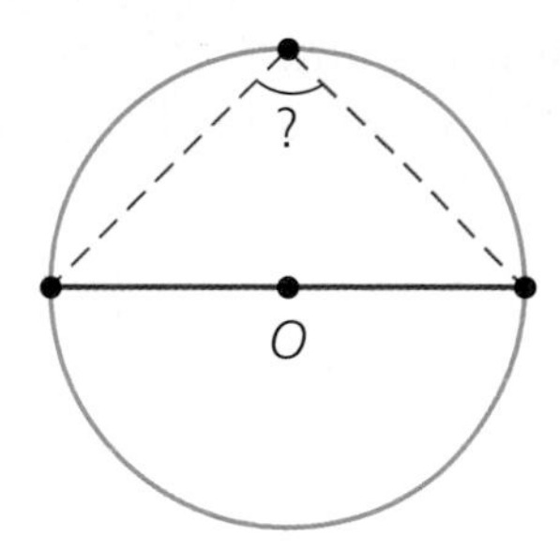

Nola designs fabric crafts. She cut out a circular design, and sewed a blue ribbon on the circle that passes through the circle's centre, O. She wants to sew on two more blue ribbons to the circle, as shown.

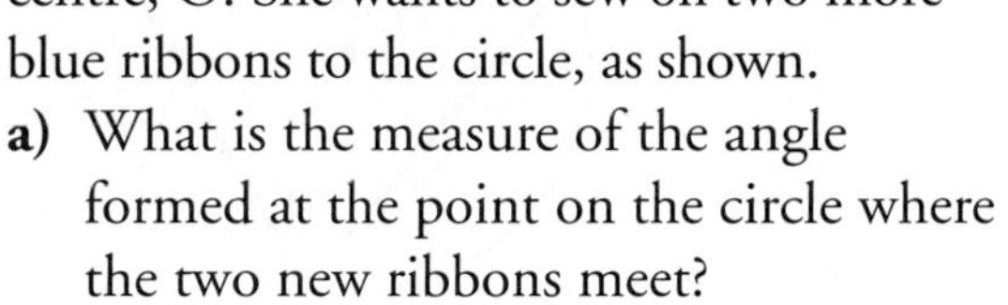

a) What is the measure of the angle formed at the point on the circle where the two new ribbons meet?

b) If the point where the new ribbons meet is moved, does the measure of the angle change?

Nola's Solution

a)

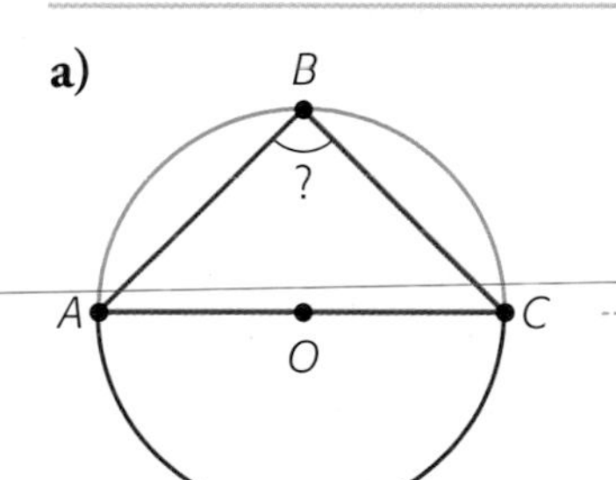

I drew a diagram of my fabric design and labeled the points where the blue ribbon touches the circle.

Since AC passes through O, the centre of the circle, I knew that AC is a diameter of the circle. This means that arc AC is a semicircle and that $\angle AOC = 180°$.

$$\angle ABC = \frac{1}{2}\angle AOC$$
$$= \frac{1}{2}(180)$$
$$= 90°$$

Since O is the centre of the circle, $\angle AOC$ is a central angle subtended by arc AC. $\angle ABC$ is an inscribed angle subtended by the same arc AC. I knew that the inscribed angle is half the measure of the central angle subtended by the same arc.

The angle formed by the two new ribbons is a right angle.

b)

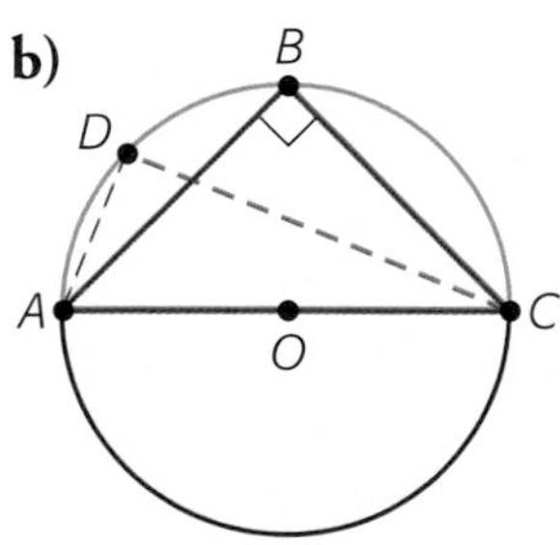

I drew in a new point D, and added chords to A and C.

I reasoned that changing the location of the point where the ribbons meet on the circle will not change the size of the angle formed. It will still be 90° because the new inscribed angle is still half of the central angle of 180°, since both angles are subtended by the same arc AC.

$$\angle ADC = \frac{1}{2}\angle AOC$$
$$= \frac{1}{2}(180)$$
$$= 90°$$

EXAMPLE 3 Determining opposite angles in a quadrilateral inscribed in a circle

Quadrilateral *AREC* is inscribed in a circle.
What is the measure of $\angle E$?

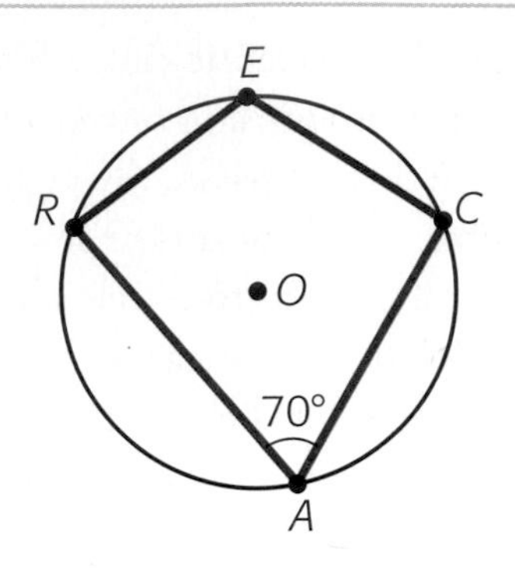

Communication | Tip

If there is only one angle at a particular vertex, the angle can be named using only the vertex letter. For example, in quadrilateral *AREC*, $\angle REC$ can be named $\angle E$.

Communication | Tip

Two points on a circle form the endpoints of two arcs: a minor arc and a major arc. Minor and major arcs can be named using only their endpoints. Sometimes a major arc is named using the endpoints of the arc and one extra point on that arc.

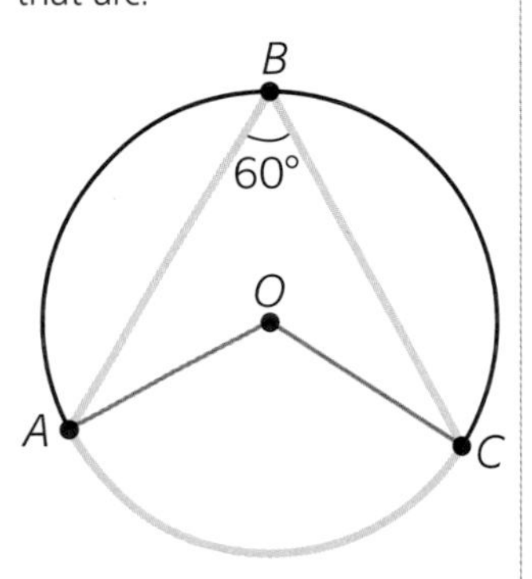

Viktor's Solution: Using central angles

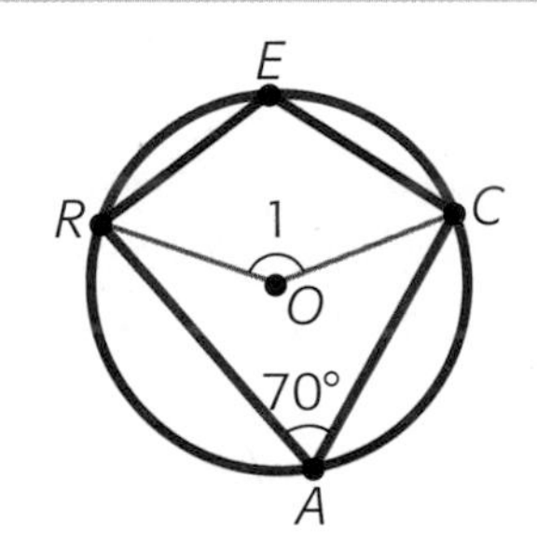

I knew that $\angle A$ is an inscribed angle subtended by minor arc *RC*. I drew radii *OR* and *OC* to form a central angle subtended by the same minor arc.

$$\begin{aligned}\angle 1 &= 2\angle A \\ &= 2 \times 70^\circ \\ &= 140^\circ\end{aligned}$$

The measure of the central angle is twice the measure of an inscribed angle subtended by the same arc. So $\angle 1$ is twice the measure of $\angle A$.

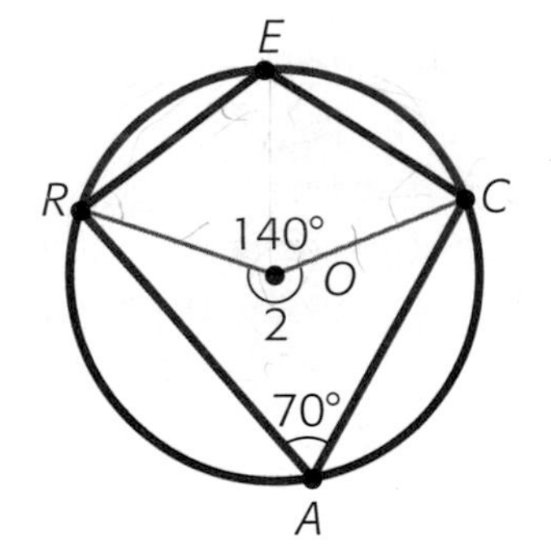

But there are two angles at *O*. I knew that the sum of these angles is 360° because together they form a circle.

$$\begin{aligned}\angle 2 &= 360^\circ - 140^\circ \\ &= 220^\circ\end{aligned}$$

$$\begin{aligned}\angle E &= \left(\frac{1}{2}\right)\angle 2 \\ &= \frac{1}{2} \times 220^\circ \\ &= 110^\circ\end{aligned}$$

$\angle 2$ and $\angle E$ are both subtended by major arc *RC*, so $\angle E$ must be half the measure of $\angle 2$.

In quadrilateral *AREC*, $\angle E$ is 110°.

In Summary

Key Ideas

- An inscribed angle is equal to half the measure of the central angle subtended by the same arc.

$$\angle I = \frac{1}{2}\angle C \text{ or } \angle C = 2\angle I$$

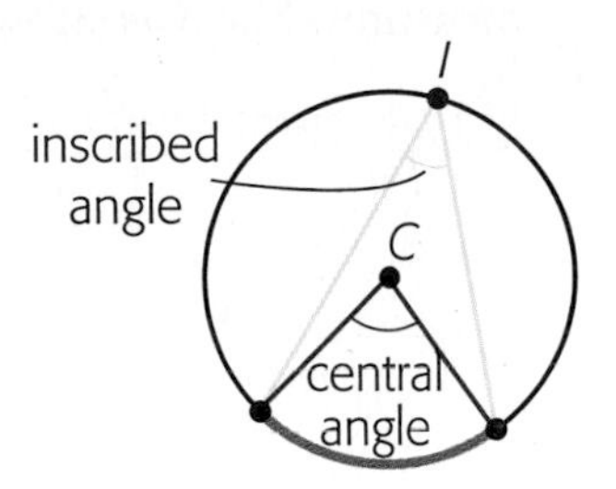

Need to Know

- An inscribed angle subtended by a semicircle measures 90°.

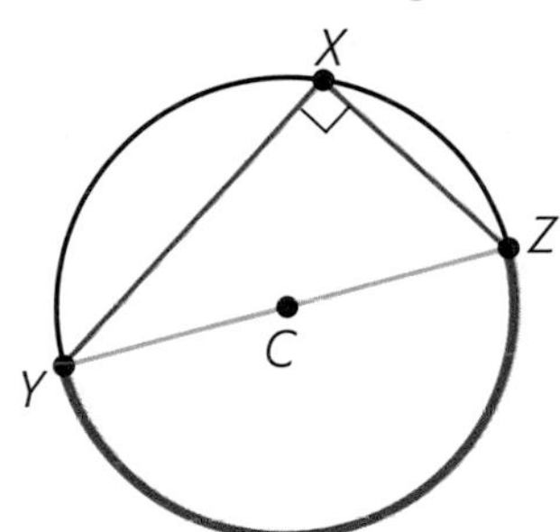

Since YZ is a diameter, arc YZ is a semicircle.
$\angle YCZ$ is a central angle equal measuring 180°.
$\angle X$ is subtended by arc YZ, so $\angle X = 90°$.

Checking

1. Determine the measure of each central angle subtended by minor arc AB. The radii divide each circle into equal parts.

a)

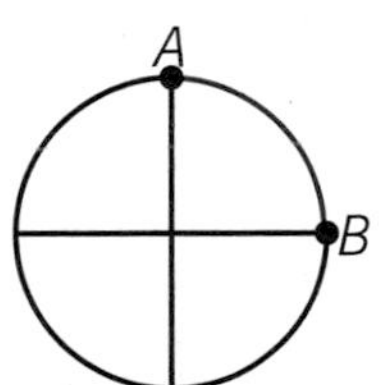

b)

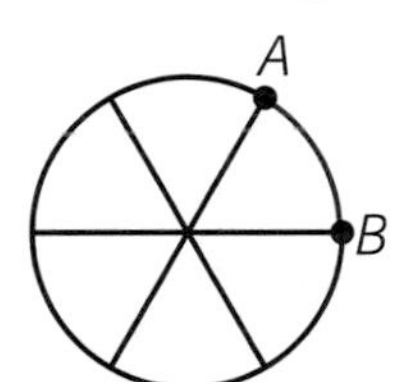

c)

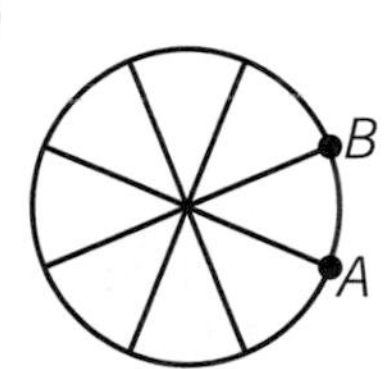

2. For each circle with centre C, determine the measure of the red angle.

a)

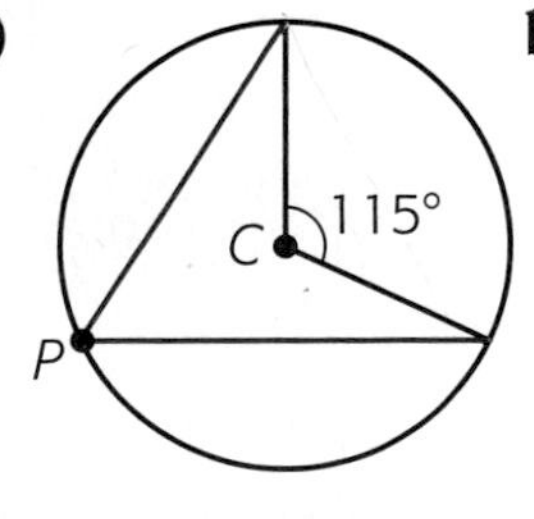

$\angle P = ?$

b)

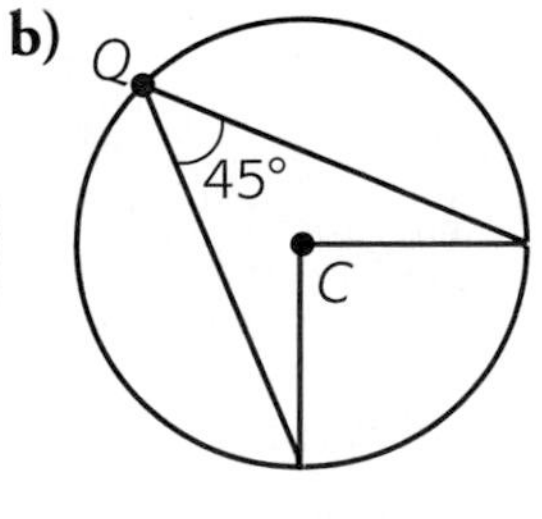

$\angle C = ?$

c)

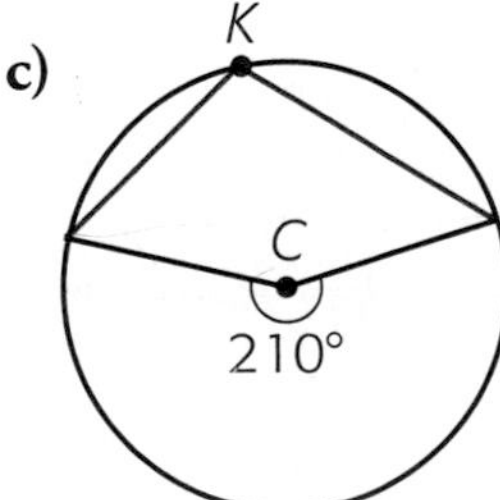

$\angle K = ?$

Practising

Reading Strategy

Activating Knowledge

Use correct mathematical terms in your work.

3. For each circle with centre C, determine the unknown angle measures. Show your work.

a)

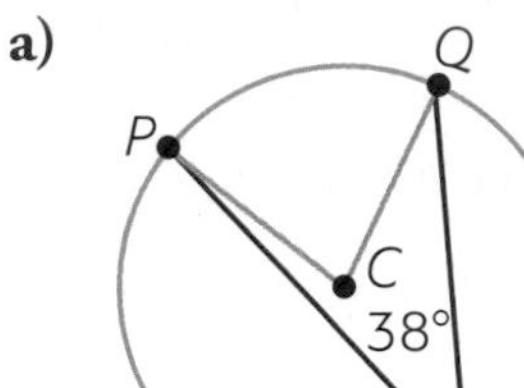

$\angle PCQ = ?$

b)

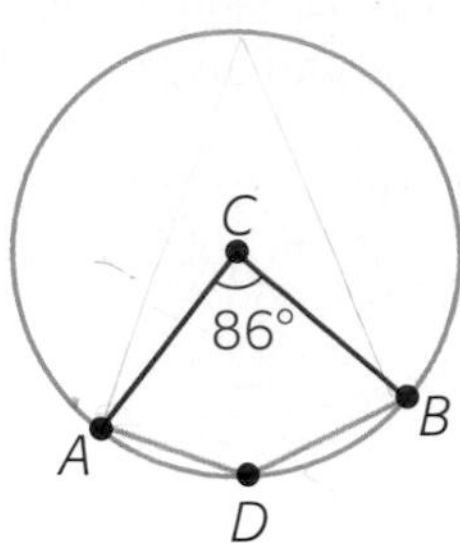

$\angle D = ?$

4. **Multiple choice.** In the diagram shown at right, $\angle F = ?$
   A. 78°
   B. 156°
   C. 24°
   D. 39°

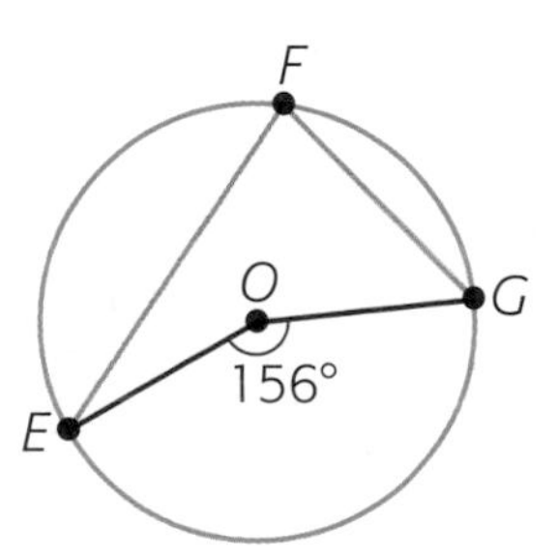

5. **Multiple choice.** In the diagram shown at right, $\angle D = ?$
   A. 18.5°
   B. 37°
   C. 106°
   D. 53°

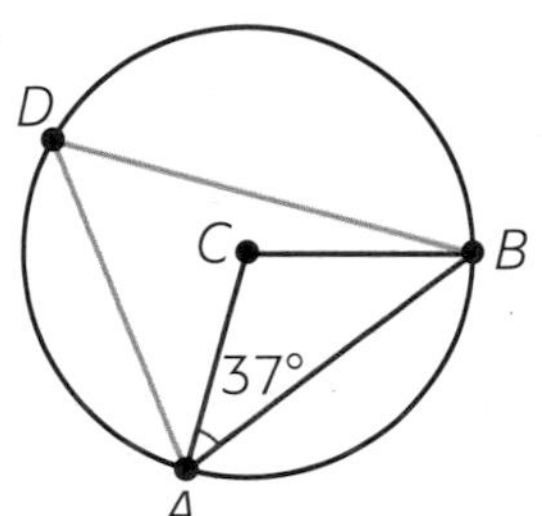

6. Identify a chord, an arc, a semicircle, and a central angle in the diagram shown at left.

7. Use your knowledge of central and inscribed angles to explain why each statement is true.

a)

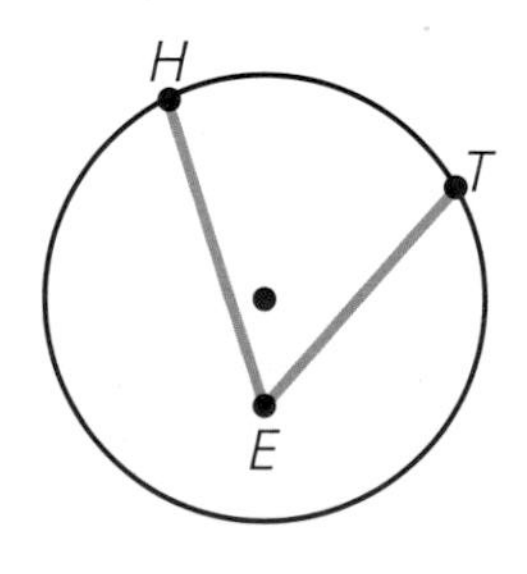

$\angle E$ is not a central angle.

b)

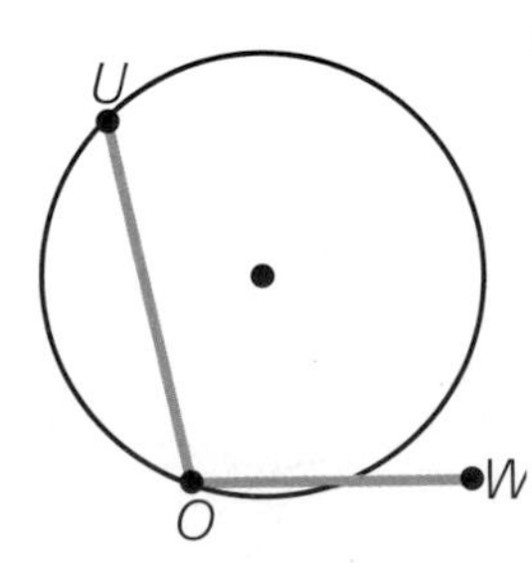

$\angle O$ is not an inscribed angle.

c)

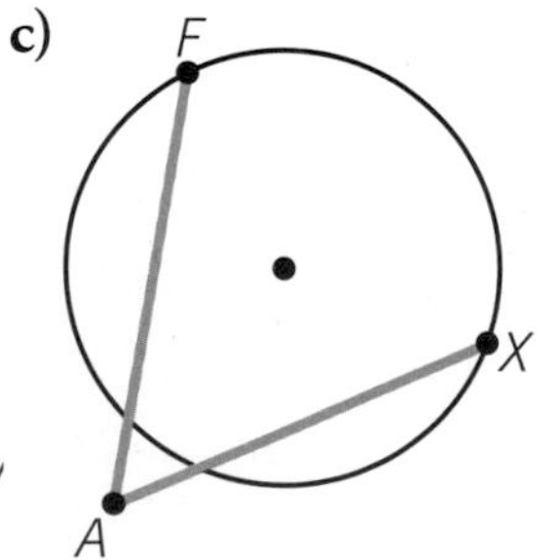

$\angle A$ is not an inscribed angle.

d)

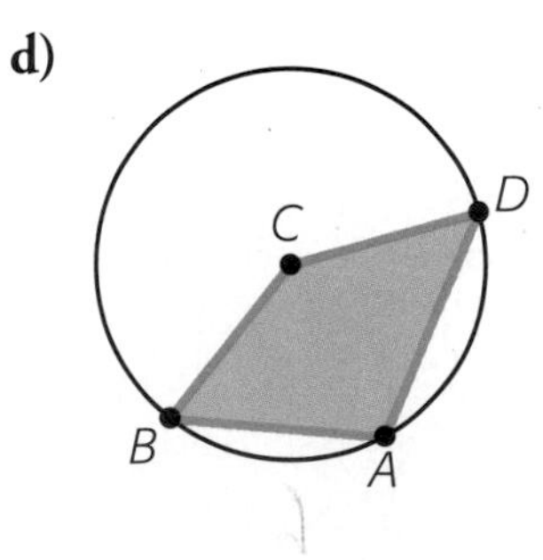

$ABCD$ is not an inscribed quadrilateral.

8. A circle can be used to determine the angle measure for any regular polygon.
   a) Using your knowledge of central and inscribed angles, how would you determine the measure of the interior angles of a regular hexagon?
   b) Determine the interior angle measures of a different regular polygon.

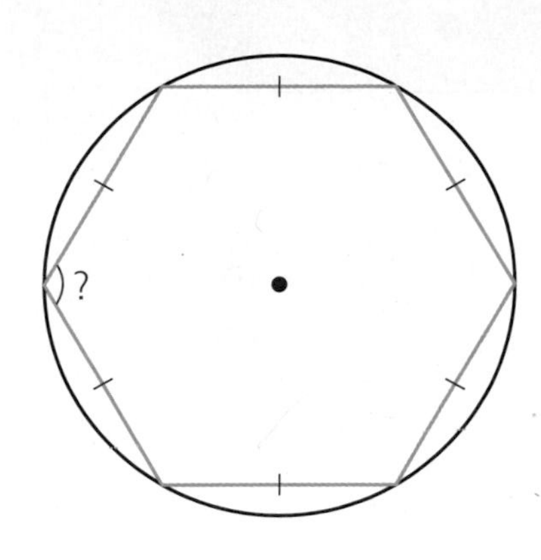

9. Show how central and inscribed angles can be used to accurately construct a right angle without using a protractor.

10. Use a circle to draw a regular eight-pointed star. What is the angle measure at each of the star's points?

11. a) Name all of the central angles in the diagram shown below, and determine their measures.
    b) Determine the measures of all inscribed angles with vertex A.

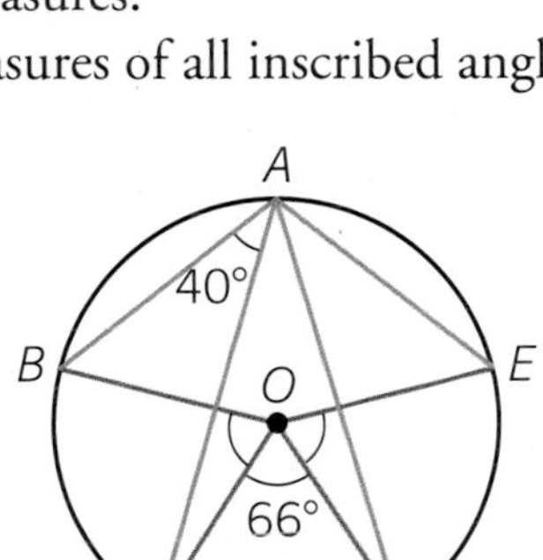

Closing

12. Explain how you can determine the measure of $\angle X$.

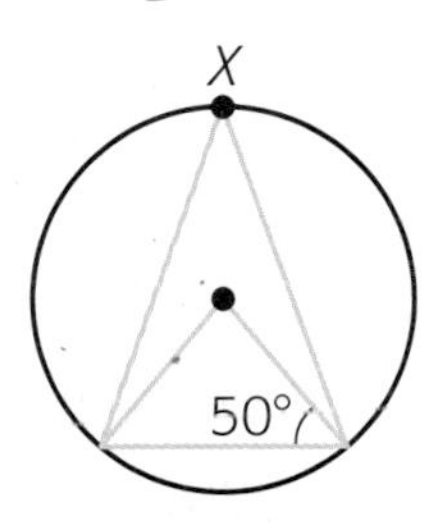

Extending

13. The circle shown at right has diameter FH and radius PE. Determine the measure of all angles in the circle.

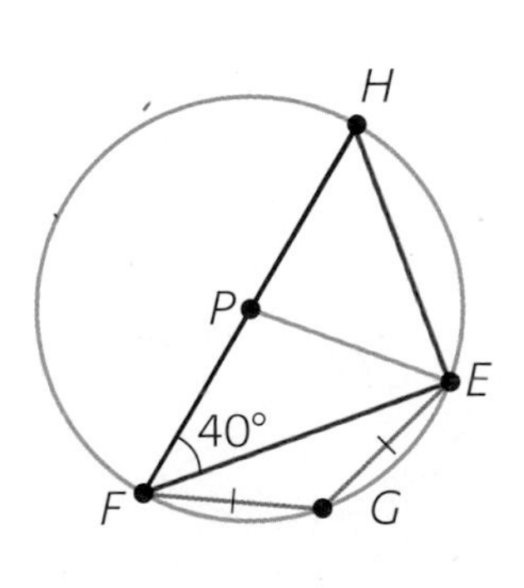

14. Two circles have centres C and P respectively. Determine the measure of $\angle APB$.

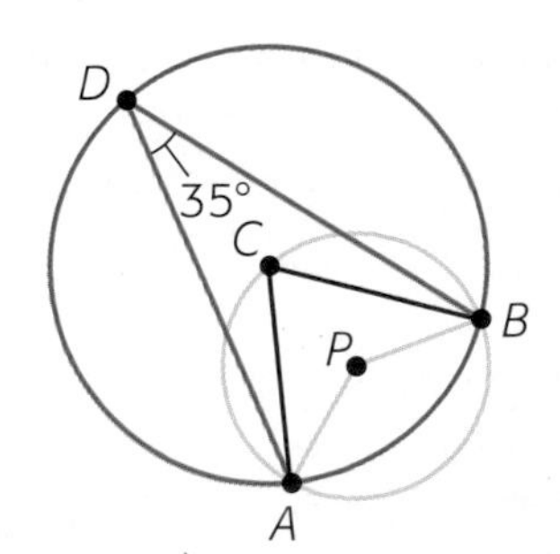

9.2 Comparing Inscribed Angles

YOU WILL NEED

- geometry software *or*
- a compass
- a protractor
- a ruler

GOAL

Relate the measures of inscribed angles in a circle.

INVESTIGATE the Math

Francis is making a dreamcatcher for his young sister. The first part of his design is shown.

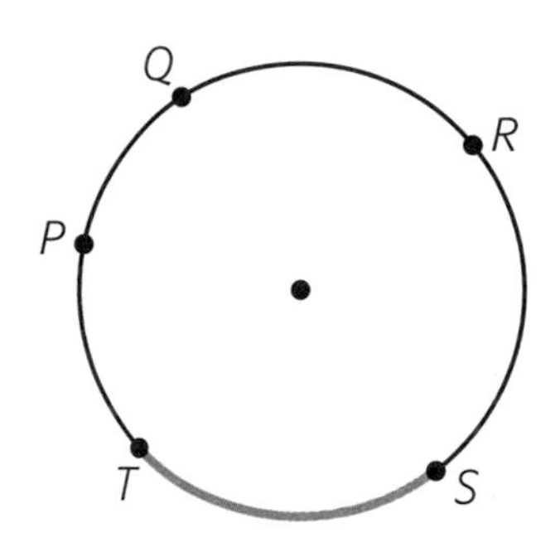

? What is the relationship among the inscribed angles in Francis's design?

A. Draw a circle. Define a minor arc by placing points S and T on the circle. Place three points, P, Q, and R on the major arc.

B. Draw the three inscribed angles ($\angle P, \angle Q$, and $\angle R$) subtended by minor arc ST. Use a different colour for each angle as shown at left. Measure these angles. What do you notice?

C. Place point P at a different location on major arc TS. What happens to the measure of $\angle P$?

D. Repeat step C for points Q and R. Does your observation for point P also hold for points Q and R?

E. Repeat steps A to D using a different minor arc ST.

F. Summarize the relationship among the inscribed angles in Francis's design.

Reflecting

G. How are the measures of inscribed $\angle P$, $\angle Q$, and $\angle R$ related to the central angle subtended by minor arc ST?

H. Why does changing the location of points P, Q, and R not change the measure of the inscribed angle?

I. Explain why changing the size of minor arc ST causes the measure of the inscribed angles to change but remain equal.

WORK WITH the Math

EXAMPLE 1 | Determining the measure of inscribed angles

The lighting engineers for a circus are hanging spotlights on tubing shaped in an arc as shown. They want each light to illuminate the floor area. The tubing lies on a minor arc of the circle centred at O. At what beam angle setting should each spotlight be set to fully illuminate the floor?

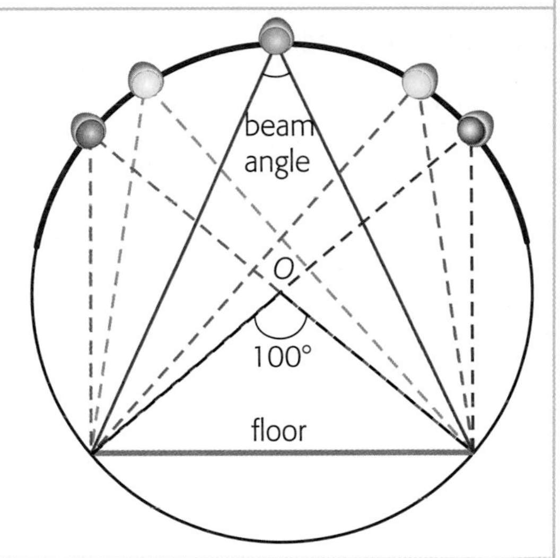

Rani's Solution

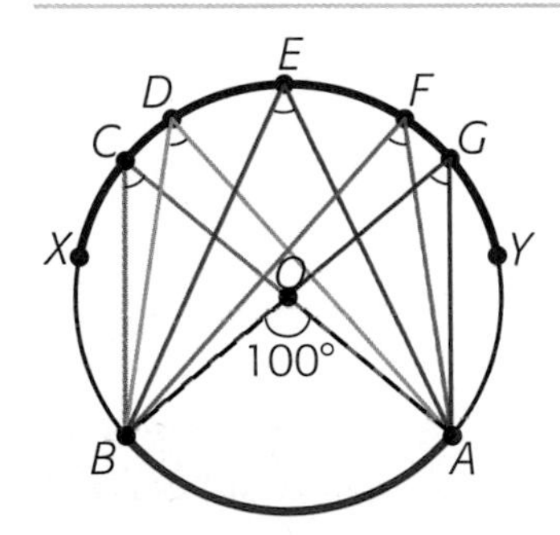

I used my drawing program to represent the stage, arc, and lights as a circle.
I chose A and B to represent the ends of the floor and X and Y to represent the ends of the tubing arc.
I named the places where the lights go as points C to G.
I knew that points C, D, E, F, and G all lie on the circle centred at O.

I needed to know the measure of the inscribed angles.

$$\angle BOA = 100°$$

$$\angle C = \left(\frac{1}{2}\right)\angle BOA$$
$$= \frac{1}{2} \times 100°$$
$$= 50°$$
$$\angle C = \angle D = \angle E = \angle F = \angle G = 50°$$

$\angle BOA$ is a central angle subtended by minor arc AB. $\angle C$, $\angle D$, $\angle E$, $\angle F$, and $\angle G$ are all inscribed angles subtended by minor arc AB. So I knew these inscribed angles were all the same measure, which is half the central angle.

The beam angle setting for each spotlight should be 50°.

EXAMPLE 2 | Determining missing angles

A magician is designing a logo for his business. His logo is drawn in a circle centred at C. What are the measures of $\angle QPR$, $\angle PQS$, $\angle PRS$, and $\angle QSR$ in the logo?

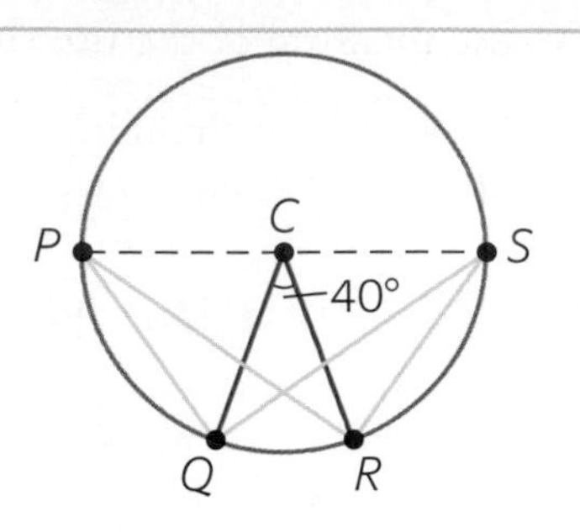

Zachary's Solution

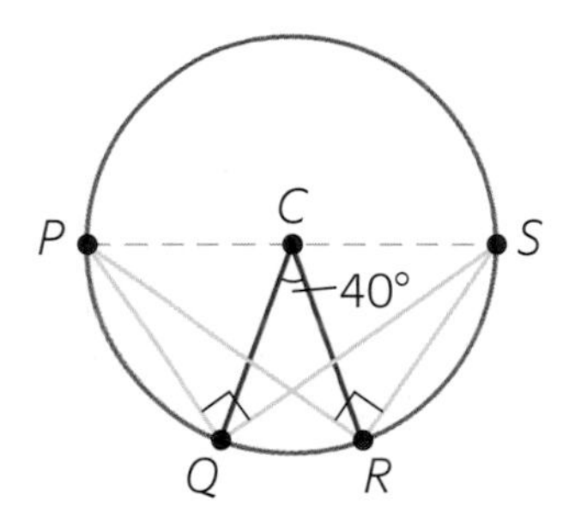

I copied the logo.
I knew that *PS* is a diameter because it goes through the centre of the circle, so arc *PS* is a semicircle. This means that $\angle PQS$ and $\angle PRS$ are inscribed angles subtended by a semicircle, so they are each 90°.

$\angle PQS = \angle PRS = 90°$

$$\angle QPR = \left(\frac{1}{2}\right)\angle QCR$$
$$= \frac{1}{2} \times 40°$$
$$= 20°$$

$\angle QPR = \angle QSR = 20°$

I noticed that $\angle QPR$ and $\angle QSR$ are inscribed angles subtended by minor arc *QR*. This minor arc also subtends central $\angle QCR$. So $\angle QPR$ and $\angle QSR$ are half of $\angle QCR$.

In the logo, $\angle QPR = \angle QSR = 20°$ and $\angle PQS = \angle PRS = 90°$.

In Summary

Key Idea

- It is possible to have many inscribed angles subtended by the same arc. Angles 1, 2, and 3 have the same measure. If the arc is a semicircle, the inscribed angles are 90°.

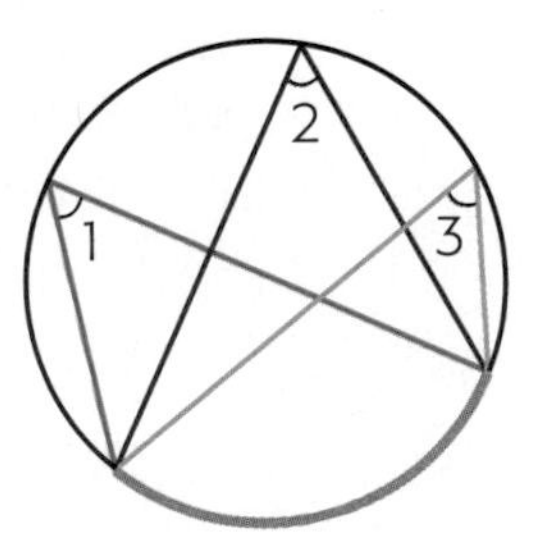

$\angle 1 = \angle 2 = \angle 3$

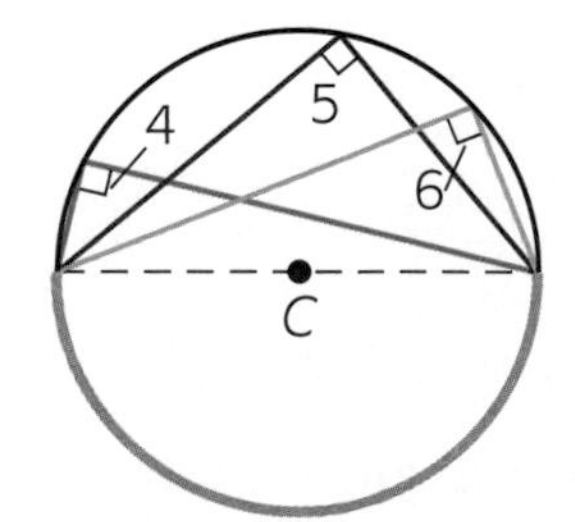

$\angle 4 = \angle 5 = \angle 6 = 90°$

Checking

1. For each circle with centre C, determine the measure of the inscribed angles indicated.

a)

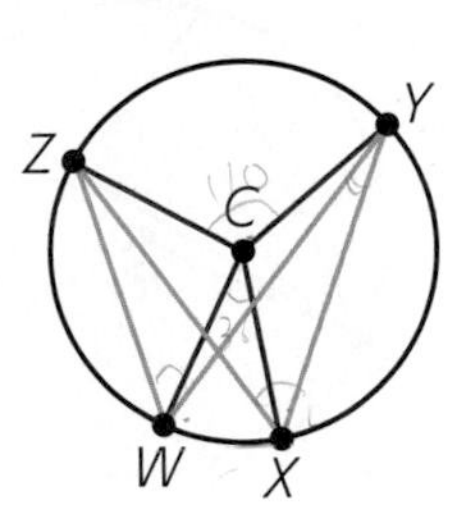

$\angle WCX = 36°$,
$\angle ZCY = 110°$
$\angle ZWY = ?$,
$\angle WYX = ?$

b)

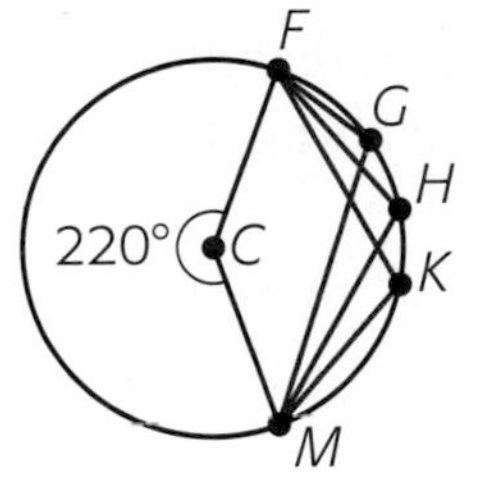

$\angle G = ?$, $\angle H = ?$,
$\angle K = ?$

c)

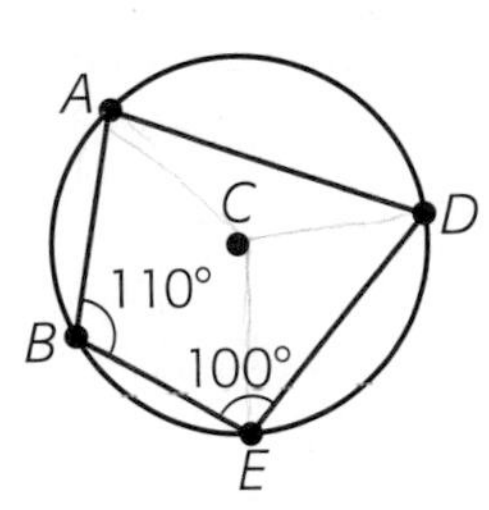

$\angle A = ?$, $\angle D = ?$

Practising

2. Determine the unknown angle measures indicated. Show your work.

a)

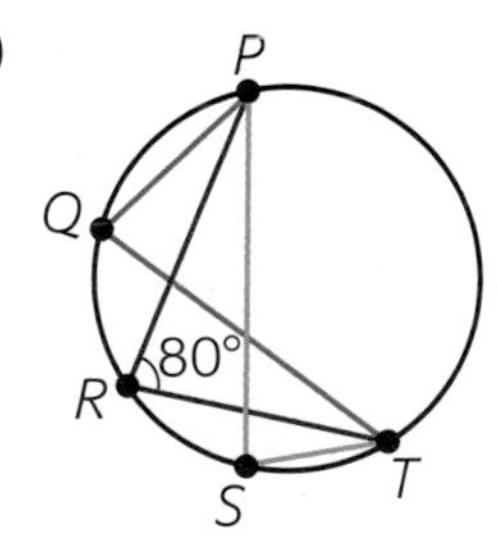

$\angle Q$ and $\angle S$

b)

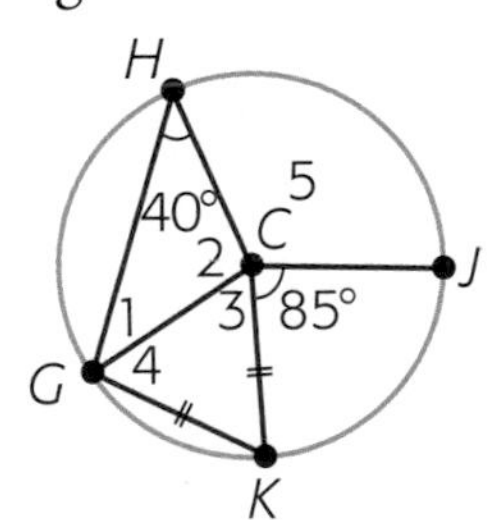

$\angle 1$, $\angle 2$, $\angle 3$, $\angle 4$,
$\angle 5$, and $\angle K$

c)

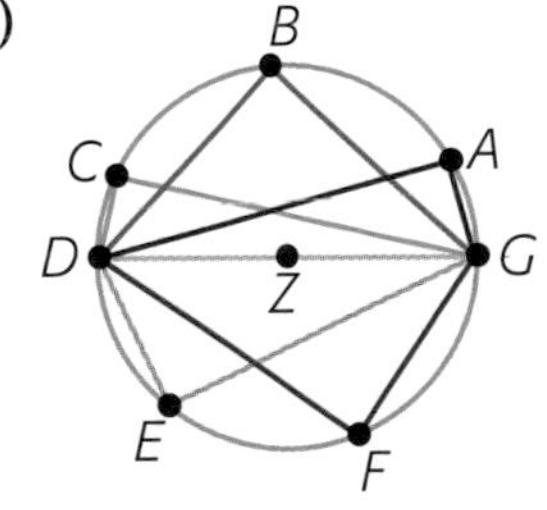

DG is a diameter.
$\angle A$, $\angle B$, $\angle C$, $\angle E$, and $\angle F$

3. Determine the measures of $\angle A$, $\angle B$, $\angle D$, and $\angle E$ shown at right. Explain how you determined the measure of each angle.

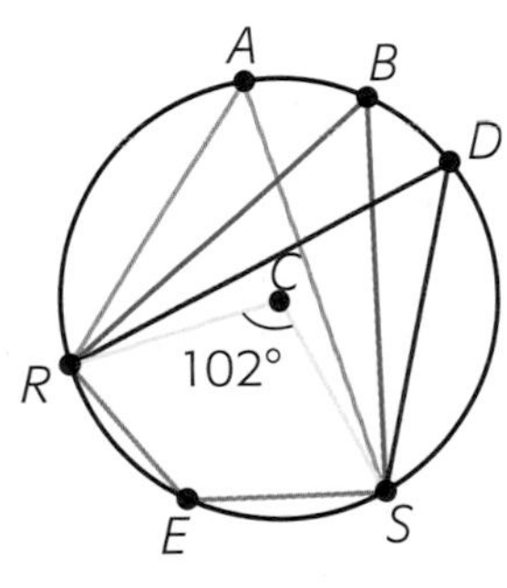

4. In each diagram, state which inscribed angles are equal. Explain how you know.

a)

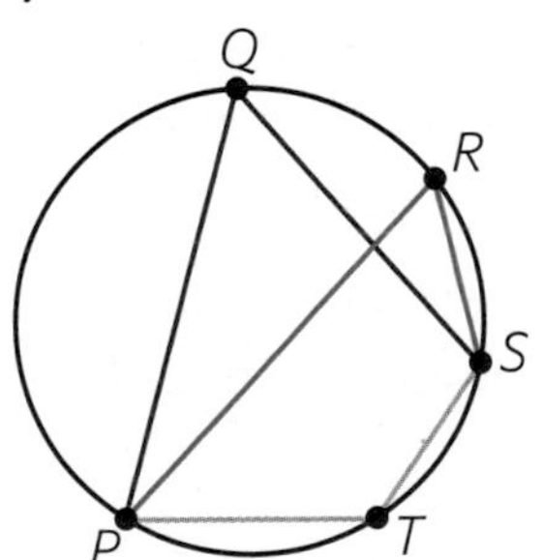

b)

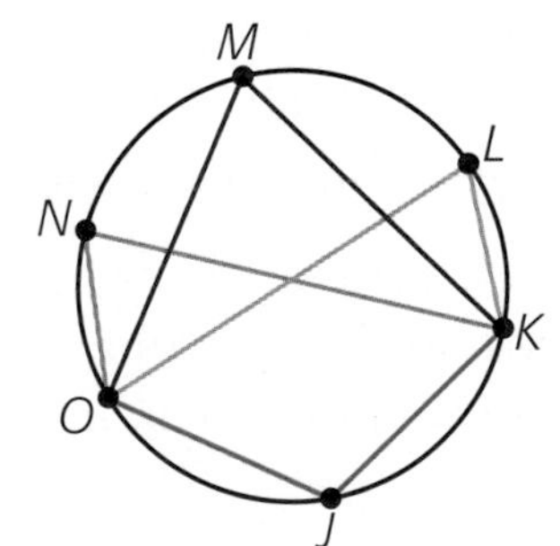

5. **Multiple choice.** R is the centre of the circle. Which statement is *false*?

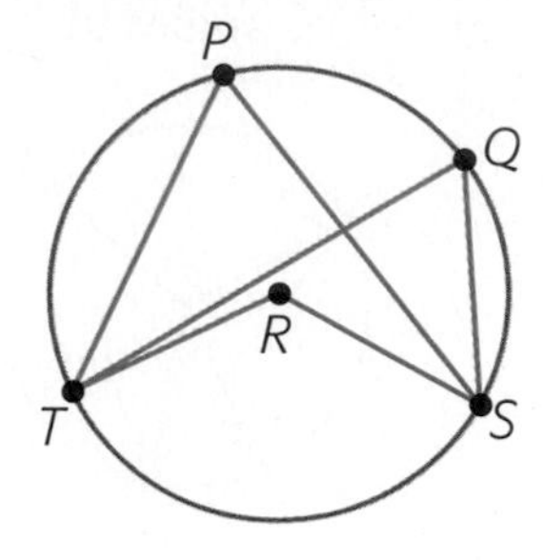

A. $\angle P = \angle Q$
B. $\angle P$ may be greater than 90°.
C. $\angle P$ and $\angle Q$ will always be less than $\angle R$.
D. $\angle P$, $\angle Q$, and $\angle R$ are all subtended by arc ST.

6. Draw a circle. Describe how to inscribe a rectangle in the circle without using a protractor or geometry software.

7. Determine the measures of the angles indicated. Show your work.

a)

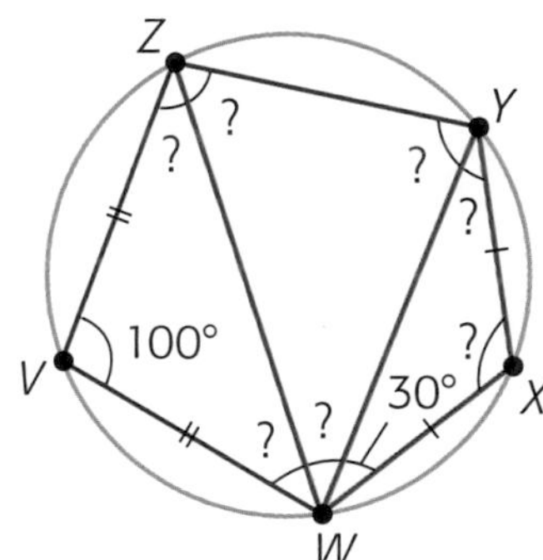

b)

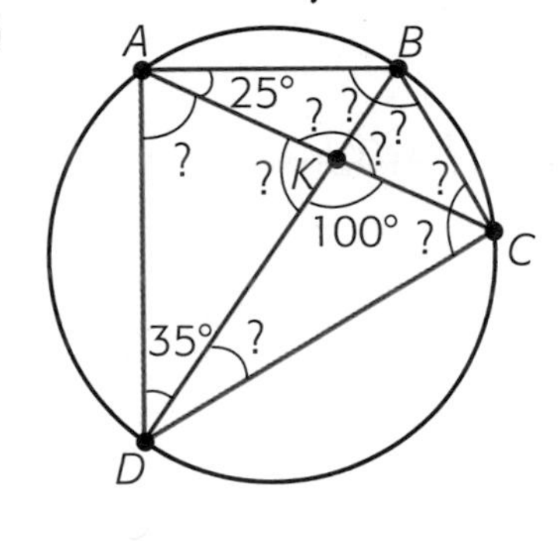

8. Construct a circle with centre O. Then draw any inscribed quadrilateral $PQRS$.
   a) Measure each angle of the quadrilateral.
   b) Determine the sum of opposite angles ($\angle P + \angle R$ and $\angle Q + \angle S$). What do you notice?
   c) Change the shape of the quadrilateral by moving one or more of the vertices to a different position on the circle. Examine the sums of each pair of opposite angles. What do you notice?
   d) Make a **conjecture** about opposite angles in a quadrilateral inscribed in a circle.
   e) Draw radii OS and OQ. What is the measure of each central angle? Can you explain why your conjecture works?

9. Create a question involving two or more inscribed angles. Write a solution to your question. Exchange questions with a classmate and solve each other's questions.

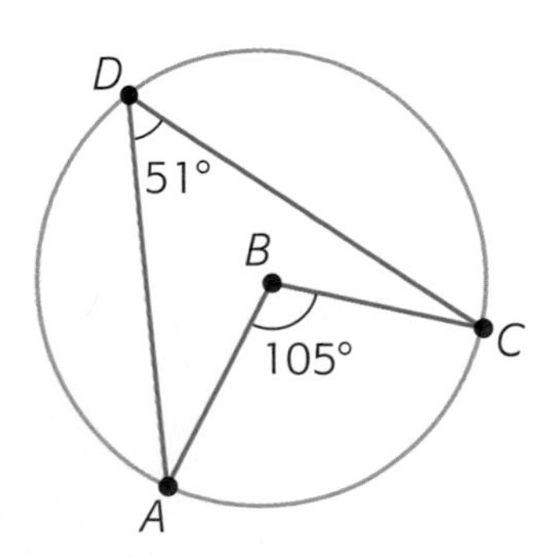

10. Is point B the centre of the circle at left? Explain how you know.

Closing

11. How does knowing that $\angle DEF = 80°$ help you to draw other 80° angles without a protractor?

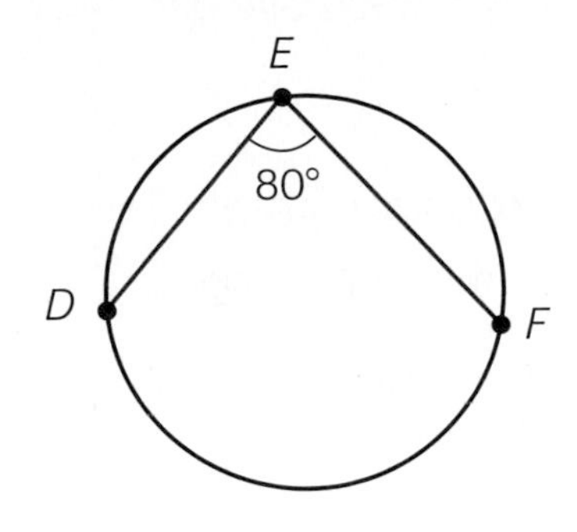

Extending

12. Rani claims that, if she randomly places four points at different locations on a circle, she can always create four pairs of equal inscribed angles. Is she correct? Explain.

13. Two chords, AB and XY, intersect at P as shown. The centre of the circle is at C.

a) State all pairs of equal angles.

b) What do you know about $\triangle APY$ and $\triangle XPB$?

c) Explain why $(PB)(PA) = (PX)(PY)$.

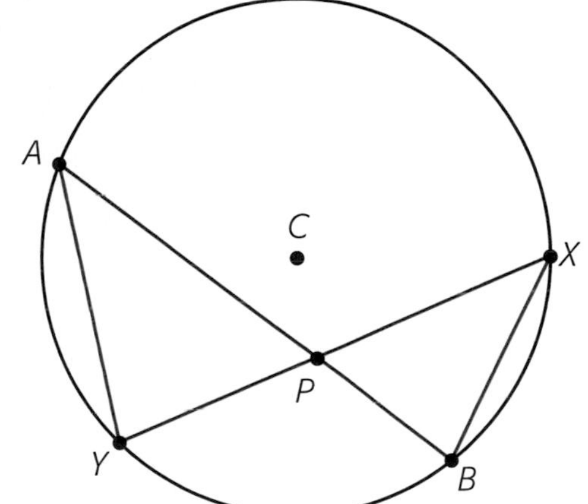

14. In a circle with centre at M, $\angle PRS = 85°$. Determine the measures of all angles indicated in quadrilateral $PRST$.

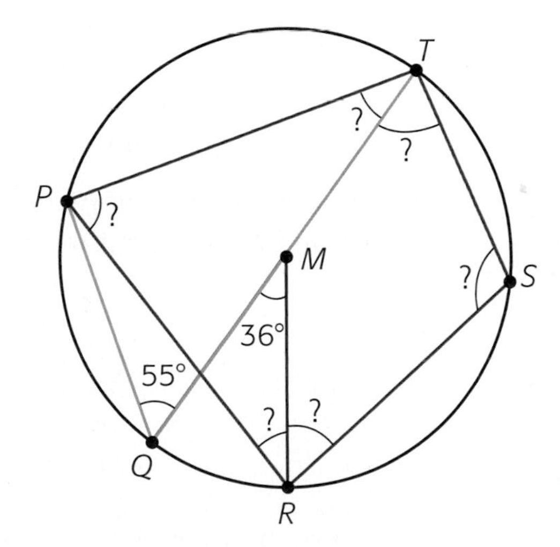

9.3 Chord Properties

YOU WILL NEED

- geometry software
  or
- a compass
- a protractor
- a ruler

GOAL

Examine the relationship between the centre of a circle and chords.

INVESTIGATE the Math

Nola designs lamps. The shade of one of her lamps has six different coloured glass inserts, which are connected to a wire frame. Each insert needs to be perpendicular to the frame. A **cross-section** of the shade is shown.

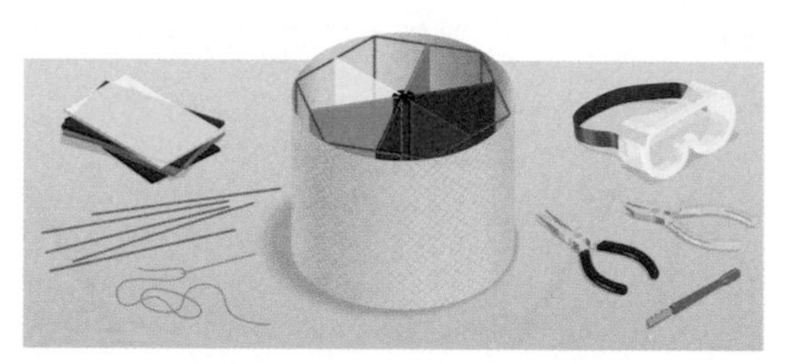

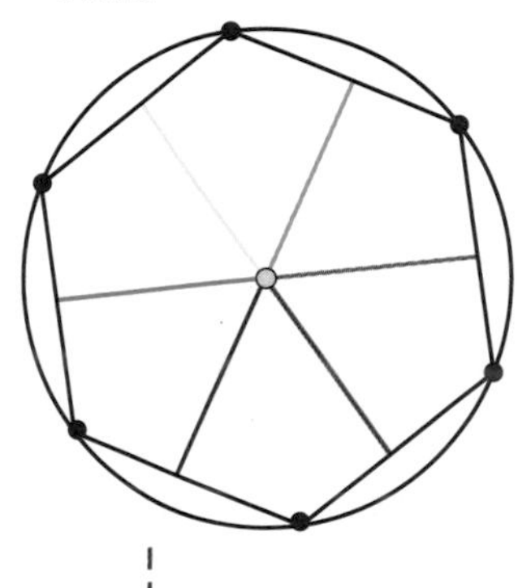

? How can Nola check that the glass inserts are connected correctly to the frame?

A. Draw a circle with centre C and radius CA. Place point P anywhere on radius CA.

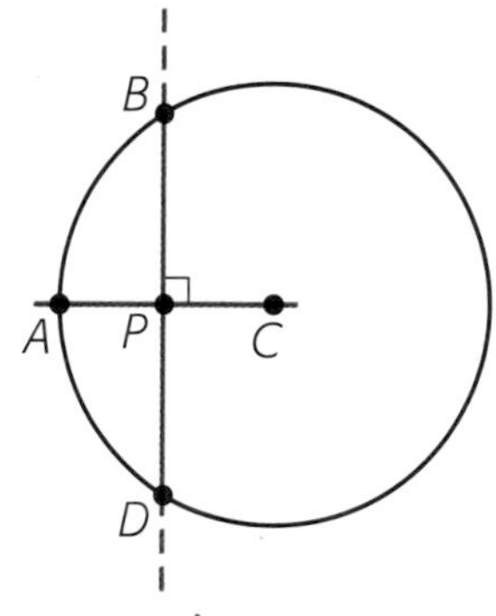

B. Draw a line perpendicular to the radius through P as shown at left. Label the points where the line intersects the circle as B and D.

C. Measure segments PB and PD. How do their measures compare?

D. Move point P to a different location on radius CA and repeat step C. Does your answer to part C depend on where P is on the radius?

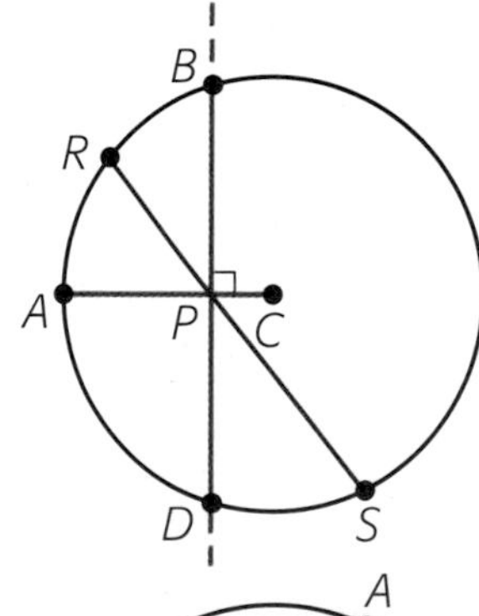

E. Draw another chord RS through P, but not perpendicular to radius CA. Measure segments PR and PS. Does the relationship you discovered in part C still hold?

F. At what point on each chord of the wire frame should the glass insert be connected to ensure that it is perpendicular to the frame?

Reflecting

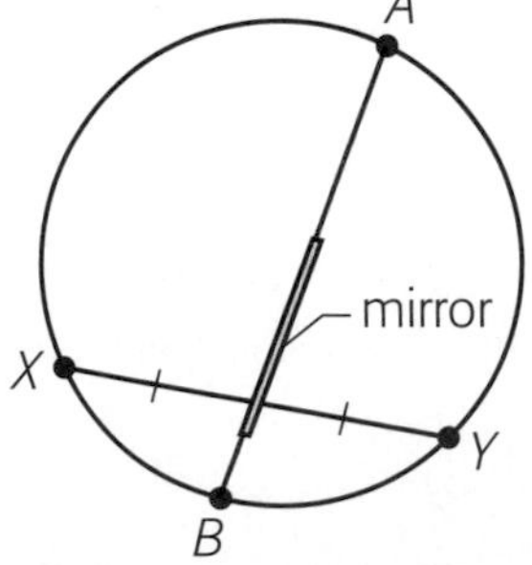

G. If you held a mirror as shown, how could you tell if line segment AB goes through the centre of the circle?

H. What conclusions can you draw about the angle created by joining the centre of a circle to the midpoint of a chord?

EXAMPLE 1 | Verifying A Chord Property

Show that:

a) A line drawn from the centre of a circle that is perpendicular to a chord, bisects the chord.

b) The perpendicular bisector of a chord passes through the centre of the circle.

Luc's Solution

a)

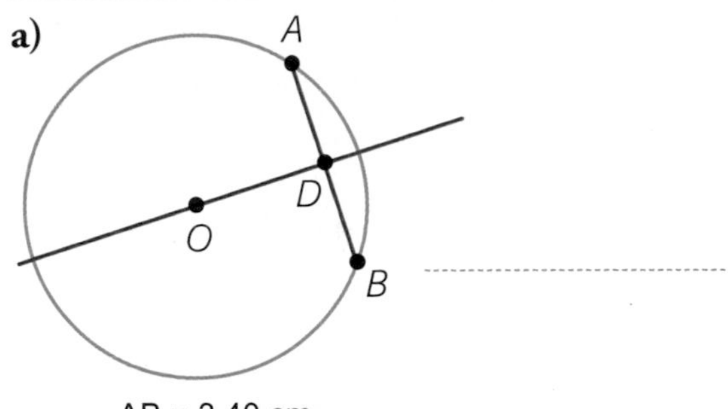

AB = 3.40 cm
AD = 1.70 cm
BD = 1.70 cm
m∠ODA = 90.00°

I used geometry software to construct a circle. I constructed two points on the circle and joined them to create chord *AB*. I selected the chord and the centre of the circle and constructed a perpendicular line. Then I located the point of intersection between the two lines and labeled this point *D*. I measured the lengths of *AB*, *AD*, and *BD*. I also measured ∠ *ODB*.

D is the midpoint of *AB*, since $AD = BD$.

The line through *OD* is perpendicular to *AB* and bisects the chord.

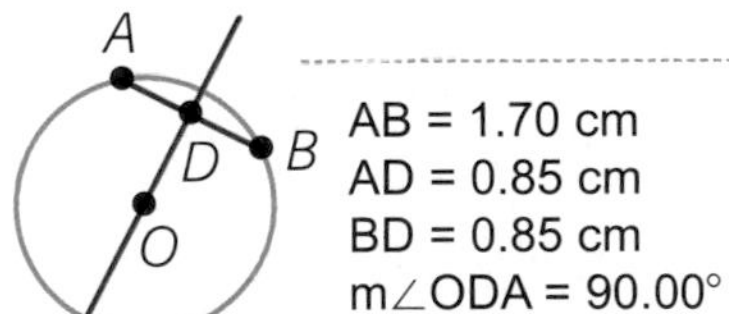

I repeated this process for a different circle and a different chord. The result was the same.

D is the midpoint of *AB*, since $AD = BD$

The perpendicular line from the centre of a circle to a chord bisects the chord.

Every time I repeated this process using a different circle and a different chord, the result was the same.

b)

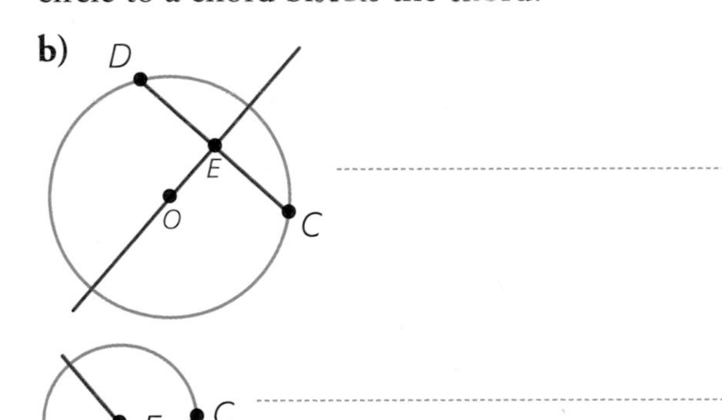

I used geometry software to construct a circle. I constructed two points on the circle and joined them to create chord *CD*. Then I constructed the midpoint of the chord, *E*. I selected the chord and the midpoint and constructed a perpendicular line. This line passed through the centre of the circle.

I repeated this process for a different circle and a different chord. The result was the same.

The perpendicular bisector of a chord passes through the centre of a circle.

Every time I repeated this process using a different circle and a different chord the result was the same.

EXAMPLE 2 | Determining which chords can locate the centre of a circle

Is it possible to locate the centre of a circle using any two chords?

Erin's Solution: Trying with non-parallel chords

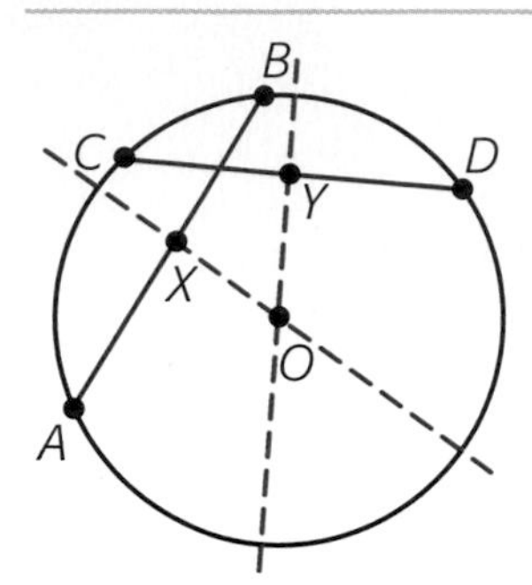

I decided to try to locate the centre of a circle using two chords, *AB* and *CD*, that are not parallel to each other. I constructed the perpendicular bisectors of each chord. I used perpendicular bisectors since I know they pass through the centre of the circle. I reasoned that their point of intersection, *O*, might be the centre of the circle.

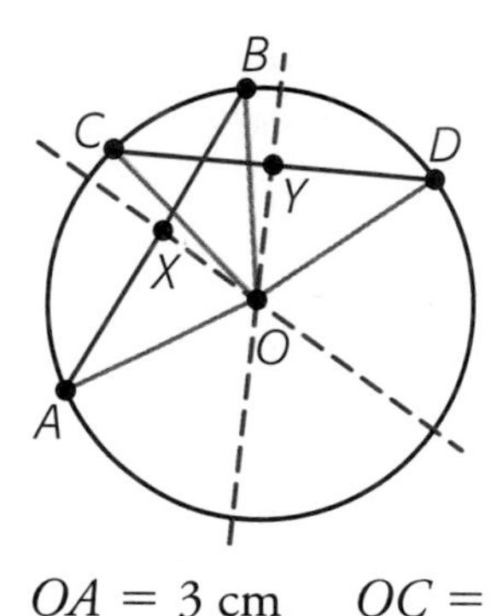

I drew line segments *OA*, *OB*, *OC*, and *OD*. Then I measured them. They were all equal. Since a circle is the set of points that are the same distance from a centre point, *O* must be the centre of the circle.

$OA = 3$ cm $OC = 3$ cm
$OB = 3$ cm $OD = 3$ cm

Check:
I put the point of my compass at *O* and the pencil on *D*, and drew a circle. The circle went through *A*, *B*, and *C*, so *O* is the centre of the circle.

The centre of a circle is at the intersection of the perpendicular bisectors of any pair of non-parallel chords.

Zachary's Solution: Trying with parallel chords

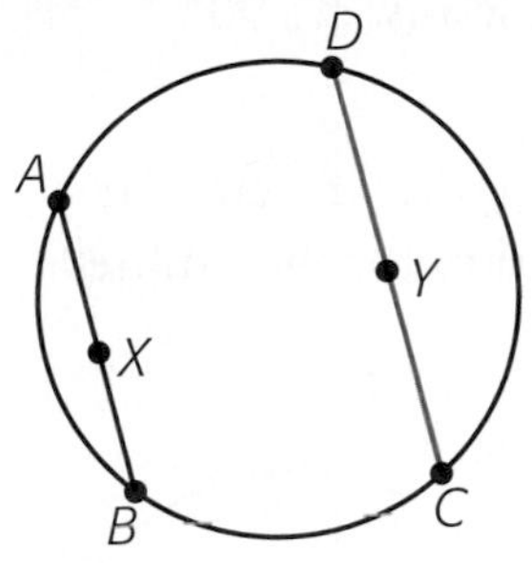

I wondered if it was possible to locate the centre of a circle if the chords were parallel.
I drew a circle with two parallel chords, *AB* and *CD*.
I constructed the midpoints, *X* and *Y*, of each chord.

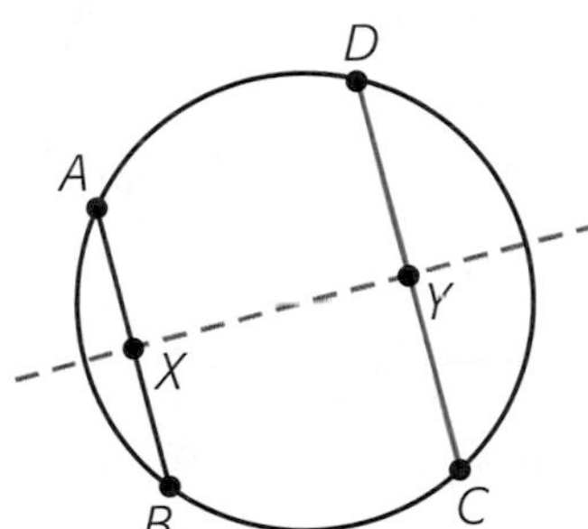

I constructed a perpendicular line through *X*. I noticed that the perpendicular bisector of *AB* went through *Y*. Then I constructed a perpendicular line through *Y*. The perpendicular bisector of *CD* went through *X*.

If two chords are parallel, you cannot locate the centre of a circle directly using only their perpendicular bisectors.

Since both perpendicular bisectors are the same line, I could not determine the location of the centre. I know the centre is on line segment *XY*, but I don't know where.

In Summary

Key Idea

- A line that passes through the centre of a circle and the midpoint of a chord is perpendicular to the chord. Another way of saying this is that a line that is perpendicular to a chord and also passes through the centre of the circle bisects the chord.

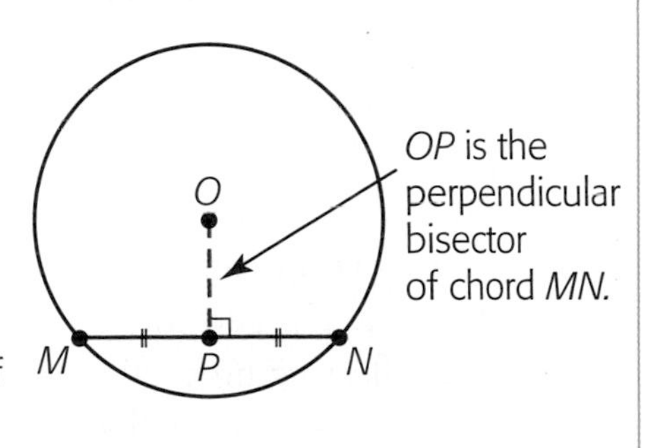

Need to Know

- The perpendicular bisector of a chord passes through the centre of a circle.
- The centre of a circle is located at the intersection of the perpendicular bisectors of two non-parallel chords.

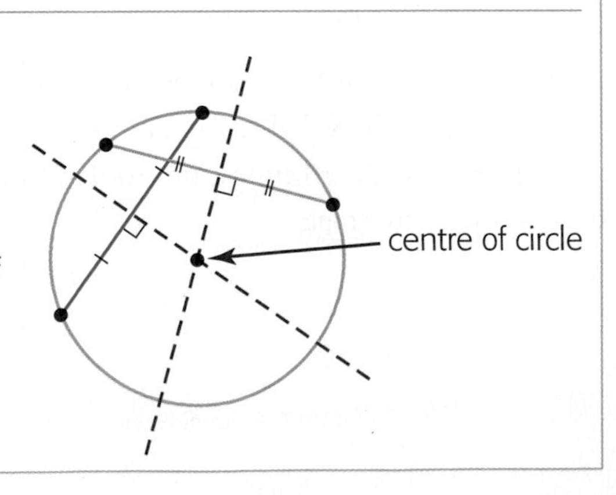

Checking

1. In the diagram, $RP = RT$. State which angles, if any, are $90°$. Explain how you know.

2. Erin wants to place an umbrella holder at the centre of a circular sandbox. How can Erin locate the correct position for the umbrella holder?

Practising

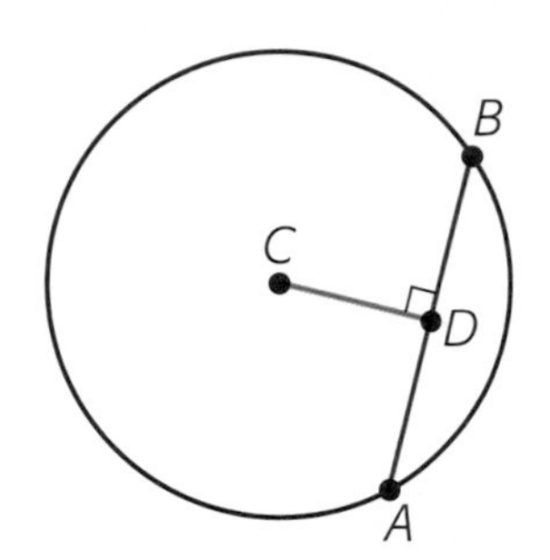

3. **Multiple choice.** In the circle shown, $AB = 12$ cm. Which statement is true?
   - **A.** The radius is 12 cm.
   - **B.** $AD = 6$ cm
   - **C.** $CD = 12$ cm
   - **D.** $CD = AB$

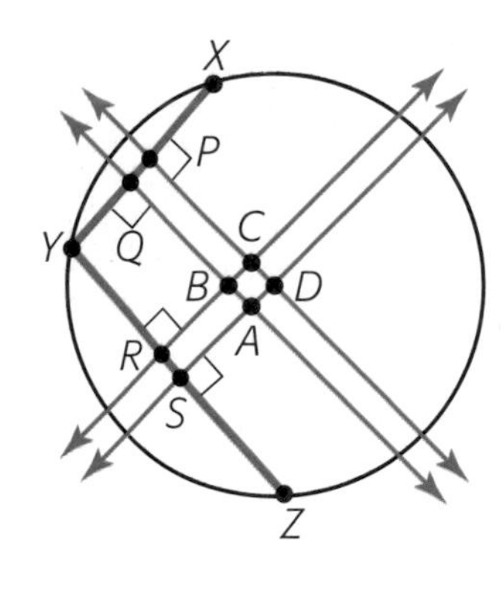

4. **Multiple choice.** In the diagram, $PX = PY$ and $SY = SZ$. Which point is at the centre of the circle?
   A. A **B.** B **C.** C **D.** D

5. **a)** Is it possible to locate the centre of a circle using two non-parallel chords if one of the chords is a diameter? Use a diagram to show why or why not.
   b) What would happen if both chords were diameters?

6. **a)** Draw a circle with radii and points as shown.
   b) Draw chords through P and Q, perpendicular to each radius. Measure the chords. What do you notice?
   c) Make a **conjecture** based on what you discovered in part b).
   d) Use reflecting properties to determine if your conjecture will work for any position of P and Q when $CP = CQ$.

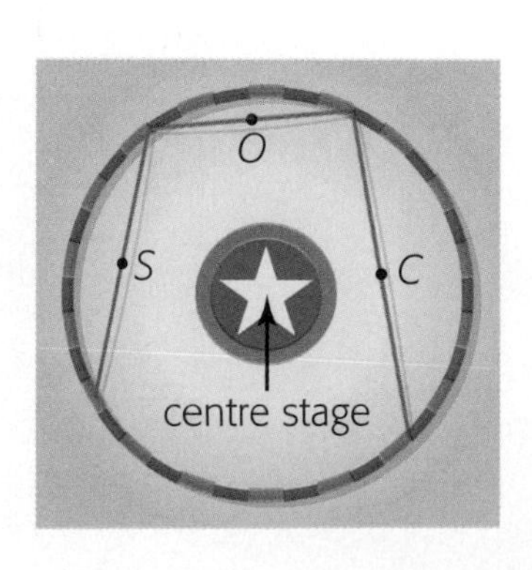

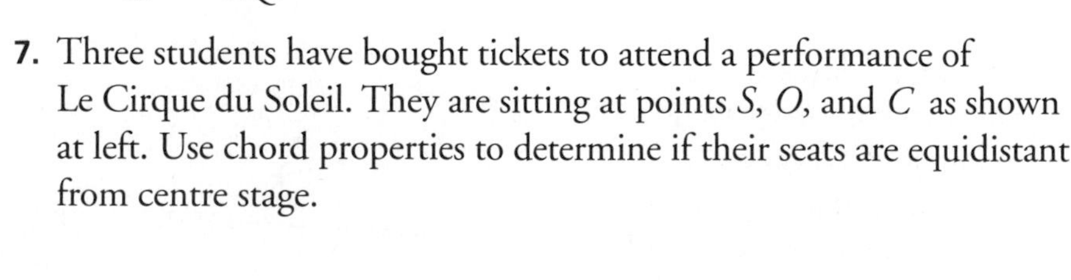

7. Three students have bought tickets to attend a performance of Le Cirque du Soleil. They are sitting at points S, O, and C as shown at left. Use chord properties to determine if their seats are equidistant from centre stage.

8. Luc goes to his favourite bakery, where pies are \$12.00 each. He orders one fourth of a pie for \$3.00, and is given the wedge shown. Even though the angle is 90°, he wonders if he has been short-changed. Is the wedge less than, greater than, or really one fourth of a pie?

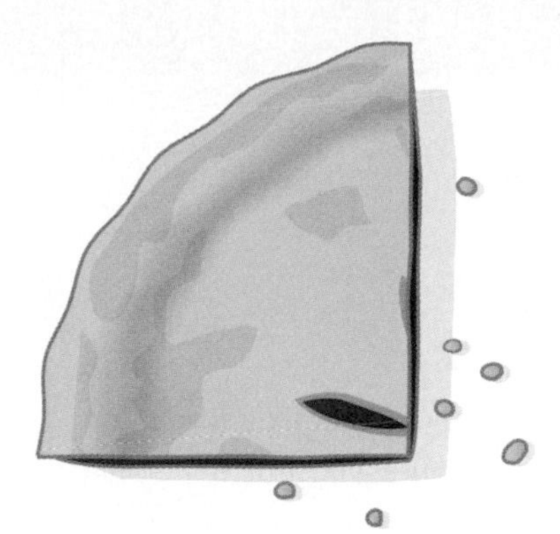

9. A carpenter's apprentice has been asked to determine the centre of the circular part of an arch, and provides the explanation below. Do you agree with his thinking? Why or why not?

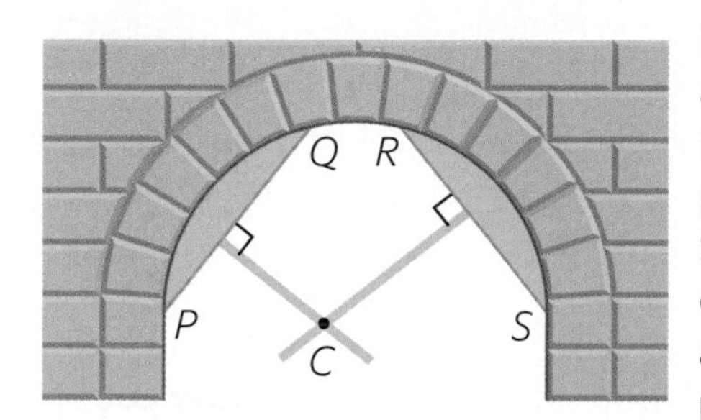

First, I attached two planks, *PQ* and *RS*, to the ceiling.
I nailed two pieces of wood perpendicular to each plank.
Since a line perpendicular to a chord goes through the centre of a circle, the intersection of the two pieces of wood must be the centre of the circle.

10. A landscape architect has staked out a circular garden as shown. She has marked one diameter in the soil for the gardener to plant his first row of flowers. However, children playing in the garden have added more lines. Explain how, using chord properties, the gardener could determine which chord is the diameter.

11. Show that a circle can be drawn through any three points that do not lie on a straight line. Is it possible to draw more than one circle through these points? Explain, using chord properties.

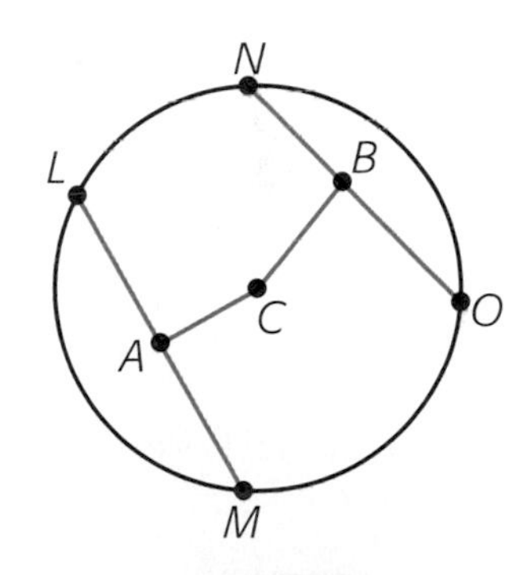

Closing

12. Explain how you can use chord properties to determine which chord is longer and which angles are right angles.

Extending

13. Two fragments of plates were found during an archeological dig. Is it possible that these fragments came from the same plate? Explain.

14. **a)** Copy the diagram below. Draw chord *PR*. What do you know about this chord?

b) Use chords to locate the centre, *S*, of the circle.

c) Label the midpoints of *PQ* and *QR* as *T* and *V*. Draw quadrilateral *STQV*. What kind of a quadrilateral is it? How do you know?

Q R

P

Mid-Chapter Review

FREQUENTLY ASKED Questions

Study | *Aid*

- See Lesson 9.1, Examples 1 and 2.
- Try Mid-Chapter Review questions 1, 2, and 3.

Q: How are inscribed angles and central angles in circles related?

A: If the same arc subtends both the inscribed angle and the central angle, the central angle is twice the inscribed angle. For example,

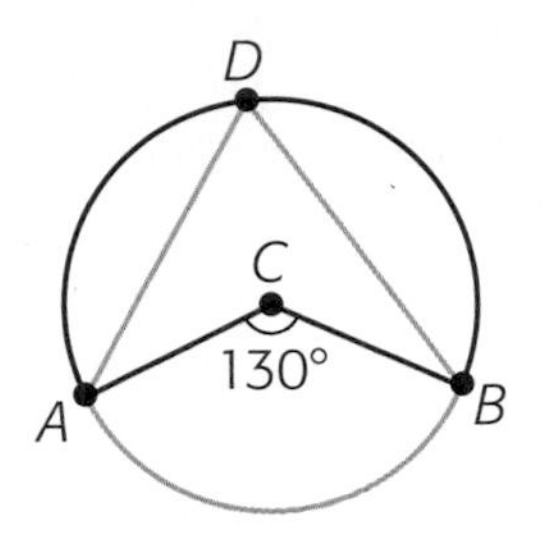

$\angle C$ and $\angle D$ are both subtended by minor arc AB.

Since $\angle C = 130°$,

$\angle D = \angle C \div 2$ Inscribed angles subtended by the same arc

$= 130° \div 2$

$\angle D = 65°$

Study | *Aid*

- See Lesson 9.2, Examples 1 and 2.
- Try Mid-Chapter Review questions 4, 5, and 6.

Q: If you are given one inscribed angle in a circle, how could you draw other inscribed angles of the same measure?

A: If the same arc subtends inscribed angles, they are equal. For example,

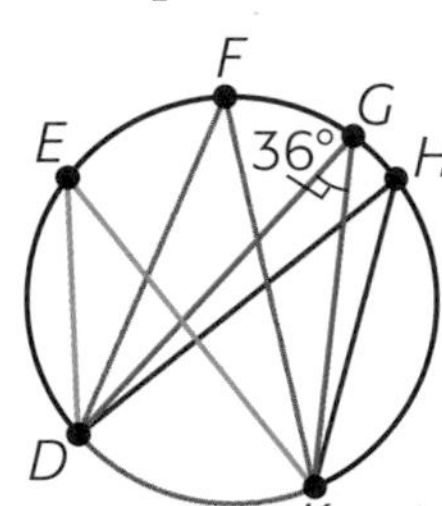

$\angle E$, $\angle F$, $\angle G$, and $\angle H$ are inscribed angles all subtended by minor arc DK.
$\angle G = 36°$, so $\angle E$, $\angle F$, and $\angle H$ are also 36°.

Study | *Aid*

- See Lesson 9.3, Examples 1 and 2.
- Try Mid-Chapter Review question 7.

Q: How is the centre of a circle related to chords in the circle?

A: The centre of a circle always lies on the perpendicular bisector of any chord. By drawing a pair of non-parallel chords and their perpendicular bisectors, the resulting point of intersection locates the centre of the circle. For example,

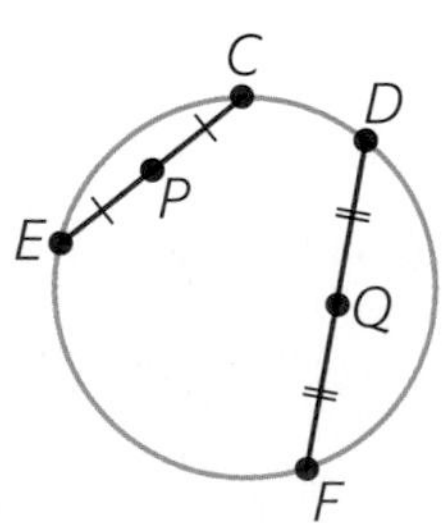

To locate the centre of the circle, draw two chords that are not parallel. Determine the midpoints of these chords.

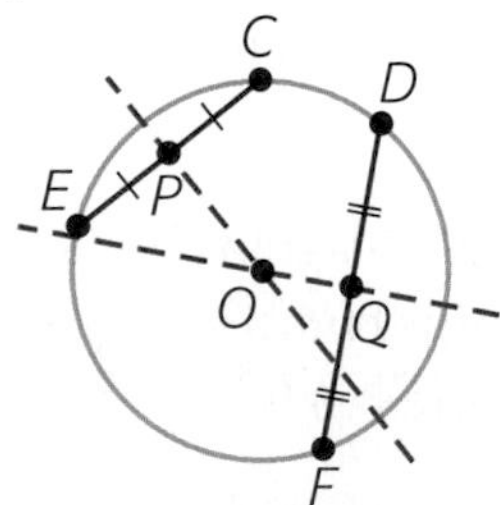

Draw a perpendicular line through the midpoint of each chord. The centre of the circle is where the perpendiculars intersect.

Practice

Lesson 9.1

1. For each circle with centre C, determine the unknown angle measures. Show your work.

   a)

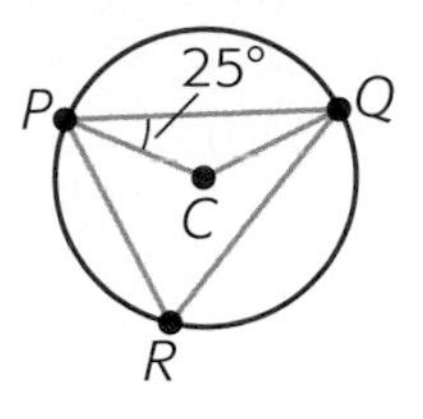

$\angle R = ?$

   b)

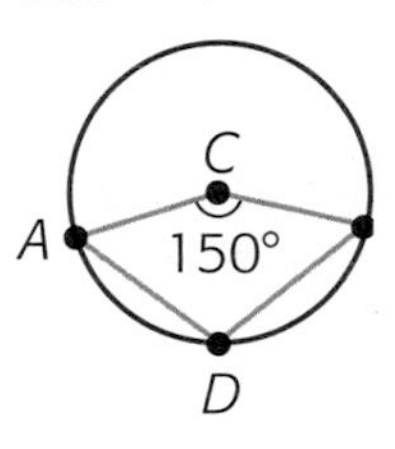

$\angle D = ?$

   c)

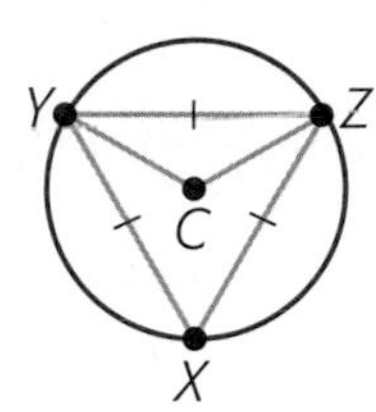

$\angle YCZ = ?, \angle CYZ = ?$

   d)

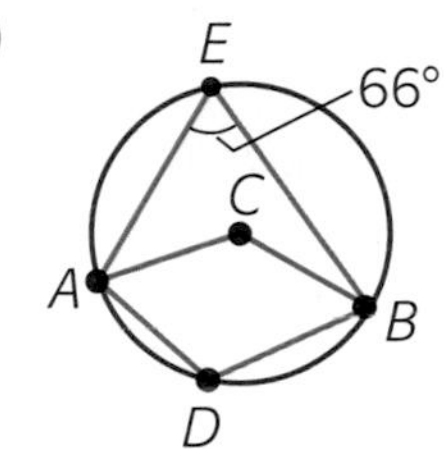

$\angle ACB = ?, \angle D = ?$

2. Draw a regular dodecagon (a 12-sided figure) inscribed in a circle. What is the measure of each interior angle of the dodecagon?

3. For each circle with centre C, determine the measure of the angles indicated.

   a)

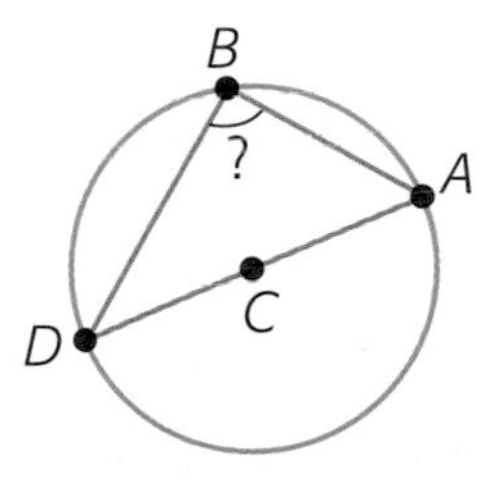

   b)

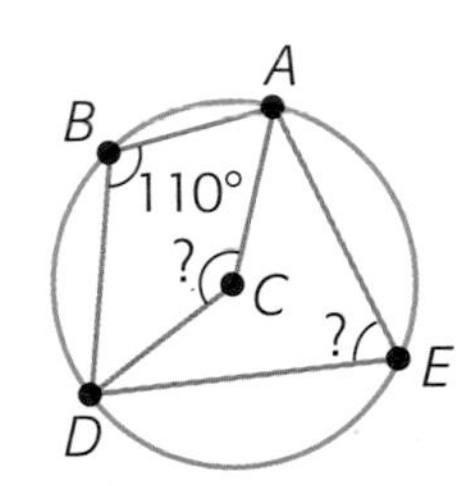

Lesson 9.2

4. In the circle shown at right, determine the measure of the indicated angle.

5. A kite is a quadrilateral that has two pairs of adjacent sides that are equal. Can you draw a circle through all four vertices of a kite? Explain why or why not.

6. Determine the measures of $\angle R$, $\angle S$, $\angle U$, and $\angle P$.

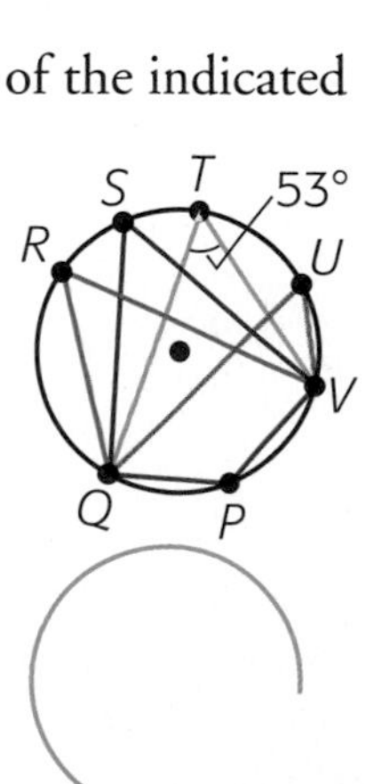

Lesson 9.3

7. Explain how you could draw a complete circle if you have only an arc of that circle as shown at right.

9.4 Applying Chord Properties

YOU WILL NEED

- geometry software
  or
- a compass
- a protractor
- a ruler

GOAL

Use chord properties and the Pythagorean theorem to solve circle problems.

LEARN ABOUT the Math

Rani is building a wooden drop-leaf table of diameter 100 cm. She plans to use a rectangular frame to support the table as shown. The drop leaves will be attached along the long sides of the rectangle.

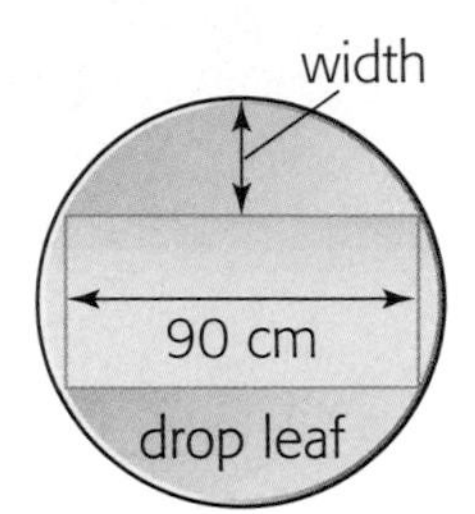

? Will the two drop leaves be the same size?

EXAMPLE 1 | Using properties of circles and triangles

Rani's Solution: Comparing sides in right triangles

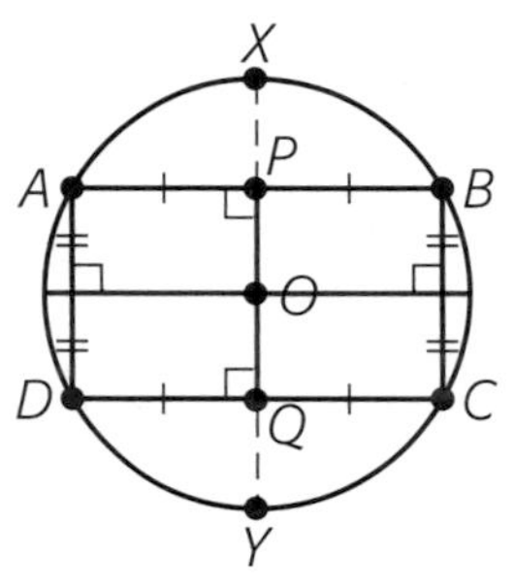

I traced the diagram for the table. Then I constructed perpendicular bisectors of chords *AB* and *DC*. They formed one line with points on the circle at *X* and *Y*.
I labelled the points *P* and *Q*, which are the midpoints of the chords *AB* and *DC*.
Then I drew the perpendicular bisectors of *AD* and *BC*. They also formed one line.
I knew that the two bisectors intersect at the centre, at point *O*.
This means that *OX* and *OY* are radii.

I need to show that the width of each leaf is the same, that is, that $PX = QY$. Since *OX* and *OY* are radii, $OX = OY$. So all I have to show is that $OP = OQ$.

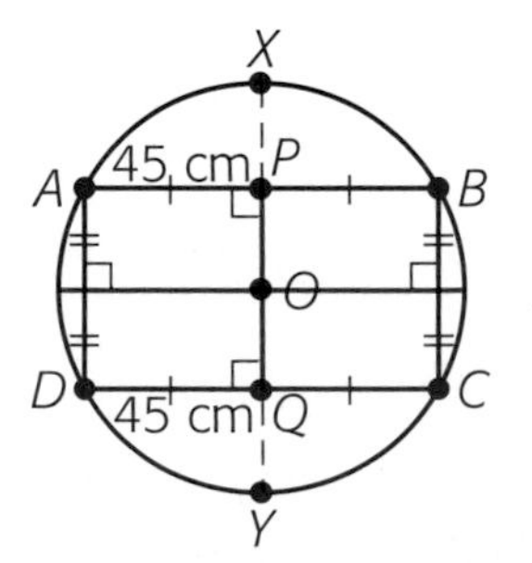

I knew that *AB* and *CD* are both 90 cm, so *AP* and *QD* are each 45 cm.

I can show that $OP = OQ$ using properties of triangles.

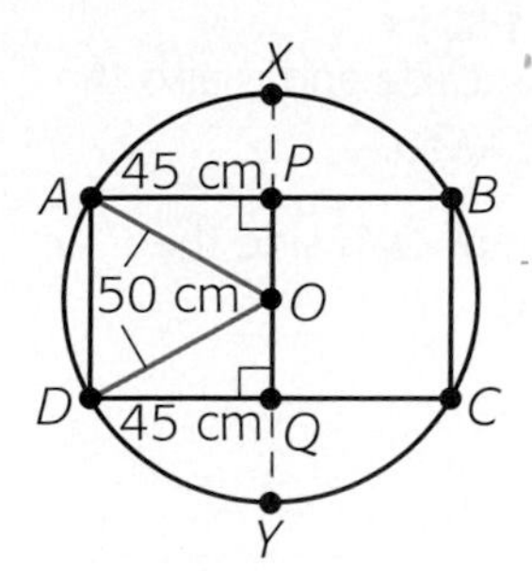

I made right triangles by drawing radii OA and OD. Since the diameter of the circle is 100 cm, I knew that each radius is 50 cm.

$AO = DO$ and $AP = DQ$,
so $\triangle APO$ and $\triangle DQO$ are congruent.

This means that $OP = OQ$.

The drop leaves are the same size.

I examined the sides in right $\triangle APO$ and right $\triangle DQO$.
Since the hypotenuse and one other side are the same length, I knew the triangles were congruent.

Reflecting

A. What chord property did Rani use to locate the centre of the circle in her diagram?

B. How did drawing radii OX and OY help Rani solve the problem?

WORK WITH the Math

EXAMPLE 2 | Calculating the radius of a circle

The lenth of a chord XY is 10 cm. The length of a line segment perpendicular to chord XY from the centre of the circle, O, is 12 cm. Calculate the radius of the circle.

Francis's Solution

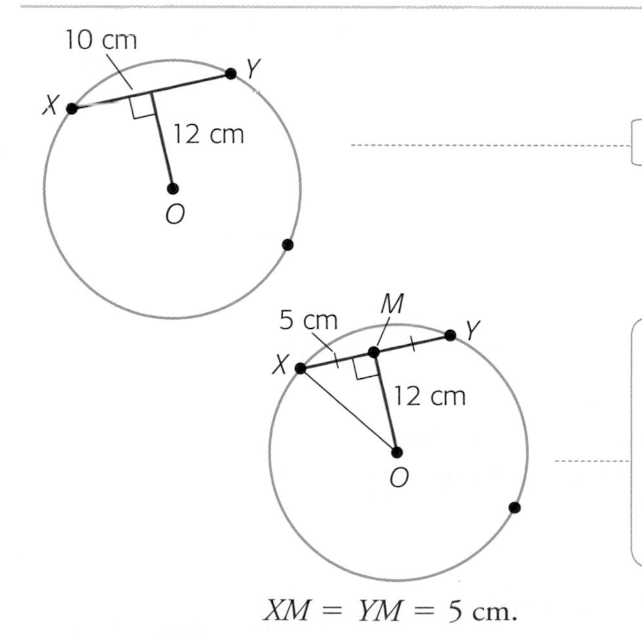

I drew a diagram of the situation.

I added the point M, where the perpendicular intersects the chord.

Since OM is perpendicular to XY, and O is the centre of the circle, M is the midpoint of XY, since a perpendicular line from the centre of a circle to a chord bisects the chord.

$XM = YM = 5$ cm.

$OX^2 = 5^2 + 12^2$
$OX^2 = 25 + 144$
$OX^2 = 169$
$OX = \sqrt{169}$
$OX = 13$ cm

The length of the radius of the circle is 13 cm.

OX is the radius of the circle and is also the hypotenuse in right △*XMO*.

I calculated the length of *OX* using the Pythagorean theorem.

EXAMPLE 3 | Calculating the length of equidistant chords

A circle of diameter 40 cm contains two chords that are both 10 cm from the centre. How long are the chords to the nearest centimetre?

Viktor's Solution

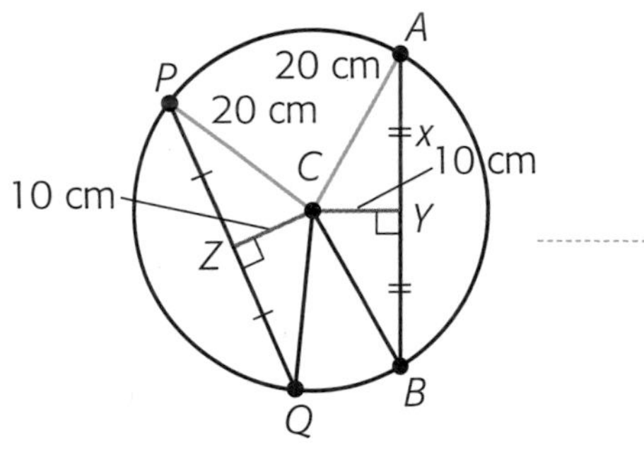

I need to determine the lengths of chords *PQ* and *AB*.

I drew a sketch and labelled all the measurements that I knew.
Since the diameter is 40 cm, I knew that radii *AC* and *PC* were both 20 cm. I marked midpoints of *AB* and *PQ* called *Y* and *Z*. I drew line segments from *Y* and *Z* to the center *C*. I knew that the line from the centre of the circle to the midpoint of a chord is the perpendicular bisector of the chord, so the triangles I created are all right triangles.
I labelled *AY* as *x*.

△*PZC* and △*AYC* are congruent. This means that $PZ = x$ and $PQ = AB$.

I examined the sides in right △*PZC* and right △*AYC*. Since the hypotenuse and one other side are the same length, I knew that these triangles are congruent. So *PZ* must be equal to *x*, and both chords are the same length.

$x^2 + 10^2 = 20^2$
$x^2 + 100 = 400$
$x^2 = 400 - 100$
$x^2 = 300 \text{ cm}^2$
$x \doteq 17.3$ cm

I used the Pythagorean theorem to calculate *x*.

length of each chord $= 2x$
$= 2(17.3)$
$\doteq 35$ cm

Since the line from the centre of a circle to a chord bisects the chord, the length of *AB* is twice *x*.

Each chord is about 35 cm long.

EXAMPLE 4 | Calculating the depth of a water slide

An engineer who designs waterslides created a slide made of circular plastic tubing measuring 120 cm in diameter. To construct the slide, a section of tubing 90 cm wide must be cut off as shown. How deep is the waterslide to the nearest centimetre?

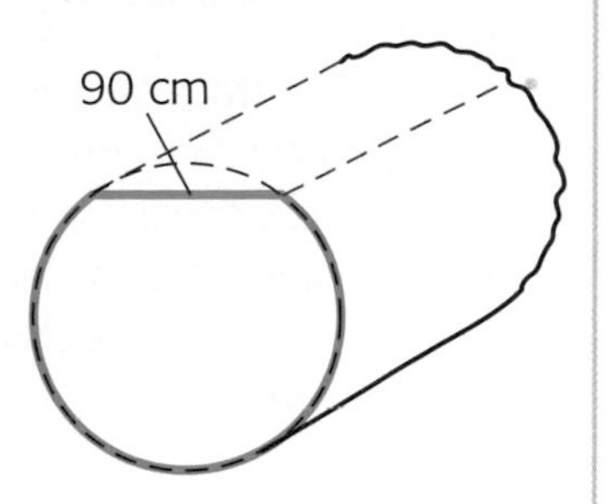

Zachary's Solution

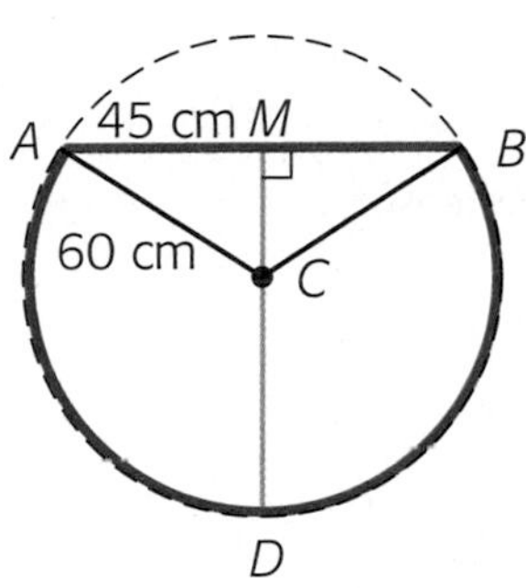

I need to determine the length of MD.

I drew a sketch of the cross section of the slide. The horizontal cut, AB, is a chord of the circle. I drew radii AC and BC. Since the diameter is 120 cm, the radius is 60 cm. I constructed the perpendicular bisector of the chord through the centre of the circle. So, $AM = BM = 45$ cm.

In $\triangle AMC$,

$$CM^2 + 45^2 = 60^2$$
$$CM^2 + 2025 = 3600$$
$$CM^2 = 3600 - 2025$$
$$CM^2 = 1575 \text{ cm}^2$$
$$CM \doteq 39.7 \text{ cm}$$

I needed to determine the length of CM before calculating the total depth, DM. I used the Pythagorean theorem to calculate the length of CM.

$$\text{depth of slide} = CM + CD$$
$$= 39.7 + 60$$
$$\doteq 100 \text{ cm}$$

Since CD is a radius, I knew that $CD = 60$ cm. I added CM and CD to determine the total depth.

The waterslide is about 100 cm deep.

In Summary

Key Idea

- Since a line from the centre of a circle to the midpoint of a chord is the perpendicular bisector of the chord, the Pythagorean theorem can be used to calculate how far the chord is from the centre of the circle.

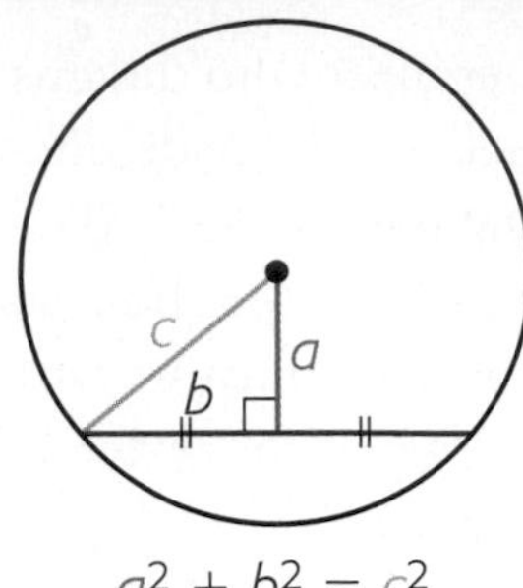

$a^2 + b^2 = c^2$

Need to Know

- Chords equidistant from the centre of a circle are of equal length.
- Chords of equal length are equidistant from the centre of a circle.

Communication | Tip

To describe the distance between the centre of a circle and a chord, use the measured distance from the centre of the circle to the midpoint of the chord.

Checking

1. Calculate the missing lengths to the nearest centimetre.

a)

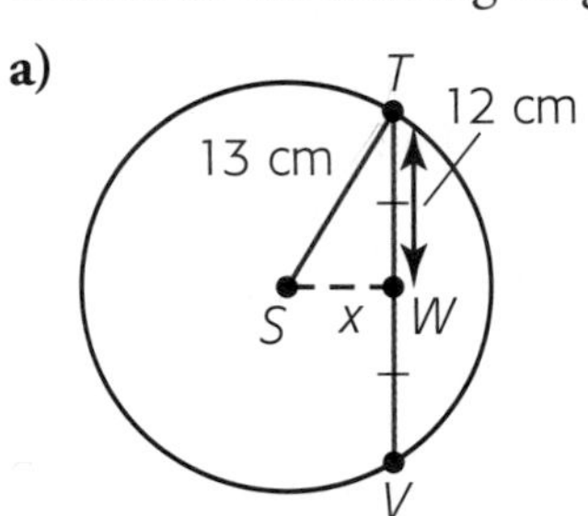

$x = ?$

b)

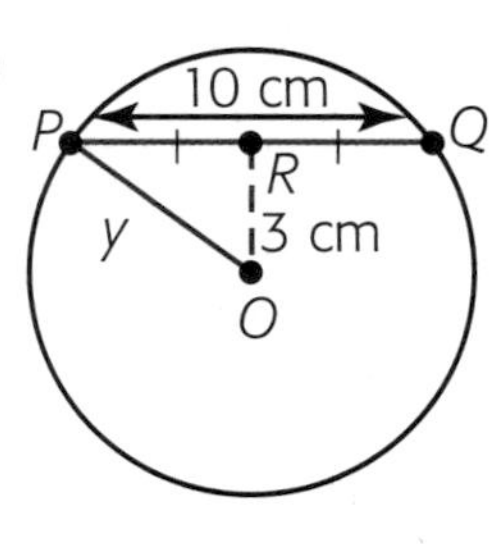

$y = ?$

c)

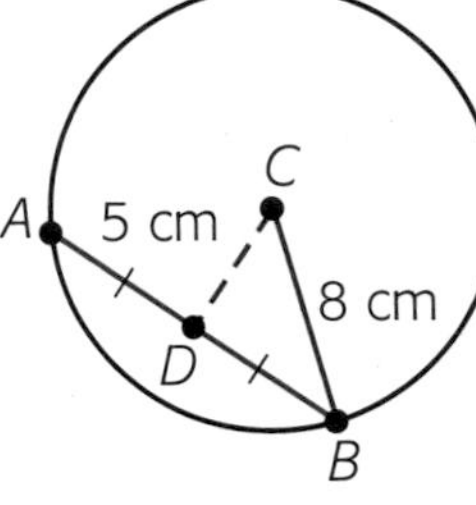

$AB = ?$

2. A sand timer can be set into a circle as shown. The heights of the top and bottom sections are equal. Are the widths of the top and bottom the same? Explain how you know.

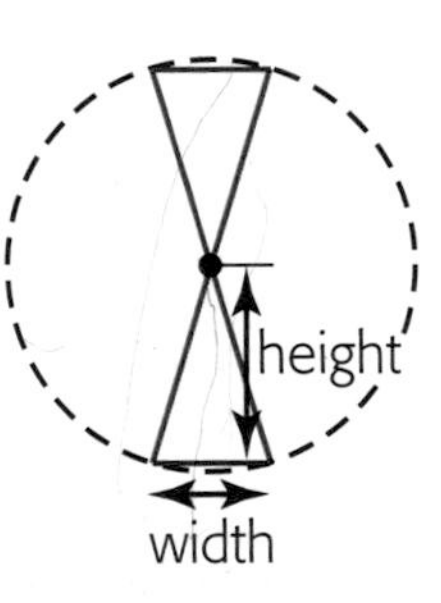

Practising

3. Calculate the missing lengths to the nearest unit.

a)

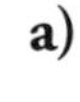

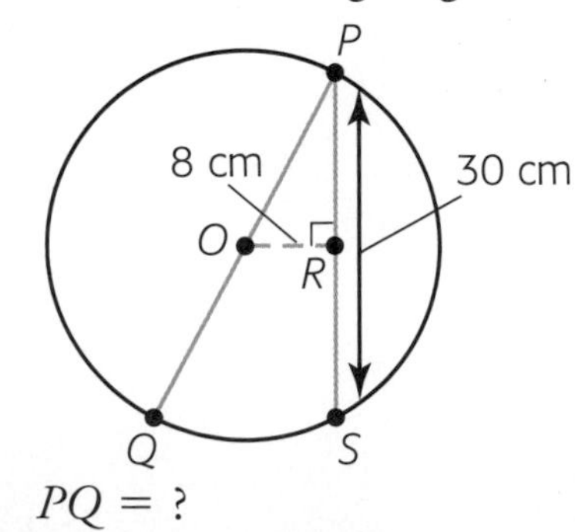

$PQ = ?$

b)

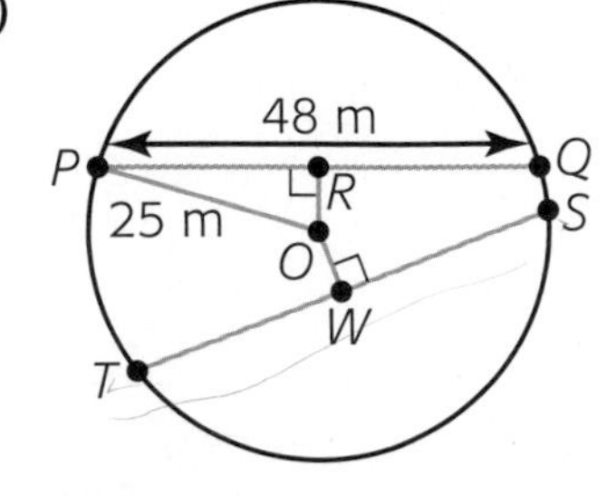

$OW = 7$ m, $ST = ?$

4. **Multiple choice.** The length of PQ in the circle shown is approximately
   A. 10.0 cm **B.** 7.0 cm **C.** 5.3 cm **D.** 2.6 cm

5. **Multiple choice.** A chord 24.0 cm long is 5.0 cm away from the centre of the circle. The radius is
   A. 24.5 cm **B.** 13.0 cm **C.** 23.5 cm **D.** 10.9 cm

6. **Multiple choice.** In the diagram, M and N are the midpoints of chords QR and ST respectively. $QM = 8.0$ cm and $OM = 6.5$ cm. The length of ST is
   A. 8.0 cm
   B. 10.3 cm
   C. 14.5 cm
   D. 16.0 cm

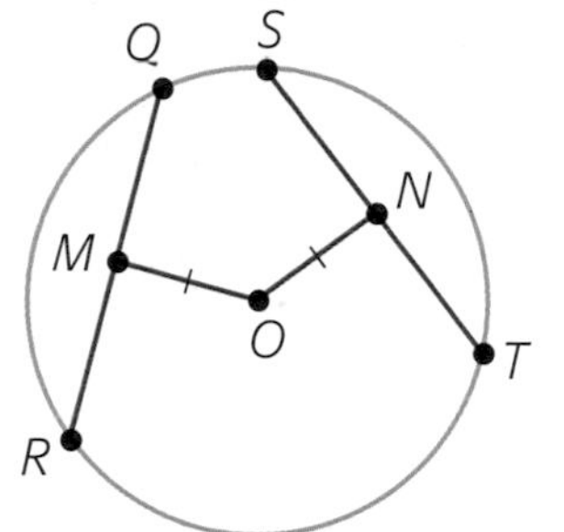

7. P is the centre of the circle at right. Determine the measures of arcs QR and ST.

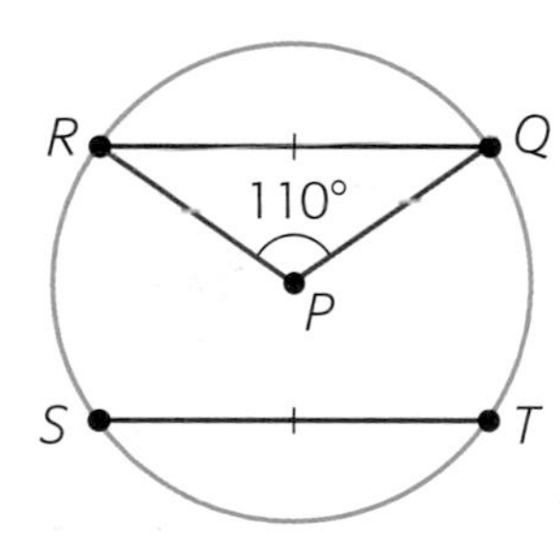

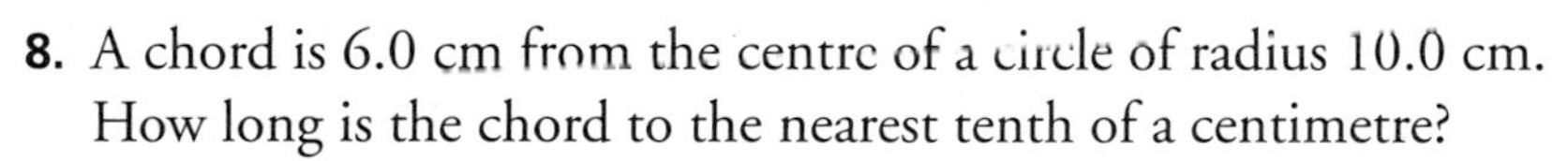

8. A chord is 6.0 cm from the centre of a circle of radius 10.0 cm. How long is the chord to the nearest tenth of a centimetre?

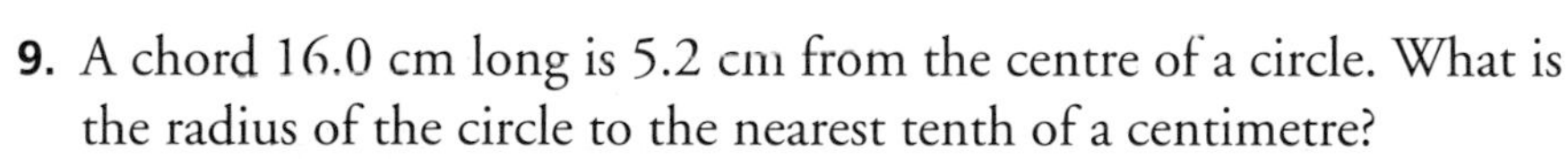

9. A chord 16.0 cm long is 5.2 cm from the centre of a circle. What is the radius of the circle to the nearest tenth of a centimetre?

10. Draw a circle and a chord.
    a) How many other chords can you draw that are parallel to and the same length as the first chord? Draw them.
    b) Measure the perpendicular distance from these chords to the centre of the circle. What do you notice?

11. **a)** How many chords can you draw on a circle that are the same length as a given chord?
    b) Make a statement about the relative perpendicular distance from each chord to the centre of the circle.

12. A circular tunnel, 20 m in diameter, is blasted through a mountain. A 16 m wide road is to be constructed along the floor of the tunnel as shown at right. What will be the maximum height of the tunnel to the nearest metre?

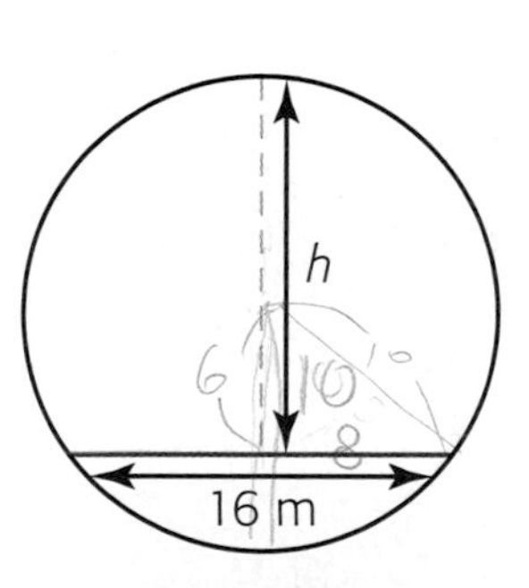

13. A circular picnic table of diameter 2.50 m has a rectangular base supporting it. Calculate the length and width of the rectangular base to the nearest hundredth of a metre.

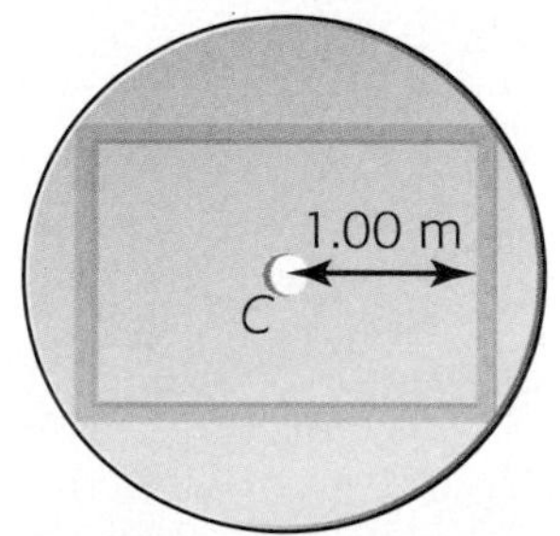

14. Carousels have been popular carnival rides for over 100 years. Originally, carousels had a circular base, with a platform made of wooden beams as shown.

a) How do the outer beams relate to the circle?

b) How can a carousel manufacturer ensure that each outer beam will be the same distance from the centre?

c) Each series of beams also forms chords within smaller circles. How do all of these circles relate to each other?

15. In a circle with radius 10 cm, two chords AB and FG are drawn. $AB = 12$ cm and $FG = 16$ cm.

a) Which chord is closer to the centre of the circle?

b) Draw the circle and the chords. Label each chord.

c) How far is each chord from the centre?

16. Calculate each length to the nearest centimetre and the area to the nearest square centimetre.

a) PQ

b) QR

c) area of $\triangle PQR$

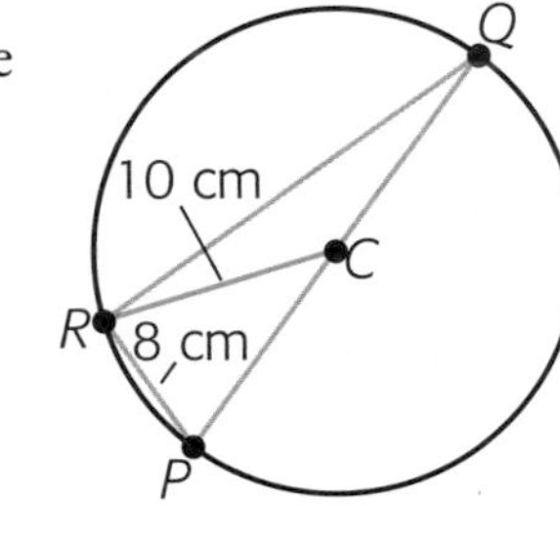

Closing

17. A Ferris wheel is circular in shape. The beams connecting the seats form chords of the circle.

a) Use your knowledge of chords to explain why each beam is the same length.

b) The diameter of a Ferris wheel is 18.5 m and each beam is 9.0 m from the centre of the wheel. State the steps you would use to calculate the length of each beam.

Extending

18. The front of a goldfish bowl is in the shape of a circle of diameter 28.0 cm. When you look at the front, the width of the water's surface is 24.0 cm.

a) What is the depth of the water to the nearest tenth of a centimetre?

b) Is there more than one answer?

19. A square of side length 4.24 cm is inscribed in a circle.

a) What is the diameter of the circle?

b) How far, to the nearest hundredth of a centimetre, is each side of the square from the centre of the circle?

9.5 Tangent Properties

GOAL

Determine how a tangent to a circle is related to the radius, and use this relationship to solve circle problems.

YOU WILL NEED

- geometry software
  or
- a compass
- a protractor
- a ruler

INVESTIGATE the Math

From the top of the Calgary Tower, Francis looks east toward the horizon.

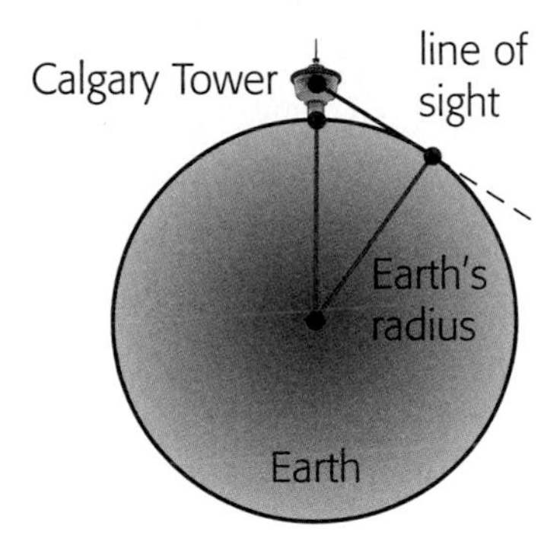

? How does his line of sight relate to the the centre of the Earth?

A. Draw a circle with radius KL. Place point M anywhere on the circle. Draw **secant** LM. Measure $\angle KLM$.

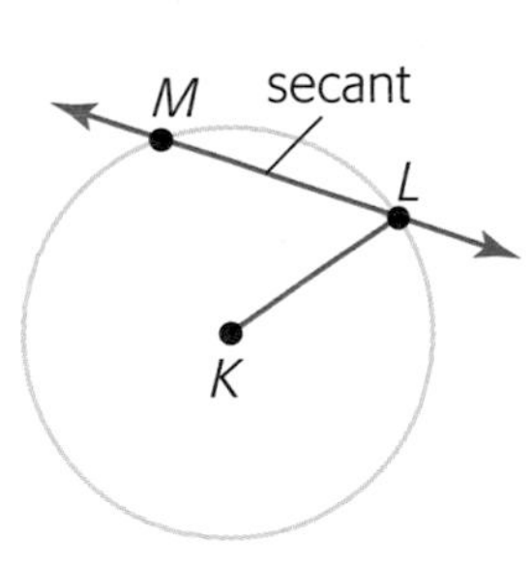

B. Shift M along the circle until point M meets point L. How does the resulting line relate to the circle? What is the measure of the angle between the **tangent** and the radius?

C. Draw a new circle with radius CA. Place point P on radius CA.

D. Draw a secant through P that is perpendicular to CA. Label the points where the secant intersects the circle as Q and R.

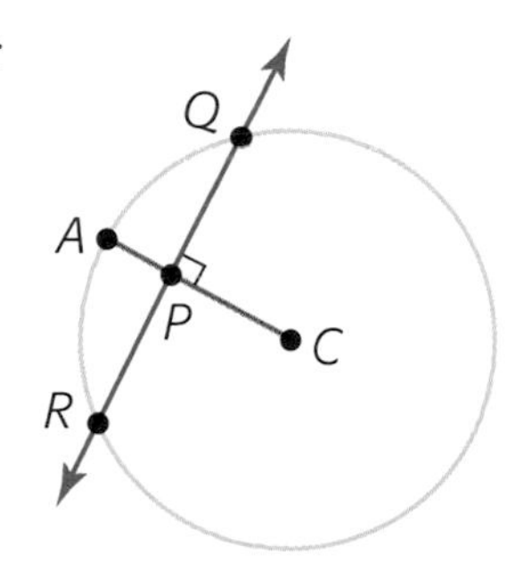

E. Move P toward point A. What do you notice about points Q and R? What happens when point P reaches point A?

F. State how Francis's line of sight relates to the centre of the Earth.

secant

a line that intersects a circle at two points

tangent

a line that intersects a circle at exactly one point; e.g., point Z is called the **point of tangency**.

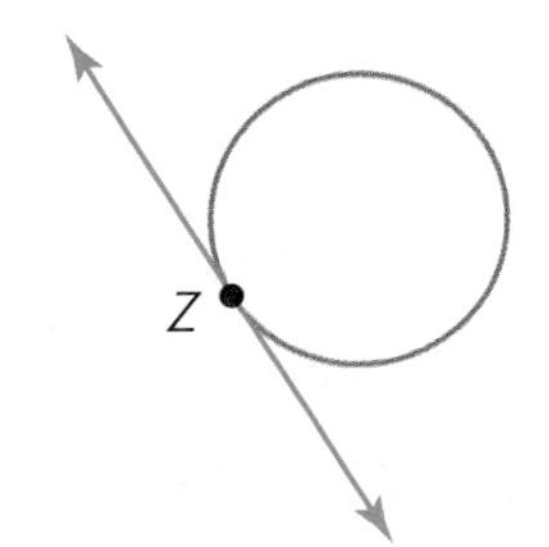

Reflecting

G. What is the relationship between the tangent to a circle and the radius drawn to the point of tangency?

H. Will the relationship you discovered in part E be true for any position of A? Explain how you know.

I. O is the centre of a circle, Z is a point of tangency on the circle, and X is a point on the tangent line. What type of triangle is created by joining these points?

WORK WITH the Math

EXAMPLE 1 Tangent segments through an external point

Erin is a jewellery designer. She is designing a gold pendant using three circles. She wants to attach a silver angle that is tangent to the largest circle for the chain to loop through. Where will the arms of the silver angle be attached and will they be the same length?

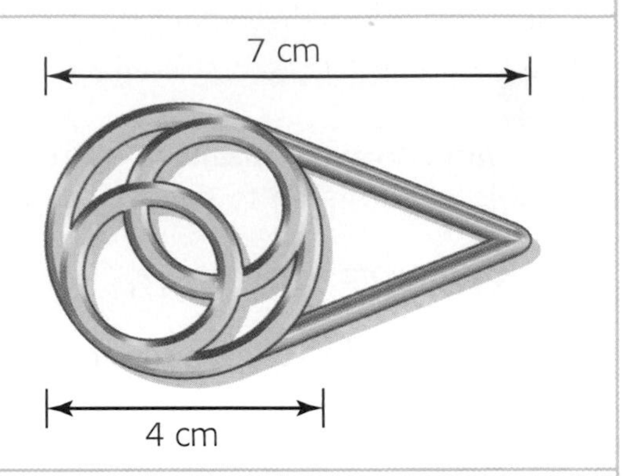

Erin's Solution

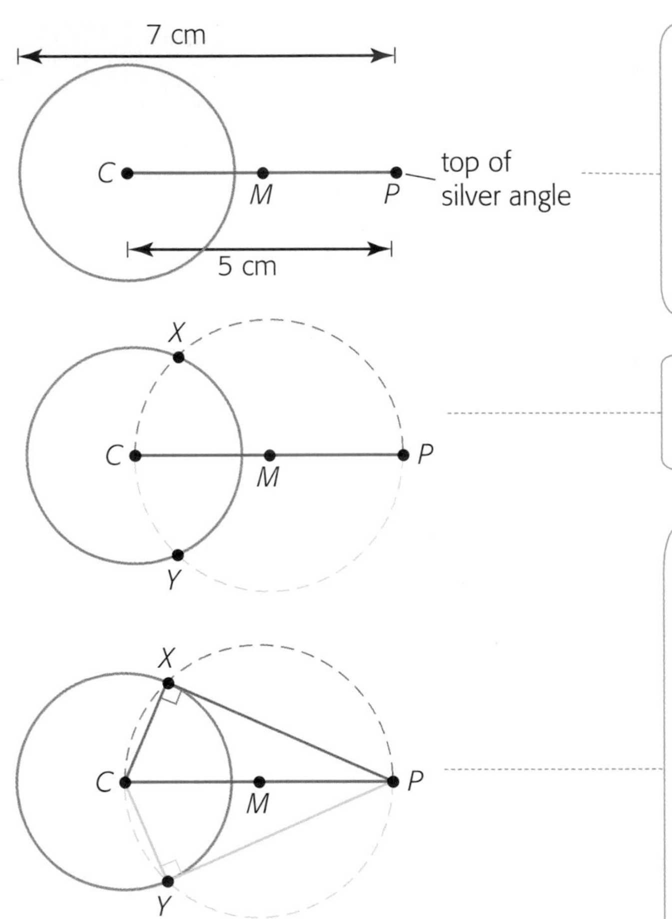

I drew a circle 4 cm in diameter, with centre C, for the pendant.
Since the pendant is 7 cm long and the radius of the largest circle is 2 cm, I reasoned that the top of the pendant would be 5 cm from the centre of the circle.
I drew line segment CP, 5 cm in length. I marked the midpoint as M.

I drew a new circle around M with diameter CP, and marked the points where this circle intersected my original circle as X and Y.

I drew $\triangle CXP$ and $\triangle CYP$.
I knew that $\angle CXP$ and $\angle CYP$ are right angles because they are angles inscribed in a semicircle.
I knew that PX and PY are tangent to the circle with centre C because they are perpendicular to radii CX and CY. So X and Y are points of tangency.
The arms of the silver angle should be attached at X and Y.
I examined the diagram. I knew that $CX = CY$ because they are radii. The two right triangles also have the same hypotenuse, PC. Since two pairs of sides are equal, the third pair of sides has to be equal by the Pythagorean theorem.

The silver arms will be the same length and should be attached at the points of tangency, X and Y.

EXAMPLE 2 | Ensuring that a line is a tangent

Luc drew a circle, then a point on its circumference. He then drew a line through the point. Can he be certain his line is a tangent?

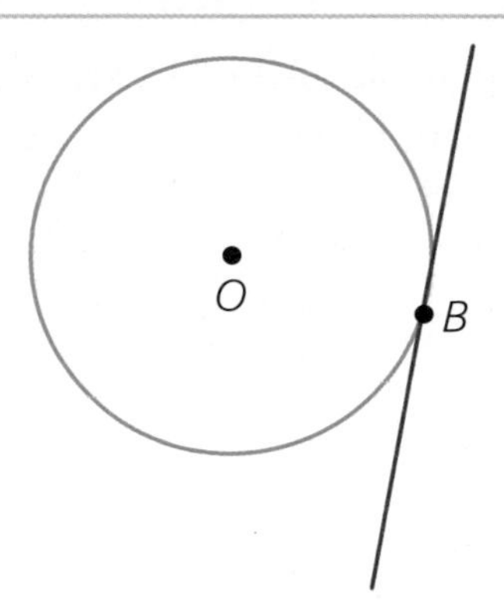

Luc's Solution

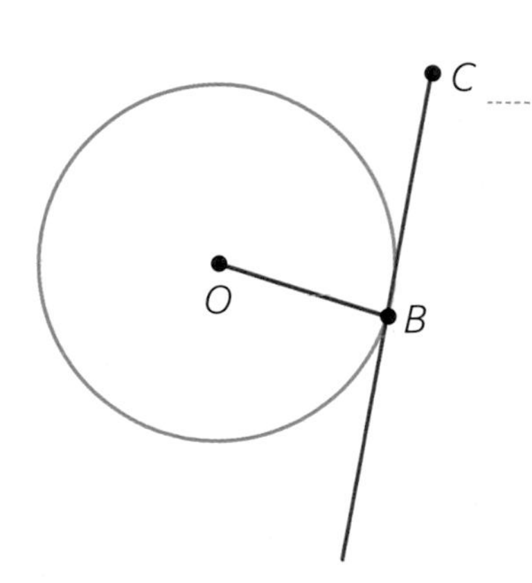

If the angle formed between the radius and the line at the point B is 90°, then the line is a tangent. I drew the radius OB on the diagram and measured $\angle OBC$ with a protractor. It wasn't a right angle.

$\angle OBC = 83°$, so the line is not a tangent.

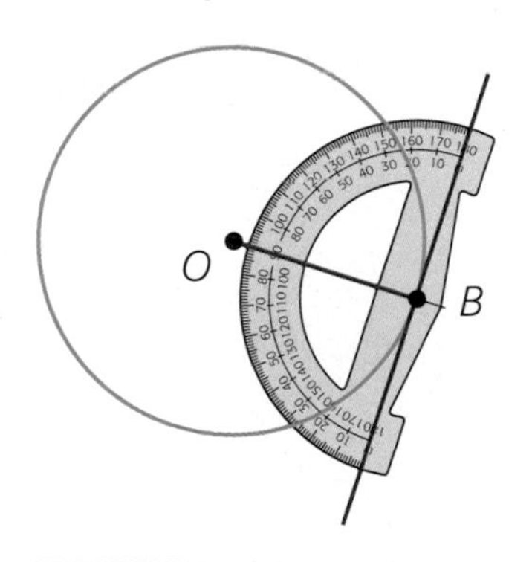

I erased my old line and drew a true tangent.
I used a protractor to draw a line perpendicular to the radius. This ensures that the line is a tangent at point B.

EXAMPLE 3 | Using tangents to solve problems

An aircraft is at an altitude of 11 km. Earth has an average radius of about 6378 km. How far from the plane is the horizon, to the nearest kilometre?

Nola's Solution

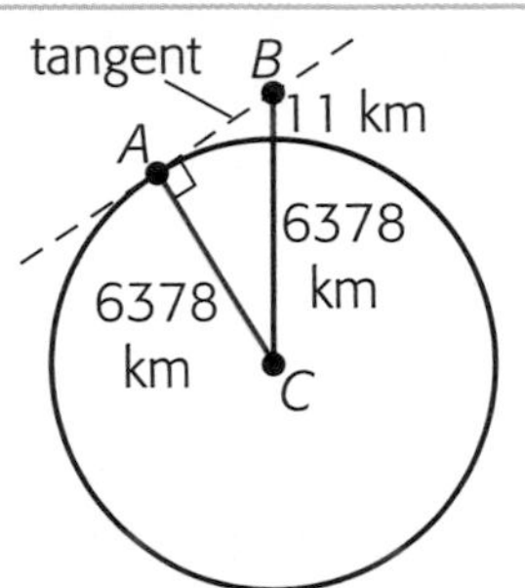

First, I drew a sketch of the problem.
I drew a tangent from the plane to Earth's surface at point A (the horizon).

I knew that A is a point of tangency because the line of sight from the plane to the horizon touches the Earth only at point A.

I drew Earth's radius and formed a right triangle.

$$BC = 11 + 6378$$
$$= 6389 \text{ km}$$

I calculated the length of BC by adding the altitude to Earth's radius.

$$AB^2 + AC^2 = BC^2$$
$$AB^2 = BC^2 - AC^2$$
$$AB^2 = 6389^2 - 6378^2$$
$$= 140\ 437$$
$$AB \doteq 375 \text{ km}$$

I used the Pythagorean theorem to calculate the distance to the horizon.

The horizon is about 375 km from the plane.

In Summary

Key Idea

- A tangent to a circle is perpendicular to the radius drawn to the point of tangency.

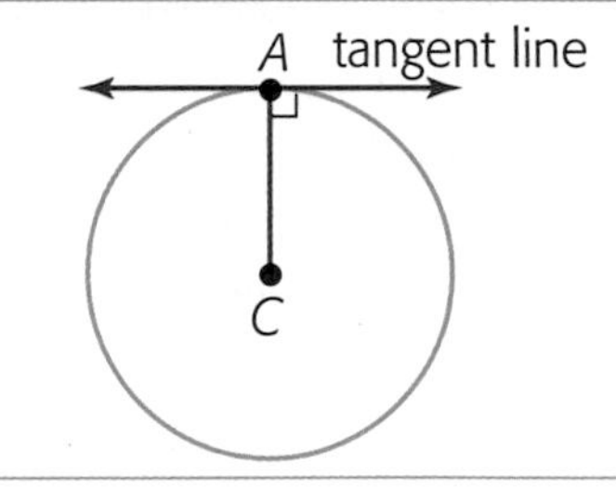

Need to Know

- Tangent segments drawn from an external point to a circle are equal.
- Tangent properties and the Pythagorean theorem can be used to solve circle problems.

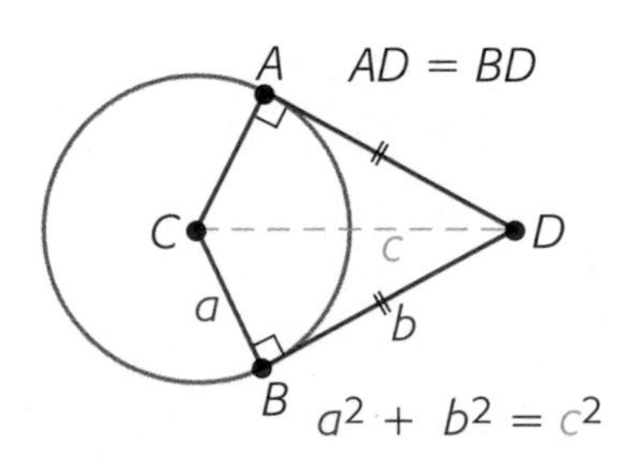

Checking

1. AB is tangent to the circle at B as shown at right. Calculate AD.

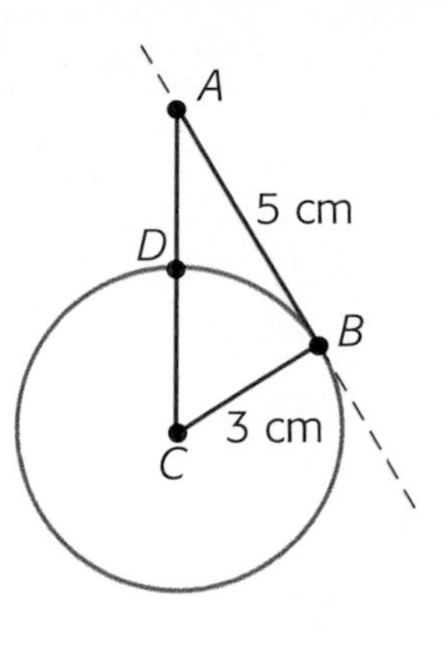

Practising

2. **Multiple choice.** AB is tangent to the circle at A. The length of AB is
   A. 10.9 cm
   B. 13 cm
   C. 17 cm
   D. 12 cm

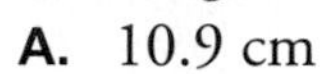

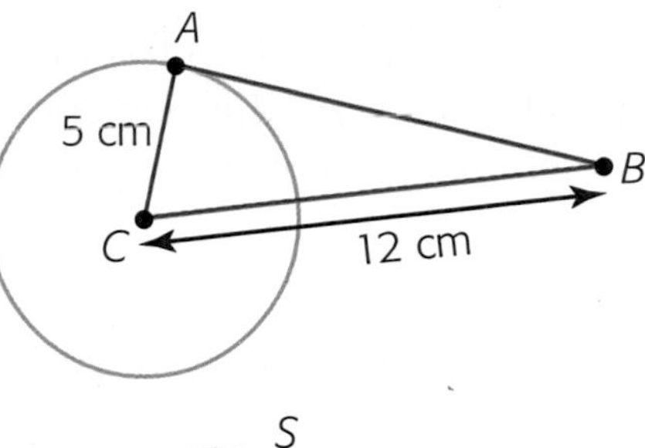

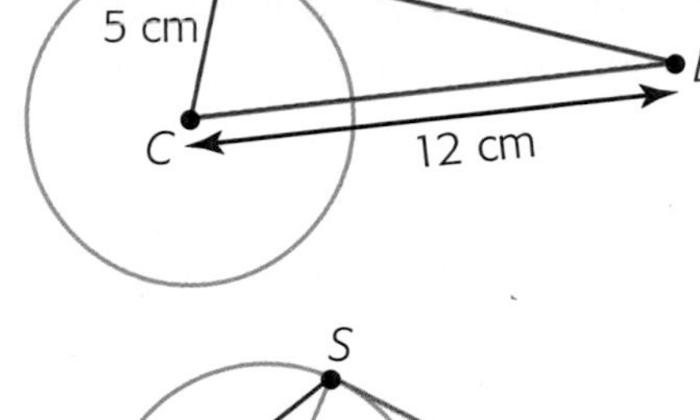

3. **Multiple choice.** In the diagram, RS is tangent to the circle at S, and RQ is tangent to the circle at Q. $\angle R = ?$
   A. 48°
   B. 132°
   C. 24°
   D. 66°

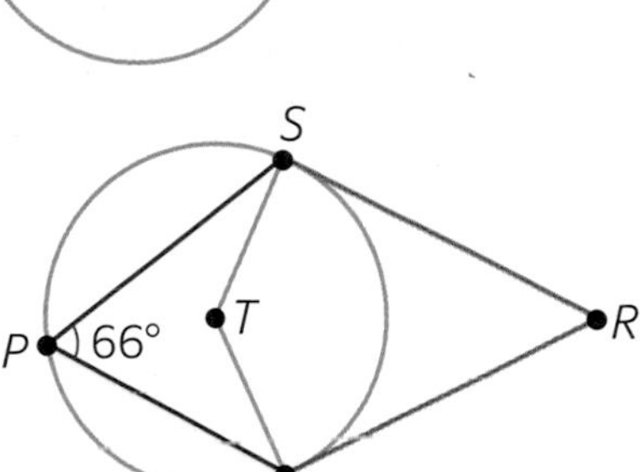

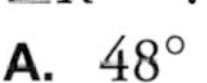

4. **Multiple choice.** The circle that is inscribed in quadrilateral $PQRS$ has tangents at J, K, L, and M as shown at right. The perimeter of the quadrilateral is
   A. 7.5 cm **B.** 15.0 cm **C.** 5.8 cm **D.** 7.6 cm

R 1.6 cm
1.1 cm K L
Q S
J M 1.2 cm
3.6 cm
P

5. **a)** Draw a circle with three radii dividing the circle into three equal areas. Draw tangents to each radius.
   b) Mark the points of intersection of the tangents to each other. Use these points to draw a triangle.
   c) Measure the sides of the triangle. What kind of triangle is it?
   d) How do the angle measures of the triangle compare to the measures of the central angles of the circle?

6. The gears of a bicycle are connected by a chain. Use tangent properties to explain why the straight portions of this chain are the same length.

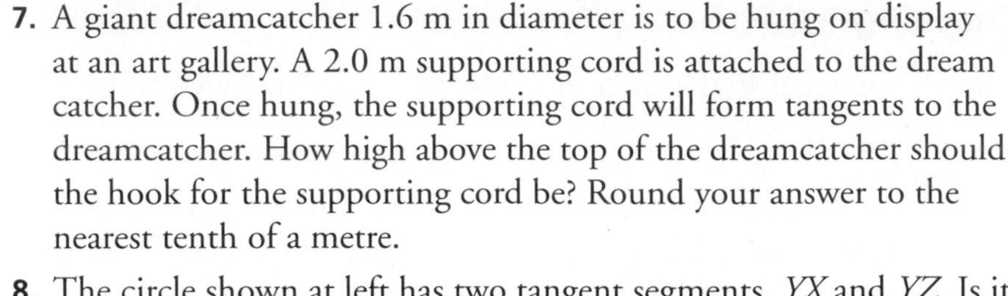

7. A giant dreamcatcher 1.6 m in diameter is to be hung on display at an art gallery. A 2.0 m supporting cord is attached to the dream catcher. Once hung, the supporting cord will form tangents to the dreamcatcher. How high above the top of the dreamcatcher should the hook for the supporting cord be? Round your answer to the nearest tenth of a metre.

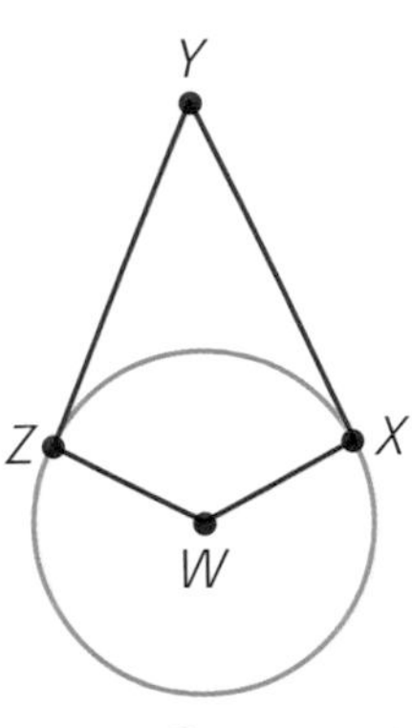

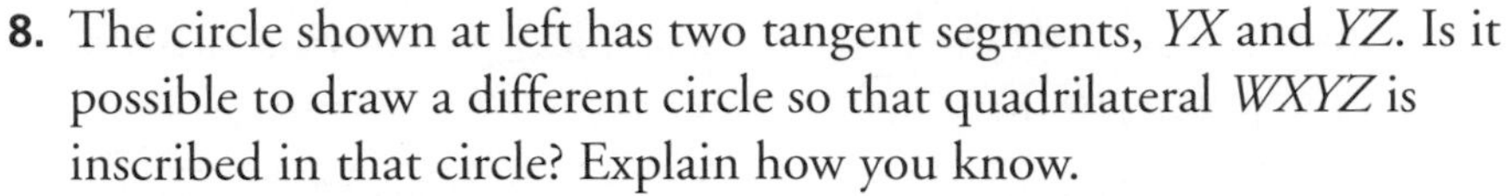

8. The circle shown at left has two tangent segments, YX and YZ. Is it possible to draw a different circle so that quadrilateral $WXYZ$ is inscribed in that circle? Explain how you know.

9. Two circles have a common centre, C. Two chords of the larger circle, AB and PQ, are tangent to the smaller circle.
   a) Draw a diagram of the situation.
   b) Explain why the chords are equal.
   c) The radius of the large circle is 13 cm and $AB = 24$ cm. What is the radius of the small circle?

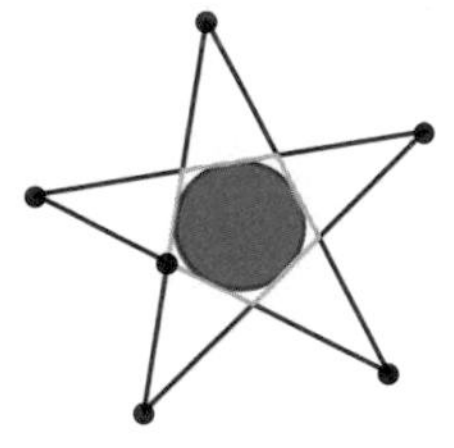

10. An artist wants to create a decoration by having a five-pointed star set around a circle as shown at left. Explain how you can use central angles and tangent lines to construct the star. Construct this star, using a circle of radius 4 cm.

11. Burj Dubai is currently the tallest skyscraper in the world. Its height is just over 807 m, or about 0.8 km, tall. Earth has an average radius of 6378 km. If you were standing at the top of the skyscraper, how far could you see to the nearest kilometre?

Closing

12. Use tangent properties to explain why the higher you fly in a hot-air balloon, the farther you can see.

Extending

13. Draw a circle and two diameters. Draw tangents at the endpoints of each diameter. Draw a quadrilateral using the intersections of the four tangent lines. Under what conditions will the quadrilateral be
   a) a square?
   b) a non-square rhombus?

14. Satellite television is broadcast to homes in Canada from a satellite stationed in orbit 36 210 km above Earth. Earth has an average radius of 6378 km. What percentage of Earth's circumference lies within the transmission range of the satellite?

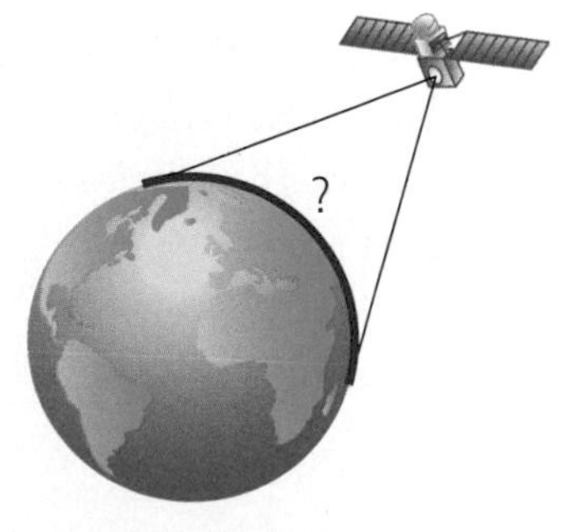

Curious MATH

Lunar Eclipse

A lunar eclipse can only occur during a full Moon when it passes through some part of Earth's shadow. The shadow is composed of two cone-shaped parts: the *penumbra* (where Earth blocks some of the Sun's rays), and the *umbra* (where Earth blocks all direct sunlight from reaching the Moon).

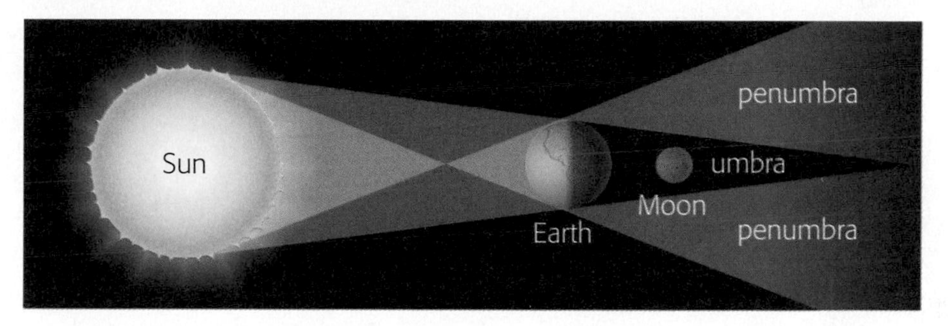

When only part of the Moon passes through the umbra, a partial lunar eclipse is visible. If the entire Moon passes through the umbra, then a total lunar eclipse occurs.

Two to four times each year, the Moon passes through some part of Earth's shadow and a total or partial eclipse may be seen, depending on where you are on Earth.

1. Examine the tangent lines in the diagram above. Which tangent lines determine
   a) the penumbra? **b)** the umbra?
2. A total solar eclipse can only occur during a new Moon when it is exactly in line with Earth and the Sun. Use tangent lines to illustrate how the Moon blocks sunlight from reaching Earth. Assume that the point of the Moon's umbra is just touching Earth's surface.

9.6 Solve Problems by Using a Model

YOU WILL NEED

- geometry software
  or
- 3 identical cans or cardboard tubes
- 2 elastic bands and string
- a compass
- a protractor
- a ruler

GOAL

Solve circle geometry problems by using a model.

LEARN ABOUT the Math

Zachary's neighbour is a farmer who requires water management on his land. Zachary was watching as three identical steel pipes were delivered. The pipes were fastened together with straps. Zachary thinks that he can use the diameter of one pipe to calculate the length of strap needed, not including the length required to fasten the strap together.

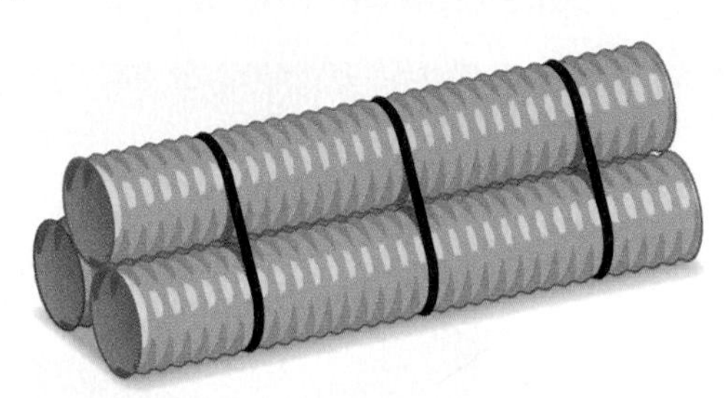

? How can Zachary check that his thinking is correct?

EXAMPLE 1 | Using an experiment to solve a problem

Zachary's Solution

1. Understand the Problem
There are three pipes packed together. The strapping goes around all three pipes.

2. Make a Plan
I decided to use a model. I built a model using three cans of the same diameter and some elastic bands. I reasoned that the model would help me see how the elastic fits around the cans.

3. Carry Out the Plan
I fitted the three cans together. The cans were bundled in a triangular shape. I drew a sketch of my model.

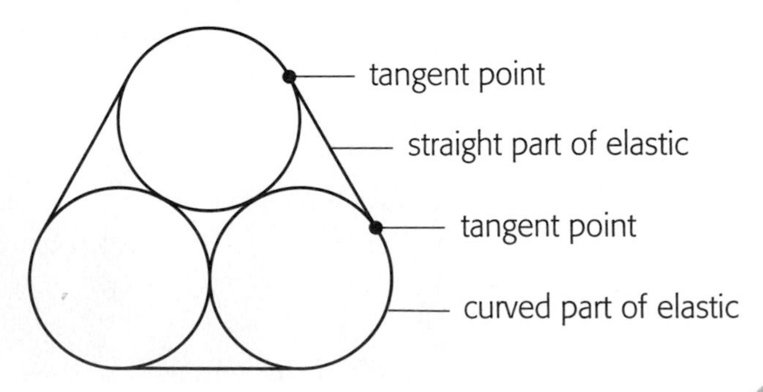

I needed to determine the total length of elastic that goes around the three curves and the total length of elastic that is straight. I decided to determine the straight lengths first.

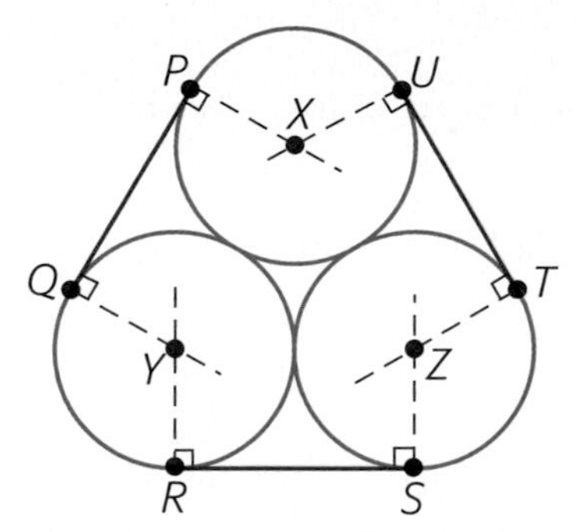

I knew that a line that is perpendicular to a tangent at the point of tangency goes through the centre of the circle, so the intersections of these perpendicular lines would be the centres of the circles.

I sketched perpendicular lines to the tangent points of the elastic.
I marked the centre of each circle where the perpendicular lines intersected.

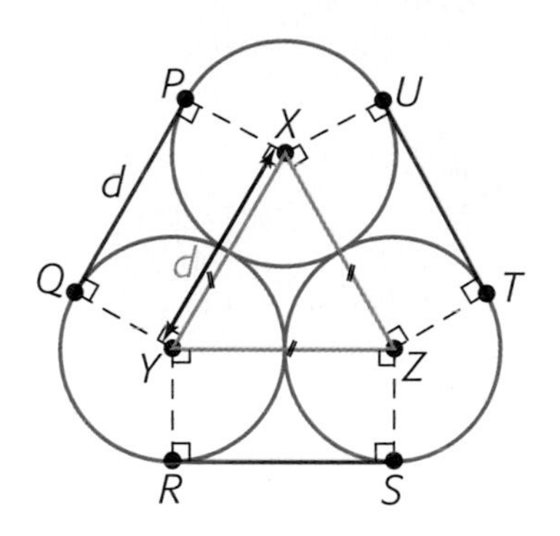

Each side of the triangle is made up of two radii, so I knew that the sides of the triangle were equal and had length *d*.

The quadrilaterals on the sides of the triangle are rectangles because they each contain two right angles. This means that the opposite sides are equal, so *PQ* must be the same length as *XY*, which is *d*.

I sketched line segments to join the three centres. I noticed that these segments form an equilateral triangle with side length *d*, the diameter of the circles.

Each straight part of the elastic is a diameter, *d*, long. The sum of the lengths of the straight parts is $d + d + d = 3d$.

Next, I needed to determine the lengths of the curved parts of the elastic. Each curve is an arc of a circle.

$$\begin{aligned} \angle PXY + \angle YXZ + \angle ZXU + \angle PXU &= 360^\circ \\ 90^\circ + 90^\circ + 60^\circ + \angle PXU &= 360^\circ \\ 240^\circ + \angle PXU &= 360^\circ \\ \angle PXU &= 120^\circ \end{aligned}$$

Each angle of an equilateral triangle is 60°. That left the central angle for the arc as the only angle I did not know. I knew that the sum of the angles must be 360°.

$\angle PXU$ has a measure of 120°. That is $\frac{1}{3}$ of a circle, but there are three equal arcs, *PU*, *QR*, and *ST*, which together form one whole circle. So the sum of the curved parts of the elastic is equal to the circumference, or πd. The total length of elastic is the sum of the lengths of the straight parts and the curved parts.

total length $= 3d + \pi d$

The length of strapping for the three pipes depends on the diameter of the pipes.

Reflecting

A. Does Zachary's formula work for identical pipes of any size? How would you check?

B. How could you modify Zachary's formula for six pipes arranged in a triangular bundle?

WORK WITH the Math

EXAMPLE 2 | Using technology to create a model and solve problems

Three wading pools have common drainpipes with each end at the centre of a pool as shown at right. Determine the radius of each pool.

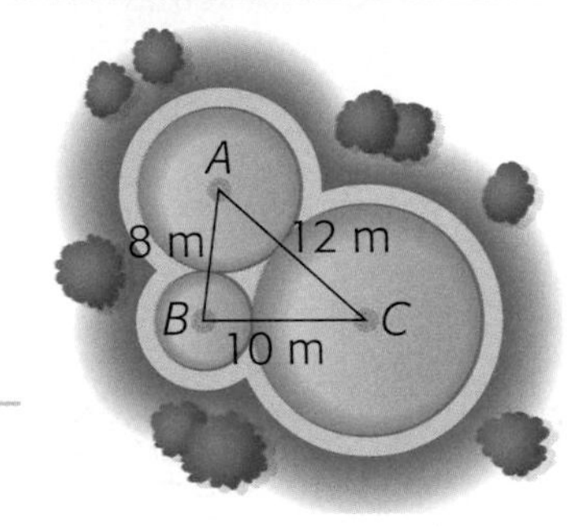

Rani's Solution

1. Understand the Problem
I have to determine the radii of the 3 circles that are tangent to each other whose centres are the vertices of $\triangle ABC$.

2. Make a Plan
I decided to use geometry software. I will first construct $\triangle ABC$ with sides 8, 10, and 12. On each vertex I will construct a circle. I will adjust the size of each circle until I can make them touch each other at one point. Then I will measure the radii of the circles.

3. Carry Out the Plan

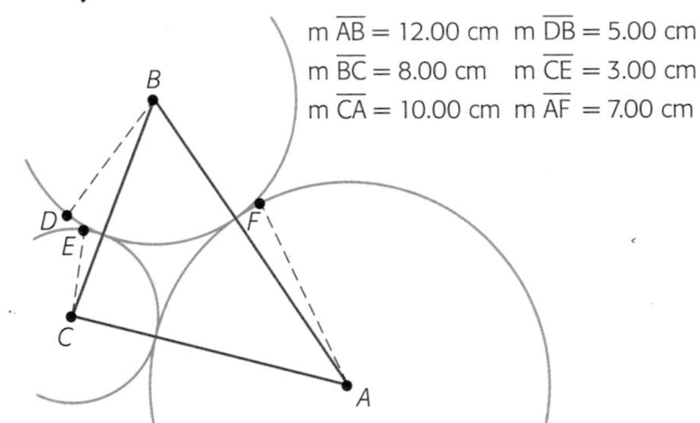

The radii of the pools are 3 m, 5 m, and 7 m.

I plotted 3 points and joined them to create a triangle. I moved the vertices until all three sides matched the lengths in the diagram.

My software measured the distances in centimetres, so I was working with a scale model where 1 cm represents 1 m.

Then I constructed a circle at each vertex. I adjusted the radii one at a time until all 3 circles touched each other. Then I measured the radius of each circle.

4. Look Back
I noticed that the sum of the radii of the circle around A and the circle around C should be the same as the length of AC. I checked my solution by adding pairs of radii.

$$3 + 5 = 8; 3 + 7 = 10; \text{and } 5 + 7 = 12$$

The lengths match, so my answer seems reasonable.

In Summary

Key Idea

- A model can be used to test conjectures about specific cases and to make generalizations about circle geometry problems.

Checking

1. Determine if it is possible that the sides of a triangle inscribed in a circle are equidistant from the centre. Model different types of triangles. What kind of triangle satisfies this condition?

Practising

2. In the circle below, chords AB and CD are equal. Use a model to determine the relationship between the arcs that subtend these chords.

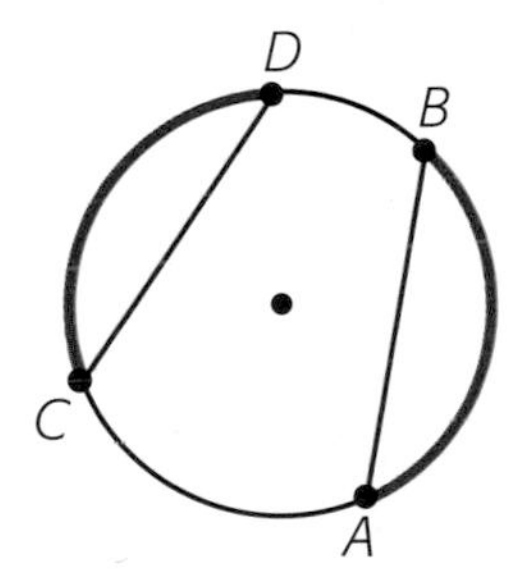

3. Gretchen is designing a new logo for her softball team, the Medicine Hat Marvels, as shown below. She begins by drawing a circle, and marking off arc XY. She wants arcs BA and AX to be the same length as XY, but she does not have a protractor. How can she use chords to mark off the correct positions for points A and B?

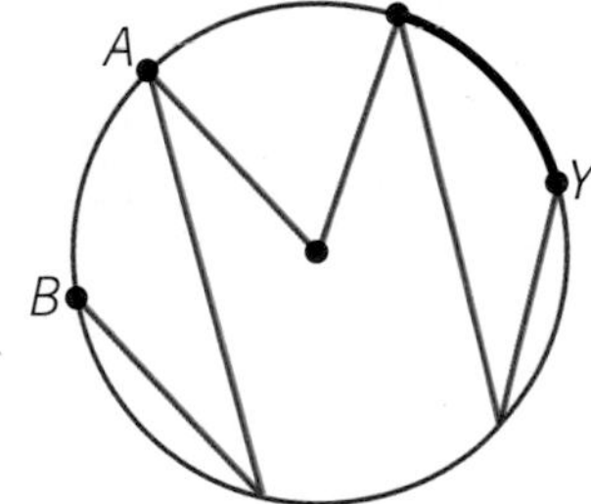

4. Can any triangle be inscribed in a circle?

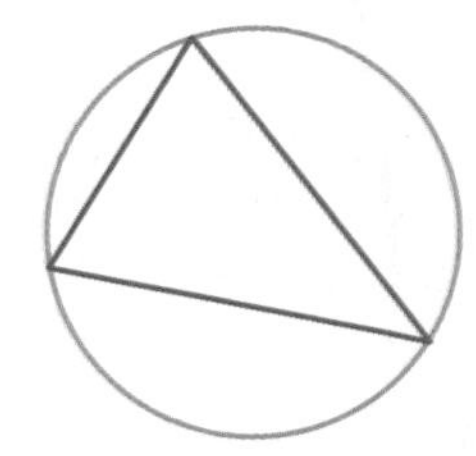

5. Four steel pipes of diameter 1.2 m must be fastened together for shipment. The pipes are stacked two by two.
   a) Determine a formula for the length of each strap needed to fasten the pipes together. Note that the length does not include the length for fastening the strap together.
   b) What is the length of each strap needed, not including the length to fasten the strap together?

6. Which of the quadrilaterals below can be inscribed in a circle? What property must a quadrilateral have to ensure that it can be inscribed in a circle?

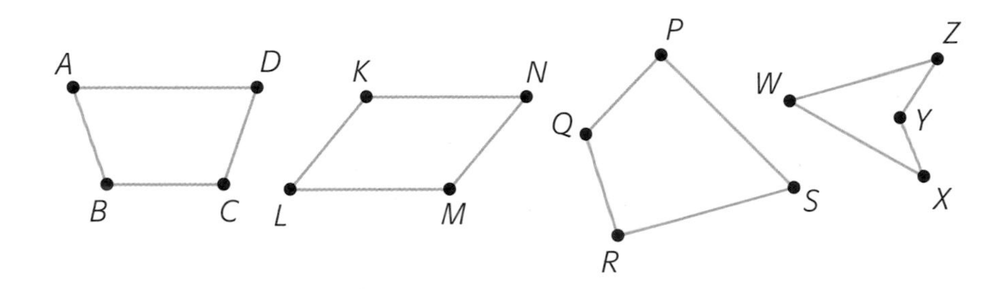

Closing

7. It is sometimes easier to solve a problem by experimenting with specific cases. How can this method help you make generalizations about the problem?

Extending

8. String art involves fastening strings to nails to create designs. For the art shown, the string appears to form multiple circles, if there are enough nails. Are the circles an optical illusion or a fact?

9. *AC* and *BD* are tangent to both circles as shown. Determine if the chords will be parallel for any two circles.

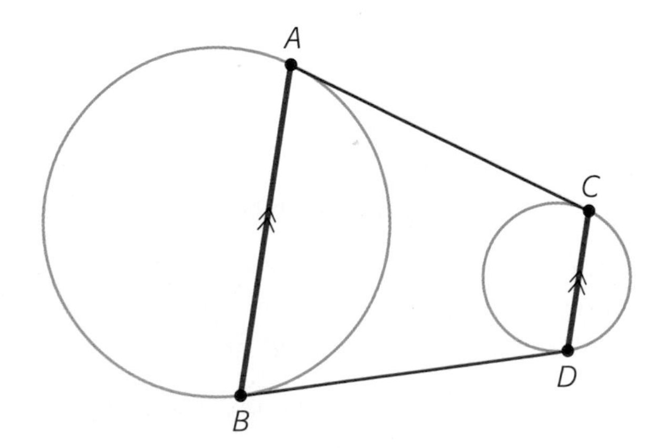

Math GAME

Circo

Number of players: any number

YOU WILL NEED
- one blank Circo Game Card
- a set of answers

How to Play

1. Choose one person to be the game master. The game master will get a set of questions from the teacher.
2. Each player has a game card with four categories: Inscribed Angles, Central Angles, Chords, and Tangents.

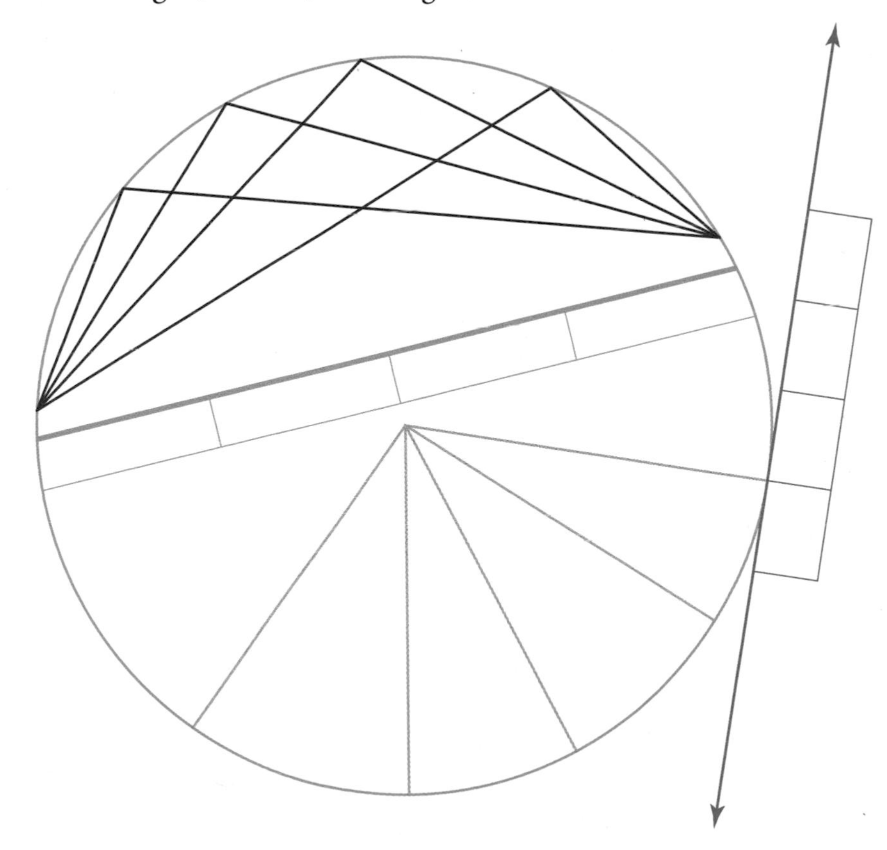

3. Each player chooses four answers from each category, and writes them on the game card in the appropriate places.
4. The game master will pick questions at random from a bowl, one at a time. Each time, the category and the question will be called out. If you have the correct answer written on your card, draw a circle around it.
5. Once you have circled all four answers in any one category, call "Circo."

Chapter Self-Test

1. Determine the measure of each indicated angle.

a)

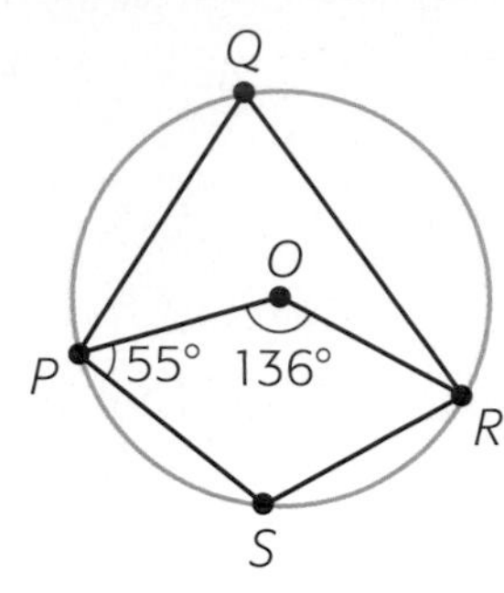

$\angle Q = ?$
$\angle S = ?$
$\angle ORS = ?$

b)

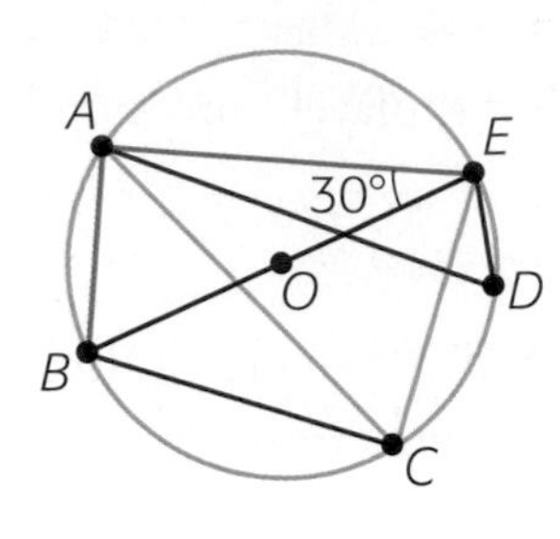

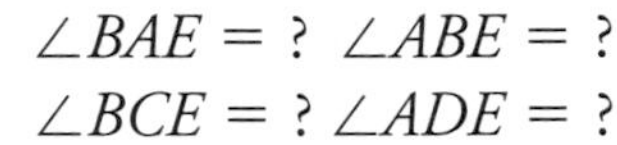

$\angle BAE = ?$ $\angle ABE = ?$
$\angle BCE = ?$ $\angle ADE = ?$
$\angle ACE = ?$ $\angle BCA = ?$

2. In the diagram shown at right, WX and YX are tangent segments. Determine the measures of
   a) $\angle W$, $\angle Y$, and $\angle Z$
   b) XY

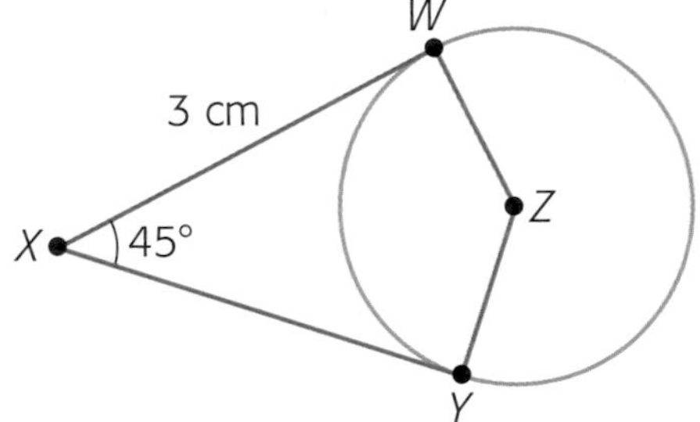

3. Use a circle to determine the interior angles of a regular 11-sided polygon.

4. A chord 30 cm long is 12 cm from the centre of a circle. What is the diameter of the circle?

5. A chord 16.0 cm long is drawn in a circle of radius 12.0 cm. How far, to the nearest tenth of a centimetre, is the chord from the centre of the circle?

6. Chords AB and FG are drawn in a circle of radius 12 cm. AB is 5 cm from the centre of the circle and FG is 7 cm from the centre.
   a) Which chord is longer?
   b) Draw a sketch of the problem. Label each chord.
   c) How long is each chord?

7. A waterslide is constructed from circular tubing. A handrail at the top allows people to grip the slide before pushing off as shown at left. What is the maximum height, h, of the cross-section of the slide?

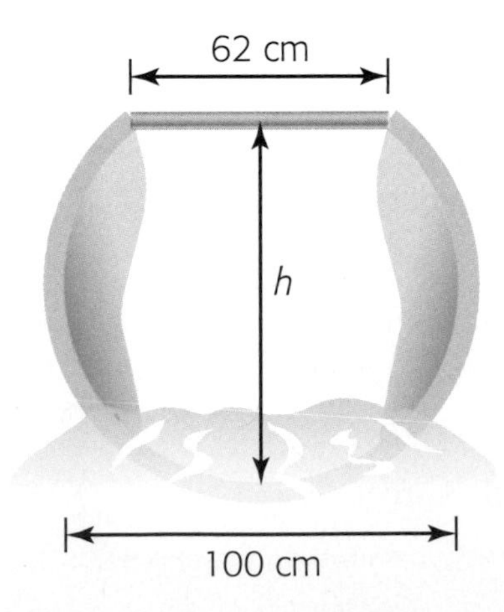

WHAT DO You Think Now?

Revisit What Do You Think? on page 411. How have your answers and explanations changed?

Chapter Review

FREQUENTLY ASKED Questions

Q: How can you determine the length of a chord, if you know how far the chord is from the centre of the circle?

A: A perpendicular line from the centre of a circle to a chord intersects the chord at its midpoint. If you know the radius of the circle and the distance from the chord to the centre of the circle, you can use the Pythagorean theorem to calculate the length of half the chord. Then, double this value to determine the length of the chord. For example,

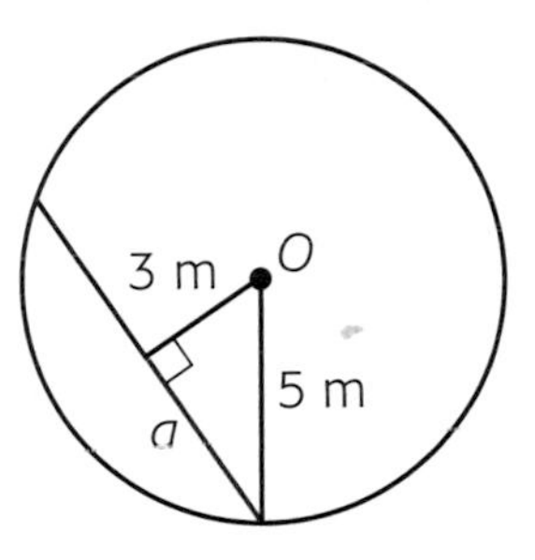

a is the length of half the chord.

$$a^2 + 3^2 = 5^2$$
$$a^2 + 9 = 25$$
$$a^2 = 25 - 9$$
$$a^2 = 16$$
$$a = 4 \text{ m}$$

Use the Pythagorean theorem to calculate *a*.

$$\text{chord length} = 2a = 2 \times 4 = 8 \text{ m}$$

Since the perpendicular line from *O* bisects the chord, the length of the chord is 2*a*.

Study Aid

- See Lesson 9.4, Examples 1, 2, and 3.
- Try Chapter Review questions 5, 6, and 7.

Q: How is a tangent line related to the centre of a circle?

A: All tangent lines are perpendicular to the radius drawn from the centre of the circle to the point of tangency.

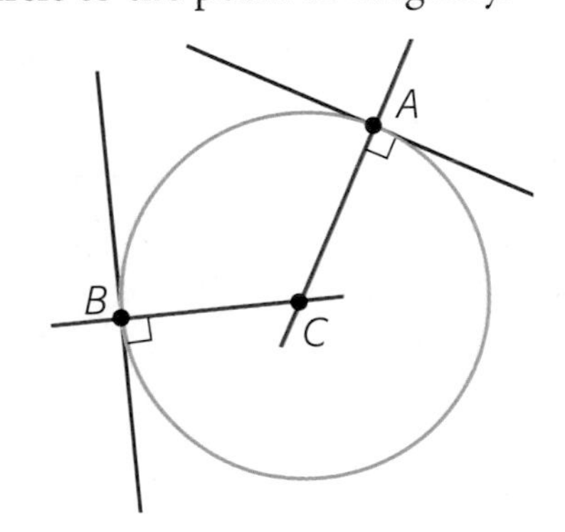

Study Aid

- See Lesson 9.5, Example 2.
- Try Chapter Review question 10.

Study | Aid

- See Lesson 9.5, Example 3.
- Try Chapter Review questions 9 and 10.

Q: How can you determine the length of a tangent segment, if you know the radius and the distance that the endpoint of the segment is from the circle?

A: Draw the radius to the point of tangency. Join the centre of the circle to the endpoint of the tangent segment. Use the Pythagorean theorem to calculate the length of the tangent segment. For example,

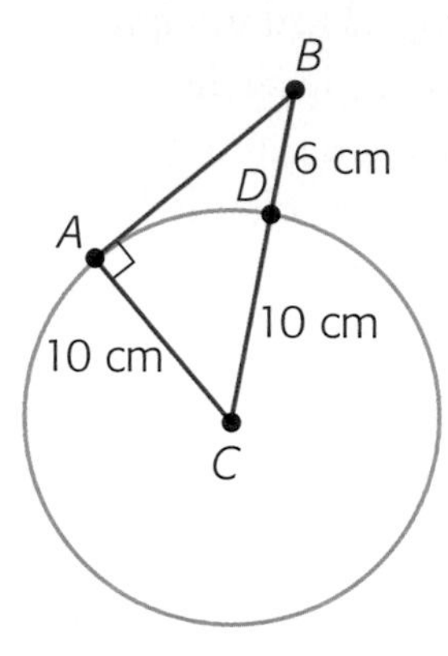

Construct right $\triangle CAB$ as shown.
Since CA and CD are radii, $CD = 10$ cm.
$BC = 16$ cm
Calculate BA using the Pythagorean theorem.

$$\begin{aligned} BA^2 &= BC^2 - CA^2 \\ &= 16^2 - 10^2 \\ &= 256 - 100 \\ &= 156 \text{ cm}^2 \\ BA &\doteq 12 \text{ cm} \end{aligned}$$

Practice

Lesson 9.1

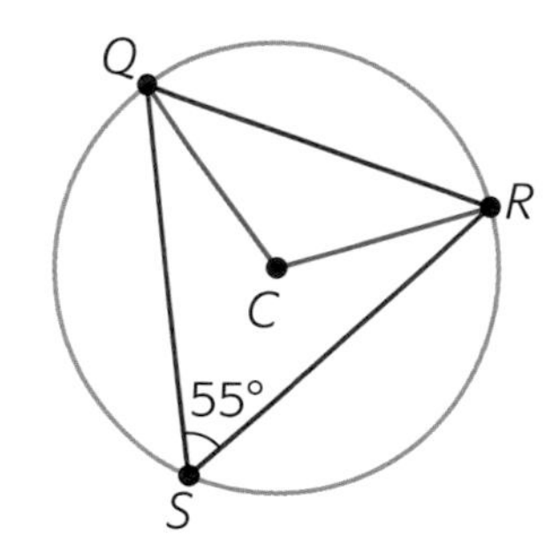

1. In the circle shown at left, determine the measure of $\angle QCR$ and $\angle CQR$.
2. Draw a circle with a diameter AB. Draw inscribed $\angle ACB$. Determine the measure of $\angle ACB$. Explain how you know.

Lesson 9.2

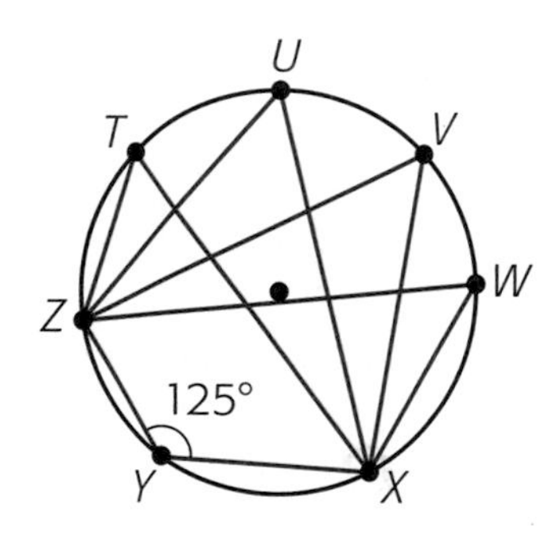

3. Determine the measures of $\angle T$, $\angle U$, $\angle V$, and $\angle W$.

Lesson 9.3

4. Examine the circles with common centre C. Use your knowledge of chords to determine all line segments that are the same length. Show your work.

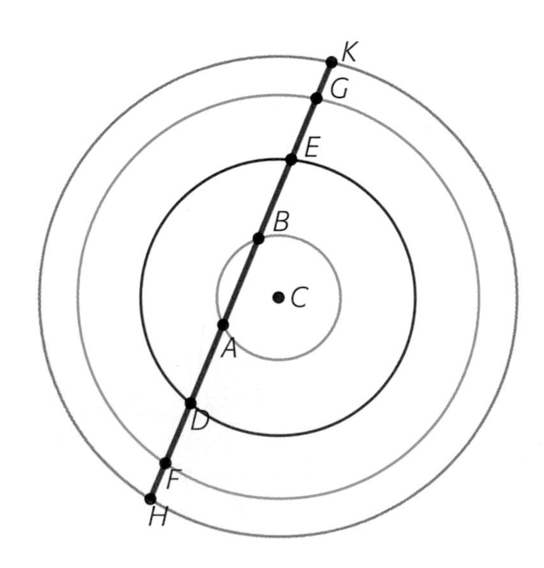

Lesson 9.4

5. A chord 9.0 cm long is 5.0 cm from the centre of a circle. What is the diameter of the circle to the nearest tenth of a centimetre?

6. In the diagram shown at right, the circle has a radius of 5 cm. How long is *QS* to the nearest centimetre?

7. The depth of water in a circular pipe of radius 30 cm is 20 cm. What is the width of the water's surface across the pipe to the nearest centimetre?

Lesson 9.5

8. *QR* is tangent to the circle at *Q* as shown below. Calculate *OQ*.

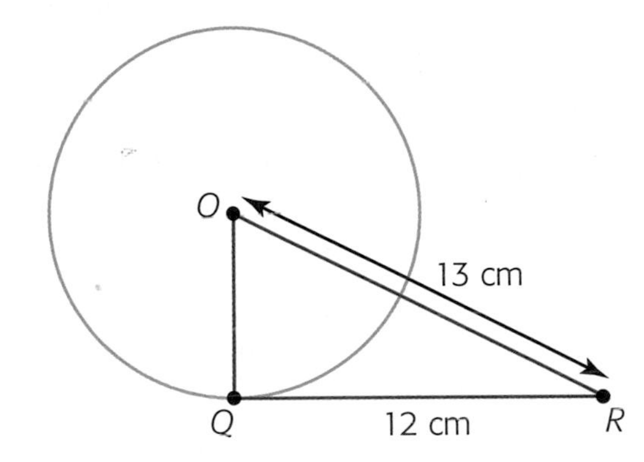

9. Two circles have common centre *P* as shown. Three chords in the larger circle are tangent to the smaller circle and form $\triangle QRS$. Determine the perimeter of the triangle.

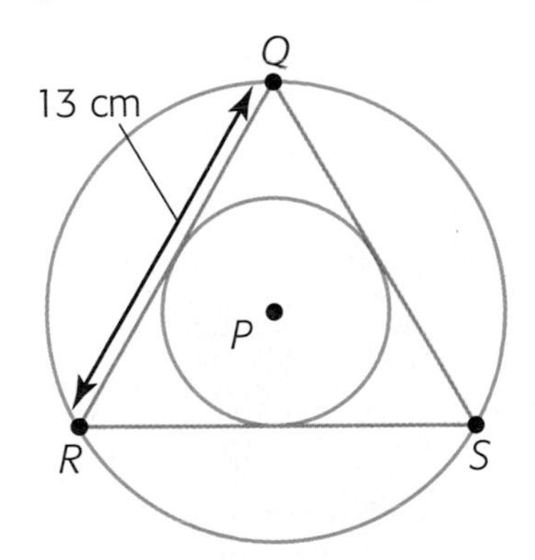

10. A circle is inscribed in $\triangle CTA$ as shown.
    a) Determine the measures of *CP*, *ST*, and *AQ*.
    b) What kind of triangle is $\triangle CTA$? Explain how you know.
    c) What is the radius of the circle?

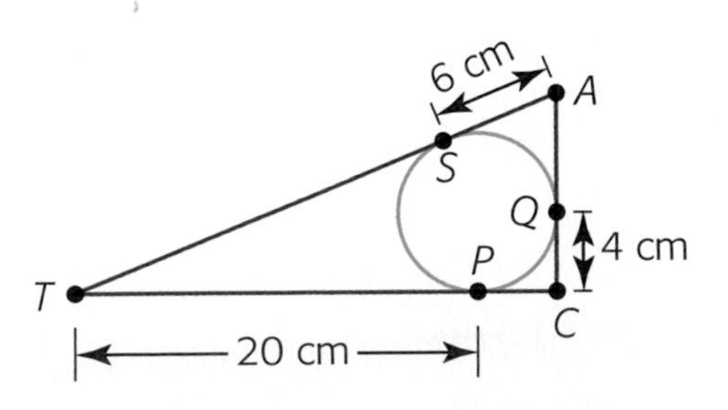

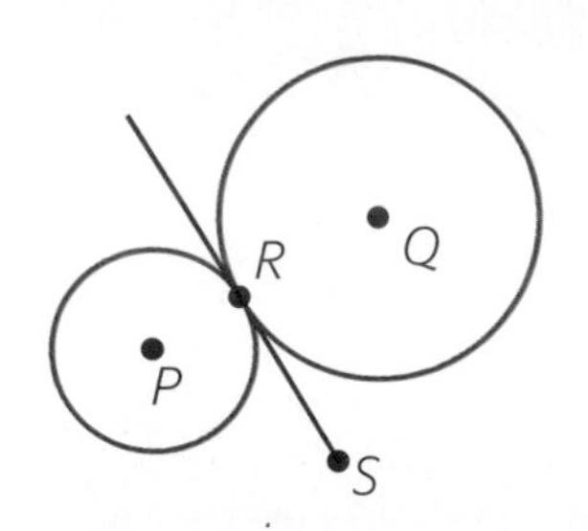

11. What shape is formed by each pair of tangent segments and the radii drawn to them?
   a) Two tangent segments to a circle intersect at 90°.
   b) Two tangent segments to a circle intersect at 60°.

12. Segment *RS* shown at left is tangent to two circles, with centres *P* and *Q* respectively, at *R*. The circles touch at one point. Can a straight line be drawn through *P*, *Q*, and *R*? Explain how you know.

Lesson 9.6

13. Many storm sewers have grates covering the openings to prevent children and animals from entering and possibly drowning. A storm sewer of diameter 180 cm has bars on the grate 20 cm apart. Determine the number of bars and the length of each bar.

14. Businesses use logos so that customers recognize products. Logos are often drawn inside a circle.
   a) Research logos for various companies. Which logos use circles in their design?
   b) Choose one logo. State the circle properties that you would use to create the design.
   c) Create a logo of your own, using circle properties. State which properties you used in your design.

Reading Strategy

Summarizing

Recall the properties of chords to help you develop a design.

15. A stained glass window consists of a large rectangle with a semicircle on top as shown below.

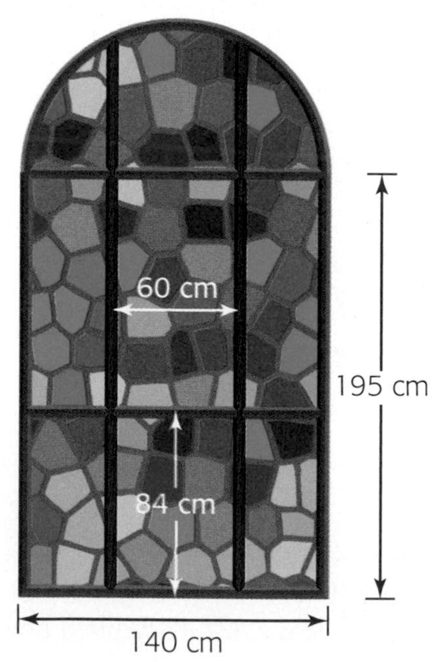

   a) What is the total height of the window?
   b) What is the length of the two red vertical bars?

Chapter Task

Designing a Circular House

Circular houses have many advantages over standard houses.

- A circular house loses less energy (18–20% less) through its walls than a similarly sized square or rectangular house.
- Circular homes are more stable in hurricanes.
- Circular houses have a smaller footprint or foundation. So, building costs are reduced.

Most circular houses are not actually in the shape of a circle, but a regular polygon, whose sides form chords in a circle. Your task is to design a circular house for your family.

? What will be the design of your "circular" house?

A. Research circular houses on the Internet. Examine floor plans and photographs to get ideas for your home design.

B. Decide on the number of sides that your home will have. Use circle properties to draw the perimeter of your home.

C. Make a list of the rooms that your home will have. About how large should each room be?

D. Estimate the number of square metres you will need. What will be the diameter of your house?

E. Do any of the corners in your rooms need to be 90°? If so, why?

F. Use circle properties to design the floor plan. Where will the entrances be? Where will the windows be?

G. Write a final report, describing your home with labelled diagrams. The report should explain how circle properties would help contractors build it.

Task | *Checklist*

- ✔ Does your house have enough sides to look circular?
- ✔ Did you check that your rooms are a reasonable size?
- ✔ Did you use circle properties in your design?
- ✔ Did you include a clearly drawn diagram?

Chapter 10

Data Collection and Analysis

GOALS

You will be able to

- explain how the way data are collected can influence results or conclusions
- distinguish between a sample and a population, and explain when each might be used
- plan and carry out a data project to answer a question
- create and use a rubric to assess the project

The front of your school is getting a new landscape. A group of students is involved in choosing the landscape design. How would the students collect, display, and analyze data in order to decide on the most popular design?

Getting Started

YOU WILL NEED

- grid paper

Picking a Winner

The graph below was created by the Trackstar Equipment Company.

? How would the graph look different if Breakaway Sports had created it?

A. Examine the graph. What does the scale on the graph say about sales at Trackstar compared to sales at Breakaway?

B. How do the two skate images used suggest a different answer than the one in part A?

C. Why do you think Trackstar has created the graph this way?

D. Create a graph that you think Breakaway Sports might use.

WHAT DO You Think?

Decide whether you agree or disagree with each statement. Be ready to explain your decision.

1. If you want to know the favourite subject of ninth graders in my school, it is reasonable to ask only students in my class.
2. If you ask people if they have ever cheated, you are likely to get honest answers.
3. Most people would be comfortable with a stranger asking them about their religious practices.
4. You are likely to get different responses about the safety of air travel the week after a big plane crash.

Chapter Task

? How effectively can you plan and carry out a data investigation?

Your Chapter Task will be a data project in which you will identify a question or questions, create a data collection method, collect data to answer your question(s), analyze the data, and communicate your findings.

A. What might be some issues or information that you would be interested in gathering data about? These may be topics around your school or community, or in the world.

Task | *Checklist*

- Topic chosen?
  - Can you use a survey or an experiment for this topic?
- Question(s) written?
- Method chosen?
- Sample or population chosen?
- Display and analysis methods chosen?
- Project completed and assessed?

10.1 Collecting Data: Asking Appropriate Questions

GOAL

Decide whether survey questions will lead to the desired information.

LEARN ABOUT the Math

Mountview city council is considering building an indoor swimming pool. The council decides to conduct a survey of the local residents to determine how much public support there is for the new pool.

? What would be an appropriate survey question?

EXAMPLE 1 | Using simple questions

Thomas's Solution

Do you think people would use a new swimming pool?
or
Do you think the city should build a swimming pool?

I focused on the popularity of the plan.

I wrote two possible questions that lead to a Yes/No answer.

EXAMPLE 2 | Using questions with multiple choices

Larissa's Solution

respondent
a person who answers the questions in a survey or census

Put the following projects in your order of preference, from 1 (first choice) to 4 (last choice):

- a new library
- a new swimming pool
- a new multi-level parking garage
- a new leisure centre

I decided to ask **respondents** to rank several projects in order of preference. This would show how popular the pool is in comparison to other projects.

To do this, I thought about possible alternatives to the plan.

Reflecting

A. What are the advantages and disadvantages of Thomas's questions compared to Larissa's?

B. Whose data, Thomas's or Larissa's, do you think would be more useful to the municipality? Why?

WORK WITH the Math

EXAMPLE 3 | Writing and analyzing questions

A group of students is planning a fundraising campaign for a class trip. Write a question to find out what kind of campaign to run.

David's Solution

Possible questions:

> I brainstormed some questions and then analyzed how well they might work.

How much money should we raise?

> This is important, since it may influence the type of fundraiser, but it doesn't get the information we need.

Would you help raise money?

> Participation is important but the question still doesn't give the answer needed.

How long should the campaign be?

> Again, important but the question isn't effective in telling us what kind of campaign to run.

Chosen question:
Which fundraising campaign might be the easiest and generate good returns?

- chocolate bar sales
- bake sales
- calendars
- magazine subscriptions
- rummage sales
- other? ____________

> This question may limit choices but it gives people an idea of what might be possible.
>
> Including "Other" gives people a chance to make their own suggestions.
>
> I think this is the best question.

EXAMPLE 4 | Questioning techniques

A survey about a series of "Do-It-Yourself" books asked these four questions.

> **CUSTOMER SURVEY: DO-IT-YOURSELF BOOKS**
>
> 1. Rate each of the following as Excellent, Good, Average, or Poor.
>   - Readability – engaging and interesting
>   - Diagrams – clear and easy to follow
>   - Instructions – clear and complete
> 2. Thinking about all of our books you have read, how long did it generally take to read each one?
> 3. Did you learn anything new from our books?
> 4. How many of our books have you read?

a) Rearrange the questions so that the order makes more sense to the respondent.

b) Identify a possible question that has not been asked, and place it in your order from part a).

Sam's Solution

a) New question order:

1. How many of our books have you read?

   This one should be first because if you haven't read any of the books you wouldn't be able to answer the rest of the survey.

2. Thinking about all of our books you have read, how long did it generally take to read each one?

   This is a useful question to get respondents thinking about the books they have read.

3. Rate each of the following as Excellent, Good, Average, or Poor:
   - Readability–engaging and interesting
   - Diagrams–clear and easy to follow
   - Instructions–clear and complete

   I picked this as the third question because even if the book is a quick read, it ought to be useful and usable.

4. Did you learn anything new from our books?

   I kept this question for last because it finds out whether the reader got value from the book.

b) Insert after question 2:
Did the books take longer to read than you thought was reasonable?

This question would find out whether the books are useful as quick reference guides. It follows on naturally from question 2.

In Summary

Key Idea

- When preparing to collect data, you must create appropriate questions.

Need to Know

- Appropriate questions are clearly written, easy to answer, and effective in generating the desired data.
- Multiple choice questions are useful for identifying respondents' preferences.
- Order questions appropriately. Think about which order makes most sense to a respondent.

Checking

1. Write a question to generate data on each of the following:
   a) the number of students in the class who play hockey
   b) the music group most popular with Grade 7 students
   c) how often students go to the library

Practising

2. What question may have been asked to lead to each conclusion?
   a) Most pet owners have dogs or cats.
   b) In a survey of dentists, 3 out of 4 preferred Spark-L-Dent toothpaste over other leading brands.
   c) Blue is the most popular colour for jeans.
   d) TV talk shows are more popular than the weather channel.

3. Write a question to generate data on each of the following:
   a) the most popular summer activity last year
   b) the number of students in French-immersion programs in your community
   c) the most popular automobile in the community

4. Would it make sense to use a survey to collect this information? Explain.
   a) On January 5, 2 cm of snow fell.
   b) The town council makes good decisions for its residents.
   c) Tanya's birthday is on June 10.
   d) Spinach is delicious.
   e) Jonathon's weekly gross earnings are $800.

5. These questions were asked by the manager of a school cafeteria, to determine whether any changes should be made.
   i) What do you dislike most about school lunches?
   ii) How satisfied are you with the quality of school lunches?
   iii) Are you satisfied with the choices given?
   iv) What types of health-conscious items should be added to the menu?
   v) Do you eat lunch in the cafeteria or do you bring your own?

   a) Would you change the order? Explain.
   b) Identify a relevant question that hasn't been asked.

6. The organizing committee for the Grade 9 year-end celebration prepared this survey.

Please complete this questionnaire regarding the Grade 9 year-end banquet and return it to your homeroom teacher by Friday.

1. Are you male _____ or female _____ ?

2. Do you think a year-end banquet is a good idea?
___Yes ___No ___No Opinion

3. Do you think formal clothes should be worn at the banquet?
___ Yes ___ No ___No Opinion

4. How much would you be willing to pay to attend the banquet? ___________

   a) Comment on the survey questions. For example,
      - Which questions are worded well, and why?
      - Which are worded poorly?
      - Are there any other questions you would ask?
   b) Rewrite any questions you think are worded poorly.
   c) Explain how the data will help the organizing committee.

7. This simple rubric was written to assess the quality of questions.
   3 Written questions are clear, easy to answer, and effective.
   2 Written questions have a few flaws and are incomplete.
   1 Written questions are not clear, not well organized, contain errors or omissions, and are difficult to understand.

   Use this rubric to assess the survey in questions 5 or 6. Rewrite the questions to make them clear, easy to answer, and effective.

8. These two bar charts were created from data about respondents' ages from two different surveys.
   a) What question or questions may have been asked in the two surveys so that these bar graphs represent the data gathered?
   b) If you compare the age categories in the two graphs, which one gives you the most useful data? Why?
   c) Could the data in the two different graphs provide you with similar information? Explain.

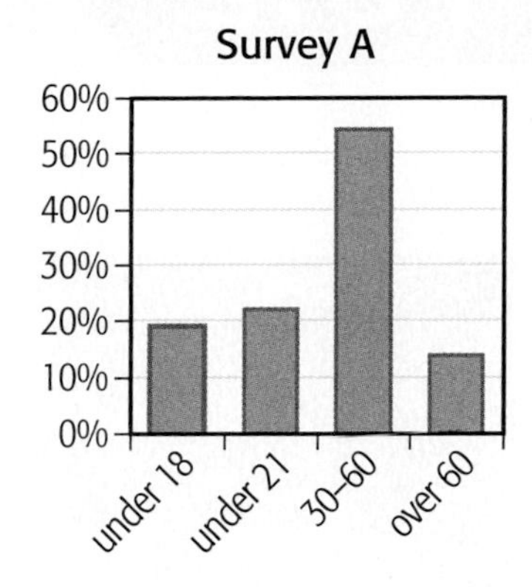

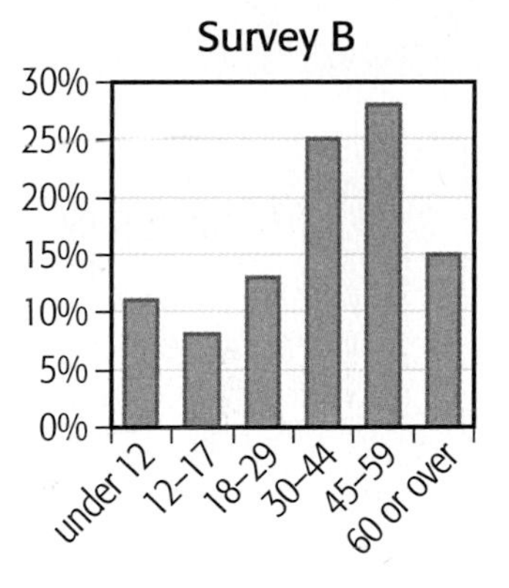

Closing

9. Appropriate questions are clearly written, easy to answer, and effective in generating the desired data. "Do your feelings about air crashes affect whether you decide to fly or to take a train or bus instead?" is a wordy question that is unclear as to the information it seeks. Rewrite the question so that it is short, clear, and direct.

Extending

10. These survey questions were written to gather information about how active people are.
    i) How much do you weigh?
    ii) How often do you exercise?
    iii) Do you have a membership at a gym?
    iv) Do you have a healthy diet?
    a) Do you think the survey questions are appropriate? Will they likely be answered honestly? Explain.
    b) How could you improve the questions?
    c) What other questions might you ask?
    d) Which would be a better way to gather this type of data: a personal interview or a questionnaire? Explain.

Chapter Task

B. Begin creating a rubric to assess your project by writing an assessment item with three levels, "not acceptable," "acceptable," and "good," for a survey question. Each level should describe the qualities of a question that reaches that level.

C. Write some possible questions for your survey in order to gather the data for your project topic.

D. Apply your rubric assessment item to your questions from step C. Then, revise your questions based on your own assessment.

Task | *Checklist*

✔ Topic chosen?

Question(s) written?
- Are your questions appropriate?
- Will your questions generate the data you need?

Method chosen?

Sample or population chosen?

Display and analysis methods chosen?

Project completed and assessed?

10.2 Collecting Data: Bias, Sensitivity, and Method

GOAL

Assess surveys for bias and sensitivity, and select appropriate survey methods.

INVESTIGATE the Math

Jia-Wen and Rachel are looking at a survey about families in their community. The survey was delivered to each resident's mailbox.

FAMILIES IN OUR COMMUNITY

Please answer the following questions about your family. Return the survey in the prepaid envelope to your mailbox for collection.

Family Structure

How many people are in your family? ________

What is the age of each member of your family?

____

How many males are in your family? ________

How many females? _____

What kind of family do you have? Choose one.

____ Traditional two-parent
____ Single parent, mother
____ Single parent, father
____ Blended with a step-parent
____ Blended with a step-parent and step-siblings
____ Other Describe ___________________

Is anyone in your family adopted?
____ Yes ____ No

Were all your family members born in Canada?
____ Yes ____ No

Family Finances

What is your family's annual income?

____

Do both parents work? ____ Yes ____ No

What are their jobs?

____

____

Do the children contribute to the household income? ____ Yes ____No

Do you own your home or rent it?
_____ Own ____ Rent

Family Education

Does anyone in the family have a university education? ____ Yes ____ No

What level of education do the parents have?

____

At what level of education is each of the children? ______________________

Family Activities

Does your family attend church?
____ Yes ____ No

Does your family use community recreational facilities such as the pool and skating rink?
_____ Yes ____ No

How does your family fill its leisure time?

____

Does your family like to watch too much television? _____ Yes ____ No

❓ How could the survey be improved?

A. Which questions do you think people might feel invade their privacy?

B. Might people be offended or embarrassed by any of the questions? Explain.

C. Are there any **biased questions**? Explain.

D. How could the survey be improved to avoid sensitivity issues? How could you improve it to avoid bias?

E. Is it ethical to conduct a survey, but not to tell people who is asking the questions or to explain the purpose of the survey? Explain.

F. What information about the organization doing the survey could you add to the form? How would this information help make respondents feel more comfortable?

Reading Strategy

Inferring

Use your own knowledge and the survey data to make inferences.

biased question

a question that is likely to influence respondents to answer in a particular way; for example, "Do you agree that dogs are friendlier than cats?"

Reflecting

G. Give examples of other issues of privacy, bias, or cultural sensitivity that might come up, but should be avoided or asked about more sensitively, in surveys on family life in Canada.

WORK WITH the Math

EXAMPLE 1 | Writing unbiased questions

A marketing agency wants to determine how Canadians spend their clothing dollars. Alexis wrote this question to determine how much is spent on imported clothing.

> **What does your closet contain more of?**
>
> **A.** less expensive foreign-made clothes
>
> **B.** high-quality made-in-Canada clothes

a) What specific information is Alexis trying to obtain?

b) Rewrite the question to avoid bias and sensitivity issues.

Sam's Solution

a) Alexis wants to know if people spend more on locally made clothing or on imported clothing. She also wants to determine information about clothing quality.

The question appears to be asking about two things: foreign-made versus made-in-Canada clothes, and quality/cost of clothing.

b) "Do you spend more on made-in-Canada clothes than on foreign-made clothes?"

The question was biased. I reworded the question to remove references to "less expensive" and "high quality" so that it wouldn't influence responses.
The information about quality could go in a separate question.

EXAMPLE 2 | Gathering data in different ways

To make valid conclusions and predictions, appropriate forms of data collection must be used. Questionnaires, interviews, and experiment and observation are some of the ways data can be collected. What would be the best way to find out about each of the following topics?

a) Do more people prefer name brand or no-name brand soft drinks?

b) Are students' marks affected by using a calculator on a math test?

c) Is there a relationship between a person's age and gender and the number of telephone calls received?

Larissa's Solution

a) I would set up a blind taste-test experiment to see if people could tell the difference between a name brand and a no-name brand.

I need to avoid bias by disguising the brand of the drinks.

b) I will interview students and ask them when they used a calculator and how their marks compared to their marks when they didn't.

I will use interviews so I can ask different questions depending on people's answers.

c) I need to be able to give a questionnaire to a number of households with various ages and genders represented.

To collect unbiased data, I need to ask a range of different types of households the same questions.

EXAMPLE 3 | Creating a survey

Due to rising printing costs, the staff of a school newspaper is thinking about increasing the price from 50¢ to 75¢ for each issue. They would like to know how this would affect the number of papers sold. To help the staff make a decision, create a set of unbiased and effective questions that are sensitive to respondents.

Thomas's Solution

NEWSPAPER SURVEY

1. How often do you read the weekly school newspaper?
   __ 4 times a month
   __ 2 or 3 times a month
   __ once a month
   __ occasionally

This question determines how often people read the newspaper.

2. Rising printing costs mean that we need to raise the price to 75¢ if we continue to publish weekly. Are you willing to pay the new price, or would you prefer a monthly paper for $1.50?

Ask this question to see if students would pay 75¢ weekly or if we should publish the paper less often.

3. How often will you buy the paper if it is published weekly at 75¢ a copy?
   __ 4 times a month
   __ 2 or 3 times a month
   __ once a month
   __ occasionally
   __ never

Ask this question to see if the newspaper will be read less often at the new price.

In Summary

Key Ideas

When preparing to collect data, you must

- ensure questions are sensitive and bias is controlled
- select a method that is appropriate for the kind of data you are collecting
- make sure that respondents know who is collecting the data, and for what purpose

Need to Know

When you create questions to collect data, analyze how the phrasing might affect the data collected. Ask yourself questions such as the following:

- If I ask this question, will I get the information I need?
- Am I making one response sound right and another one wrong?
- Is the question respectful? If I walked up to a stranger and asked this question, would the person be upset?

Checking

1. Tell why each question may be biased. Describe what changes you would make to improve the question.
   a) Are you in favour of replacing the hockey arena that has been used by the hometown teams since 1920 with a new sports complex?
   b) A survey of voters in the province shows that 80% would support a candidate who favours a decrease in taxes. Do you favour a decrease in taxes?

2. For each question, which is the most appropriate method of collecting data: questionnaires, interviews, or experiment and observation?
   a) Do all brands of batteries have the same life span?
   b) What proportion of students in your school speak more than one language?
   c) Do the shape and size of a container of water have an effect on how fast the water evaporates?

Practising

3. Kandace asks this question: "Do you prefer top-quality stainless steel appliances to ordinary appliances?"
   a) Is the question biased? Explain how you know.
   b) What would be a better question to ask?

4. For each question, state the most appropriate method of collecting data. Explain your choice.
   a) What is the most popular household pet in your school?
   b) What are students' attitudes to bullying and harassment?
   c) Is there a relationship between the length of a word and the number of vowels it contains?

5. Mountview city council is considering building an outdoor swimming pool. The mayor's special assistant suggests conducting a survey of local support for the pool in July, because the data will likely show a greater level of public support. Discuss the ethics (honesty, fairness) of the timing for the survey.

6. A music teacher wants to know if there is student support for more music courses. He hands out this short questionnaire to all of his students.
   a) Why might the data collected not represent students' real opinions?
   b) How would you improve the questionnaire to get more useful data?

Name: ____________________

Do you think music is

A) a very interesting subject,

B) an interesting subject,

C) an important subject?

(Circle one answer.)

7. In a school survey about bullying and harassment, some of the questions ask students about times when they have been bullied, or times that they have bullied others. The students do not write their names on the surveys. When the students have finished the surveys, however, the homeroom teacher collects them and reads through the responses. Explain why this is unfair.

8. Two groups of students generated different sets of survey questions to gather information about students' grades and after-school jobs.

SURVEY I	SURVEY II
A. Do you think it is important to get good grades at school?	**A.** Is getting good grades the most important thing in school?
B. Do you think the long hours a student works at an after-school job make it more difficult to get good grades?	**B.** Do you think it is a good idea for a student to have an after-school job where they learn important skills outside the classroom?
C. Do you think it is a good idea for a student to have a job?	**C.** Do you think it is a good idea for a student to have a job?
D. If a student does have a job, what do you think is the maximum number of hours he or she should work in a week?	**D.** If a student does have a job, what do you think is the maximum number of hours he or she should work in a week?

a) Do the questions in the two surveys ask about the same information? Explain.

b) Do you think the results from the two surveys will be similar? Explain.

c) Question A asked about the importance of good grades. According to the two surveys, does it appear that one group thinks good grades are more important than the other group does? Do you think this is really the case? Explain.

d) Suppose questions C and D were the first two questions in each survey. Do you think the results from these questions would be different? Explain.

e) Rewrite survey questions that you believe are biased.

9. Use this rubric to assess the questions from either survey in question 8.
   3 Written questions are unbiased, sensitive toward respondents, and effective at getting the information required.
   2 Written questions have a few flaws and are incomplete in at least one way.
   1 Written questions are biased, not sensitive, contain major errors or omissions, and/or are difficult to understand.

   Rewrite any or all of the questions from the survey to make them unbiased, sensitive toward respondents, and effective at getting the information required.

Closing

10. Why is it important to think about whether a survey question may be biased or offend respondents?

Extending

11. Write the topics shown below on cards and place the cards in a box.

Television	Newspapers	Movies	Magazines
Internet	Social Networks	Video Games	Blogs

With a partner, choose one of the cards.

a) Write a question about the topic that needs data to answer it.
b) Write a second question that is likely to bias the results of the data gathered.
c) Have classmates answer each of your questions and decide whether bias may have occurred.

Chapter Task

E. Add a row to your Chapter Task rubric to assess whether a question avoids bias and is sensitive toward respondents. Use the attainment levels "not acceptable," "acceptable," and "good." Review and, if necessary, revise your question(s).

F. Add a row to your rubric, including the three attainment levels, to assess the method of collecting data. Take social considerations into account.

G. Identify the method you will use to collect your data.

H. Apply your rubric assessment item from step F to your method as determined in step G. Based on your self-assessment, review and, if necessary, revise your method.

✔ Topic chosen?

Question(s) written?
- Are your questions appropriate?
- Will your questions generate the data you need?
- Are your questions biased or insensitive?

Method chosen?
- Is your method practical and appropriate?

Sample or population chosen?

Display and analysis methods chosen?

Project completed and assessed?

10.3 Selecting a Sample or Population

GOAL

Compare the choice of a sample or the population to gather information.

INVESTIGATE the Math

Thomas has volunteered to run the smoothie stand at the school's Fun Fair. Before buying the ingredients, he wants to know flavour preferences. Instead of taking a **census** of the whole **population** of people likely to visit the Fun Fair, he decides to survey his class as a **sample** that represents all the visitors. He is wondering if his sample will give similar results to the whole population, and if the size of his sample is appropriate.

census
collects data about (and counts) a whole population

population
the total set of people or things under investigation

sample
part of a population, selected to give information about the whole

? How does Thomas's choice of sample affect his conclusions?

A. Have each student in your class secretly record his or her smoothie preference on a slip of paper, from this list: banana blaster, very berry, citrus sunshine, other, none.

B. Tally the results.

C. Based on the results, predict the percentage of Fun Fair visitors who will prefer each flavour.

D. What kinds of people might attend the Fun Fair? How might this affect your prediction about the most popular flavour?

E. Is your class a **representative sample** of the population? Explain.

F. Whom could you survey to make your sample more like the population attending the Fun Fair?

representative sample
a sample that is similar to the whole population; for example, in terms of gender, age group, and/or other characteristics

Reflecting

G. Why do you think a sample of respondents is often used instead of a population?

H. Why does using a sample make sense in Thomas's case?

I. Why is a large sample likely to be more representative than a small one?

WORK WITH the Math

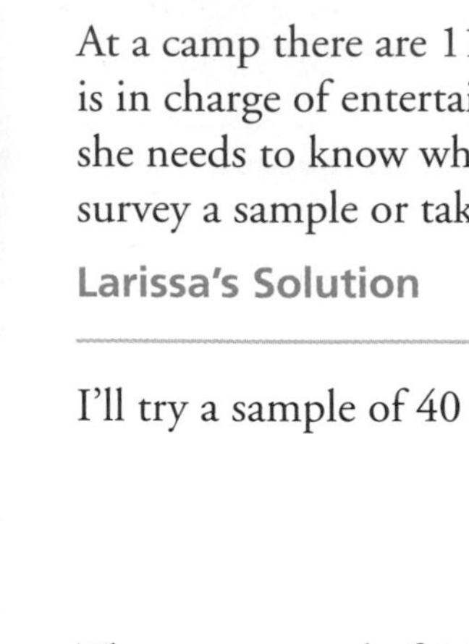

EXAMPLE 1 | Sample versus population

At a camp there are 115 children, 78 teenagers, and 52 adults. Larissa is in charge of entertainment. In order to set up for Saturday evening she needs to know what the most popular entertainment is. Should she survey a sample or take a census of the population?

Larissa's Solution

I'll try a sample of 40 people.

I'm guessing that a sample of 40 is big enough to be a fair sample. I think I'll get most opinions with that many.

There are a total of 245 people at the camp, of which children are about half, so I will include 20 children in my sample. Teenagers are about 30% of the population, so I will ask 12 teenagers. The other 8 in the sample will be adults.

I decided that age probably makes the most difference in terms of what entertainment the campers would like. I can use approximate percents to make sure my sample has the same age proportions as the population.

Sam's Solution

Use the population. Ask everyone by putting a questionnaire at the entrance to the dining hall. As they all come in to breakfast and are waiting in line, they can quickly fill it out.

The whole population is small enough that it can be easily surveyed.

Jia-Wen's Solution

Use a sample of 25 children only.

I think the camp is really for the children and they should be the ones to choose the type of entertainment.

EXAMPLE 2 | **Conducting efficient surveys with representative samples**

Farley, a market researcher, wants to find out what kinds of reality television programs are most popular in Canada. He decides to do face-to-face interviews and must therefore select possible interviewees. Comment on each of these methods that Farley could use.

a) advertise in a national newspaper

b) advertise in an adventure magazine

c) advertise in local newspapers across the country

Rachel's Solution

a) People who answer the ad might not be a fair sample.

Many Canadians don't read national newspapers.

b) Interviewees may be biased toward a particular type of reality show.

Only people interested in adventure buy the magazine, and only these people would see the ad. This may also result in too small a survey.

c) This method should remove regional biases. However, the interviewer will need to travel. This may lead to high costs.

If we get responses from all parts of the country, the regions of the respondents should not bias the data. Method c) is the most expensive.

EXAMPLE 3 | **Representative sampling**

Fred and his group wanted to survey 25 out of all 512 students in Mountview High to determine if the cafeteria should alter its menu. The group developed the following three plans:

Plan 1 Select 25 students at **random** from the cafeteria at lunch.

Plan 2 Choose a class in the school that has 25 students and survey the whole class.

Plan 3 Using an alphabetical list of all students, pick every 20th name, and then survey those students.

Compare the plans. Which plan should Fred use, and why?

random

each item or individual is equally likely to be chosen

David's Solution

Plan 1 is unrepresentative. Students who do not eat in the cafeteria cannot be selected, but they are also part of the population.

I could see this plan gives a **biased sample** of the population of all 512 students because it excludes a group. Students who don't use the cafeteria might do so if the menu changed.

biased sample

a sample whose responses are likely to be different from the responses of the whole population

Plan 2 is unrepresentative. Students whose classes contain fewer or more than 25 students are eliminated.

This plan could exclude a lot of classes. For example, it might exclude all Grade 9 classes, so the sample would be biased in terms of age.

Plan 3 is representative. Each of the 512 students has an equal chance of being randomly selected.

I decided that this plan was unbiased because it creates a random sample.

Fred should use Plan 3.

This is the only plan that gives a representative sample.

In Summary

Key Ideas

- Data can be collected using a sample or a population.
- When collecting data from a sample, it is important that the sample be representative (not biased).

Need to Know

- A census for a large population can be time consuming and costly, so using a reasonably sized sample often makes sense.
- One way to select a fair sample is to make the proportions for age groups, genders, and/or other categories roughly the same as in the population.

Checking

1. Identify each data collection method as using a population or a sample.

a) To decide on a family vacation, each family member was questioned.

b) To check the lifespan of fluorescent bulbs in a particular production run, every 1000th bulb was tested.

2. State, with reasons, whether each conclusion is likely to be valid.

a) All the people living near the railroad tracks in a city were asked if they wanted the tracks moved. Conclusion: Most people in the city wanted the tracks moved.

b) People waiting in line for a carnival were asked whether they liked to go on rides. Conclusion: Most Canadians like to go on carnival rides.

c) A store looked at sales of jeans over a one-year period. Conclusion: Most of the store's customers preferred to wear styled jeans.

Practising

3. Would you use a sample or the whole population to gather data about each topic? Explain.
   a) the most popular movie among your classmates
   b) the life expectancy of a brand of battery, determined by testing
   c) the quality of a shipment of apples, based on inspection
   d) the popularity of a new local band at the club where they usually play
   e) the effectiveness of a new pain medication, according to people who have used it

4. Suppose you want to know the cartoon-watching habits of students in your school. You decide to use a sample from a single class. Is this a representative sample of your school? Explain.

5. Identify each data collection method as using a population or a sample.
   a) To determine preferences for local attractions in the Edmonton area, 300 households in the area were telephoned.
   b) After bumping his trolley into a wall, a grocery store employee opened all of the egg cartons on the trolley.
   c) To determine feelings about working conditions, all the employees of a company were personally interviewed.

6. For each population, why is the sample not representative?
   a) Population: teenage Canadians. Questionnaires are mailed to 120 teenagers randomly chosen from a single school in each Canadian city.
   b) Population: adult Canadian women. A questionnaire is included in a popular cooking magazine.
   c) Population: Grade 9 students in a particular school. Students are interviewed in the library before school, at lunch in the cafeteria, and after school.
   d) Population: Canadian families. Door-to-door interviews are conducted during the day across the country.
   e) Population: bilingual school children. Questionnaires for students were sent to all Francophone and French-immersion schools.

7. A survey was sent out randomly across Canada, asking if people thought that the age to qualify for a learner's permit should be raised to 16 and for a driver's license be raised to 18. The 1000 surveys were distributed as shown in the table.

Western Provinces	100 each
Ontario	225
Québec	100
Maritime Provinces	50 each
Territories	25 each

   a) How could you check if this distribution is representative of Canada's population distribution?
   b) Do you think that the people who respond to the survey will be representative of all interested parties? Explain.
   c) How can it be ensured that different age groups will be able to respond to the question?

8. A Kindergarten to Grade 12 school in a small town has 75 students in K to Grade 3, 80 students in Grades 4 to 6, 65 students in Grades 7 to 9, and 80 students in Grades 10 to 12. A parent committee has raised money to make improvements to the playground and outdoor equipment.
   a) Should the parents survey a sample or conduct a census of the school's population? Explain.
   b) If they choose to do a sample, how should it be organized to be representative of each group of students?

9. The managers of a movie theatre chain want to find out how many movies people in the community usually see in the theatre each month. Each manager suggests a different sampling method for gathering data.
   i) Have ticket sellers at each theatre survey customers when they purchase their tickets.
   ii) Place an ad in the local newspaper and ask people to mail in their responses.
   iii) Randomly select phone numbers from the phone book and call people to ask their opinions.
   a) For each suggestion, will the sample likely produce a biased response? Explain.
   b) For each sample, tell how these timing factors might influence the survey results: time of day, day of the week, time of year.

10. For each case, analyze potential problems with the conclusion made. Present a way that the sample could have been selected to provide a more reasonable conclusion.
   a) A grocery store created a survey about how the store needed to change in order to bring in more customers. A store employee handed out a questionnaire to every fifth person entering the store. The data collected indicated that no changes were needed, so the store owner decided not to change anything.
   b) A student council wanted to survey students about school activities. It randomly selected 25 students from each grade to answer the survey. The results indicated a number of different ideas, of which the council chose to implement the three most popular.
   c) An orange seller tested the quality of oranges in a shipment by opening one crate and testing a few of the oranges on the top. Since the oranges tested were good, the whole shipment was passed as good.
   d) As the spacecraft Mariner 4 flew past Mars in 1965, it photographed about 10% of Mars' surface. Since there was no plant or animal life in these pictures, a study concluded that Mars was a dead planet.

Closing

11. a) Discuss ways in which a sample can be chosen to be representative.
    b) Under what circumstances might you use a population?

Extending

12. The Canadian government conducts a census every five years to gather information about the population of the country. The last census was in 2006. Research some data gathered from a recent Canadian census. Write a question about the data and have a classmate answer it.

Chapter Task

I. Add a row to your rubric to assess the choice of sample or population.

J. Decide whether your survey should be conducted using a sample or a population. Use your rubric to assess, and, if necessary, revise your choice.

K. Describe in detail the method you will use to collect data (survey/census/other).

Task | *Checklist*

✔ Topic chosen?

✔ Question(s) written?

✔ Method chosen?

Sample or population chosen?

- Is choice of sample or population practical?
- If you chose a sample, is it representative?

Display and analysis methods chosen?

Project completed and assessed?

10.4 Communicating about Collected Data

GOAL

Communicate clearly and accurately about the results of a survey.

INVESTIGATE the Math

Larissa wanted to know if, after downloading free music, people shared it with others. She conducted a survey, organized her data, and made this presentation. David wrote down some comments during the presentation.

? How can Larissa improve her report?

Larissa's Report

I created this questionnaire to survey the students in my class about music downloads.

1. Do you download music from free sites? Yes ___ No ___
2. Do you allow others to copy it? Yes ___ No ___ Not Applicable ___
3. If someone does share it, do you think that it is stealing? Yes ___ No ___ Don't Know ___ Explain. ______________________________
4. When you download from a "legal" site, what do you think it means? ______________________________

David's Comments

- Your questions are clear and easy to answer, and should get the data you need.
- Should you include options to check off with each question?
- You may want to put the questions in a more natural order.
- Do you think the question about allowing copying will be answered honestly? How can you change it to get more truthful answers?

I asked my teacher if my classmates could take a few minutes to fill out the questionnaire one morning during homeroom period.

- Were any students absent that morning? What did you do if there were?

I tallied the results and made this table.

Q	Yes	No	Not Applicable	Don't Know
1	20	5		
2	2	18	5	
3	8	2		15

"Yes"–it is stealing, the download is meant only for the original person (paraphrased from 8 responses)

"No"–it is not stealing, they could go download for themselves anyway (paraphrased from 2 responses)

"Don't Know"–no explanations

4 Don't know–15

Site creator paid the royalties to the label–5

Site creator also "stole" the music–5

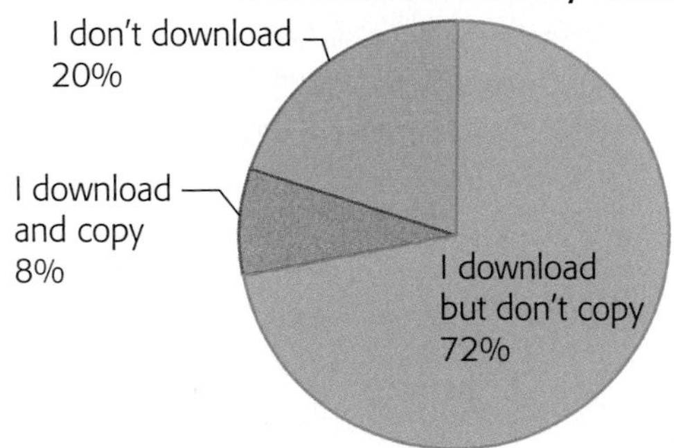

From the data, I concluded that though many of my classmates do use free download sites, most of them don't allow others to copy what they have downloaded. There are a number of students who don't know about the "stealing" idea, and a number of them do not know what it means when they use a "legal" site.

- Are you sure about your first conclusion? Do you think the respondents told the truth?
- After reviewing the data you gathered, are there any other questions you might have asked?

A. Use David's comments, this Communication Checklist, and any ideas of your own to improve Larissa's report.

Reflecting

B. What parts of the Communication Checklist did Larissa cover well?

C. How did David's questions help you analyze Larissa's report?

Communication | ***Checklist***

✔ Did you include all of the important details?

✔ Did you justify your choice of sample?

✔ Did you justify your type of graph?

✔ Did you make reasonable conclusions and justify them?

WORK WITH the Math

EXAMPLE 1 | Displaying data

Thomas was in charge of surveying the students in his school about the preferred destination for a year-end field trip in the Calgary area. What is good about his report, and how would you improve it?

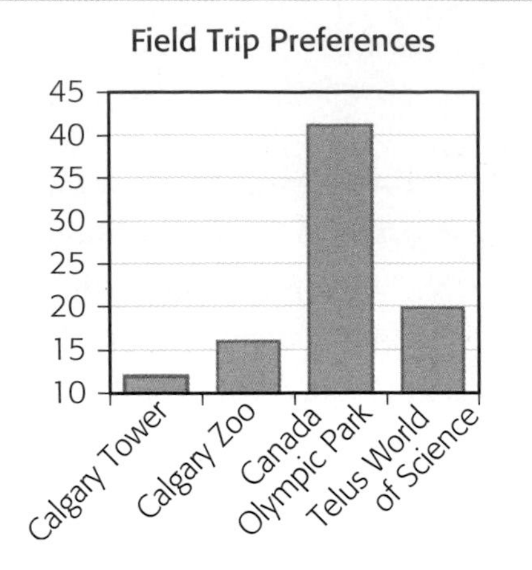

Report on Field Trip Destinations

I asked a sample of 80 students to choose a preferred destination for the field trip. This bar graph shows the results of my survey.

I concluded that the Canada Olympic Park was the most popular destination.

Jia-Wen's Solution

Thomas should say how he selected the sample.

To decide whether the sample was representative, I needed to know if Thomas asked students from each grade in fair proportions, and if he selected students randomly within each grade.

Thomas should have stated the exact question he asked.

Did the students have only the four choices shown? Was there an "Other" option?

Thomas should say whether he told students the cost per person for entrance fees and transportation of each choice.

The cost of going to the Canada Olympic Park may be more than parents want to spend. By not stating the costs, Thomas may have made the question biased.

A bar graph is a good way to show these data.

As well as showing all the data in one graph, Thomas could have used more bars to show the popularity of destinations for each grade.

The most popular destination shown here may not have been the most popular for each grade.

Thomas's conclusion is fine as long as the other changes are made.

It does appear that the Canada Olympic Park is much more popular than the other choices. However, we do not know if either the sample or the question was biased.

EXAMPLE 2 | Validity of conclusions

The same conclusion was drawn from two surveys conducted in a school of 500 students.

Sample A: 10 students were asked, 2 of them eat pizza on Friday nights.

Sample B: 100 students were chosen at random, 28 eat pizza on Friday nights.

Conclusion: About 30% of students eat pizza on Friday nights.

Based on the samples, would you accept or reject the conclusion? Justify your answers.

Sam's Solution

Sample A–reject
The sample is probably too small.

2 out of 10 is only 20%, not 30%. Also, 10 out of 500 students is only 2% of the population. As well, we don't know if the students were chosen at random. They might all be from one grade.

Sample B–accept
The sample is probably representative and the data support the conclusion.

I think a sample of 100 is large enough, and its randomness should make it representative. The result of 28 out of 100 is 28%, which is close to 30%.

In Summary

Key Ideas

For your audience to judge if your conclusions are reasonable, communication about how data are collected should describe

- the method of collection
- the sample or population from whom the data were collected
- why the survey was conducted

Need to Know

A good report should include

- the question(s) asked in the survey
- appropriate display of the data
- valid conclusions based on the data

Checking

1. A survey concludes that "Four out of five dentists surveyed recommend sugarless gum for their patients who chew gum."

a) Use the Communication Checklist on page 485 to help you write some questions about the survey.

b) Do you have enough information to decide if the claim is valid? Explain.

Practising

2. People walking on a busy street in Edmonton were stopped at random and asked the following question:

> **When you go on vacation, what is your preferred mode of transport:**
>
> airplane (P), car (C), bus (B), or train (T)?

The responses of the first 20 people stopped were

B C C P B C C B P B P C T T C P T P C C

These data can be organized in a table, a bar graph, or a circle graph.

a) Identify advantages and disadvantages of each method of display.

b) Is one display better than the others to communicate the results of the survey?

c) Might the results of the survey be different in a more rural area?

3. Describe how the data might have been gathered to support each claim.

a) Nine out of 10 cats prefer Katto Treats.

b) Out of a random sample of 10 cats, 9 preferred Katto Treats.

c) Out of a random sample of 10 cats, 9 preferred Katto Treats to their regular brand.

4. A radio news program asked listeners to phone in a vote for or against increasing funding for the development of electric cars. The overwhelming response was "for," so the radio station concluded that the population was in favour of increasing funds. Do you think this conclusion was valid?

5. Explain whether you would accept or reject each conclusion, based on the sample. Assume all samples are random.
   a) Conclusion: 18% of the students in your school have blue eyes.
      Sample: 36 students in a class completed a questionnaire and 18% said they have blue eyes.
   b) Conclusion: "Teen Teen," a magazine for teenagers, is read by very few teens.
      Sample: Out of 200 people of various ages interviewed in downtown Winnipeg, only 3 people had read the magazine, while 23 people were aware of it.
   c) Conclusion: All Francophone schools have a band as a part of their music program.
      Sample: During the annual band competition, all band members were from Francophone schools.
   d) Conclusion: 98.9% of light bulbs met the required standards.
      Sample: 1000 light bulbs were tested daily and about 11 were found to be defective.

Reading Strategy

Finding Important Information

What is the most important information in each conclusion?

Closing

6. When you describe the results of a survey, why is it important to make clear what the whole population is, how a sample is selected, and the purpose of the data collection?

Chapter Task

L. Add two lines to your rubric to assess the display and analysis of data and the conclusions about the question(s) asked.

M. Decide on the methods you will use to display and analyze your data. Assess and, if necessary, revise your methods.

Task | ***Checklist***

✔ Topic chosen?

✔ Question(s) written?

✔ Method chosen?

✔ Sample or population chosen?

Display and analysis methods chosen?

- Are displays appropriate?
- Does your analysis help you answer your question(s)?

Project completed and assessed?

Curious MATH

Weird and Wonderful Maps

Cartograms are world maps that are resized or "morphed" to show data such as population, land area, births, or carbon emissions. These maps, from Worldmapper, show population distributions for specific years in history and a prediction for the future.

1. Which regions show the most significant increases from 1 CE to 1900?
2. The world population approximately doubled from 1 CE to 1500. What do those two maps say about the distribution of the increase?
3. From 1500 to 1900 the world population more than tripled. Compare Canada and the United States. Estimate the population increases in these two regions.
4. a) To what possible question do you think each cartogram is an answer?
   b) How do you think the data for these cartograms were collected? Do you think populations or samples were used?
   c) Are these cartograms good visuals for presenting this type of data? Explain.
5. Use an Internet search to find more cartograms. Create a question that some of the cartograms will help you answer.

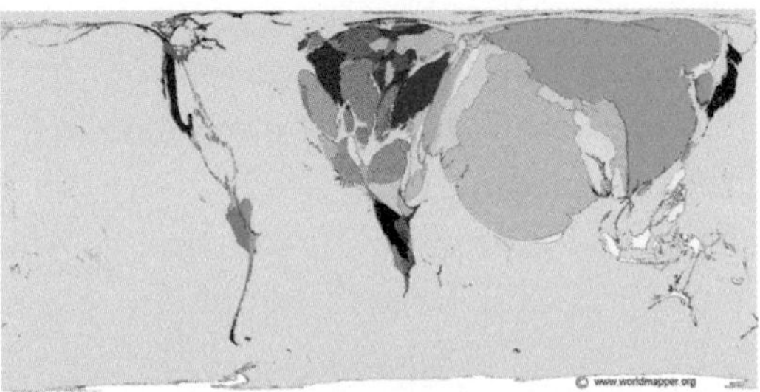

World population, 1 CE (Common Era).

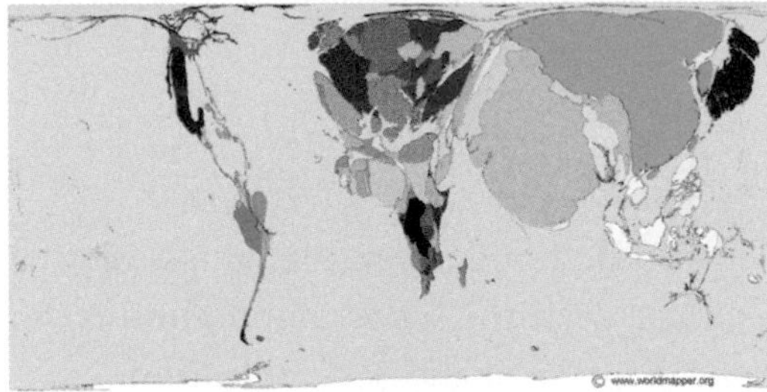

World population in 1500 CE.

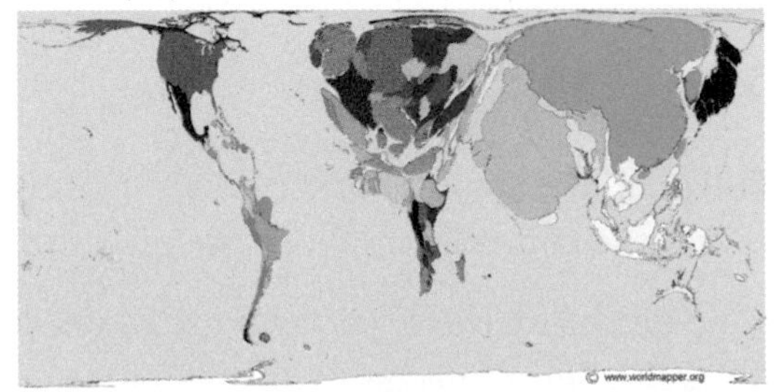

World population in 1900 CE.

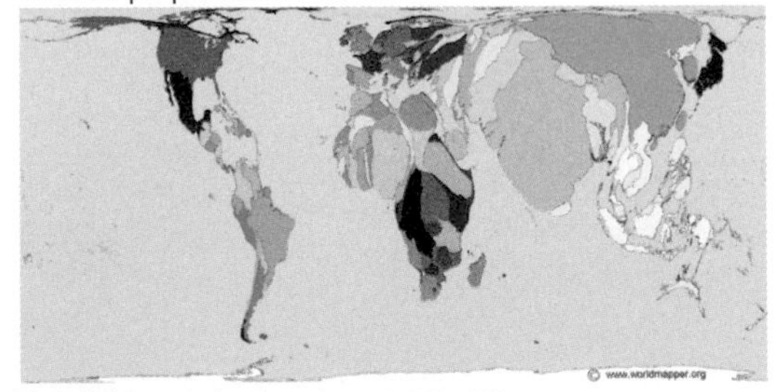

World population in 2050 CE.

CHAPTER 10 Chapter Self-Test

1. The following questions will likely not be effective at generating the required data. Rewrite them so that it will be clear and easy to understand what is being looked for.
   a) Does your family eat a lot of candy?
   b) You are against smoking, aren't you?
   c) Are you aged ___ over 14, ___under 21, ___ under 18?
   d) Can you afford to pay your school fees?

2. Emergency rooms are reporting an increased number of serious accidents because of all-terrain vehicles (ATVs) among young people. Write four or five questions for a survey to gather data about young people operating ATVs.

3. Describe problems with the plan for selecting a sample to collect data about each question. Explain how the sample could be improved.
   a) Are red Fancy Candies the ones produced in the greatest quantity? Sample: Open one box and count each colour.
   b) What is the most popular high-school sport? Sample: Ask all the people leaving a volleyball game.
   c) What do you think about the wages paid to a particular group of public employees? Sample: Ask a group of public employees who earn below-average wages.
   d) How sweet is a shipment of oranges? Sample: Cut open all the oranges in a case and taste them.

4. Would you use a sample or the whole population to gather data about each topic? Explain what is wrong with the other choice.
   a) the average base circumference of all the trees on your block
   b) the average base circumference of all the trees in Canada
   c) the number of "Spirit" T-shirts the student council should print to sell for a fundraiser

5. A local sports station wants to find out how many hours per week people in their viewing area watch sporting events on television. The station surveys people at a nearby sports stadium.
   a) Is the sample biased? Explain.
   b) How else could the survey be conducted?

6. Andrea says that, based on her survey, she believes that taller women have higher incomes in Canada. Name two items Andrea should put in a full report that would convince you that her conclusion is valid.

7. This questionnaire was distributed to the members of a Grade 9 class just before Christmas.

Name ______________________

We are planning a ski trip to the mountains in February. The fee of $295 will cover transportation, two nights' lodging, and two days of lift tickets. Rentals ($50 per day), lessons ($25 per hour), and food (about $40 per day) will be extra.

1. Would you be interested in coming? ___Yes ___No
2. Can you afford the cost? ___Yes ___No
3. Would you be interested in a fundraising event to defer some of the cost? ___ Yes ___No
4. Would you ask your parents to give you the ski trip as a Christmas present? ___Yes ___No
5. Have you ever skied before? ___Yes ___No
6. Will you need rentals and/or lessons? ___Rentals ___Lessons ___Both

a) Which questions may be insensitive or invade a student's privacy? Explain.
b) Is there a better order for the questions? Explain.
c) Is the timing of the questionnaire good? Explain.

8. Evaluate the questions in the survey in question 7 according to this rubric.

	3 Good	2 Acceptable	1 Not Acceptable
Survey/ Interview Questions (1)	Appropriate questions are asked; questions should generate all of needed data.	Fairly appropriate questions are asked; questions should generate most of needed data.	Inappropriate questions are asked to gather needed data.
Survey/ Interview Questions (2)	Questions are sensitive and do not create bias.	Questions are fairly sensitive; some may create bias.	Questions are biased and/or likely to offend respondents.

WHAT DO You Think Now?

Revisit What Do You Think? on page 463. How have your answers and explanations changed?

Chapter Review

FREQUENTLY ASKED Questions

Q: What are the characteristics of an appropriate survey question?

A: Survey questions should be clearly written, easy to answer, and effective in generating the desired data. For example, "Is your annual household income a) below $25 000, b) $25 000 to $50 000, c) $50 000 to $100 000, or d) more than $100 000?" is clearer, easier to answer, and more effective than "Is your income a) low, b) medium, c) high?"

Study *Aid*

- See Lesson 10.1, Examples 1, 2, and 3.
- Try Chapter Review questions 1 and 2.

Q: How can I tell if a survey question may be biased?

A: If a question influences you to answer in a particular way then it may be biased. For example, "If you knew that dozens of people die each year because there are not enough organ donors, would you express an intention to become an organ donor?"

Study *Aid*

- See Lesson 10.2, Examples 1 and 2.
- Try Chapter Review questions 4, 5, and 6.

Q: What are possible reasons for using a sample rather than the population to gather data?

A: A census may cost too much or be too difficult or time-consuming to manage.

Study *Aid*

- See Lesson 10.3, Example 1.
- Try Chapter Review questions 8, 9, and 10.

Q: What are the elements of a clear and accurate report on a survey?

A: You should

- state your questions exactly as you asked them
- clearly explain your method of collecting data and how you chose your sample or population
- use tables, graphs, or diagrams as appropriate
- state and explain conclusions that are well supported by the data

Study *Aid*

- See Lesson 10.4, Examples 1 and 2.
- Try Chapter Review question 12.

Practice

Lesson 10.1

1. This questionnaire was developed to collect data about the activities students would like for a Spring Fiesta activity day.

> SPRING FIESTA ACTIVITIES
>
> 1. Rank the activities from 1 to 10 to determine which ones should be included in the day.
>
> _____ Tug of War _____ Jello Pool _____ Pudding Toss
>
> _____ Water Balloon Toss _____ Noodle Jousting ______ Sumo Suits
>
> _____ Astro Castle _____ Astro Obstacle _____ Dodge Ball
>
> _____ Frisbee Baseball
>
> 2. List any other activities that you would like to see.
>
> 3. Will you participate in a Spring Fiesta activity day, or will you stay home that day?
>
> 4. How much should the school spend on renting equipment for the day?
>
> 5. Would you be willing to pay a fee to participate in the day?

a) Are the questions clear and easy to answer, and will they generate the information the organizing committee will need?
b) Which question(s) might not be answered? Explain.
c) Should the questions be in a different order? Explain.
d) Should some questions be removed?

2. Write an appropriate question that might be used to gather data in each situation.
a) The staff at your school wants a staff-only cafeteria.
b) You want to find the fastest way to school.
c) You're having a party and want to know what foods to serve.

Lesson 10.2

3. For each situation in question 2, what method would you use to get an answer?

4. Explain why each question may be biased.

a) Many national forests are being damaged by acid rain. Do you favour government funding to help prevent acid rain?

b) Police officers ask mall visitors, "Do you wear your seatbelt regularly?"

5. What errors in data collection could be caused in each survey?

a) asking respondents to phone in if they are in favour of age restrictions for operating all-terrain vehicles (ATVs) as a means of reducing fatalities among young people

b) a newspaper questionnaire to gather data about the possibility of instituting a curfew for teens in your community

6. Identify the bias in each question, and rephrase it to remove the bias or potential influence on the respondent.

a) Do you agree with most doctors and the Canadian Medical Association that smoking is bad for your health?

b) Should reckless adventure seekers pay for any expenses incurred if they need to be rescued?

c) Should roller-bladers be allowed to cause danger to walkers on walking paths?

7. Which method of gathering data—questionnaire, interview, or experiment and observation—would you use for each of the following? Explain.

a) the popularity of a reality show on television

b) whether boxes of cereal coming off an assembly line contain the posted mass

c) the effectiveness of an air-purifying system

Lesson 10.3

8. For each situation, decide whether to use a sample or the population to make a decision. Give reasons for your choice.

a) determining the quality of the picture in a shipment of television sets

b) determining the quality of a number of parachutes

c) deciding on the effectiveness of a moisturizing cream

d) predicting the amount of oil in a new discovery

e) drawing blood to measure glucose levels

f) checking the conditions of the pistons in a car engine

g) determining the attendance at a football game

9. The Science Club at school wants to conduct a survey about recycling.

a) Should the club survey a sample of your school's population or do a census? Give reasons for your answer.

b) Describe how a random sample can be selected so that it is representative.

10. Give reasons why you would take samples in each case.

a) crash resistance of automobiles

b) heights of Canadians

c) noise level of a jet at an airport

d) protection given by firefighters' clothing

e) the proportion of a tree species in a forest

11. A department store wants to know customers' opinions about its service and merchandise. They offer a free gift as an incentive to fill out the survey. Which customers are most likely to fill out the survey?

Lesson 10.4

12. In a group of 40 people, the following pulse rates in beats per minute were obtained.

66	61	79	71	53	86	81	73
84	87	76	72	76	71	67	64
67	83	71	68	81	86	56	62
67	77	72	79	76	82	78	62
76	76	56	82	88	73	67	65

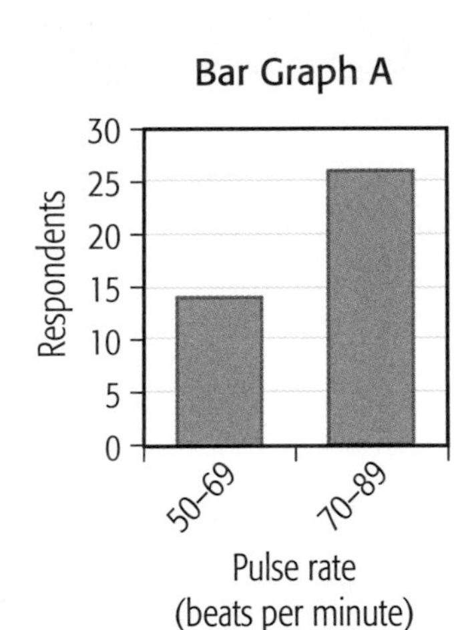

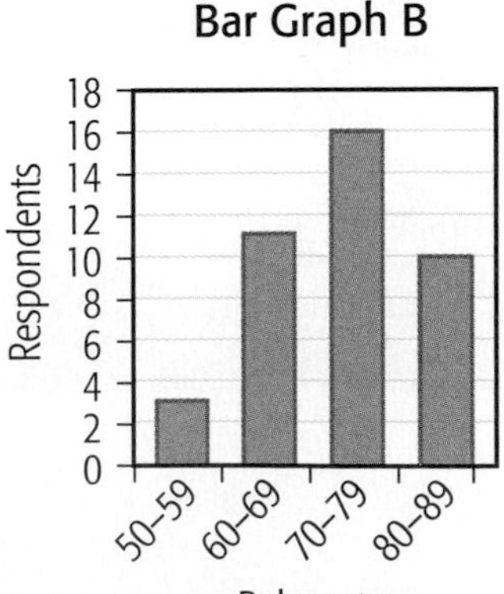

a) Why is it difficult to make observations about the data in "raw" form?

b) Bar graphs A and B were created as displays to show which pulse rates are more common. Which bar graph communicates the data more clearly, and why?

c) Based on each bar graph, what conclusion can you draw about the most common pulse rate?

d) If you record the pulse rates of 1000 people, about how many would you expect to have a rate in the interval 80–89? Give reasons for your answer.

e) What assumptions did you make in obtaining your answer?

Chapter Task

Data Project

How effectively can you plan and carry out a data investigation?

During the course of this chapter you may have already done much of the work for your project. Use the following steps to ensure that your project is complete:

A. Describe
- your chosen topic
- your questions
- the method you chose to collect the data, including choice of sample or population
- how you plan to organize and display your data

B. Obtain your teacher's approval for your project plan and rubric.

C. Carry out your plan.

D. Analyze your data and make appropriate conclusions.

E. Use your rubric to self-assess your project.

Task | *Checklist*

✔ Topic chosen?

✔ Question(s) written?

✔ Method chosen?

✔ Sample or population chosen?

✔ Display and analysis methods chosen?

Project completed and assessed?
- Plan and rubric approved?
- Collection, display, and analysis completed?
- Report completed?
- Project self-assessed using rubric?

CHAPTERS 8–10 Cumulative Review

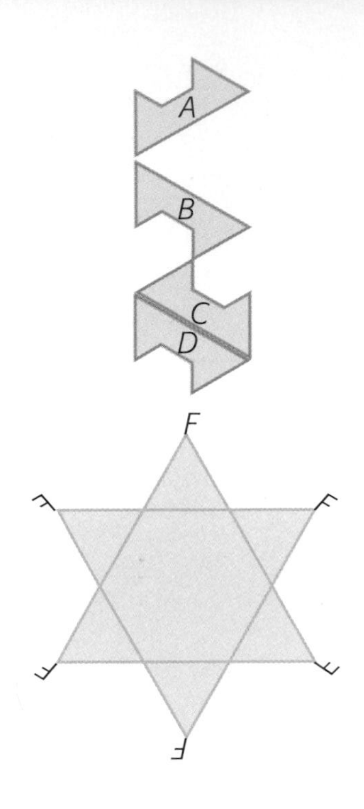

1. Which two shapes at left create a design with line symmetry?
   A. A and C **B.** B and C **C.** B and D **D.** A and D

2. Which two shapes create a design with rotation symmetry?
   A. B and C **B.** A and C **C.** A and D **D.** B and D

3. Which two shapes create a design with more than one line of symmetry?
   A. C and D **B.** A and D **C.** A and B **D.** B and C

4. What is the order of rotation symmetry in this star design?
   A. 1
   B. 2
   C. 3
   D. 6

5. Which is *not* an angle of rotation for rotation symmetry in this tessellation?
   A. 60°
   B. 90°
   C. 120°
   D. 180°

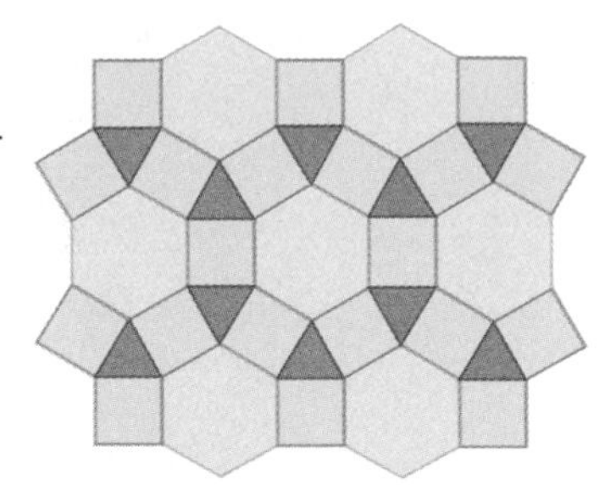

6. A triangle with vertices $A(1, 1)$, $B(2, 3)$, and $C(5, 1)$ is translated (L5, D4). Which point is a vertex of the image?
   A. $(-3, 6)$ **B.** $(-2, -2)$ **C.** $(-3, -1)$ **D.** $(0, 5)$

7. A triangle with vertices $(-4, -1)$, $(0, -1)$, and $(-4, -5)$ is reflected across the line $y = x$. Choose the correct description of the design created by the triangle and its image.
   A. It has no line symmetry and no rotation symmetry.
   B. It has line symmetry but no rotation symmetry.
   C. It has no line symmetry but does have rotation symmetry.
   D. It has line symmetry and rotation symmetry.

8. A quadrilateral with vertices $P(1, 1)$, $Q(2, -1)$, $R(3, 2)$, and $S(4, 0)$ is reflected across the x-axis, and then rotated 180° about the origin. Determine the coordinates of $P'Q'R'S'$.
   A. $P'(1, -1)$, $Q'(2, 1)$, $R'(3, -2)$, and $S'(4, 0)$
   B. $P'(-1, 1)$, $Q'(-2, -1)$, $R'(-3, 2)$, and $S'(-4, 0)$
   C. $P'(-1, -1)$, $Q'(-2, 1)$, $R'(-3, -2)$, and $S'(-4, 0)$
   D. $P'(1, 1)$, $Q'(-1, 2)$, $R'(2, 3)$, and $S'(0, 4)$

9. The measure of $\angle COD$ is
   A. 56° **B.** 112° **C.** 136° **D.** 62°

10. Determine the measures of $\angle T$ and $\angle W$.

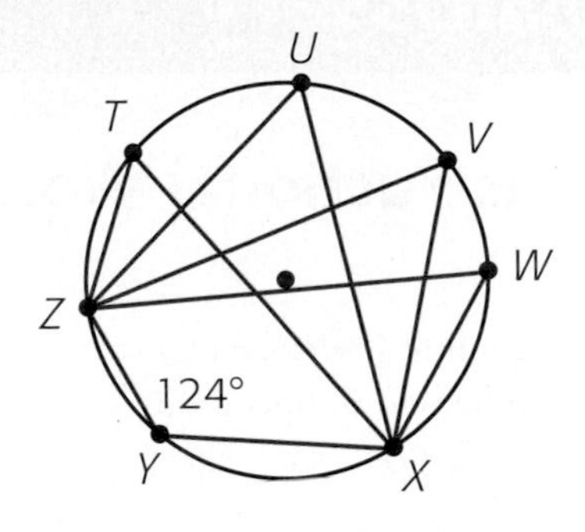

A. $\angle T = 56°, \angle W = 56°$
B. $\angle T = 62°, \angle W = 62°$
C. $\angle T = 56°, \angle W = 62°$
D. None of the above

11. A chord 9.0 cm long is 6.0 cm from the centre of a circle. What is the diameter of the circle to the nearest tenth of a centimetre?

A. 7.5 cm B. 10.8 cm C. 15.0 cm D. 21.6 cm

12. The sides of $\triangle QRS$ are tangent to the smaller circle. P is the centre of both circles. Determine the perimeter of $\triangle QRS$ to the nearest tenth of a centimetre.

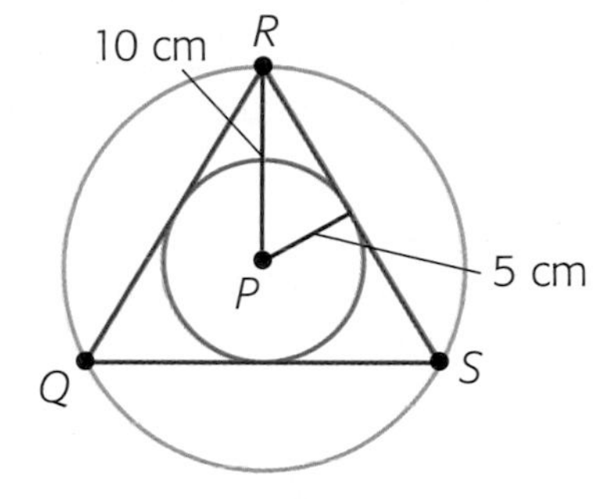

A. 52.0 cm B. 26.0 cm C. 8.7 cm D. 67.1 cm

13. How could you gather reliable data to decide the popularity of a soap opera at your school?

A. ask a random sample of students at your school to complete a questionnaire about soap operas
B. interview one of the stars of the soap opera
C. interview all students who watch the soap opera
D. ask a random sample of students in one class to complete a questionnaire about soap operas

14. How could you gather reliable data to decide if boxes of crackers contain the posted mass?

A. ask managers of grocery stores to complete a questionnaire
B. interview the owner of the cracker factory
C. measure the mass of a sample of boxes of crackers
D. measure the mass of every box of crackers

15. Identify the phrase that creates bias in this question: Do you agree with most dentists and the Canadian Dental Association that sugar is bad for your teeth?

A. sugar is bad
B. with most dentists
C. Canadian Dental Association
D. B and C

16. In which situation would a population be used rather than a sample?

A. An advertising firm wants to know the music preferences of 14- to 17-year-olds.
B. Shipments of video games are being tested for defective products.
C. Your school is voting for student council grade representatives.
D. A medical team is researching the exercise habits of Canadian teenagers.

Glossary

Instructional Words

C

calculate [*calculer*]: Complete one or more mathematical operations; compute

clarify [*clarifier*]: Make a statement easier to understand; provide an example

classify [*classer* ou *classifier*]: Put things into groups according to a rule and label the groups; organize into categories

compare [*comparer*]: Look at two or more objects or numbers and identify how they are the same and how they are different

conclude [*conclure*]: Judge or decide after reflection or after considering data

construct [*construire*]: Make or build a model; draw an accurate geometric shape (e.g., Use a ruler and a protractor to construct an angle.)

create [*inventer* ou *créer*]: Make your own example

D

describe [*décrire*]: Tell, draw, or write about what something is or what something looks like; tell about a process in a step-by-step way

determine [*déterminer*]: Decide with certainty as a result of calculation, experiment, or exploration

draw: 1. [*dessiner*] Show something in picture form (e.g., Draw a diagram.)
2. [*tirer*] Pull or select an object (e.g., Draw a card from the deck. Draw a tile from the bag.)

E

estimate [*estimer*]: Use your knowledge to make a sensible decision about an amount; make a reasonable guess (e.g., Estimate 3210 + 789.)

evaluate [*évaluer*]: 1. Determine if something makes sense; judge
2. Calculate the value as a number

explain [*expliquer*]: Tell what you did; show your mathematical thinking at every stage; show how you know

explore [*explorer*]: Investigate a problem by questioning, brainstorming, and trying new ideas

extend [*prolonger*]: 1. In patterning, continue the pattern
2. In problem solving, create a new problem that takes the idea of the original problem further

J

justify [*justifier*]: Give convincing reasons for a prediction, an estimate, or a solution; tell why you think your answer is correct

M

measure [*mesurer*]: Use a tool to describe an object or determine an amount (e.g., Use a protractor to measure an angle.)

model [*représenter* ou *faire un modèle*]: Show or demonstrate an idea using objects and/or pictures (e.g., Model addition of integers using red and blue counters.)

P

predict [*prédire*]: Use what you know to work out what is going to happen (e.g., Predict the next number in the pattern 1, 2, 4, 7,...)

R

reason [*raisonner* ou *argumenter*]: Develop ideas and relate them to the purpose of the task and to each other; analyze relevant information to show understanding

relate [*établir un lien* ou *associer*]: Describe how two or more objects, drawings, ideas, or numbers are similar

represent [*représenter*]: Show information or an idea in a different way that makes it easier to understand (e.g., Draw a graph. Make a model. Create a rhyme.)

S

show (your work) [*montrer son travail* ou *présenter sa démarche*]: Record all calculations, drawings, numbers, words, or symbols that make up the solution

simplify [***simplifier***]**:** Rewrite an expression as an equivalent expression that uses fewer terms (e.g., The polynomial $2x - 3x + 8 + 9$ can be simplified to $-x + 17$.)

sketch [***esquisser***]**:** Make a rough drawing (e.g., Sketch a picture of the field with dimensions.)

solve [***résoudre***]**:** Develop and carry out a process for finding a solution to a problem

sort [***trier*** ou ***classer***]**:** Separate a set of objects, drawings, ideas, or numbers according to an attribute (e.g., Sort 2-D shapes by the number of sides.)

V

validate [***valider***]**:** Check an idea by showing that it works

verify [***vérifier***]**:** Work out an answer or solution again, usually in another way; show evidence of

visualize [***imaginer***]**:** Form a picture in your head of what something is like; imagine

Glossary

Mathematical Words

A

algebraic expression [*expression* (n.f.) *algébrique*]: The result of applying arithmetic operations to numbers and variables (e.g., $3x$ or $5x + 2$)

angle bisector [*bissectrice* (n.f.)]: A line that cuts an angle in half to form two equal angles

arc [*arc* (n.m.)]: Part of the circumference of a circle; called a major arc when the arc is greater than a semicircle or a minor arc when the arc is less than a semicircle

area of overlap [*bande* (n.f.) *de recouvrement*]: The area covered when two component parts are joined to form a composite object

associative property [*opération* (n.f.) *associative*]: The property that brackets can be disregarded. Multiplication and addition are associative, so $2 \times (3 \times 4) = (2 \times 3) \times 4$ and $2 + (3 + 4) = (2 + 3) + 4$, but division and subtraction are not associative.

B

base [*base* (n.f.)]: 1. The side of a shape that is measured for calculating the area or perimeter of a shape. Each base has a corresponding height that creates a 90° angle with the base. Any side of a shape can be the base of the shape.
2. The number used as a factor in a power; e.g.,

base ⟶ 2^3 ⟵ exponent

biased question [*question* (n.f.) *manquant d'objectivité*]: A question that is likely to influence respondents to answer in a particular way (e.g., "Do you agree that dogs are friendlier than cats?")

biased sample [*échantillon* (n.m.) *déséquilibré*]: A sample whose responses are likely to be different from the responses of the whole population

C

Cartesian coordinate system [*système* (n.m.) *de coordonnées cartésiennes*]: A method (named after mathematician René Descartes) for describing a location by identifying the distance from a horizontal number line (the x-axis) and a vertical number line (the y-axis). The location is represented by an ordered pair of coordinates (x, y). The axes intersect at (0, 0), which is called the origin.

census [*recensement* (n.m.)]: Collects data about (and counts) a whole population

central angle [*angle* (n.m.) *au centre*]: An angle whose vertex is at the centre of a circle

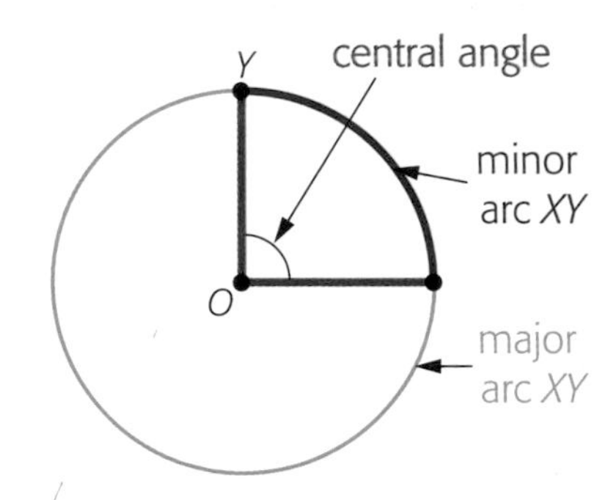

centre of rotation [*centre* (n.m.) *de rotation*]: A fixed point around which other points in a shape rotate in a clockwise (cw) or counterclockwise (ccw) direction. The centre of rotation may be inside or outside the shape.

chord [*corde* (n.f.)]: A line segment joining two points on a circle

circle graph [*diagramme* (n.m.) *circulaire*]: A graph that shows how the parts make up a whole

circumference [*circonférence* (n.f.)]: The boundary of a circle; the length of this boundary

clockwise (cw) [*dans le sens* (n.m.) *des aiguilles d'une montre*]: Turning in a sense similar to the hands of a clock (e.g., A turn from direction OP to direction OQ is a clockwise turn. Also see **counterclockwise**.)

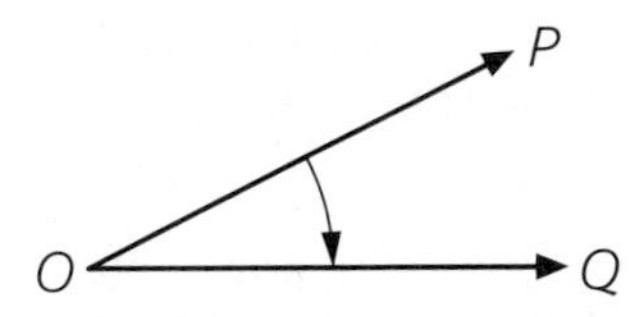

coefficient [***coefficient*** (n.m.)]**:** The multiplier of a variable (e.g., In $2n + 5$, 2 is the coefficient of n.)

common denominator [***dénominateur*** (n.m.) ***commun***]**:** A common multiple of two or more denominators (e.g., For $\frac{2}{3}$ and $\frac{3}{6}$, a common denominator would be any multiple of 6.) If you use the least common multiple of the denominators, the common denominator is called the lowest common denominator.

common factor [***diviseur*** (n.m.) ***commun***]**:** A whole number that divides into two or more other numbers with no remainder (e.g., 4 is a common factor of 12 and 24.)

common multiple [***multiple*** (n.m.) ***commun***]**:** A number that is a multiple of two or more given numbers (e.g., 12, 24, and 36 are common multiples of 4 and 6.)

commutative property [***opération*** (n.f.) ***commutative***]**:** The property that elements can be combined in any order. Multiplication and addition are commutative, so $2 \times 3 = 3 \times 2$ and $2 + 3 = 3 + 2$, but division and subtraction are not commutative.

complementary event [***événement*** (n.m.) ***complémentaire***]**:** The set of outcomes in the sample space in which the event does not happen (e.g., When rolling a die, the event "rolling 2" has the complementary event "rolling 1, 3, 4, 5, or 6".)

composite object [***objet*** (n.m.) ***composite***]**:** An object that can be decomposed into component parts, such as prisms and cylinders

constant [***constante*** (n.f.)]**:** A quantity that does not change (e.g., In $2n + 5$, 5 is a constant.)

congruent [***congruent***]**:** Identical in shape and size (e.g., △A is congruent to △B but is not congruent to △C (different size) or △D (different shape).)

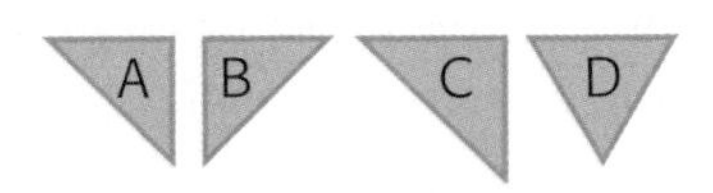

convex [***convexe***]**:** A design where all interior angles measure no greater than 180°

coordinates [***coordonnées*** (n.f.pl.) ***d'un point*** ou ***coordonnées*** (n.f.pl.)]**:** An ordered pair, used to describe a location on a grid labelled with an x-axis and a y-axis (e.g., The coordinates (1, 3) describe a location on a grid that is 1 unit horizontally from the origin and 3 units vertically from the origin.)

corresponding angles [***angles*** (n.m.) ***correspondants***]**:** Angles that match when two shapes are arranged to look the same (e.g., In the parallelograms below, $\angle CDA$ and $\angle GHE$ are corresponding angles.)

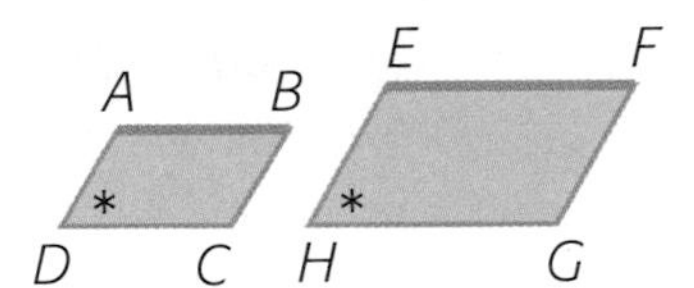

corresponding sides [***côtés*** (n.m.) ***correspondants***]**:** Sides that match if two shapes are arranged to look the same (e.g., In the parallelograms above, AB and EF are corresponding sides.)

counterclockwise (ccw) [***dans le sens*** (n.m.) ***contraire des aiguilles d'une montre***]**:** Turning in a sense opposite to the hands of a clock (e.g., A turn from direction OQ to direction OP is a counterclockwise turn. Also see **clockwise**.)

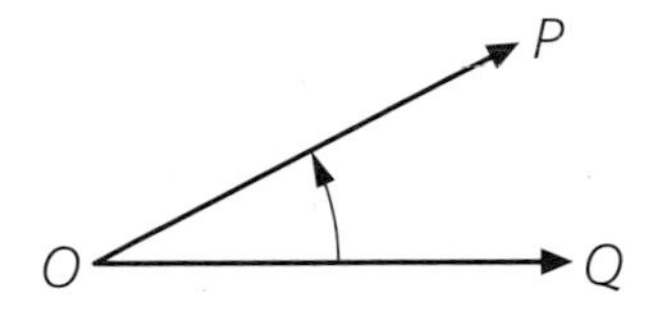

D

degree of a polynomial [***degré*** (n.m.) ***d'un polynôme***]**:** The greatest of the degrees of the polynomial's terms (e.g., first-degree polynomials: $-5a + 2$, $8 + 6q$; second-degree polynomials: $3a + 4a^2 - 2$, $2pq - p^2$, $st + 8$)

degree of a term [***degré*** (n.m.) ***d'un terme***]**:** The power to which the variable in a term of a polynomial is raised; if a term contains two variables, its degree is the sum of the powers of the variables (e.g., first-degree terms: $2a$, $-b$; second-degree terms: $4a^2$, $-3b^2$, ab, $-6rs$). The degree of a constant term is 0.

diameter [*diamètre* (n.m.)]: A line segment that joins two points on the circumference of a circle and passes through the centre; the length of this line segment

digital root [*racine* (n.f.) *numérique*]: The number obtained by adding the digits of a number, then repeating the digit addition for each new number found, until a single-digit number is reached (e.g., The digital root of 123 is $1 + 2 + 3 = 6$.)

distributive property [*opération* (n.f.) *distributive*]: The property that says $a \times (b + c) = a \times b + a \times c$. Multiplication is distributed over addition, but division is not distributed over addition.

divisibility rule [*règle* (n.f.) *de divisibilité* ou *caractères* (n.m.pl.) *de divisibilité*]: A way to determine if one whole number is a factor of another whole number without actually dividing the entire number

dodecagon [*dodécagon* (n.m.)]: A polygon with 12 straight sides and 12 angles

E

equally likely outcomes [*résultats* (n.m.pl.) *également probables*]: Two or more outcomes that have an equal chance of occurring (e.g., The outcome of rolling a 1 and the outcome of rolling a 2 on a 6-sided die are equally likely outcomes because each outcome has a probability of $\frac{1}{6}$.)

equation [*égalité* (n.f.); *remarque: en français, une équation comporte obligatoirement une inconnue*]: A statement that two quantities or expressions are equivalent (e.g., $4 + 2 = 6$ and $6x + 2 = 14$)

equivalent [*équivalent*]: Equal in value (e.g., Two equivalent fractions are $\frac{1}{2}$ and $\frac{2}{4}$, two equivalent ratios are 6:4 and 9:6, and the fraction $\frac{1}{2}$ is equivalent to the decimal 0.5.)

equivalent equation [*équation* (n.f.) *équivalente*]: An equation that has exactly the same solutions as another (e.g., $y = 3x + 4$ and $2y = 6x + 8$ are equivalent equations.)

equivalent rate [*rapport* (n.m.) *équivalent*]: A rate that describes the same comparison as another rate (e.g., 2 for $4 is equivalent to 4 for $8.)

equivalent ratio [*rapport* (n.m.) *équivalent*]: A ratio that represents the same relationship as another ratio (e.g., 2:4 is an equivalent ratio to 1:2 because both ratios describe the relationship of the blue counters to the red counters. There are 2 red counters for each blue counter, but also 4 red counters for every 2 blue counters.)

event [*événement* (n.m.)]: A set of one or more outcomes in a probability experiment (e.g., The event of rolling an even number with a six-sided die consists of the outcomes of rolling a 2, a 4, or a 6.)

experimental probability [*probabilité* (n.f.) *expérimentale*]: In a probability experiment, the ratio of the number of observed favourable outcomes to the number of trials, or repetitions, of the experiment

exponent [*exposant* (n.m.)]: The number used to express the number of factors in a power

base → 2^3 ← exponent

expression [*expression* (n.f.) *numérique*]: See **algebraic expression [*expression algébrique* (n.f.)]**

extrapolate [*extrapoler*]: Predict a value by extending a pattern beyond known values

F

factor [*facteur* (n.m.)]: One of the numbers you multiply in a multiplication operation

$2 \times 6 = 12$
↑ ↑
factor factor

favourable outcome [*résultat* (n.m.) *favorable*]: The desired result in a probability experiment

formula [*formule* (n.f.)]: A rule represented by symbols, numbers, or letters, often in the form of an equation (e.g., area of a rectangle = length × width, or $A = l \times w$)

G

greatest common factor (GCF) [*plus grand diviseur* (n.m.) *commun* ou *PGDC*]: The greatest whole number that is a factor of two or more whole numbers (e.g., 4 is the greatest common factor of 8 and 12.)

H

height [*hauteur* (n.f.)]: A line segment drawn to form a right angle with the side of a shape

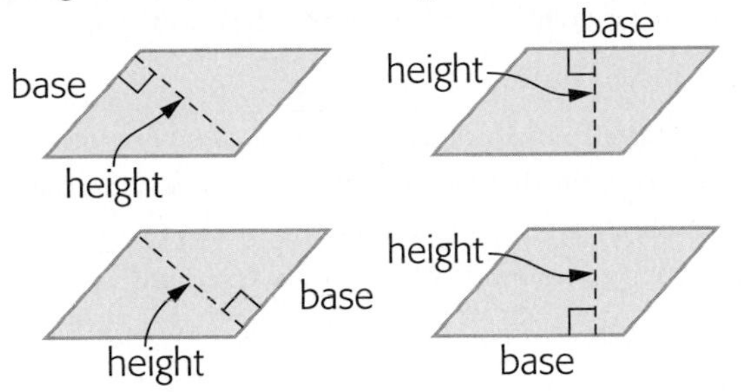

heptagon [*heptagone* (n.m.)]: A polygon with 7 straight sides and 7 angles

hexagon [*hexagone* (n.m.)]: A polygon with 6 straight sides and 6 angles

hypotenuse [*hypoténuse* (n.f.)]: The longest side of a right triangle; the side opposite the right angle

I

improper fraction [*fraction* (n.f.) *impropre*]: A fraction whose numerator is greater than its denominator (e.g., $\frac{5}{4}$ is an improper fraction.)

independent events [*événements* (n.m.pl.) *indépendants*]: Two events are independent if the probability of one is not affected by the probability of the other

inequality [*inéquation* (n.f.)]: A statement that two quantities or expressions are related using less than, greater than, less than or equal to, greater than or equal to (e.g., statements like $2x + 5 < 4$, $3 - 2x \leq 7$ and $4 > 7 + 2x$)

inscribed [*inscrit*]: When all the vertices of a polygon are points on a circle

inscribed angle [*angle* (n.m.) *inscrit*]: An angle formed by two chords whose vertex lies on the circle (e.g., chords PQ and RQ form inscribed $\angle PQR$.)

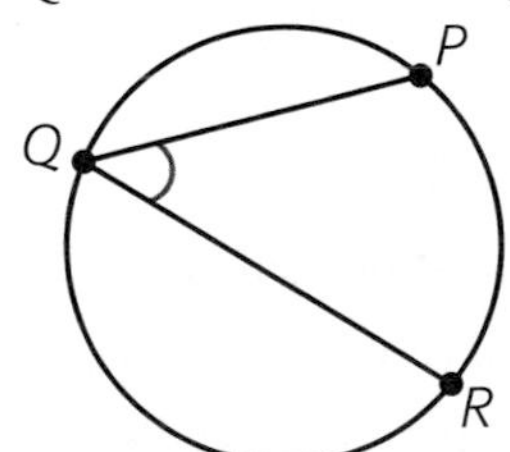

integer [*nombre* (n.m.) *entier* ou *entier* (n.m.)]: The counting numbers (+1, +2, +3,...), zero (0), and the opposites of the counting numbers (−1, −2, −3,...)

interior angle [*angle* (n.m.) *intérieur*]: The inside angle of a polygon

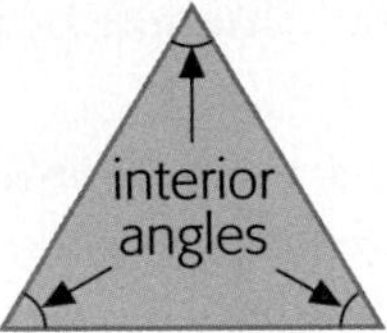

interpolate [*interpoler*]: Estimate a value between two known values

intersection point [*point d'intersection* (n.m.)]: The point where two lines or line segments cross each other (e.g., QR intersects ST at intersection point E.)

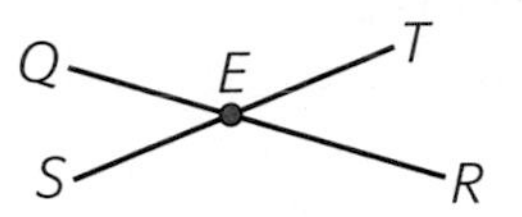

inverse operation [*opération* (n.f.) *systématique*]: An operation that undoes, or reverses, another (e.g., Subtraction is the inverse operation of addition.)

isolate a term or variable [*isoler*]: Perform an operation to get a term or a variable by itself on one side of an equation

isometric drawing [*diagramme* (n.m.) *isométrique*]: A 3-D view of an object in which

- vertical edges are drawn vertically
- width and depth are drawn diagonally
- equal lengths on the object are equal on the drawing

K

kite [*cerf-volant* (n.m.)]: A convex quadrilateral with two pairs of equal adjacent sides

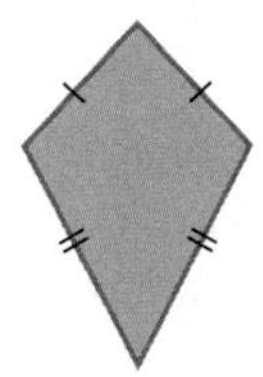

L

least common multiple (LCM) [*plus petit multiple* (n.m.) *commun* ou *PPMC*]: The least whole number that has two or more given whole numbers as factors (e.g., 12 is the least common multiple of 4 and 6.)

like terms [*termes* (n.m.pl.) *similaires*]: Terms of a polynomial that are identical (same variable and same exponent) except for their coefficients (e.g., $3x$ and $-2x$ are like terms.)

linear equation [***équation*** (n.f.) ***linéaire***]**:** An equation that represents a linear relation (e.g., $y = 4x + 2$, $C = 4t - 12$, $3x = 5 + 2x$.)

linear relation [***rapport*** (n.m.) ***linéaire*** ou ***relation*** (n.f.) ***de variation directe***]**:** A relation whose plotted points lie on a straight line

line of symmetry [***ligne*** (n.f.) ***de symétrie***]**:** A line that divides a 2-D shape in half, so that if you fold the shape on this line, the halves will match (e.g., This shape has two lines of symmetry.)

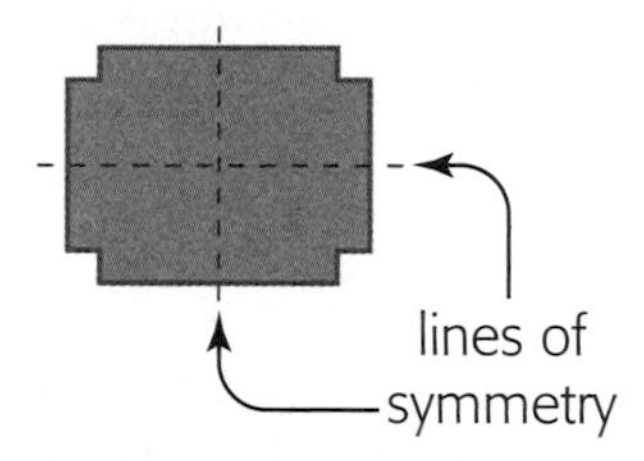

line segment [***segment*** (n.m.) ***de droite*** ou ***segment*** (n.m.)]**:** Part of a line with two endpoints. It is named using the labels of the endpoints (e.g., The line segment joining points X and Y is called XY.)

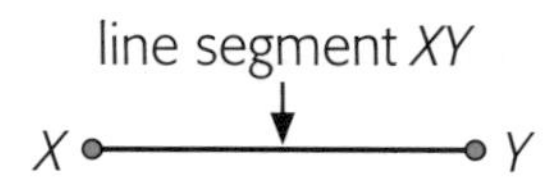

lowest terms [***sous forme*** (n.f.) ***irréductible***]**:** An equivalent form of a fraction with numerator and denominator that have no common factors other than 1 (e.g., $\frac{3}{4}$ is the lowest-term form of $\frac{12}{16}$, since $\frac{3}{4} = \frac{12}{16}$ and 3 and 4 have no common factors other than 1.)

M

mean [***moyenne*** (n.f.)]**:** A representative value of a set of data. It is determined by sharing the total amount of the data evenly among the number of values in the set (e.g., Consider the set of data: 3, 6, 8, 14, 9. There are 5 values, whose sum is 40. The mean is 8, because 40 divided equally among 5 values would give each number the value 8. That is, $40 \div 5 = 8$.)

median [***médiane*** (n.f.)]**:** A representative value of a set of data; the middle value of the ordered data. When there is an odd number of values, the median is the middle value; e.g., the median of 2, 3, and 4 is 3. When there is an even number of values, it is the value halfway between the two middle values; e.g., the median of 2, 3, 4, 5, 6 and 6 is 4.5.

midpoint [***milieu*** (n.m.)]**:** The point on a line segment that divides the line segment into two equal parts

mixed number [***nombre*** (n.m.) ***mixte***]**:** A number expressed as a whole number and a fraction (e.g., $2\frac{1}{2}$ is a mixed number.)

mode [***mode*** (n.m.)]**:** A representative value of a set of data; the value or item that occurs most often in a set of data. A set of data might have no mode, 1 mode, or more than 1 mode (e.g., The mode of 1, 5, 6, 6, 6, 7, and 10 is 6.)

monomial [***monôme*** (n.m.)]**:** A polynomial with only one term (e.g., $3x$, $4xy$, and (-5) are monomials.)

multiple [***multiple*** (n.m.pl.)]**:** The product of a whole number and any other whole number (e.g., When you multiply 10 by the whole numbers 0 to 4, you get the multiples 0, 10, 20, 30, and 40.)

N

net [***développement*** (n.m.)]**:** A 2-D pattern you can fold to create a 3-D object (e.g., This is a net for a cube.)

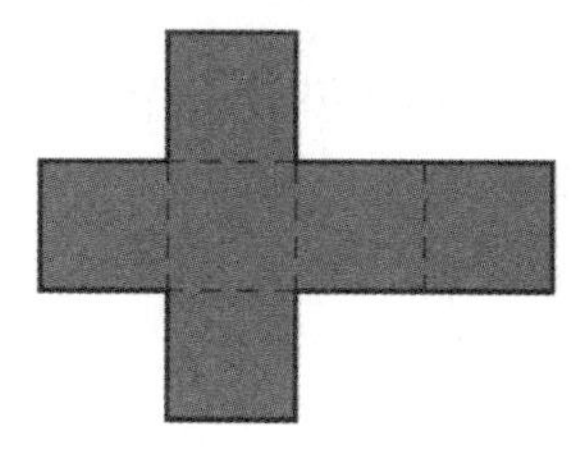

O

octagon [***octogone*** (n.m.)]**:** A polygon with 8 straight sides and 8 angles

opposites [***opposés*** (n.m.pl.)]**:** Two numbers with opposite signs that are the same distance from 0 (e.g., $+2$ and -2 and $+0.5$ and -0.5.)

order of operations [***priorité*** (n.f.) ***des opérations***]**:** A set of rules people use when calculating, in order to get the same answer. The rules for the order of operations are

Step 1: Do the operations in brackets first.

Step 2: Evaluate the powers.

Step 3: Divide and multiply from left to right.

Step 4: Add and subtract from left to right.

To remember the rules, think of "BEDMAS": **B**rackets, **E**xponents, **D**ivide and **M**ultiply, **A**dd and **S**ubtract.

order of rotation symmetry [***ordre*** (n.m.) ***d'une rotation symétrique***]**:** The number of times, within a

360° rotation about an internal point, that a shape will coincide with its original position is its order of rotation symmetry (e.g., This shape has rotation symmetry of order 2 because, during a 360° rotation, it coincides with its original position twice.)

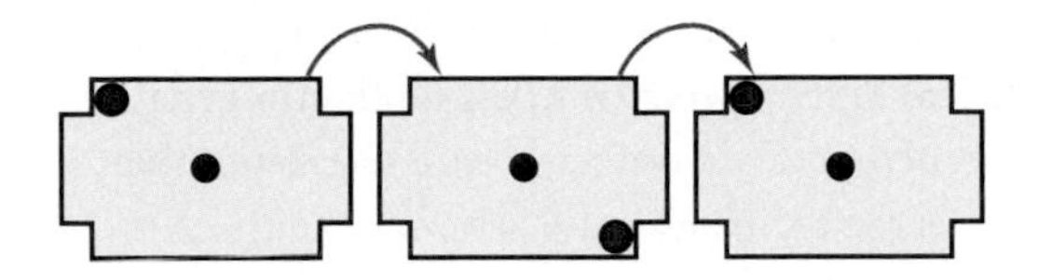

origin [***origine*** (n.f.)]**:** The point from which measurement is taken. In the Cartesian coordinate system, it is the intersection of the vertical and horizontal axes and is represented by the ordered pair (0, 0).

outcome [***résultat*** (n.m.)]**:** A result of an event or experiment (e.g., Rolling a 1 is one possible outcome when you roll a die.)

outcome table [***tableau*** (n.m.) ***des résultats***]**:** A chart that lists all possible outcomes of a probability experiment

outlier [***observation*** (n.f.) ***aberrante***]**:** A data value that is far from the other data values

P

parallel [***parallèle***]**:** Always the same distance apart (e.g., Line segments *AB* and *CD* are parallel.)

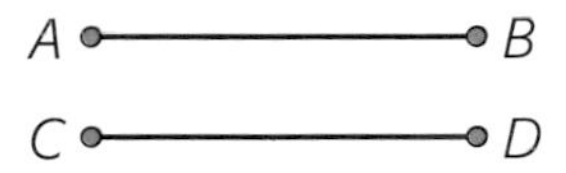

part-to-part ratio [***rapport*** (n.m.) ***partie/partie***]**:** A comparison of two parts of the same whole (e.g., 2:4 compares the number of red tiles to the number of blue tiles.)

part-to-whole ratio [***rapport*** (n.m.) ***partie/tout***]**:** A comparison of part of a whole to the whole (e.g., 2:6 compares the number of red tiles to the total number of tiles) that can be written as a fraction, such as $\frac{2}{6}$

pattern rule [***règle*** (n.f.) ***de la suite***]**:** A way to describe a pattern that compares a characteristic of the figure to the figure number (e.g., A pattern rule for the pattern shown below is $b = 4 \times n + 1$, where b is the number of blocks in figure n.)

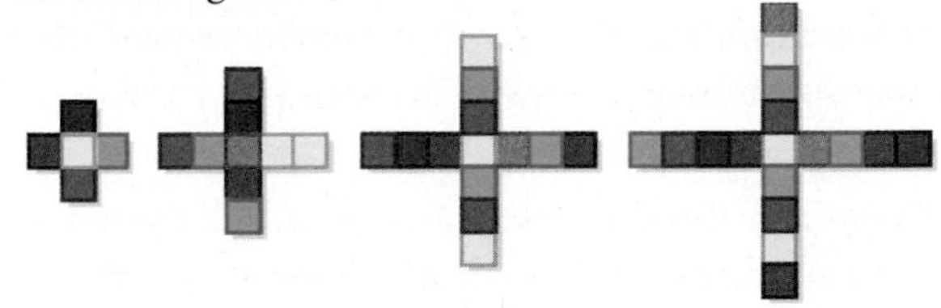

percent [***pourcentage*** (n.m.)]**:** A part-to-whole ratio that compares a number or an amount to 100 $\left(\text{e.g., } 25\% = 25:100 = \frac{25}{100}\right)$

perfect cube [***cube*** (n.m.) ***parfait***]**:** The product of a natural number multiplied by itself twice (e.g., 343 is a perfect cube because $7 \times 7 \times 7 = 343$.)

perfect square [***carré*** (n.m.) ***parfait***]**:** The product of a natural number multiplied by itself (e.g., 49 is a perfect square because $7 \times 7 = 49$.)

perpendicular bisector [***bissectrice*** (n.f.) ***perpendiculaire***]**:** A line that intersects a line segment at 90° and divides it into two equal lengths. Any point on the perpendicular bisector to *AB* is equidistant from endpoints *A* and *B*.

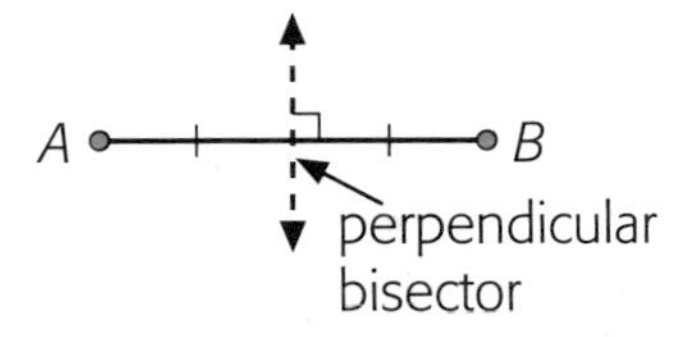

π (pi) [(***pi***) (n.m.) ou ***π***]**:** The ratio of the circumference of a circle to its diameter. Its value is about 3.14.

plane [***plan*** (n.m.)]**:** A flat surface that goes on forever in two different directions

polynomial [***polynôme*** (n.m.)]**:** An algebraic expression that is the sum of numbers and terms involving variables with exponents that are whole numbers. The variables can be multiplied by or divided by any numbers; e.g., $3a^2 + 4a + 2$ and $bh \div 2$.

population [***population*** (n.f.)]**:** The total set of people or things under investigation

power [***puissance*** (n.f.)]**:** A numerical expression that shows repeated multiplication (e.g., The power 2^3 is a shorter way of writing $2 \times 2 \times 2$.)

prime number [***nombre*** (n.m.) ***premier***]**:** A number with only two factors, 1 and itself (e.g., 17 is a prime number since its only factors are 1 and 17.)

Glossary

probability [***probabilité*** (n.f.)]**:** A number from 0 to 1 that shows how likely it is that an event will happen

proportion [***proportion*** (n.f.)]**:** A number sentence that shows two equivalent ratios or fractions $\left(\text{e.g., } 1:2 = 2:4 \text{ or } \frac{1}{2} = \frac{2}{4}\right)$

Pythagorean theorem [***théorème*** (n.m.) ***de Pythagore***]**:** Statement of a relationship in which the sum of the squares of the lengths of the legs of a right triangle is equal to the square of the length of the hypotenuse. This is written algebraically as $a^2 + b^2 = c^2$.

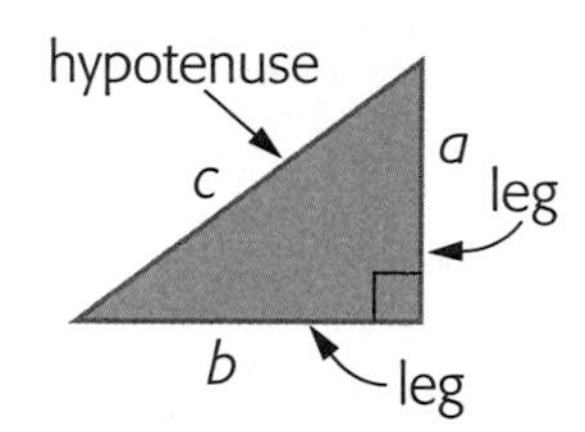

R

radius [***rayon*** (n.m.)]**:** Half the diameter of a circle; the distance from the centre of a circle to a point on the circumference

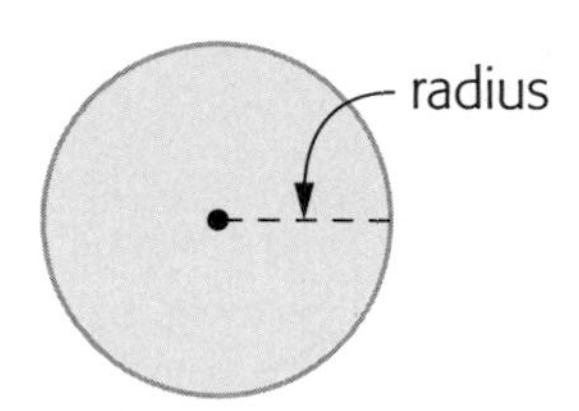

random [***aléatoire***]**:** Each item or individual is equally likely to be chosen

range [***étendue*** (n.f.)]**:** The difference between the greatest and least number in a set of data (e.g., The range of 6, 7, 7, 8, 9 is 3, because $9 - 6 = 3$.)

rate [***rapport*** (n.m.) ou ***relation*** (n.f.)]**:** A comparison of two amounts measured in different units (e.g., cost per item or distance compared to time). The word "per" means "to" or "for each" and is written using a slash (/) (e.g., a typing rate of 250 words/8 min).

ratio [***rapport*** (n.m.) ou ***relation*** (n.f.)]**:** A comparison of two numbers (e.g., 5 : 26 is the ratio of vowels to letters in the alphabet) or of two measurements with the same units (e.g., 164 : 175 is the ratio of two students' heights in centimetres). Each number in the ratio is called a term.

rational number [***nombre*** (n.m.) ***rationnel***]**:** A number that can be expressed as the quotient of two integers, where the divisor is not 0. It can be written in fraction, mixed-number, or decimal form, or as an integer $\left(\text{e.g., } 3.25, -5.8, \frac{2}{3}, -2, -1\frac{1}{4}\right)$.

ray [***demi-droite*** (n.f.)]**:** A part of a line, with one endpoint

reciprocal [***réciproque*** (n.f.)]**:** The fraction that results from switching the numerator and the denominator $\left(\text{e.g., } \frac{4}{5} \text{ is the reciprocal of } \frac{5}{4}.\right)$

reflection [***réflexion*** (n.f.)]**:** The result of a flip of a 2-D shape. Each point in a 2-D shape flips to the opposite side of the line of reflection, but stays the same distance from the line. (Also see **transformation.**)

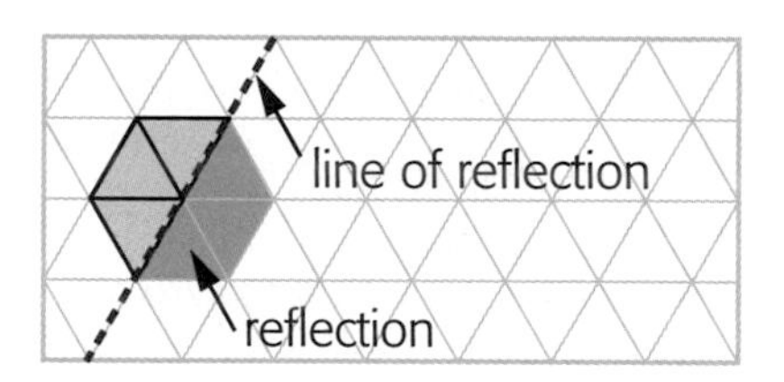

relation [***relation*** (n.f.)]**:** A property that allows you to use one number to get information about another number

repeating decimal [***suite*** (n.f.) ***décimale périodique***]**:** A decimal in which a block of one or more digits eventually repeats in a pattern $\left(\text{e.g., } \frac{25}{99} = 0.252\,525\ldots, \frac{31}{36} = 0.861\,111\,1\ldots, \frac{1}{7} = 0.142\,857\,142\,857\ldots\right)$. These repeating decimals can also be written as $0.\overline{25}$, $0.86\overline{1}$, and $0.\overline{142\,857}$.

respondent [***répondant*** (n.m.)]**:** A person who answers the questions in a survey or census

representative sample [***échantillon*** (n.m.) ***représentatif***]**:** a sample that is similar to the whole population, in terms of gender, age group, and/or other characteristics

rotation [***rotation*** (n.f.)]**:** A transformation in which each point in a shape moves about a fixed point through the same angle

rotation symmetry [***symétrie*** (n.f.) ***d'une rotation***]**:** when a rotating shape fits exactly over its original position with a turn of less than 360°, the shape has rotation symmetry. The number of times that a shape fits over its original position during a rotation of 360° is its order of rotation symmetry. (e.g., This shape has rotation symmetry of order 2.)

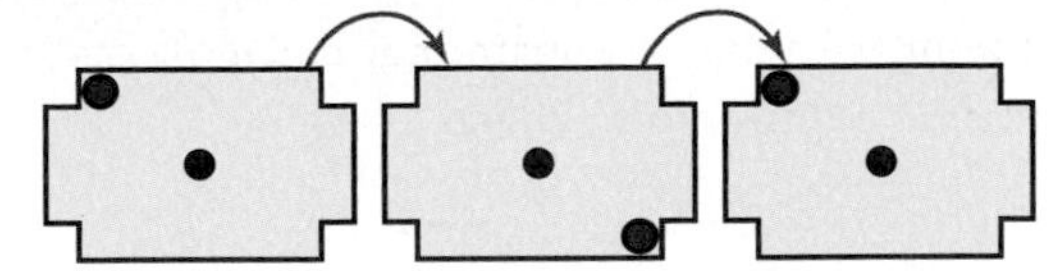

S

sample [*échantillon* (n.m.)]: Part of a population, selected to give information about the whole

sample space [*espace* (n.m.) *des échantillons*]: All possible outcomes in a probability experiment

scale factor [*facteur* (n.m.) *d'échelle*]: The factor one dimension of a polygon is multiplied by to calculate the corresponding dimension of a similar polygon

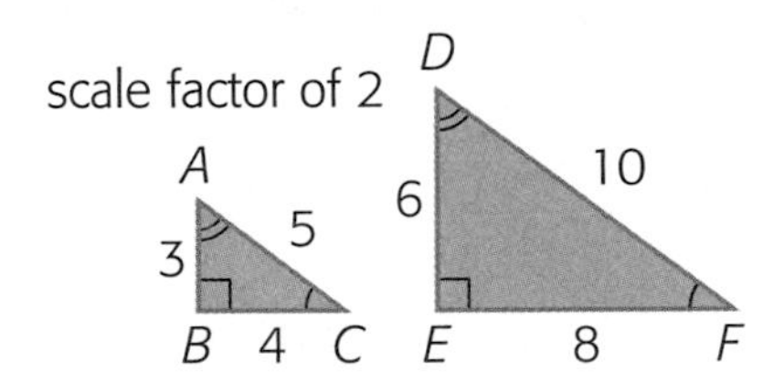

scatter plot [*diagramme* (n.m.) *de dispersion*]: A graph that attempts to show a relationship between two variables by means of points plotted on a coordinate grid

secant [sécante (n.f.)]: A line that intersects a circle at two points

similar polygons [*formes* (n.f.pl.) *similaires*]: Two or more polygons that are congruent or are enlargements or reductions of each other. The ratios of corresponding linear measurements are the same, and all corresponding angles are equal

solution to an equation [*solution* (n.f.) *d'une équation*]: A value of a variable that makes an equation true (e.g., The solution to $6x + 2 = 14$ is $x = 2$.)

speed [*vitesse* (n.f.)]: The rate at which a moving object travels a certain distance in a certain time (e.g., A sprinter who runs 100 m in 10 s has a speed of 100 m/10 s = 10 m/s.)

square root [*racine* (n.f.) *carrée*]: One of two equal factors of a number; e.g., the square root of 81 is 9 because 9×9, or 9^2, = 81. This is sometimes called a root.

statistics [*statistique* (n.f.pl.)]: The collection, organization, and interpretation of data

subtend [*sous-tendre*]: To define or limit (e.g., Arc AB subtends central $\angle AOB$, as it defines where the arms of the angle are placed.)

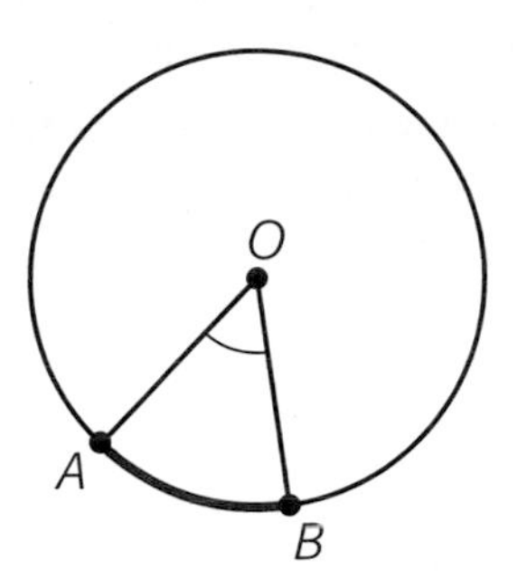

surface area [*surface* (n.f.)]: The total area of all of the faces of any 3-D object (e.g., The surface area of a cube with a side length of 2 cm is $6 \times (2 \times 2) = 24$ cm^2.)

T

tangent [*tangente* (n.f.)]: A line that intersects a circle at exactly one point

term [*terme* (n.m.)]: A part of a polynomial, separated from the other terms by addition signs (e.g., The terms of the polynomial $3a^2 + 4ab - 2$ are $3a^2$, $4ab$, and -2.)

terminating decimal [*fraction* (n.f.) *décimale finie*]: A decimal that is complete after a certain number of digits with no repetition (e.g., 0.777)

tessellation [*mosaïque* (n.f.)]: The tiling of a plane with one or more congruent shapes without any gaps or overlaps

theoretical probability [*probabilité* (n.f.) *théorique*]: The ratio of the number of favourable outcomes to the number of possible equally likely outcomes (e.g., The theoretical probability of tossing a head on a coin is $\frac{1}{2}$, since there are 2 equally likely outcomes and only 1 is favourable.)

three-term ratio [*rapport* (n.m.) *à trois termes*]: A ratio that compares three quantities (e.g., The ratio 2:3:5 (or, 2 to 3 to 5) describes the ratio of red to blue to yellow squares.)

transformation [***transformation*** (n.f.) ***géométrique***]: The result of moving a shape according to a rule. Transformations include translations, rotations, and reflections.

translation [***translation*** (n.f.)]: The result of a slide. The slide must be along straight lines, left or right, up or down. (Also see **transformation**.)

tree diagram [***diagramme*** (n.m.) ***en arbre*** ou ***arbre*** (n.m.)]: A way to record and count all combinations of events, using lines to connect the two parts of the outcome

1st toss 2nd toss
H — H (HH)
H — T (HT)

1st toss 2nd toss
T — H (TH)
T — T (TT)

trial [***essai*** (n.m.) ou ***événement*** (n.m.)]: A single event or observation in a probability experiment

U

unit rate [***valeur*** (n.f.) ***unitaire***]: A rate in which the second term is 1 (e.g., In swimming, 12 laps/6 min can be written as a unit rate of 2 laps/min.)

V

variable [***variable*** (n.f.)]: A letter or symbol, such as a, b, x, or n, that represents a number (e.g., In the formula for the area of a rectangle, the variables A, l, and w represent the area, length, and width of the rectangle.)

Z

zero principle [***principe*** (n.m.) ***de la somme des nombres opposés***]: When two opposite integers are added, the sum is zero; e.g.,

$$(-2) + (+2) = 0$$

Answers

Chapter 1

Lesson 1.1, pages 7–8

1. e.g., **a)** $-1 \div 2$ **b)** $-9 \div 4$ **c)** $-41 \div 7$ **d)** $72 \div 10$
2. **a)** -0.25 **b)** -2.375 **c)** $-7.833...$ **d)** 4.3
3. e.g., **a)** $-0.7, -0.75, -0.77$ **b)** $-0.1, 0.1, 0.22$ **c)** $0.7, 0.8, 0.9$
4. D
5. B
6. e.g., B: $8 \div 3$; D: $4 \div 3$; K: $(-2) \div 3$; M: $(-7) \div 3$; T: $(-11) \div 3$
7. e.g., **a)** $51 \div 10$ **b)** $(-21) \div 5$ **c)** $(-302) \div 100$ **d)** $29 \div 3$
8. **a)** 5.4 **b)** -7.5 **c)** $-6.333...$ **d)** 2.6
9. Number line from −10 to 2 with points labelled:

-8.4, -7.2, -6.9, $-3\frac{2}{3}$, $-\frac{5}{2}$, -0.78, $\frac{2}{3}$, $1\frac{2}{3}$

−10 −8 −6 −4 −2 0 2

10. **a)** e.g., a debt of \$1.20

    b) e.g., a drop of $\frac{2}{3}$ in the height of a snow bank
11. $-\frac{3}{4} = (-1)\frac{3}{4} = \frac{-1}{1} \times \frac{3}{4} = \frac{-3}{4}$

    $-\frac{3}{4} = (-1)\frac{3}{4} = \frac{1}{-1} \times \frac{3}{4} = \frac{3}{-4}$
12. **a)** e.g., $\frac{9}{32}, \frac{10}{32}, \frac{11}{32}$

    b) Divide opposite of numerator by denominator. **c)** yes
13. **a)** agree **b)** disagree
14. rational numbers include all of the integers, which include all of the whole numbers, which include all of the natural numbers
15. e.g., A rational number is either a positive or negative fraction or decimal.
16. **a)** $\frac{5}{9} = 5 \div 9$ **b)** $-0.5555...$ **c)** $-0.055\ 55...$

    d) e.g., One is ten times greater than the other.
17.

Lesson 1.2, pages 13–15

1. e.g., -5, -5.1, and -5.2
2. e.g., $3\frac{1}{8} < 3\frac{3}{4}$, so $-3\frac{1}{8} > -3\frac{3}{4}$
3. the one who moved –0.9; west
4. **a)** $>$ **b)** $<$ **c)** $<$ **d)** $=$ **e)** $=$ **f)** $<$
5. e.g., **a)** $-2.3 < -1.4$ **b)** $-1.0 < -0.8$ **c)** $-0.9 < 0.9$ **d)** $1.9 < 2.4$ **e)** $-1.3 > -1.7$ **f)** $5.8 > 4.5$
6. **a)** $-14\frac{1}{2}, -12.2, -4\frac{2}{3}, 3\frac{1}{4}$

   b) $-10.3, -10.2, -8.4, 8\frac{2}{3}, 8.8$

   c) $-\frac{3}{8}, -\frac{3}{15}, \frac{3}{15}, \frac{3}{8}$

   d) $-2.9, -2\frac{3}{4}, 10.1, 14.2$
7. **a)**, **b)** e.g.,

X Y

−3.0 −2.8 −2.6 −2.4 −2.2 −2.0

8. A
9. C
10. tremor at -12.2 s
11. e.g., For $+8.1$ and -4.3, one is negative and one is positive; -4.3 and $-4\frac{1}{3}$ are both negative and have the same integer.
12. **a)** e.g., benchmarks, decimal forms, common denominators

    b) $-7.5, -\frac{11}{2}, -2\frac{1}{2}, -1\frac{1}{2}, -\frac{7}{5}, \frac{1}{100}, \frac{5}{8}$
13. **a)**, **b)**, **c)** e.g.,

R Q S T U V P

-1.3 -1.25 -1.23 -1.22 -1.21 -1.205 -1.2

    d) e.g., You can always add another digit to the end of the decimal.

    e) an infinite number of rational numbers
14. $-a > -b$
15. e.g., decimals, because I can compare the digits, as I do for whole numbers and integers
16. e.g., agree
17. $-\frac{1}{4}, -\frac{24}{98}, -0.242\ 424..., -\frac{24}{100}$
18. 7, 8, or 9
19. $\frac{9}{140}$

Lesson 1.3, pages 20–21

1. **a)** -8.0 **b)** $\frac{5}{24}$ **c)** $1\frac{7}{10}$ **d)** -3.1 **e)** $-\frac{7}{12}$ **f)** $-5\frac{7}{15}$
2. -0.55
3. e.g., **a)** $4 - 73 = -69$ **b)** $-12 + 19 = 7$ **c)** $-9 - 6 = -15$

   d) $\frac{1}{2} + 21\frac{1}{2} = 22$ **e)** $3 + 6 + 11 = 20$

   f) $-5 + (-6) + 5 = -6$
4. **a)** -69.26 **b)** 6.7 **c)** -15.30 **d)** 22.07 **e)** 20.32 **f)** -5.91
5. C
6. C
7. **a)** $-4.2, 9.4$ **b)** $-5.362, 1.205$ **c)** $9.4, -5.362$

   d) $-8.94, -5.362$
8. **a)** 8, 5, 8 **b)** e.g., 1, 5, 0, 5 **c)** 8, 1, 2 **d)** 1, 3, 9
9. **a)** -5.5 **b)** -12.3
10. **a)** $1\frac{3}{8}$ **b)** $-2\frac{5}{6}$ **c)** $-\frac{3}{10}$ **d)** $-1\frac{13}{20}$ **e)** $-7\frac{13}{15}$ **f)** $3\frac{1}{24}$
11. \$53.87
12. **a)** e.g., $-\left(-3\frac{1}{4}\right) > \left(-3\frac{1}{4}\right)$ **b)** e.g., $-2.3 - \left(-3\frac{1}{4}\right) \doteq -2 + 3 = 1$
13. **a)** $2\frac{3}{4}$ **b)** $-2\frac{3}{4}$
14. 1:31:57.7
15. **a)** -0.9 **b)** -9.4 **c)** $1\frac{1}{4}$ **d)** $\frac{3}{4}$
16. **a)** e.g., $3.8 - 0.68$ **b)** $1.5 + 0.68 + 2.3 + (3.8 - 0.68)$
17. e.g., **a)** $a = -\frac{1}{2}, b = -\frac{3}{2}$ **b)** $a = -\frac{1}{2}, b = \frac{3}{2}$ **c)** $a = -\frac{3}{2}, b = -\frac{1}{2}$
18. e.g., Amy is 4.5 km west of my house and I am 3.2 km west. How far must Amy walk and in what direction to get to me? (1.3 km east)
19. sum 1.605, difference -8.405
20. $-\frac{10}{40}, \frac{33}{40}$
21. e.g., $-4.2, -8.7$

Lesson 1.4, pages 25–27

1. a) -19 b) $\frac{24}{35}$ c) -16 d) $-\frac{16}{25}$
2. $\frac{11}{40}$
3. $\frac{1}{3}$
4. a) $-\frac{5}{12}$ b) $\frac{5}{12}$ c) $-\frac{16}{15}$ d) $-\frac{15}{16}$ e) $\frac{16}{15}$ f) $\frac{16}{15}$
5. D
6. D
7. a) $\frac{-1}{8} \times \left(-3\frac{2}{3}\right)$ b) $\frac{8}{-1} \times \left(-3\frac{2}{3}\right)$
8. a) $-4.2, -8.4$ b) $7.3, -4.2$
9. -13.3 °C
10. a) $\frac{2}{9}$ b) $-\frac{225}{7}$ c) $-\frac{9}{10}$ d) -8 e) 0.381 f) -12
11. a) 37 °C b) -38 °C c) 32 °F
12. 4 : 15
13. a) $\frac{1}{6}$ b) no
14. e.g.,
    a) The fraction of water gained by the pail in $\frac{3}{4}$ of the time it was sitting.
    b) The comparison between the fraction of water gained in the time the pail was sitting $\left(-\frac{1}{8}\right)$ and the fraction gained in twice as much time $\left(-\frac{1}{4}\right)$.
15. e.g., $-1\frac{1}{3}$
16. a) If both were negative or positive, the product would be negative.
    b) e.g., $\frac{1}{2}, -\frac{2}{3}$
17. a) -16.18 b) -54.59 c) $-\frac{25}{8}$ d) $-\frac{13}{6}$
18. e.g., Multiply and divide rationals as you would integers. The result is positive if both numbers have the same sign and negative if they have opposite signs.
19. a) -2 b) -23
20. e.g., $\frac{1}{2}, -5$
21. 2 m by 8 m

Mid-Chapter Review, pages 29–30

1. e.g., A: -4.5; B: -3.6; C: -0.2
2.

$-8\frac{1}{3}$ $\frac{23}{-3}$ $-\frac{18}{4}$ -2.6

-10 -8 -6 -4 -2 0 2

3. Portage la Prairie
4. a) $>$ b) $>$ c) $=$ d) $<$
5. a) $-1\frac{1}{3}, -\frac{3}{5}, \frac{1}{-3}$ b) $-2\frac{1}{5}, \frac{-2}{5}, \frac{4}{5}$ c) $-0.\overline{3}, -0.3, 0.7$ d) $-2, -1.5, 0$
6. e.g., $-\frac{13}{32}, -\frac{14}{32}, -0.4, -0.41$
7. -4
8. a) $-3\frac{1}{12}$ b) $-\frac{13}{45}$ c) -2.4 d) $-\frac{23}{24}$ e) -11.2 f) $-7\frac{9}{28}$
9. 3.4 km west
10. $\frac{7}{15}, -\frac{2}{15}$
11. $-\$2.26$
12. a) e.g., $1\frac{3}{4}\left(-5\frac{1}{3}\right)$ or $-3\frac{1}{2}\left(\frac{8}{3}\right)$
    b) e.g., You walk $1\frac{3}{4}$ km west (negative) each hour. What is your position after $5\frac{1}{3}$ h? $\left(-9\frac{1}{3}\text{ km}\right)$
13. $1.5 \div (-2)$
14. e.g., Elliot walked 3.9 km west. Derek walked $\frac{1}{3}$ as far in the same direction. How far and in what direction did Derek walk? (1.3 km west)

Lesson 1.5, pages 33–34

1. a) addition in brackets b) subtraction in brackets
2. -0.063
3. a) division by 0.7 b) adding -10.2 c) subtracting $\frac{27}{20}$
4. -0.36
5. A
6. B
7. no
8. a) $2\frac{4}{9}$ b) $-2\frac{1}{3}$
9. It was 3.8° C more than double the Thursday temperature.
10. a, b, d
11. e.g., a) $-4.7 + (-5.3) \times 2.1$ b) yes
12. $\frac{1}{24}$ s
13. Because integers are rational numbers.
14. e.g., $\left(-\frac{2}{3} + \frac{3}{4}\right) \times 2 \div \frac{1}{2} = \frac{1}{3}$
15. a) $\left(3\frac{1}{2} + 4\right)$ b) $(-1.2 + -3) \div (1.5 + 1.5)$
16. $\frac{1}{3}$

Lesson 1.7, page 39

1. $-\frac{5}{16}$
2. e.g., $-21, -10, 1, 2, 3$
3. 1.0 km
4. $\frac{1}{2}, \frac{1}{8}$, and $-\frac{5}{8}$
5. $-1.35, 1.35$
6. e.g., $-\frac{1}{4}, \frac{1}{2}, -\frac{1}{2}, \frac{3}{8}, -\frac{3}{8}$
7. \$0.15
8. $-\frac{7}{9}$
9. e.g., $\frac{1}{2}, -\frac{1}{2}$
10. e.g., Because there were only a few possibilities.
11. e.g., The mean of five numbers is -4. The sum of the positive numbers is 22 greater than the sum of the negative numbers. What could the numbers be? $\left(-7, -7, -7, \frac{1}{2}, \frac{1}{2}\right)$

Chapter Self-Test, page 41

1. D
2. C
3. $-4\frac{1}{3}$
4. e.g., $-\frac{105}{32}, -\frac{106}{32}, -\frac{107}{32}$

5. a) $\frac{27}{14}$ b) $-\frac{32}{9}$ c) $-0.0333\ldots$ or $-\frac{1}{30}$
d) $\frac{16}{9}$ e) $-7.2888\ldots$ f) $-\frac{7}{3}$

6. a) 2.9° C decrease b) 0.58° C decrease

7. $\frac{3}{10}$

8. e.g., The second number is negative. The first number can be either positive or negative. If the second number is negative, then it is less than 1.

Chapter Review, pages 43–44

1.

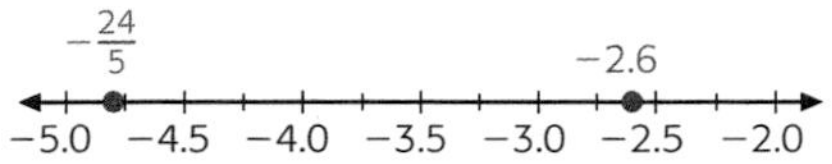

2. $-\frac{29}{3}$, since $-\frac{29}{3} = -9\frac{2}{3}$

3. e.g., a) $-42 \div 10$ b) $9 \div 5$ c) $-3 \div 8$

4. e.g., The time before a rocket launch is $-1\frac{2}{3}$ h.

5. The integers circle should be completely inside the rationals circle.

6. a) $-5.1, \frac{-8}{3}, -\frac{1}{5}, 0.3, 1.2$ b) $\frac{-8}{9}, -\frac{2}{3}, -\frac{1}{4}, \frac{4}{7}, \frac{3}{5}$

7. e.g.,
a) $-4\frac{1}{2}, -4.4, -4.6$
b) $-5.007, -5.008, -5.009$
c) $-0.7, -0.71, -0.75$

8. e.g., $-\frac{8}{2}$ is 4 units to the left of 0 and $\frac{-1}{2}$ is $\frac{1}{2}$ units to the left.

9. e.g., $-\left(\frac{3}{4} + 1\frac{1}{2} + \frac{2}{3}\right)$

10. e.g., a) 5 b) −1 c) −21 d) −2

11. a) $5\frac{1}{4}$ b) $-\frac{11}{15}$ c) −20.8 d) $-\frac{38}{15} = -2\frac{8}{15}$

12. \$0.02 increase

13. $-\frac{4}{5}, \frac{3}{10}$

14. a) 2 b) $\frac{4}{3}$ c) $-\frac{20}{27}$ d) $-\frac{4}{9}$ e) $\frac{9}{5}$ f) $\frac{9}{5}$

15. $\frac{25}{3}$

16. a) e.g., $\frac{3}{8}, -\frac{1}{4}$ b) Use the opposite of each rational.

17. a) $-\frac{4}{5}$ b) $-1\frac{13}{18}$ c) $-\frac{1}{2}$ d) $-\frac{2}{5}$

18. no

19. $2\frac{5}{6}$

20. e.g., −4, −2

21. $\frac{1}{3}, -\frac{2}{3}, \frac{4}{3}$

Chapter 2

Lesson 2.1, pages 52–53

1. a) 2^2 b) 3^3
2. a) 6^3 b) 11^2
3. a) 9 m b) 2 cm
4. a) 4 b) 3 c) 10 d) 3 e) 49 f) 125
5. a) 5^2 m^2 or 25 m^2
6. a) 144 cm^2 b) 864 cm^2 c) 1728 cm^3
7. a) cube with 15 cm side length b) 125 cubes
8. 21
9. C
10. A
11. D
12. 4^2 is a flat square, 4^3 is a three-dimensional cube
13. disagree
14. a) 13 or 1 apart b) 2197 or 21 421 apart
15. 0, 1
16. e.g.,

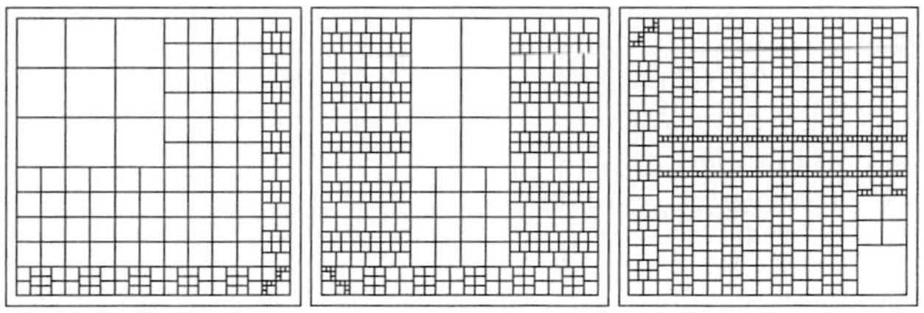

17. e.g., There will always be more perfect squares than perfect cubes between two numbers, because cubes are always farther apart than squares of numbers (greater than 1).
18. 4 plates
19. yes
20. 729, 4096

Lesson 2.2, pages 56–58

1. a) 5^6 b) 3.2^4 c) $(-4)^3$ d) -7^5 e) $\left(\frac{5}{7}\right)^3$ f) $\left(\frac{3}{4}\right)^5$
2. a) 4^6 b) 6^4 c) $(-5.4)^3$ d) -8^5 e) $\left(\frac{8}{9}\right)^4$ f) $\left(\frac{2}{3}\right)^4$
3. a) (2)(2)(2)(2) b) (−2)(−2)(−2)(−2)
c) −(2)(2)(2)(2) d) −(−2)(−2)(−2)(−2)
4. a) −343 b) −343 c) 81 d) −81 e) −153.76 f) 144
5. a) 9, 4, (9)(9)(9)(9)
b) 5^3, 3, 125
c) $(-2)^5$, (−2)(−2)(−2)(−2)(−2), −32
d) -6^3, 6, 3, −216
e) 4, 6, −(4)(4)(4)(4)(4)(4), −4096
6. C
7. A
8. C
9. disagree
10. yes
11. $-2^4, (-1)^{31}, (-1)^{100}, -(-2^2), (-2)^4$
12. a) 3150 cm^2 b) 22.9 cm
13. a) 16, 81, 256, 625
b) 32, 243, 1024, 3125
c) 4, 3
d) e.g., The difference, 13, is quite small, and the larger the numbers get, the larger the difference gets.
14. a) 1, 1, 1, 1 b) 1
15. a) $6^0, 6^1, 6^2, 6^3, 6^4$
b) with 5, no; with −5, yes; with 0, cannot be ordered
16. $2^3, 3^2, 4^3, 3^4, 5^3, 3^5$
17. a) s^4 b) $(-y)^2$ c) t^4 d) $-p^3$
18. a) pennies 7^2, nickels 2^5, dimes 3^2, quarters 5^2, loonies 2^3, toonies 2^4
b) $N = 7^2 + 2^5 + 3^2 + 5^2 + 2^4$
19. no
20. a) −128, 256, 64
b) $-128 = (-2)^7, 256 = (-2)^8, 64 = (-2)^6$
c) e.g., Add the exponents.
21. a) 6 rounds, plus 2 extra calls b) 2^7

Answers

Lesson 2.4, pages 64–66

1. a) 9^9 b) 7^8 c) 2^1 or 2 d) 5^0 or 1 e) 11^{31} f) 8^5
2. a) e.g., 2^4 b) 2^6 c) e.g., 3^8
3. a) x^{10} b) a^2 c) m^{12}
4. a) 10^{13} b) 3^{11} c) 12^3 d) 2^5 e) 6^7 f) 5^2
5. a) -32 b) -1 c) 121 d) -8 e) 81 f) 46 656
6. a) 3 b) 2 c) 4 d) 12
7. A
8. B
9. D
10. e.g., a) $(4^4)(4^3) = 4^7$ b) $3^8 \div 3^2 = 3^6$ c) $(5^3)^5 = 5^{15}$
11. $2^3 \times 2^8 = 2^{11}$, not 2^{24}
12. a) x^5 b) y^5 c) s^{11} d) p^4
13. a) correct b) incorrect c) incorrect
14. a) 1 b) 1 c) 1
    d) If $a \neq 0$, then $\frac{a^m}{a^m} = 1$ and $\frac{a^m}{a^m} = a^{m-m} = a^0$, so $a^0 = 1$.
    e) yes
15. Any power of 10 is divisible by 5 and any power of 8 is not, so they cannot be equal.
16. a) 2^{12} b) 3^9 c) $(-3)^{12}$ d) $(-5)^9$
17. a) x^8 b) m^2 c) y^9 d) a^4 e) a^6 f) b^5
18. You can add exponents when the bases are the same but not when they are different.
19. a) no b) yes c) no

Mid-Chapter Review, page 68

1. a) square with side lengths of 21
   b) square with side lengths of 8
   c) cube with side lengths of 15
   d) cube with side lengths of 11
2. a) 14 cm b) 4 cm × 4 cm × 4 cm
3. e.g., 64 and 729
4. a) e.g., $(-2)(-2)(-2)$ b) $(-2)^3$, $-(2)^3$
5. a) e.g., $6 \times 6 \times 6$ b) e.g., 6^3
6. a) 1 b) -125 c) -81 d) 8 e) 1 f) $\frac{16}{81}$
7. $-125, -81, \frac{16}{81}, 1, 1, 8$
8. a) 10^{11} b) 3^{12} c) 9^2 d) 2^5 e) 5^7 f) 6^2
9. e.g., $\frac{2^{14}}{4^2} + 3^4 - 9^2$
10. 2^1
11. a) b^7 b) n^3 c) d^{27} d) a^3

Lesson 2.5, pages 73–75

1. a) $2^4 \times 3^4$ b) $\frac{2^5}{3^5}$ c) $3^6 \times 5^{12}$ d) $\frac{3^6}{7^4}$
2. a) 2^3 b) 3^{12} c) 4^{24} d) 5^4
3. a) 21^2 b) 24^3 c) 3^2 d) 8^3
4. a) $8^{12} \times 5^8$ b) $4^{21} \times 3^{10}$ c) $2^{14} \times 3^{15}$ d) 4^6 e) $\frac{2^{12}}{7^6}$ f) 10^2
5. a) 5184 b) 59 049 c) 15 625 d) 1024
6. A
7. D
8. A
9. e.g., a) Enter $(5^2)^4$. b) Enter $(4^2)^2$.
10. 1 000 000 000
11. a) 354 294 units^2 d) 14 348 907 units^3
    b) 354 294 units^2 e) 14 348 907 units^3
    c) e.g., method in b) f) e.g., method in e)
12. (3×2^3) m^2
13. a) e.g., 8^3 cm^3 b) 4 times as high
14. 27
15. e.g., Simplify $2^8 \times 25^4$.
16. 200 000 000
17. a) yes b) no c) when exponent of base 0.9 is even
18. a) e.g., 0.25^{15} b) e.g., 1.2^{10} c) 0.4^9

Lesson 2.6, pages 78–79

1. a) 36 b) 82 c) 24
2. a) 30 b) 15 c) e.g., b)
3. a) 252 b) 160 c) 4032 d) 215
4. a) 82 b) 25 c) $-\frac{7}{11}$
5. a) 165 b) e.g., yes
6. e.g., $(2^1)(2^1) = 2 + 2 = 4$
7. e.g., 2 is the only number for which its square is also its double.
8. yes
9. 3^{20}
10. a) B
    b) e.g., $(18 \times 2) + (12 \times 2^2)$ cubes of meat
    c) 84 cubes of meat
11. e.g., Otherwise, the answer might be wrong.
12. a) e.g., Use guess and test.
    b) $7^2 + 3^3 - 12 \div 2^2 = 73$
13. No, not always.

Lesson 2.7, pages 84–85

1. a) $\sqrt{7 \times 7}$ b) $\sqrt{121}$ c) $\frac{2}{3}$ d) $\sqrt{\frac{49}{81}}$ e) $\frac{12}{15}$ f) $\frac{\sqrt{100}}{\sqrt{169}}$
2. 1.2 km by 1.2 km
3. a) 1.9 b) $\sqrt{0.0049}$ c) $\frac{10}{17}$ d) $\frac{\sqrt{16}}{\sqrt{36}}$
4. a) 3 b) 3 c) 3
5. 2
6. a) 79 b) 23
7. A
8. a) 1.6 b) 1.4 c) 1.3 d) 1.2 e) 0.9 f) 0.7 g) 0.6 h) 0.5
9. 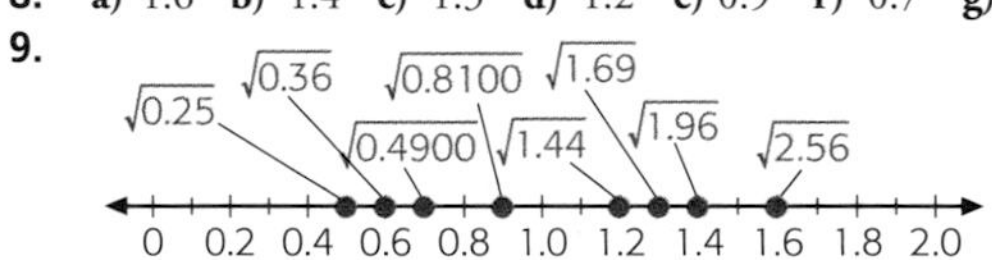

10. no
11. 272.25
12. e.g., $\sqrt{5.76}$, $\sqrt{0.0576}$
13. yes
14. a) A. $\sqrt{0.25}$ B. $\frac{1}{5}$ C. e.g., $\sqrt{0.0625} = \frac{1}{4}$
    b) e.g., Evaluate both sides using calculator.
15. a) incorrect b) incorrect c) correct d) correct
16. a) 0.3 b) 0.03 c) 0.003 d) 0.0003
17. When the value under the square root sign is divided by 100, the square root is divided by 10.
18. 24 cm^2
19. 0.49 and 0.0049
20. no
21. 4.00 cm
22. 1.75 cm

Lesson 2.8, pages 89–90

1. a) 2, 3 b) 7, 8 c) 12, 13 d) 0, 1
2. a) 2.92 b) 7.24 c) 12.24 d) 0.75
3. The values of the square roots were between the pairs of whole numbers in question 1.
4. about 2.5 cm
5. about 5.6 cm
6. e.g.,
   a) estimate 1.2, calculation 1.2
   b) estimate 8.5, calculation 8.7
   c) estimate 0.1, calculation 0.1
   d) estimate $\frac{1}{2}$, calculation 0.5
   e) estimate $\frac{4}{12}$, calculation 0.333...
   f) estimate $\frac{6}{5}$, calculation 1.2
7. C
8. C
9. a) She will have enough paint. b) about 3 m
10. 7.2 m
11. a) $0.7 > 0.64$, so $\sqrt{0.7} > 0.8$ b) no
12. $\sqrt{6.4}$ must be between 2 and 3 since $2^2 = 4$ and $3^2 = 9$.
13. e.g., about 38.2 m
14. no
15. e.g., Try numbers less than 50.
16. e.g., about 8 cm by 20 cm

Chapter Self-Test, page 91

1. a) cube with side lengths of 18
   b) square with side lengths of 1.2
   c) cube with side lengths of 9 cm
2. a) 5 cm, 150 cm^2 b) 10 cm, 1000 cm^3
3. a) 32 b) 117 649
4. a) 2^5 mysteries, 10^1 action, $2(3^2)$ comedies, 2^2 cartoons
   b) 64 DVDs = $2^2 \times 4^2$
5. a) 65 536 b) 8192 c) 1 d) 1 e) −191 102 976 f) 36
6. a) x^6 b) a^6 c) c^5
7. 44
8. a) 7.48 b) 5.29 c) $\frac{9}{12}$ d) $\frac{\sqrt{36}}{\sqrt{49}}$ e) 2 f) 0.6
9. a) 8 m, 9 m b) $s = 8.72$ m

Chapter Review, pages 93–94

1. a) square with side lengths of 15 m
   b) square with side lengths of 10
   c) cube with side lengths of 3
2. a) 14 mm b) 5 cm
3.

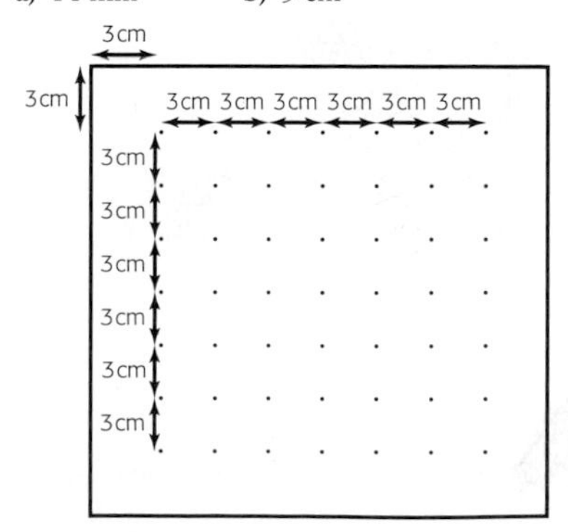

   b) 24 cm by 24 cm c) 576 cm^2
4. a) −3, 4, $(-3)(-3)(-3)(-3)$, 81
   b) $-(6)^3$, 6, 3, −216
   c) $(-4)^4$, 4, $(-4)(-4)(-4)(-4)$
5. a) 36 b) −12.167 c) 1
6. yes
7. a) 5^{27} b) 12^4 c) 19^2
8. a) 1 679 616 b) 256 c) 1
9. a) x^{14} b) a^3 c) v^9
10. a) $\frac{8 \times 8 \times 8 \times 8 \times 8}{8 \times 8 \times 8} = 8 \times 8 = 8^2$
    b) $(6 \times 6) \times (6 \times 6 \times 6 \times 6 \times 6)$
    $= 6 \times 6 \times 6 \times 6 \times 6 \times 6 \times 6 = 6^7$
11. 2^{10}
12. a) 6^{22} b) 7^{12}
13. a) 240 b) 46
14. e.g., B
15. a) 17 b) 6.3 c) $\frac{4}{6}$ d) $\frac{11}{12}$ e) 1 f) 8.42
16. a) incorrect b) incorrect c) correct
17. a) 14 m, 15 m b) 14 m c) 14.14
18. 6.3 m
19. about 5.8 m

Chapter 3

Lesson 3.2, pages 106–109

1. a) no b) no c) yes d) no e) no f) yes
2. yes
3. A and C
4. a) no b) yes c) no
5. a) B b) D c) A
6. e.g., Corresponding sides have the same scale factor and corresponding angles are equal.
7. *A* & *G*, *C* & *H*, *E* & *J*
8. B
9. B
10. *ABCD* ~ *EFGH*, 1:1.5
11. e.g., a) isosceles triangles: 2:3; scalene triangles: 5:2; equilateral triangles: 1:3
    b) isosceles triangles: 7:9; scalene triangles: 2:1; equilateral triangles: 15:13
12. a) 5.1 m b) 3.4
13. They are not similar.
14. a) true b) false c) false
    d) true e) true f) false
15. A. disagree B. disagree C. disagree D. agree
16. no
17. a) b)

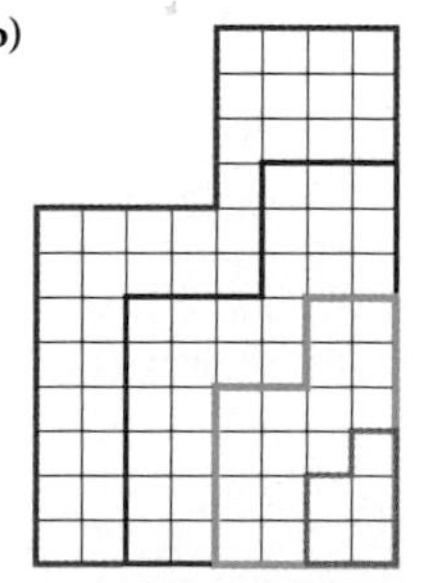

18. a) $\angle L$ b) $PR = 36$ cm, $QR = 39$ cm
19. e.g., Corresponding angles are equal.

Lesson 3.3, pages 114–116

1. **a)** $\triangle ABC$ is an enlargement of $\triangle DEF$ by a scale factor of $\frac{3}{2}$.

b) $\triangle DEF$ is a reduction of $\triangle ABC$ by a scale factor of $\frac{2}{3}$.

2. **a)** 24 cm **b)** 50 m **c)** 40 km **d)** $\frac{1}{3}$

3. **a)** *AB* **b)** *FE* **c)** 12

4. 2

5. **a)** e.g., Corresponding sides are related by the same scale factor, and corresponding angles are equal.

b) $\frac{5}{3}$

6. A

7. C

8. not similar

9. $FD = 9$, $AB = 3$, $FE = 12.6$

10. **a)** 150 000 **b)** 30 km

11. **a)** $BC = 8$, $EF = 30$, $FG = 24$, $HG = 18$

b) $PR = 20$, $RQ = 16$ **c)** longest side $= 6$, other side $= 4.2$

d) both sides $= 10$

12. 10

13. e.g., all are about similar

14. **a)** e.g.,

1 cm:1 m

b) e.g.,

1 cm:2 m

15) **a)** e.g.,

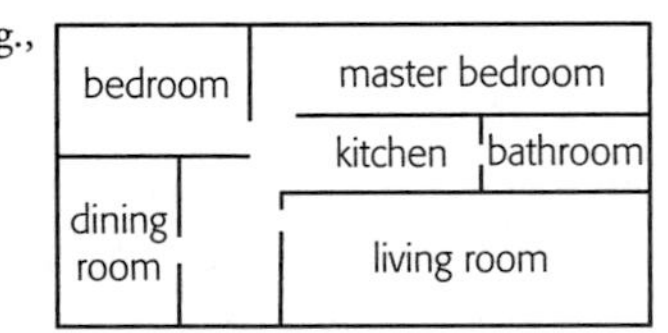

b) 100

c) e.g., based on size of sheet of paper

16. **a)** $\frac{1}{2}$ **b)** $\frac{1}{2}$

c) e.g., shaded triangles increase by $3^0, 3^1, 3^2, 3^3, \ldots$

17. e.g., a magnifying glass to represent scale. It shows 2 cm on the map represents 2 m in its normal size.

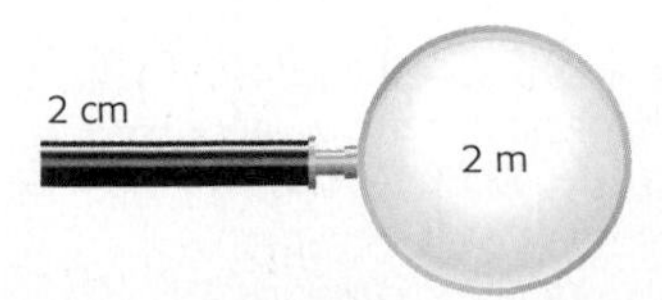

Mid-Chapter Review, pages 120–121

1. a, b

2. **a)** *AB* & *FG*, *BC* & *GH*, *AE* & *FJ*, *CD* & *HI*, *DE* & *IJ*, $\angle A$ & $\angle F$, $\angle B$ & $\angle G$, $\angle C$ & $\angle H$, $\angle D$ & $\angle I$, $\angle E$ & $\angle J$

b) *QR* & *UV*, *SR* & *TV*, *SQ* & *TU*, $\angle Q$ & $\angle U$, $\angle S$ & $\angle T$, $\angle R$ & $\angle V$

c) e.g., *LM* & *JO*, *MN* & *OY*, *NO* & *YC*, *OP* & *CE*, *PQ* & *EH*, *QL* & *HJ*, $\angle L$ & $\angle J$, $\angle M$ & $\angle O$, $\angle N$ & $\angle Y$, $\angle O$ & $\angle C$, $\angle P$ & $\angle E$, $\angle Q$ & $\angle H$

3. Corresponding angles are the same and corresponding sides have the same scale factor.

4. 2.4

5. **a)** 7.5 m **b)** 10.7 cm **c)** 3

6. **a)** not similar

b) similar; scale factor 0.25

c) not similar

d) similar; scale factor 1.5

Lesson 3.4, pages 127–128

1. **a)** 3 cm by 6 cm **b)** 1.5 cm by 3 cm **c)** 1.2 cm by 2.4 cm

2. **a)** The corresponding sides of each figure will be half as long as the original's sides.

b) The corresponding sides of each figure will be three times as long as the original's sides.

c) The corresponding sides of each figure will be twice as long as the original's sides.

3. **a)** One octagon will have sides of length 0.75 cm and the other sides of 0.5 cm.

b) One octagon will have sides of length 6 cm and the other sides of 4 cm

4. **a)** The corresponding sides will be half as long as the original's sides.

b) The corresponding sides will be 1.3 times as long as the original's sides.

c) The corresponding sides will be twice as long as the original's sides.

d) enlargement: b and c; reduction: a

5. e.g., **a)** With a scale factor of 2, the side lengths would be 18 and 30.

b) With a scale factor of $\frac{1}{3}$, the side lengths would be 3 and 5.

6. e.g., 1.5, $\frac{3}{4}$

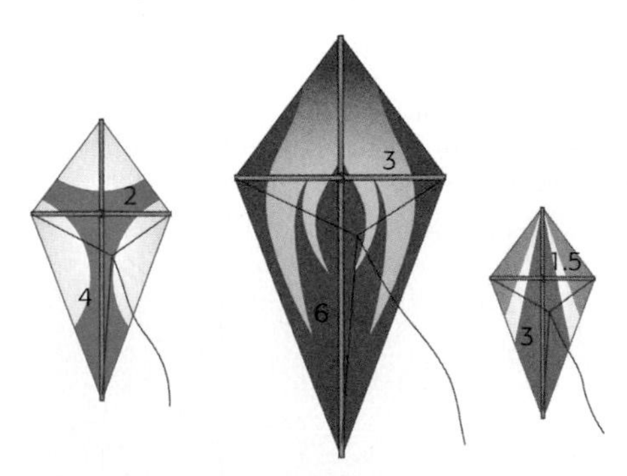

7. **a)** The ratio between their dimensions is not equal.

b) 17.5 cm by 24.5 cm

8. a) e.g.,

b) e.g.,

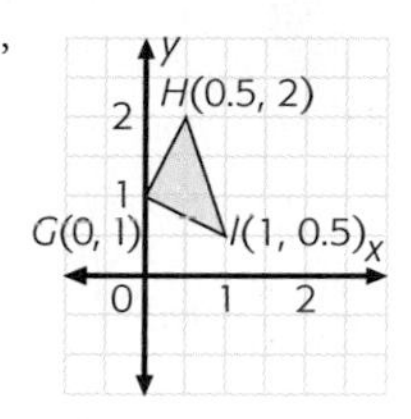

9. a) 4 cm b) 45 km
10. 9.5 m
11. e.g.,

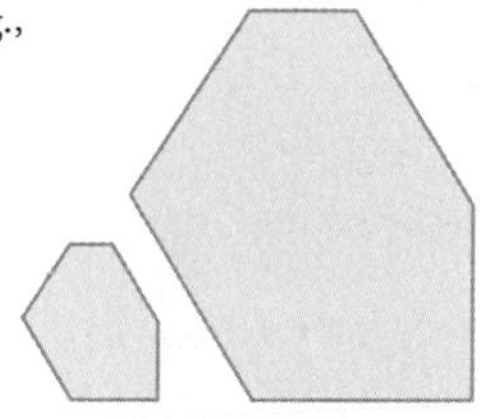

12. e.g., Measure the length of one side of the star polygon. Measure the internal angles. Multiply the length of the side by $\frac{5}{3}$. Draw a new star notepad with the longer lengths and the same angles as the original star polygon.

Lesson 3.5, pages 134–138

1. 10.64 m
2. 1.9 m
3. e.g., They are both right-angled triangles and the corresponding sides of each triangle seem to be related by the same ratio. The blue side would be 5.2.
4. e.g., a) 1.3 cm b) 22 cm c) 1:17 d) 17 cm
5. 50 cm by 75 cm
6. 14 similar parallelograms
7. C
8. D
9. 66
10. reduction: 0.4
11. 12 cm
12. 4
13. 110 mm long by 50 mm wide
14. 9.375 cm
15. 46.9 cm
16. 5.7 m
17. 4
18. 25 m
19. 520 m
20. 5.3 m
21. 167 m
22. 2 m

Lesson 3.6, pages 142–143

1. e.g., The octagons, because they are both regular, so they must be similar.
2. a) false b) false c) true
3. e.g., All circles have the same angle of 360°.
4. e.g., The area of the larger triangle is four times as large.
5. If the triangles are similar, then $\frac{8}{6} = \frac{SQ}{3}$, and $SQ = 4$. But then $\triangle PQS$ doesn't satisfy the Pythagorean theorem: $6^2 \neq 3^2 + 4^2$.
6. 1:3 means the poster should be 3 times as large as the ad. 2:1 means that for every 2 units on the ad the postcard dimension should be reduced to 1.
7. 7 m long
8. e.g.,

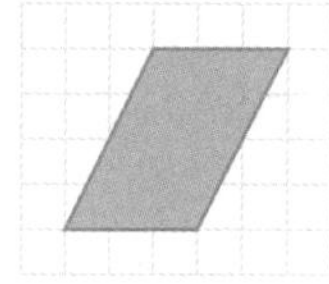

9. yes
10. C
11. a) e.g., about 6 cm b) about 80:1
12. a) Divide the length of the building's shadow by the length of the metre stick's shadow.
    b) e.g., 30 m high
13. e.g., Comparing corresponding sides to see if they have the same ratio.

Chapter Self-Test, pages 144–145

1. Set A
2. yes
3. a) *ABCD* is an enlargement of *EFGH* by a scale factor of 2.
   b) *EFGH* is a reduction of *ABCD* by a scale factor of $\frac{1}{2}$.
4. a triangle 2.5 the size of the original
5. e.g., 20 cm by 28 cm, 22 cm by 30 cm, 28 cm by 39 cm
6. 2.2 m
7. 11.5 m
8. e.g., The leftmost sides of each polygon are the same lengths while the horizontal sides are not.

Chapter Review, page 147–148

1. a) the octagons
2. e.g., Two polygons are similar if all corresponding sides have the same scale factor and all corresponding angles are equal.
3. a) 2.5 b) 12.5 cm c) 90°
4. a) 135 cm by 135 cm
   b) e.g., a scale factor of 20% and drew the design 18 cm by 18 cm.
5.

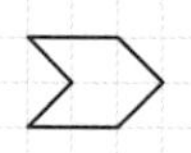

6. 25 cm by 35 cm
7. 70 m
8. yes
9. 4.7 m
10. 81 m
11. e.g., Determine if corresponding interior angles are equal and if corresponding sides have the same scale factor.
12. a) e.g., Scale factor requires multiplication, not subtraction.
    b) e.g., Write the relationship as a ratio. $\frac{4}{1} = \frac{6}{1.5}$ and include diagrams.

Cumulative Review: Chapters 1–3, pages 150–151

1. A
2. D
3. C
4. A
5. D
6. C
7. C
8. D
9. D
10. B
11. D
12. C
13. C
14. D
15. B
16. B
17. D
18. B

Chapter 4

Lesson 4.2, pages 160–162

1. a)

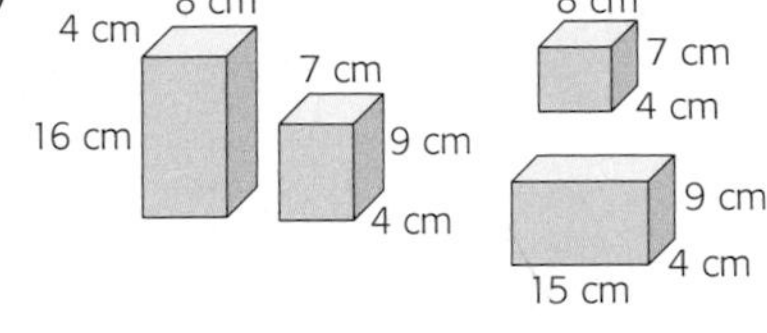

b)

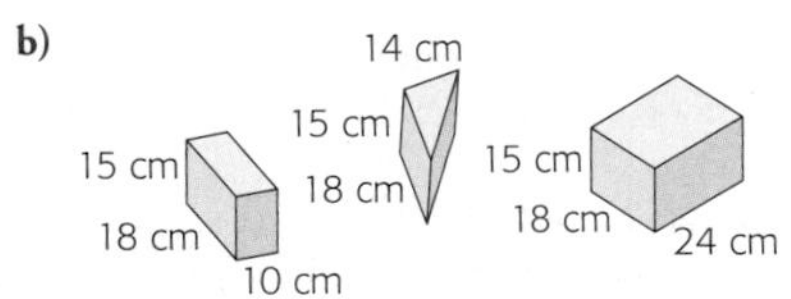

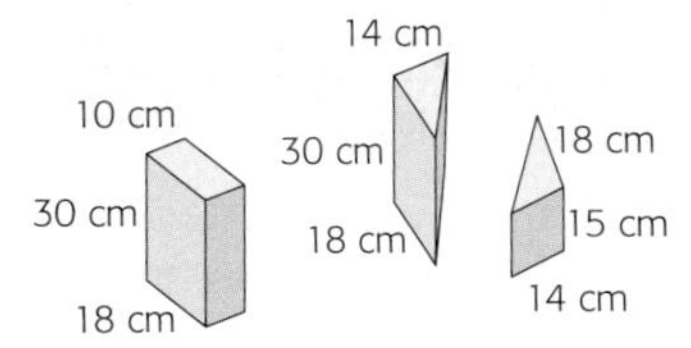

2. a)

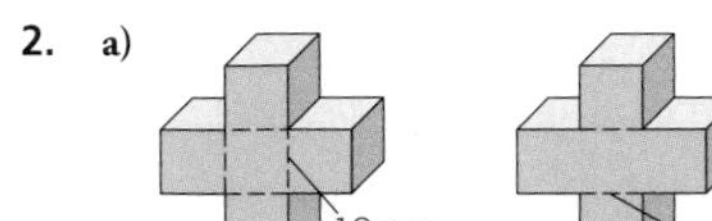

b)

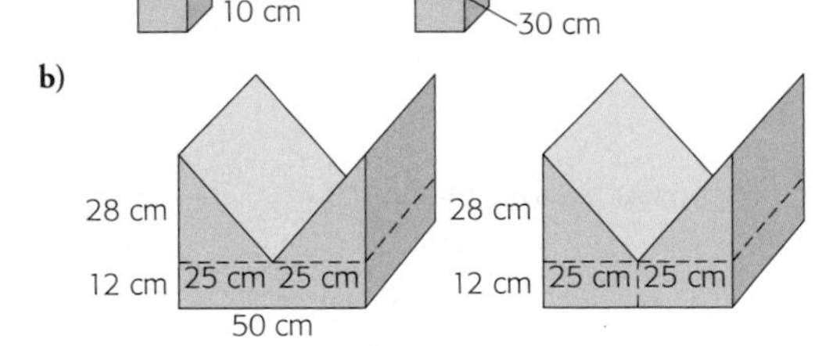

c)

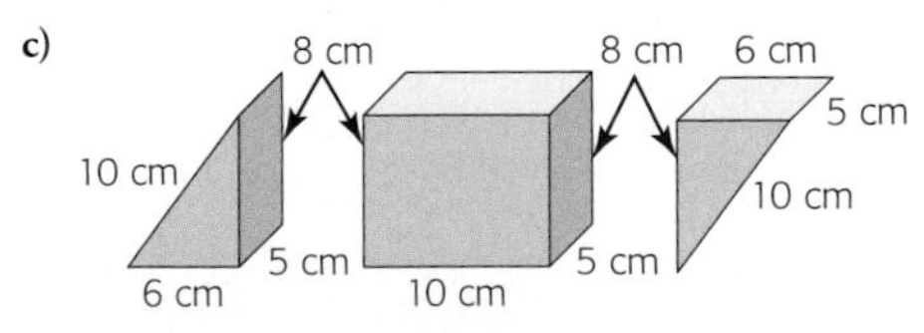

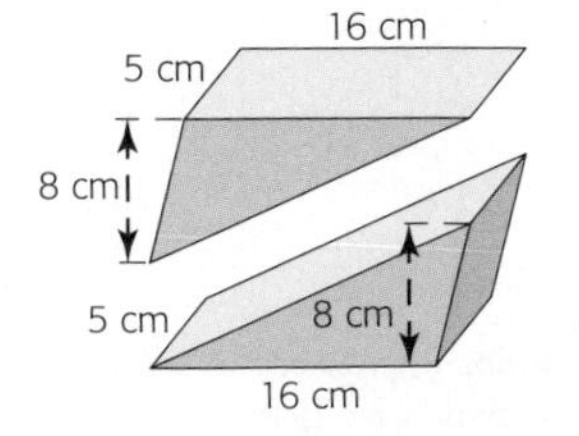

3. a) b) c)

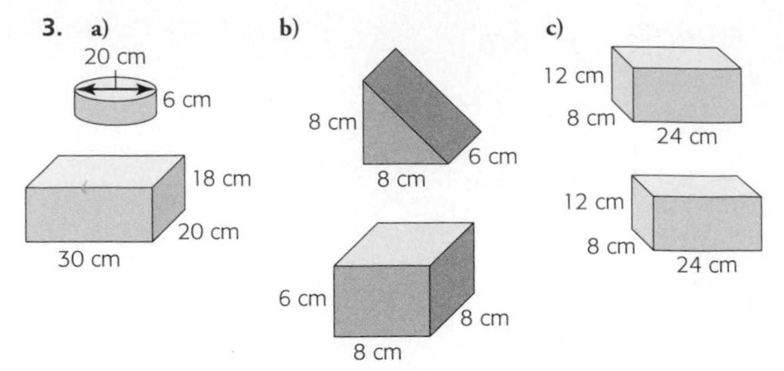

4. e.g.,

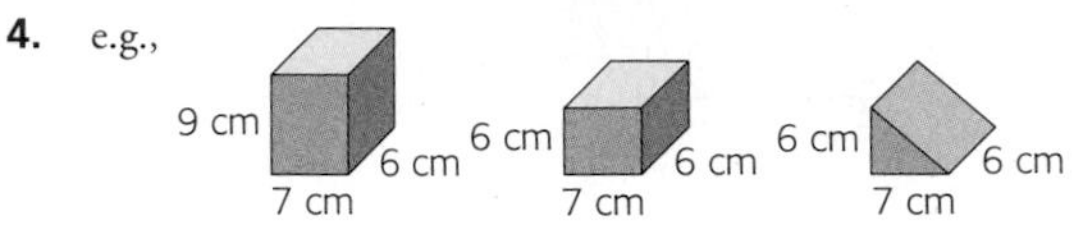

5.

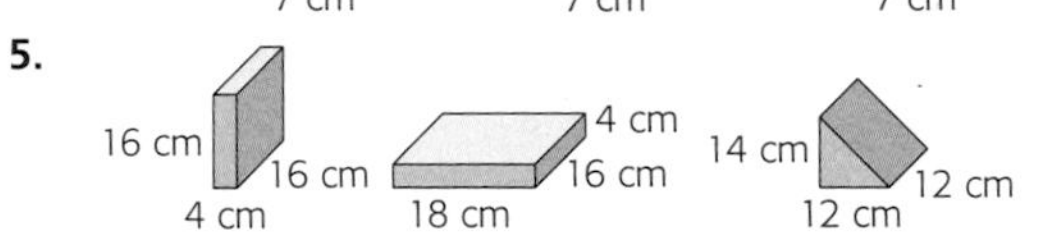

6. C
7. B
8. e.g.,

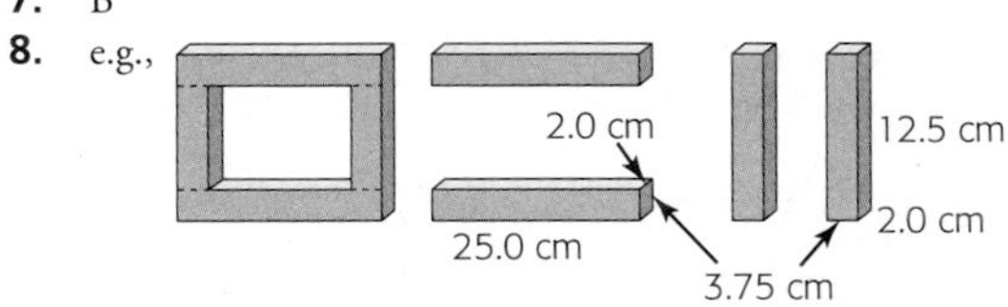

9. e.g., one rectangular prism 1.9 m by 0.9 m by 0.8 m, one rectangular prism 0.9 m by 0.8 m by 0.3 m, two half-cylinders with diameter 0.8 m and height 0.9 m
10. e.g., four cylinders 37 cm high and 5 cm in diameter, four cylinders 7 cm high and 5 cm in diameter, two rectangular prisms 130 cm by 55 cm by 3 cm.
11. a) e.g., One way involves three rectangular prisms that are 1.2 m by 0.4 m by 1.2 m, 0.7 m by 0.6 m by 1.2 m, and 0.5 m by 0.6 m by 0.6 m. b) yes
12.

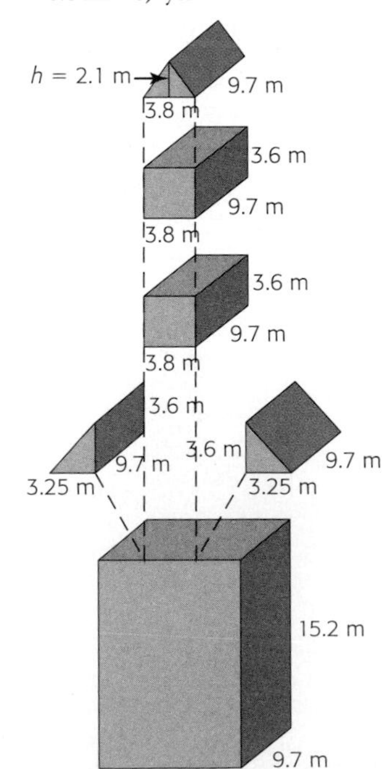

13. **a)** e.g., A stereo speaker can be divided into a rectangular prism and a triangular prism.

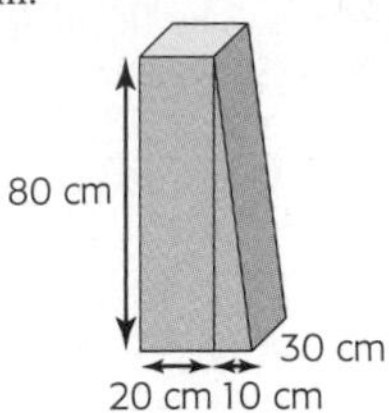

14. e.g., It's easier to calculate the volume of a rectangular prism than a triangular prism. So, if I need to determine the volume of a composite object, then it is easier to decompose it into rectangular prisms than triangular prisms.
15. e.g., The components of the packing are a rectangular prism 24 cm by 24 cm by 30 cm with half a cylinder that is 24 cm in diameter and 30 cm high subtracted out.
16.

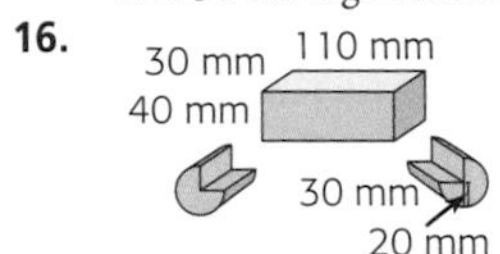

Lesson 4.3, pages 168–170

1. e.g., The area of overlap is shaded in yellow.

   a) **b)** **c)**

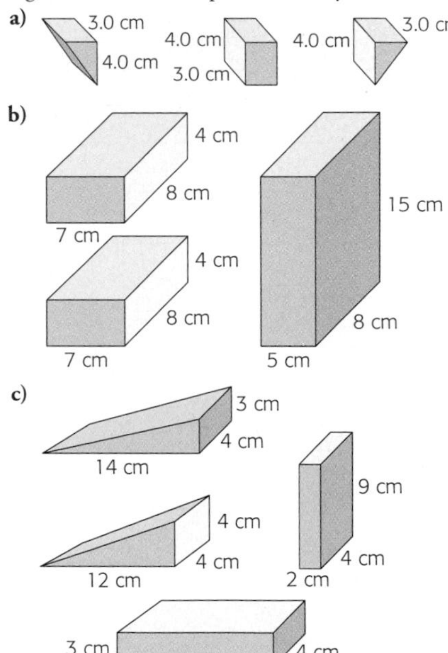

2. **a)** 24.0 cm^2 **b)** 64 cm^2 **c)** 80 cm^2
3. 72 cm^2
4. A
5. D
6. 170 cm^2
7. 3.06 m^2
8. 9 cm^2
9. e.g., This is my composite structure. The area of overlap for one cube is 4 cm^2. The cubes overlap in 8 places, so the area of overl is 8×4 cm^2 = 32 cm^2.

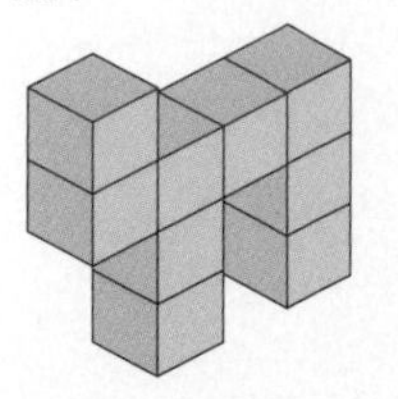

10. 235.6 cm^2
11. **a)** 15 120 cm^2 **b)** eg., 23 520 cm^2

   c) eg., 23 520 cm^2

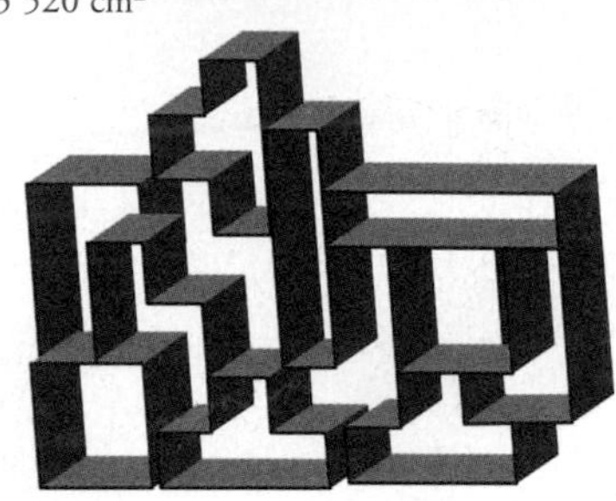

12. no
13. **a)** a rectangle 4.25 cm by 2.60 cm **b)** 41.14 cm^2
14. 1510 cm^2

Mid-Chapter Review, page 172

1. e.g., rectangular prisms, triangular prisms, cylinders
2. e.g., **a)**

   b)

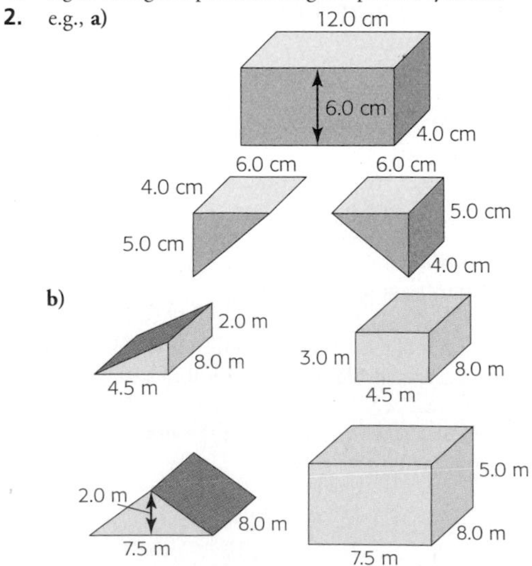

3. a) 48 cm^2 b) 136 m^2
4. 101 cm^2
5. about 857 cm^2

Lesson 4.4, pages 179–181

1. a) 1016 cm^2 b) 1140 cm^2
2. about 37 707 cm^2
3. 544 cm^2
4. 6072.9 cm^2
5. 1982.0 cm^2
6. 25 440 cm^2
7. 846.8 cm^2
8. 826.8 cm^2
9. 14 688 cm^2
10. a) 3131 cm^2 b) 7 L
11. A
12. B
13. 1942.5 cm^2
14. 11 654 cm^2
15. 499.8 cm^2
16. 130.1 m^2
17. no
18. 21 183.7 cm^2
19. 165.7 m^2

Lesson 4.5, pages 187–189

1. 1226.7 cm^2
2. a) 2.91 m^2 b) 3.9 m^2
3. 5.91 m^2
4. 21 601.59 cm^2
5. 38 816.7 cm^2
6. 225.3 m^2
7. 9389.3 cm^2
8. 11 880 cm^2
9. a) cylinder 117.8 cm^2, rectangle 110 cm^2, triangle 84.3 cm^2
   b) 1222 cm^2

Chapter Self-Test, pages 190–191

1. e.g., 350 cm^2
2. a)

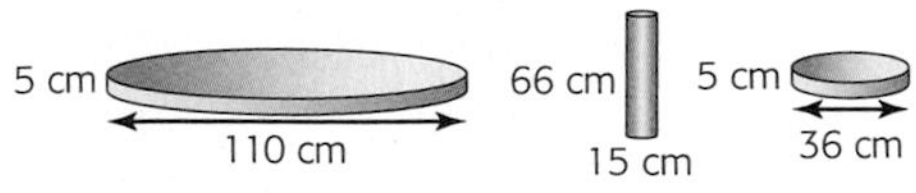

   b) 353.4 cm^2 c) 26 092.5 cm^2
3. a) e.g., split into two rectangular prisms, two congruent triangular prisms and a cylinder
   b) e.g., 314.3 cm^2 c) 1694.4 cm^2
4. 1482.0 cm^2
5. a) e.g., Find the area of the tent and subtract the windows, or divide into smaller shapes and add them together (be careful of overlap).
   b) 115.2 m^2
   c) Calculate the area of tent, then subtract the area of windows.
6. 265 747.7 cm^2
7. 37.63 m^2
8. 16 875.2 cm^2

Chapter Review, pages 193–194

1. a) a rectangular prism 12 cm by 18 cm by 10 cm and 4 congruent triangular prisms 9 cm by 6 cm by 10 cm
   b) a rectangular prism 1.15 m by 0.50 m by 0.55 m and a triangular prism 0.21 m by 0.50 m by 0.55 m
2. 900 cm^2
3. 405 cm^2
4. 25.1 m^2
5. 40 cm^2
6. 9837 cm^2
7. 5375.3 cm^2
8. a) 15.59 m^2 b) 29 965.5 m^2 c) 3307.9 cm^2
9. 6.48 m^2
10. 5889 cm^2
11. 33.5 m^2
12. e.g., 22 000 cm^2
13. 186.1 cm^2

Chapter 5

Lesson 5.1, pages 204–207

1. a) C b) B c) A
2. a)

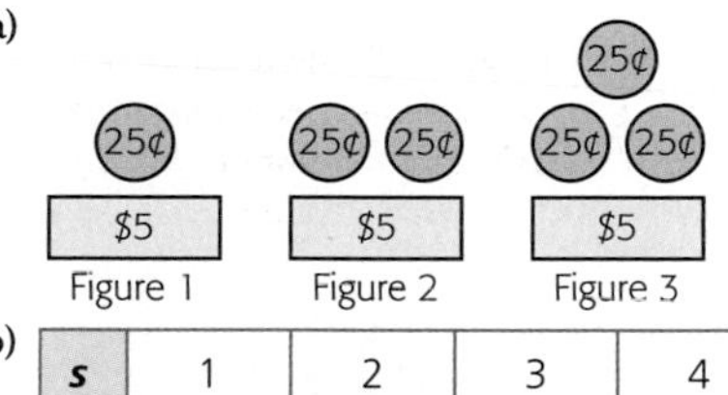

   b)

s	1	2	3	4
C	$5.25	$5.50	$5.75	$6.00

   c) 0.25
3. a)

Time (h)	Distance (km)
1	15
2	30
3	45

   b) $d = 15t$ c) 120 km d) $6\frac{2}{3}$ h
4. a) $P = 3s$ b) $C = 2.50 + 0.50d$ c) $y = 3x + 3$
5. a)

Figure	Toothpicks
1	4
2	7
3	10

   b) $t = 3n + 1$ c) 25 toothpicks d) Figure 15
6. C
7. A
8. D
9. a) e.g., $C = \frac{1}{12}T$ b) $150
10. a) 6; $y = 6x - 1$ b) -4.5; $y = 124.5 - 4.5x$

11. **a)**

x	1	2	3
y	−2	−1	0

b)

x	1	2	3
y	5	10	15

c)

x	1	2	3
y	1	−3	−7

d)

x	1	2	3
y	3.75	6.25	8.75

e)

x	1	2	3
y	$\frac{3}{5}$	$\frac{6}{5}$	$\frac{9}{5}$

f)

x	1	2	3
y	$-7\frac{1}{12}$	$-4\frac{5}{6}$	$-2\frac{7}{12}$

12. $1, 5, -4, 2.5, \frac{3}{5}, 2\frac{1}{4}$

13. e.g., The height of an elevator above street level at the bottom floor is 1.75 m. For every floor the elevator reaches, its height above street level is increased by 3.5 m.

14. **a)** $\frac{3}{5}$ **b)** no

15. **a)** 30.00, 41.50, 53.00, 64.50 **b)** $11.50
c) e.g., change in x-values is 10, not 1
d) $y = 30 + 1.15(x - 50), x \geq 50$ **e)** $64.50

16. **a)** $P = 5x$ **b)** 25 m **c)** 42 m by 21 m

17. **a)** $\frac{1}{3}$ **b)** $-4\frac{2}{3}, -4\frac{1}{3}, -4; \frac{1}{3}$
c) e.g., My prediction was correct. **d)** multiples of 3

18. e.g., A table of values gives multiple ordered pairs, which is helpful for identifying or estimating solutions to a relation. Using an algebraic representation gives an exact numerical solution to a relation.

19. **a)** $y = x$ **b)** $y = \frac{x}{2} + 3$

20. **a)**

Hours	1	2	3	4	5	6	7	8	9	10
Cost ($)	20	25	30	35	39	43	47	51	55	59

b) first 4 h: $C = 15 + 5h$, where $h \leq 4$;
after 4 h: $C = 35 + 4(h - 4), h > 4$
c) e.g., The algebraic representation will be more useful because it is easier to determine the cost for any number of hours.

Lesson 5.2, pages 214–218

1. From top to bottom: b), a), c)

2. **a)** 15 min **b)** 9 km **c)** 12 km/h

3. **a)** B **b)** A

4. **a)**

x	−2	−1	0	1	2
y	−2	$-1\frac{1}{2}$	−1	$-\frac{1}{2}$	0

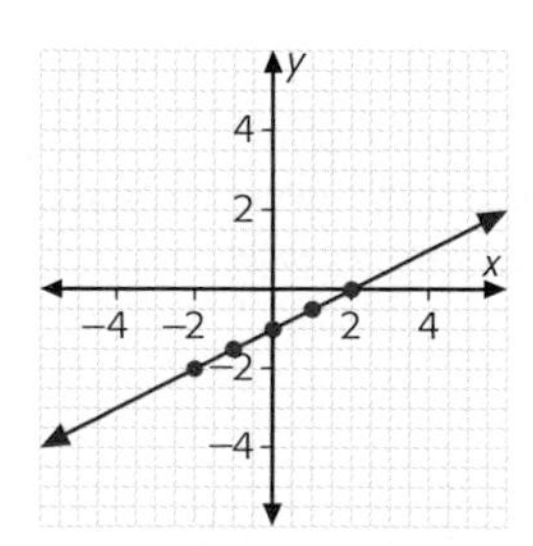

b) $\frac{1}{2}$

5. $-\frac{3}{8}$

6. D

7. D

8. $y = 2$; e.g., A car stopped at a traffic light has a zero rate of change in position.

9. **a)**

x	0	5	10	15	20
y	10	0	−10	−20	−30

b)

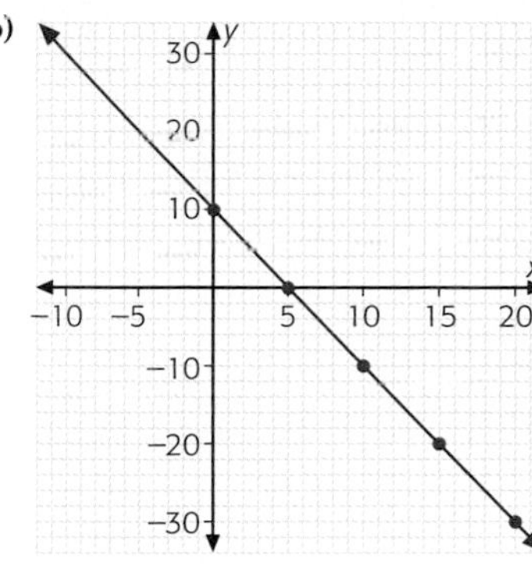

c) 2, −26, −140

10. **a)** A party of 20 people will cost $250.
b) $325 **c)** 70 people **d)** $50
e) $5; This is the rate of change of cost per person.

11. **a)** The computer is worth $500 after 2 years.
b) $550 **c)** after 6 years **d)** after 7 years **e)** $100
f) e.g., The graph is a straight line so the rate of change remains constant for all the data, which means the decrease is constant between consecutive years.

12. **a)**

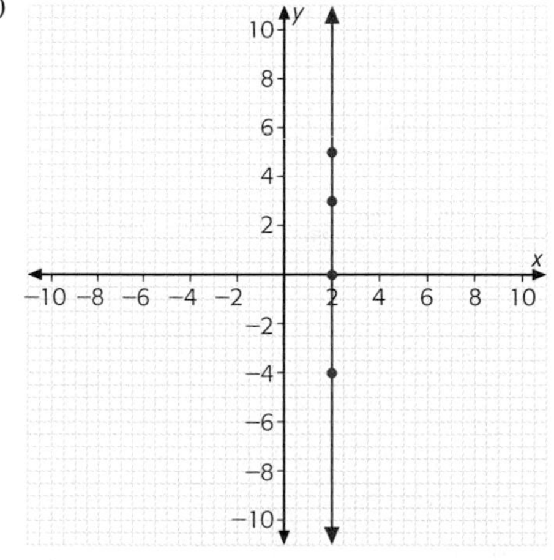

b) yes **c)** It is a vertical line.

Answers

13. a)

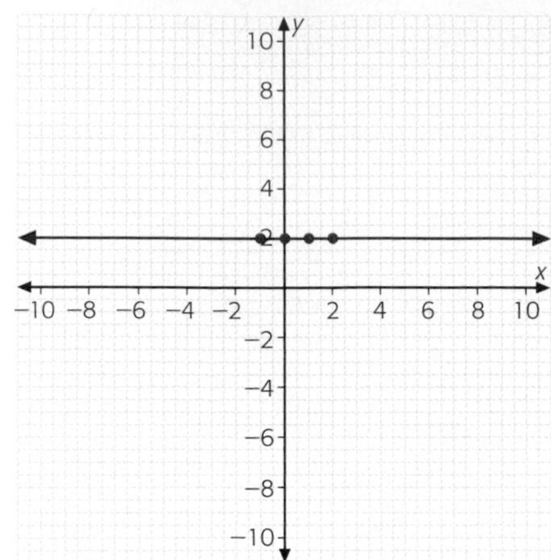

b) yes c) It is a horizontal line.

14. a)

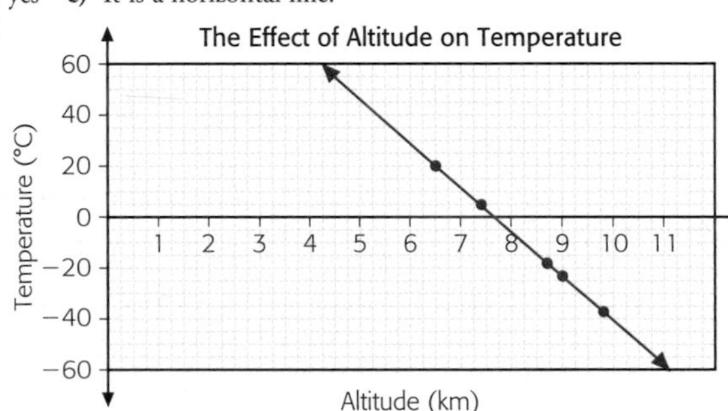

b) about 12 °C c) about 10.5 km d) yes e) about −17 °C

15. a) e.g., The graph will start high along the y-axis and will grow at a slow rate because the initial cost of the house is large and the value of the house will increase steadily but slowly as time goes on.

b)

x	1	2	3	4	5
y	132 500	140 000	147 500	155 000	162 500

c) $177 500 d) $7500

e) It is the rate of change of the value of the house.

16. D

17. a)

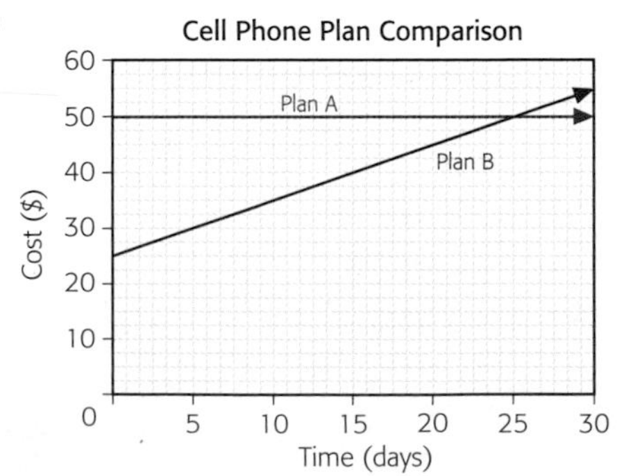

b) Both graphs are linear relations; The graph of Plan A is horizontal and the graph of Plan B increases.

c) Plan A

18. e.g., The rate of change tells by how much to multiply the independent variable to determine the value of the dependent variable in a linear relation.

19. e.g., No, she would get tired and her speed would begin to decrease.

20. a) e.g., 80 min of calls costs $10.

b) $10 for 80 min; e.g., it costs $10 more for 80 min than for 0 min.

c) $2.50 for 20 min; e.g., it costs $2.50 more for 20 min.

d) e.g., The rate is the same, $1.25 more for each 10 min, so the relation between cost and time is linear.

21. a) $\frac{1}{2}$, 1, 2, 3 b) (0, 1)

c) e.g., The coefficient of the x is the rate of change.

d) $y = -3x + 1$

Lesson 5.3, pages 223–225

1. a) $y = 4.25x - 3$ b) $y = 5 - \left(\frac{1}{4}\right)x$

2. e.g., 3; 28

3. e.g., about 73 min

4. e.g., a) −6 b) 2 c) −7.5 d) 1.5 e) 4 f) 4

5. a) incorrect b) correct c) correct d) incorrect

6. a) solution A: correct; solution B: incorrect

b) solution B: $x = \frac{2}{5}$; Nick used the y-value at $x = 1$ instead of the x-value at $y = 1$ for his answer.

7. a) $C = 25n - 250$, $n \geq 50$

b)

Cost of Hiring Party Planners

Cost ($): 0, 200, 400, 600, 800, 1000, 1200, 1400, 1600, 1800

Number of guests: 50, 55, 60, 65, 70, 75

c) $1000; $1625 d) $1500 = 25n - 250$; $n = 70$ guests

8. a) $E = 8n$ b) $720 = 8n$ c) $E = 8(90)$

d) e.g., They are the same equation with each coordinate of the solution (90, 720) substituted into a separate part of the equation.

e) part b: 90 h; part c: $720

f) part b: 90 h; part c: $720

9. 20 students and 2 adults

10. D

11. B

12. a) $c = 3n + 3$ b) 39 c) Figure 19 d) no

13. e.g., using a table of values, for the first equation, you would look for a y-value of $\frac{13}{3}$ in the table, and the corresponding x-value would be the solution. If $\frac{13}{3}$ is not in the table, you would find two values it falls between and estimate an x-value. You would do the same thing to solve the second equation except you would look for a y-value of 21 instead of $\frac{13}{3}$.

14. e.g., a) −7 b) 1 c) −1

15. $\frac{41}{15}$

Lesson 5.4, pages 229–231

1. **a)** subtraction, division **c)** subtraction, multiplication
   b) addition, division
2. **a)** $-\frac{13}{3}$ **b)** 1.99 **c)** 12
3. **a)** $10\ 000 = 5000 + 1.25n$ **c)** e.g., My solution is correct.
   b) 4000
4. **a)** addition, division **b)** subtraction, division
   c) division **d)** multiplication
   e) division **f)** multiplication, division
5. **a)** $\frac{4}{3}$ **b)** 0.2 **c)** $\frac{20}{7}$ **d)** -1200 **e)** -3 **f)** $\frac{3}{2}$
6. **a)** $10.00 = 8.00 + 0.50T$ **b)** 4
   c) $10.00 = 8.00 + 0.50(T - 2)$
7. **a)** $d = 600 - 4t$ **b)** $486 = 600 - 4t$ **c)** 28.5 s
   d) e.g., My solution is correct.
8. **a)** $d = -11$ **b)** $d = -11$
   c) e.g., The equation can be solved using subtracting and dividing in any order.
9. **a)** 8 **b)** 26 **c)** 6 **d)** –5 **e)** –12 **f)** 24
10. B
11. A
12. **a)** 3 **b)** 6 **c)** 5 **d)** 23 **e)** 6 **f)** $-\frac{5}{4}$
13. **a)** e.g., The bill is determined by multiplying the price per person, \$22.95, by one less than the number of people at one table; x represents the number of people at a table, T represents the bill total.
    b) Table 1: $22.95(x - 1) = 137.70$, $x = 7$; Table 2: $22.95(x - 1) = 68.85$, $x = 4$; Table 3: $22.95(x - 1) = 160.65$, $x = 8$; Table 4: $22.95(x - 1) = 91.80$, $x = 5$; Table 5: $22.95(x - 1) = 91.80$, $x = 5$
    c) 29
14. **a)** about 14.4 °C **b)** subtraction, multiplication
    c) multiplication, addition **d)** 77 °F
15. e.g., Performing inverse operations always keeps both sides of the equation balanced.
16. B
17. **a)** 5 **b)** $\frac{2}{3}$ **c)** no solution **d)** $-\frac{5}{3}$
18. **a)** 30 **b)** 42.5°

Mid-Chapter Review, pages 233–235

1. All the relations are linear.
2. **a)** e.g., After 1 week she has \$1200 in her account.
   b) \$1100 **c)** \$850
3. **a)** e.g.,

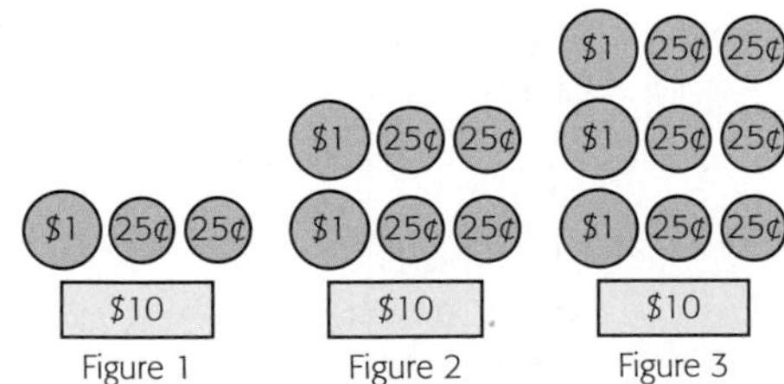

Figure 1 Figure 2 Figure 3

b)

Cost of Downloading Music				
s	0	2	4	6
C	10	13	16	19

c)

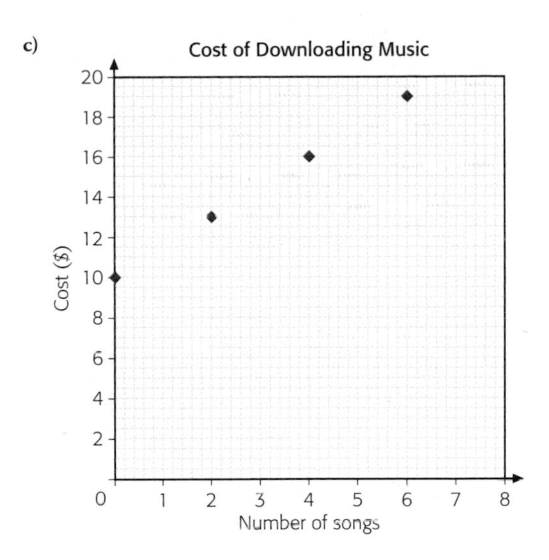

d) \$17.50 **e)** 43 songs

4. **a)** 2 **b)** 1 **c)** 3
5. **a)**

Circumference vs. Radius

Circumference (cm)

Radius (cm)

   b) about 19 cm **c)** about 2 cm
6. e.g., **a)** -1.5 **b)** 9 **c)** 34 **d)** $\frac{1}{2}$
7. **a)** incorrect **b)** correct **c)** incorrect **d)** incorrect

Answers

8. **a)**

Submarine Depth vs. Time	
Time (min)	Depth (m)
0	0
5	50
10	100
15	150
20	200
25	250
30	300

b) Submarine Depth vs. Time

Depth (m): 0, 50, 100, 150, 200, 250, 300, 350
Time (min): 5, 10, 15, 20, 25, 30, 35

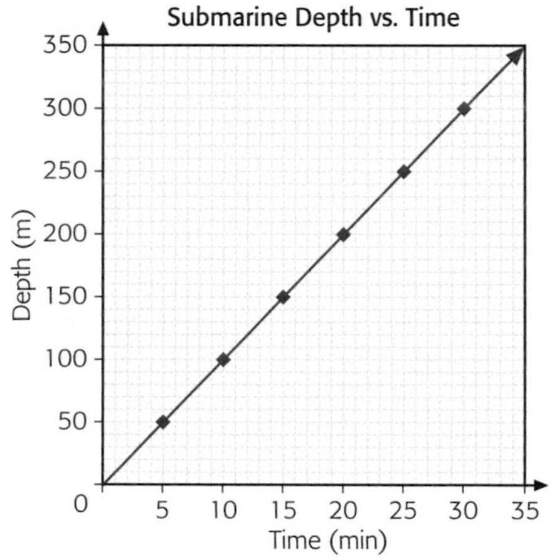

c) e.g., When the time increases by the same amount, the depth of the submarine increases by the same amount. Also, the depth is 10 times the time.
d) $d = 219 + 10t$ **e)** $428 = 10t$ **f)** 42.8 min
g) The equation is the point on the graph when $d = 428$ m.

9. **a)** 6 **b)** $\frac{27}{130}$ **c)** $-\frac{1}{5}$ **d)** 12.3 **e)** 0 **f)** 176

10. **a)** $C = 8.98(b - 6)$ **b)** $17.96
c) $53.88 = 8.98(b - 6); b = 12$

11. **a)** $k + 3 = 12; k = 9$
b) $x - 6 = 2\frac{1}{3}; x = 8\frac{1}{3}$
c) $7 = 5a; a = \frac{7}{5}$
d) $g - \frac{7}{15} = 0; g = \frac{7}{15}$
e) $h + \frac{3}{8} = \frac{21}{4}; h = \frac{39}{8}$
f) $2x = 9; x = \frac{9}{2}$

12. e.g., **a)** The position of a long-distance runner who gets a 6 m head start in a marathon and runs at 3 m/s for the rest of the race.
b) (0, 6); when $x = 0$, the race is at the very beginning and the position of the runner is 6 m from the start line.
c) When $x = -1$, which cannot be true since time is never negative.

Lesson 5.5, pages 242–245

1. 3

2. **a)** e.g., We know the width is 3 less than the length.
b) $2L + 2(L - 3) = 44; L = 12.5$ cm
c) 12.5 cm by 9.5 cm

3. **a)** e.g., A: Gather the variables on the right side of the equation. B: Gather the constants on the left side of the equation. C: Divide both sides of the equation by 2 to isolate x.
b) e.g., A: Multiply both sides of the equation by 6 to convert all numbers to integers. B: Simplify and express the equation with integers, gather the constants on the right side of the equation. C: Divide both sides of the equation by 3 to isolate x.

4. **a)** Equation 2 is equivalent to Equation 1; the left sides are the same and the right sides are equivalent. Equations 2 and 3 are equivalent; Equation 3 is just Equation 2 with all constants on one side and all variables on the other. Equation 2 is equivalent to Equations 1 and 3, so Equations 1 and 3 are equivalent.
b) Equation 2 is equivalent to Equation 3, as the terms in Equation 3 are the same as the terms in Equation 2, multiplied by 12 to make whole numbers. Equation 1 is equivalent to Equation 2 as $\frac{x}{4}$ and $\frac{3x}{12}$, 5 and $\frac{60}{12}$, and $\frac{1}{3}$ and $\frac{4}{12}$ are all equivalent fractions. Equation 2 is equivalent to both Equation 1 and Equation 3, so Equations 1 and 3 are also equivalent.
c) Equation 2 is equivalent to Equation 3, as $-\frac{4}{3}$ and $-\frac{8}{6}$ and 2 and $\frac{12}{6}$ are equivalent fractions. Equation 1 is the same as Equation 3, as each term in Equation 3 has been multiplied by 6 to make whole numbers in Equation 1.

5. **a)** -8 **b)** 7.5 **c)** -6 **d)** no solution **e)** 2 **f)** 0

6. **a)** $4x = 3 + 2x; x = \frac{3}{2}$ **b)** $5x + 9 = -4x - 18; x = -3$

7. **a)** not equivalent **b)** not equivalent **c)** equivalent **d)** equivalent **e)** equivalent **f)** equivalent

8. 2

9. **a)** 7 **b)** -2 **c)** 3 **d)** 10 **e)** -1 **f)** -1

10. D

11. A

12. D

13. **a)** $9x + 8 = 24$
b) $3 - 2x = 2$
c) $2 = 15 + 3x$
d) $x - 5 + 4 = 2$
e) $-240 = 3x + 5x$
f) $-2(x - 8) = 20$

14. **a)** 6 **b)** -4 **c)** 12 **d)** 36 **e)** $\frac{45}{2}$ **f)** 7

15. true

16. **a)** $\frac{t}{4} + \frac{t}{3} = 1; t = \frac{12}{7}$ h **b)** $\frac{t}{30} + \frac{t}{60} = 1; t = 20$ min
c) $800t = 3500 - 600t; t = 2.5$ h

17. **a)** correct **b)** correct
c)

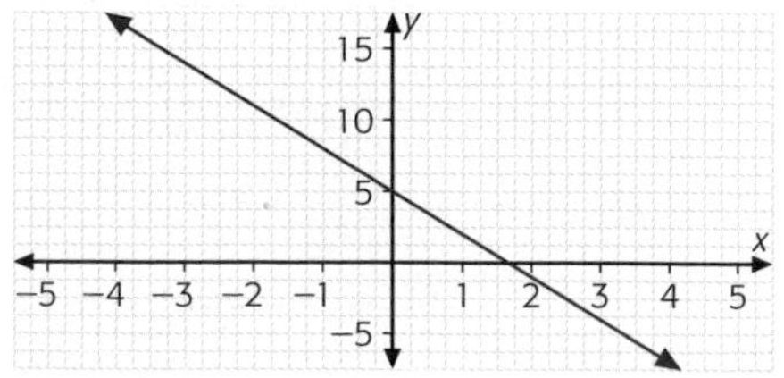

y: 15, 10, 5, −5
x: −5, −4, −3, −2, −1, 1, 2, 3, 4, 5

Both graphs are the same line.
d) all values of x

18. e.g., You can multiply by 4 to make all the numbers integers and then group the x's and numbers to solve the equation, or you can group the x's and numbers first and then multiply to solve for x.

19. a) $y = 100 - x$

b) $w = \frac{(P - 2l)}{2}$

c) $r = \frac{I}{pt}$

d) $x = \frac{(c - by)}{a}$

e) $x = \frac{(D + AC)}{(AB)}$

f) $h = \frac{(s - 2\pi r^2)}{(2\pi r)}$

20. Multiply by 2 to remove fractions and then divide by $(b_1 + b_2)$

21. a) $x = \frac{1}{2}$ b) $x = 3$

Lesson 5.6, pages 248–249

1. 1 km
2. Nola
3. 16
4. 93.75 m
5. 15.50 cm by 10.50 cm
6. 277.5 s
7. 10
8. e.g., 10
9. about 1 h 4 min
10. e.g., 8
11. e.g., Ted has 57 beads to make a bracelet and he separates them into piles of 6. If he has 3 beads left over, how many piles of 6 beads does he have? (9 piles)
12. on the roadway at 90 km from the hospital; (the ambulance will not be able to travel at 140 km/h over rough terrain).
13. Fencepost 386 from Michelle

Lesson 5.7, pages 254–256

1. a) B b) C c) A d) D
2. a)

0 1400

b)

150 275

3. a) B b) D c) A d) C
4. a) $-2 < x \leq 1$, x is rational
b) $x < 5$, x is rational
c) $x \leq -2$ or $x \geq 1$, x is an integer
d) $x \leq 4$, x is an integer
e) $-1 \leq x \leq 3$, x is an integer
f) $x \geq -2$, x is rational
5. e.g., a) Bob wants his kite to fly more than 20 m high. It is now 11 m high. How much higher must it go?
b) A tour company gives a discount to groups of more than 20 people. There are 11 people in Lisa's group. How many more are needed for the discount?
6. a)

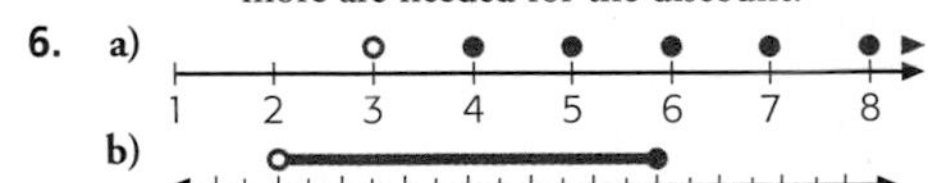

b)

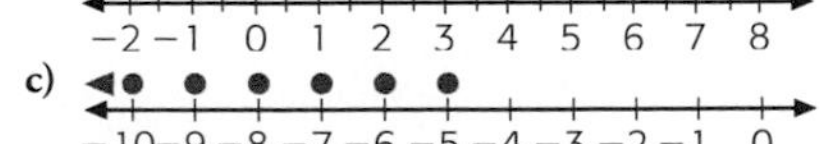

c)

d)

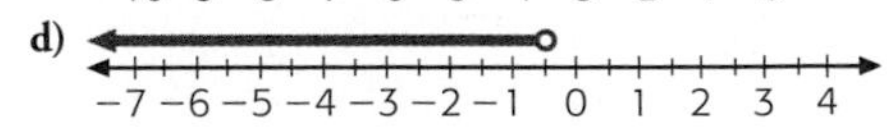

e)

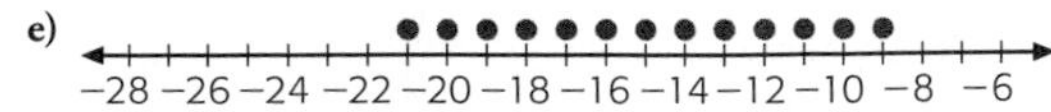

f)

7. $x > 12$
8. a) e.g., there are no values between the integer values b) $x > 1$
9. a) e.g., $x \geq 2$; x is an integer c) $x \geq -2$; x is rational
b) $x < 2$; x is an integer
10. e.g., Rebecca can silk screen 9 T-shirts in one day. She shares her studio and can only use her studio space 2 days a week. What is the maximum number of T-shirts she can make in 4 weeks?
11. a) $a > -2$ b) closed dots instead of a line
12. B
13. B
14. C
15. e.g., The graph helps you visualize the solution.
16. a) $x \leq -\frac{2}{5}$ b) e.g. Because the constant is a rational number.
17. a)

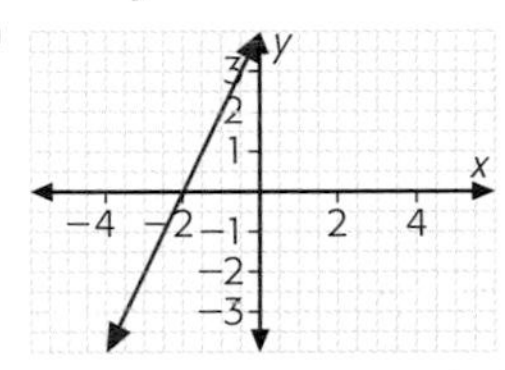

b) All points above and on the line are in the solution.
c) All points below the line $y = -3x + 1$ are in the solution. The line itself is not in the solution.

Lesson 5.9, pages 262–265

1. a) $x > 0$ b) $x \geq 4$ c) $x < -\frac{1}{2}$ d) $x \geq -7$
2. The graph of $x \leq 7$ includes the endpoint $x = 7$.
3. a) $x > \frac{3}{4}$ c) $x \geq -\frac{1}{2}$ e) $m \geq -2$
b) $x < -4$ d) $x > \frac{13}{6}$ f) $x < \frac{3}{2}$
4. a) no b) no c) yes d) no e) yes f) yes
5. a) $2x - 7 < 20$ b) $x < \frac{27}{2}$
6. a) $152 + 5g \leq 400$ c) e.g., My solution is correct.
b) 49 games
7. a) $t \leq -\frac{8}{3}$ c) $r \geq 424$ e) $p \leq -\frac{4}{3}$
b) $x < -2.31$ d) $a < 0$ f) $x > \frac{27}{40}$
8. $x > 5$
9. a) $y < -5$ c) $p < 1$ e) $x > \frac{24}{7}$
b) $a \leq -\frac{1}{7}$ d) $q \leq \frac{16}{7}$ f) $x > -90$
10. a) $\frac{(19.5 + t)}{4} > 7.5$ b) $\frac{(19.5 + t)}{4} > 7$
11. a) $15 + 1.5n$
b) $2.25n - 11.25$
c) $15 + 1.5n > 2.25n - 11.25$
d) $n < 35$
e) PRionTV to download fewer than 35; TVTitles otherwise
12. a) $8(x + 3)$ c) $x < 3.5$
b) $8(x + 3) < 52$ d) less than 6.5 cm
13. a) $a > -3\frac{1}{3}$ b) $p \geq -\frac{2}{3}$ c) $s \geq -1\frac{7}{11}$ d) $b > 3$
14. C
15. no
16. a) 32 cards b) e.g., from 28 to 38 in ones.
c)

28 29 30 31 32 33 34 35 36 37 38

17. **a)** $2(4n - 4) + 2(2n + 3) \leq 100$ **b)** $1 < n \leq \frac{17}{2}$

c) e.g., from 0 to 10 in rational numbers

d) 0 1 2 3 4 5 6 7 8 9 10

18. e.g., **a)** 19, 20, 21 **b)** 18, 17, 16

c) $\frac{x}{3} + 5 > 11$ **d)** $x > 18$

19. e.g., similar: need to perform same operation on both sides; different: may need to change the > or < signs; an equation has one solution and an inequality may have many solutions

20. **a)** $n + 2$

b) $3n$

c) $n + (n + 2) + 3n$ or $5n + 2$ **d)** 2

e) Alberta
B.C.
Québec
0 1 2 3 4 5 6 7 8 9 10

21. no

22. **a)** $x > -\frac{3}{2}$

b) $a < -2$

c) $n \leq -5$

d) $d \leq -\frac{3}{2}$

Chapter Self-Test, page 266

1. **a)** $C = 0.25a$ **b)** \$37.50

2. **a)** The cost is the same for each kilometre.

b) $C = 45 + 0.15k$ **c)** $58.50 = 45 + 0.15k$

3. **a)** The number of squares in Figure n is n.

b) The number of squares in Figure n is n^2.

4. **a)** $a = 1$

b) $x = \frac{3}{7}$

c) $x = \frac{6}{5}$

d) $x = \frac{1}{3}$

5. 2000 linear feet

6. **a)** $x < -1$, x is an integer **c)** $x \geq 1$, x is a natural number

b) $x \geq 4$, x is rational **d)** $x \geq 0$, x is a whole number

7. **a)** −6 −5 −4 −3 −2 −1 0

b) 0 1 2 3 4 5 6 7 8 9 10

c)

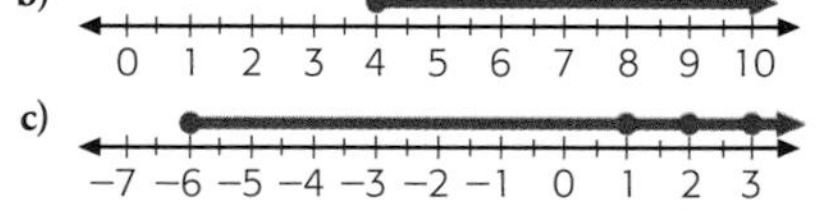

d) −7 −6 −5 −4 −3 −2 −1 0 1 2 3

Chapter Review, pages 268–270

1. **a)**

Figure number	Number of toothpicks
1	3
2	5
3	7

b) The rate of change is 2.

c) $N = 1 + 2n$

d) Figure 13

2. **a)**

x	$3x + 6$
0	6
5	21
10	36
15	51
20	66

b)

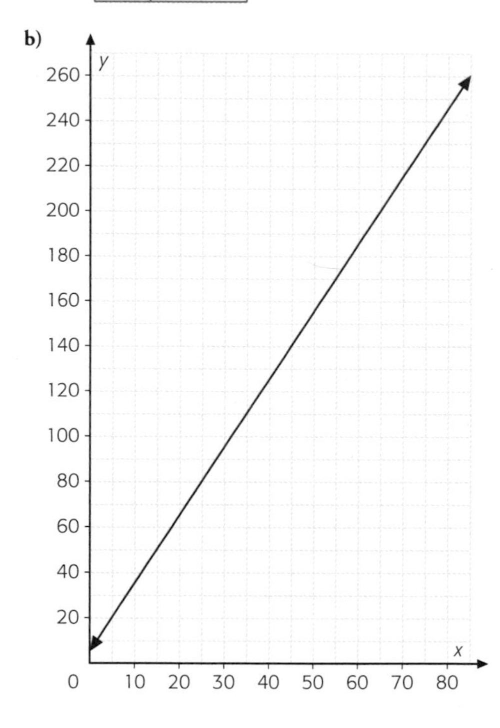

c) e.g., 18, 60, 231

3. a)

x	$4x - 8$
0	−8
5	12
10	32
15	52
20	72

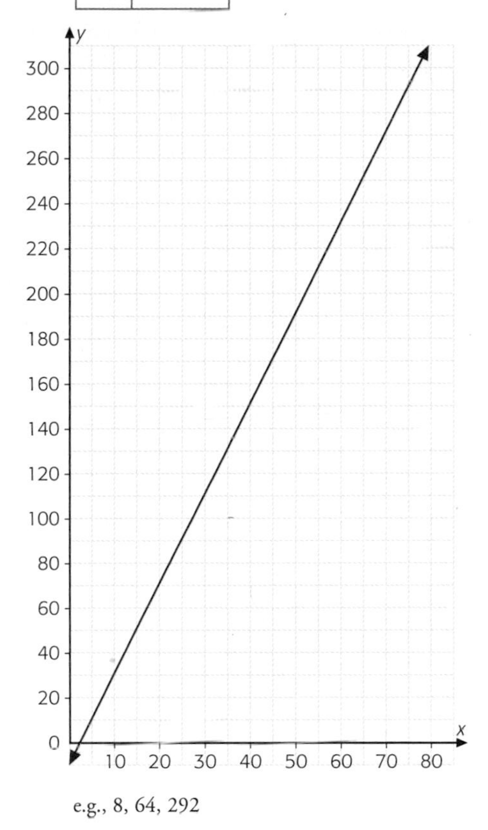

e.g., 8, 64, 292

b)

x	$5 - 2x$
0	5
5	−5
10	−15
15	−25
20	−35

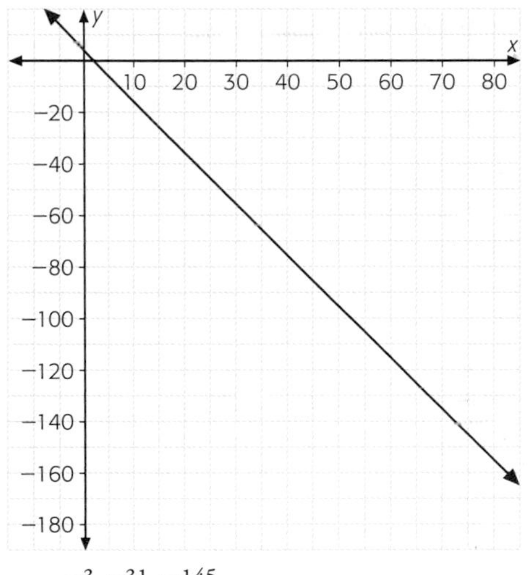

−3, −31, −145

c)

x	$-6x + 8$
0	8
5	−22
10	−52
15	−82
20	−112

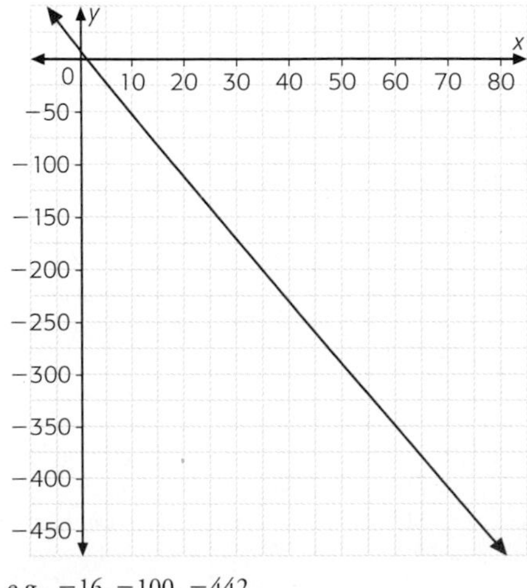

e.g., −16, −100, −442

4. a) $x = 2$ b) $x = 4$ c) $x = 5$ d) $x = -\frac{2}{5}$

5. a) $E = 15n - 150$ if $n \geq 10$, otherwise $E = 0$

b)

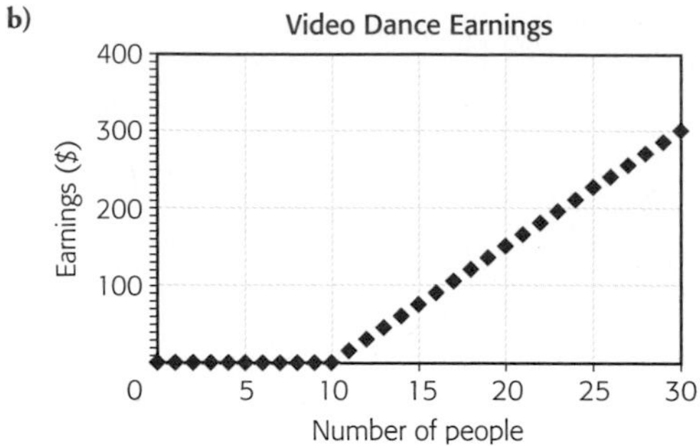

c) \$1350 d) e.g., 50

6. a) $x = \frac{64}{9}$ b) $a = 10.5$ c) $x = \frac{40}{9}$ d) $f = \frac{19}{10}$

7. a) $C = 15.95(x - 10)$ b) \$79.75 c) 12

8. a) $x = 6$ b) $x = -\frac{80}{153}$ c) $x = -10$ d) $x = 86$

9. The first trapezoid has bases 2 and 5. The second trapezoid has bases 6 and 8.

10. a) $x = 6$ b) $x = -1$ c) $x = 7$ d) $x = 0$

e) $a = \frac{18}{7}$ f) $a = -\frac{24}{7}$

11. a) 56 m b) 27 quarters, 90 dimes c) about 5 h 27 min

12. about 1 h 7 min

13. a) a solid line

b)

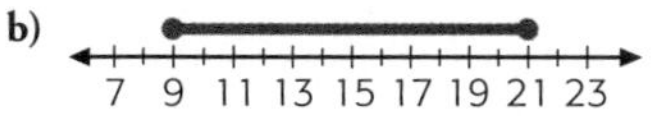

14. e.g., $3(x - 1) > 3$, x is a natural number

15. a)

1 2 3 4 5 6 7 8 9 10

b)

1 2 3 4 5 6 7 8 9 10

c) e.g., Alike: both include natural numbers ≥ 5; different: b) contains non-natural numbers ≥ 5.

16. a) $x < \frac{1}{2}$, x is rational

b) $x \geq 0$, x is a whole number

c) $x \geq 1$, x is is a natural number

d) $x \geq 12$, x is an integer

e) $w < \frac{1}{9}$, w is rational

f) $a \geq \frac{572}{511}$, a is rational

Chapter 6

Lesson 6.1, pages 281–282

1. a) degree: 2; variable: k; coefficient of k: -2; coefficient of k^2: 4; constant: 3

b) degree: 2; variable: k; coefficient of k^2: -5; constant: -2

c) degree: 2; variables: k, j; coefficient of k: -1; coefficient of j^2: 1; constant: 5

2. a) and c)

3. e.g., the perimeter of a rectangle of length 4 and width w

4. a) degree: 1; variable: p; coefficient of p: -2; constant: -7

b) degree: 1; variable: t; coefficient of t: 3; constant: 4

c) degree: 2; variables: a, b; coefficient of ab: 5; constant: -8; coefficient of b^2: 5

5. a) e.g., $3t^2 - 9$ b) e.g., $6p + 2$

c) e.g., $3m^2 + 5p - 2m + 8$

6. e.g., $-2j^2 + 4 + 3j$

7. C

8. B

9. A

10. a) -116 b) 54

11. a) $A = \frac{1}{2}(b)(h) = \frac{1}{2}b^2$ b) 50 cm^2

12. e.g., $6.4n$ tells the number of hours spent on n round trips, $54n$ tells the number of litres of gasoline needed for n round trips and $27n$ tells the number of litres of gasoline needed for $\frac{n}{2}$ round trips.

13. e.g., πr^2 tells the area of the circle and $2\pi r$ tells the circumference of the circle.

14. a) The degree is 1. The number of terms is 2. The variable is x. The coefficient of the variable is -7. The constant is 55.

b) e.g., You have \$55. You spend \$7 every week for x weeks. How much money do you have after x weeks?

15.

List A	List B
$3x^2 - 2x + 4$	$4 - 2x - 3x^2$
$-3x^2 + 2x - 4$	$-2x + 4 + 3x^2$
$-3x^2 - 2x + 4$	$2x - 4 - 3x^2$
$3x^2 + 2x - 4$	$2x + 3x^2 - 4$

16. e.g., For $50 - 3x$, there has to be a constant decrease of 3 as the value of x goes up, instead of the constant increase of 3 in $50 + 3x$.

17. a) $35 + 43.50x$ b) $41 + 38.75x$

18. e.g., There could be a rectangle with length $3x$ and width y attached to a 2-by-4 rectangle. The polynomial $3xy + 8$ describes the total area of these two rectangles.

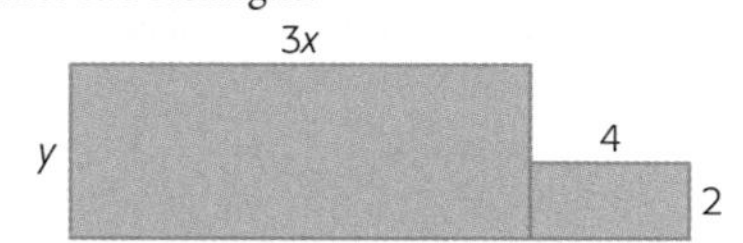

Lesson 6.3, pages 288–289

1. a) $-2x^2 + x - 4$ b) $x^2 - 5x + 2$

2. a) $x + 8 - 2x^2$ b) $-x^2 + 2y + 12$

3. a) $-2x^2 + 3x + 1$ b) $-x^2 + 3x + 1 + (-x^2)$ c) $2x^2 - 3x - 1$ d) $2x^2 - x - 3$

a and **b** are equivalent

4. a) $xy + 3x + 3 - x^2$ b) $x^2 - y^2 - x - 1$

5. a) $4x^2$ and $-4x^2$; $2x - 3$

b) $-6xy$ and $2xy$; 9 and -5; $-4xy + 2x^2 - y^2 + 4$

c) $3y$ and $4y$ and $-2y$; $15 + 5y + 6x^2$

d) $4x$ and $7x$; $-2xy$ and $-5xy$; $8x^2$ and $-5x^2$; $11x - 7xy - 3x^2 + 3y$

6. B

7. C

8. A

9. a) $-7, 11$ b) $-3, 16, -6$ c) $-7, 11, -17$ d) $3, 8, 10$

10. e.g., $3x - 4x + 2xy + 9xy - 7 + 12 = -x + 11xy + 5$

11. e.g., $12x + (-3x)$

12. a) $16x + 16$ b) $4x + 15$

13. disagree

14. a) 4x by 5; 2x + 5 by 2x

b) the grey area:

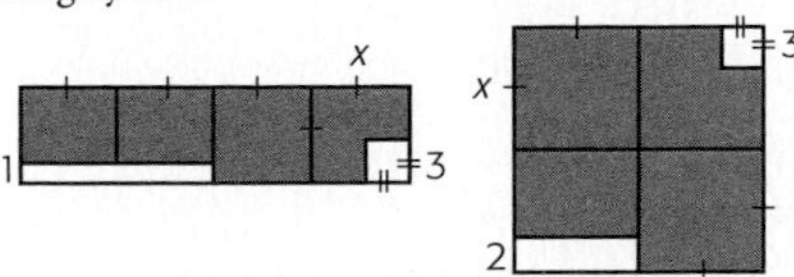

Lesson 6.4, pages 294–296

1. a) $-2x^2 + 5xy + 1$ b) $-x^2 + 3xy - 4$
c) $4y^2 + xy + 5$

2. a) $-xy - 5x + y - 2$ b) $-2x^2 - 9x + y$

3. $2x^2$ and $3x^2$; -8 and 2

4. a) $(2x^2 + x) + (y^2 + 4x) = 2x^2 + y^2 + 5x$
b) $(2x^2 + xy - 2x) + (2x^2 - x^2 + x) = 3x^2 + xy - x$
c) $-3x + (-xy + x) = -2x - xy$
d) $(-2x^2 + x - 3) + (x^2 - 3x + 4) = -x^2 - 2x + 1$

5. a) $-12y^2 - 2xy - 7$ c) $2x^2 - 10x + 3xy - 2$
b) $-8x^2 + 3y - 8$

6. a) $x + 15$ c) $2x^2 + 2y - 2$
b) $3x^2 + 4xy - 2$ d) $-2y^2 + 3xy + 5$

7. B

8. D

9. B

10. a) and c)

11. a) $5x^2 + 15x - 11$ c) $y^2 + 4x - 2$
b) $x^2 - xy - 11$ d) $-5x^2 + 2xy - 5$

12. e.g., Since there are two positive and two negative x^2 tiles, you can pair them up to get zeroes and eliminate all of them.

13. a) $5s^2 + 9$ b) $6\pi r^2$

14. $(42 - 8x) + (80 - 9x) = 122 - 17x$

15. e.g., Explain to David that he added the $-2x$ and -6 and got $-8x$ and didn't realize they were not like terms.

16. e.g., A polynomial is made up of terms. If you think of each term as a polynomial, then the sum of them is the polynomial you started with. For example, $3x^2 + 2x$ is the sum of $3x^2$ and $2x$. You can also start with a polynomial and add opposite terms and it could be a sum that way, too. e.g.,
$3x^2 + 2x = (3x^2 + 2x) + (x^2 + x) + (-x^2 - x)$

17. a) yes b) yes c) yes

18. a) e.g., $(3x^2 - 2x + 5) + (-2x^2 - 3x - 5)$
b) e.g., $(3x^2 - 2x + 5) + (-3x^2 - 3x - 5)$

Mid-Chapter Review, pages 299–300

1. a) 2, x and y, -6, 5 b) 2, x, 4, -3 c) 1, y, 0, -4

2. a) e.g., $s^2 + 4$ b) e.g., $-3k^2 + 4k + 9$
c) e.g., $5x + y + 11$ d) e.g., $-2m^2 + 7m + 2$

3. $6p + 4$

4. a) e.g., the perimeter of a square with a side length of $x + 4$
b) e.g., the amount of water you have left if you start with 20 cups and pour out c 2-cup measures
c) e.g., the amount of money you have left if you start with \$52 and buy n items costing \$16 each

5. a) $3x^2 - 3y + 3$
b) $x^2 - 2x^2 - 2x + x - 2 + 1$ or $-x^2 - x - 1$
c) $4x - x - 1$ or $3x - 1$

6. a) $-2x^2 - 2xy + 7$ c) $3x^2 - 2x - 8$
b) $4x^2 + 2y - 9$ d) $2y^2 - 7x - 2$

7. a) m c) $-5x - 2$
b) $-3k^2 + 4k$ d) $-5x^2 + 6x + 2$

8. a) x^2 x^2 x^2 x^2 $-x$ $-x$

b) e.g., $2x^2 + 5x + 2$, $9x^2$, $-9x$

9. He is not correct. He added the j coefficient and the j^2 coefficient, but they are not like terms.

10. a) $8x - 4$ b) $3x + 21$ c) $8x + 4$

11. a) $(-2x^2 + 3x) + (x^2 + 3x - 1) = -x^2 + 6x - 1$
b) $(2y^2 - xy + 2) + (-4y^2 + 2xy - 1) = -2y^2 + xy + 1$

12. a) $-5x + 3$ c) $-2xy - 2$
b) $-2y^2 + x - 2$ d) $-6x^2 - x$

13. a) e.g., $-4x^2 - 5xy + 1$ and $-2x^2$, $-3x^2 - 5xy$ and $-3x^2 + 1$, $-7x^2 - 3xy + 2$ and $x^2 - 2xy - 1$
b) e.g., $7x^2 - 7x + 6$ and $3x^2$, $5x^2 - 7x + 6$ and $5x^2$, $10x^2 - 5x$ and $-2x + 6$

14. e.g., The constant in the sum must be positive. At least one of the coefficients of x and x^2 must be negative, since it is the sum of two negatives. The other coefficient could be positive, negative, or zero.

15. e.g., Rachel had \$100 and spent \$5 a week. Alicia had \$200 and spent \$4 a week. How much money did both of them have, together, after w weeks?

Lesson 6.5, pages 305–308

1. a) $(-2x^2 + xy - 3) - (-x^2 - 2) = -x^2 + xy - 1$
b) $(2x^2 - x + 3) - (-x^2 - x - 2) = 3x^2 + 5$

2. a) $6y^2 - 3xy - 1$ b) $3x^2 + 4x - 16$

3. $(182 - 23p) - (157 - 22p) = 25 - p$

4. a) $(y^2 + 3x - 4) - (y^2 + 2x) = x - 4$
b) $(4x^2 - 2x - 3) - (-2x^2 + x + 1) = 6x^2 - 3x - 4$

5. $(-6) - 4$ and $5 - (-3)$

6. a) $(2x^2 + x) - (x^2 + 4x) = x^2 - 3x$
b) $(3x^2 - 2y) - (2x^2 - xy + y) = x^2 + xy - 3y$
c) $-3x - (-x^2 + x) = x^2 - 4x$

7. a) $(2y + 8) - (-y + 7) = 3y + 1$
b) $(x^2 - 3x + 2) - (2x^2 + 7x - 4) = -x^2 - 10x + 6$
c) $(-x^2 + 3xy + 2) - (3x^2 - xy - 4) = -4x^2 + 4xy + 6$

8. C

9. B

10. D

11. a) $(2x^2 + 7x - 9) - (3x^2 + 8x - 2) = -x^2 - x - 7$
b) $(-2y^2 + 7x - 9) - (3y^2 - 8x - 2) = -5y^2 + 15x - 7$
c) $(2x^2 + 7xy) - (-x^2 - 3xy - 2) = 3x^2 + 10xy + 2$
d) $(-8y^2 + 2y - 3) - (3y^2 - 2) = -11y^2 + 2y - 1$

12. **A** and **D**: The difference is $4x^2 + 2x + 6$.

13. e.g., I think that Rachel subtracted $5 - 2$ instead of subtracting 5 from -2. I also think she calculated $8 - (-2)$ as $8 - 2$. I would remind her that she is subtracting -2.

14. e.g., You could model $(-3x^2 - 4y + 8)$ and, using the zero principle, add sufficient tiles so that you can subtract $(-2x^2 + 5y + 2)$.

15. a) $-2x^2 - 2xy + 15$ b) $-10x^2 + 6xy + 5$
c) $6x^2 - 4xy + 16$

Answers

16. a) e.g., $-2x^2 - (4x - 3)$, $(3x^2 + x + 5) - (5x^2 + 5x + 2)$, $(8x^2 - x + 6) - (10x^2 + 3x + 3)$
b) e.g., $(6x^2 + 2y + 10) - (3x^2 + y + 18)$, $(4x^2 + 5y - 5) - (x^2 + 4y + 3)$, $(-x^2 - y - 6) - (-4x^2 - 2y + 2)$
c) e.g., $5y^2 - (xy - 7)$, $(6y^2 + xy + 5) - (y^2 + 2xy - 2)$, $(-y^2 - xy - 6) - (-6y^2 - 13)$
d) e.g., $-4x^2 - (2x^2 + 4x + 7)$, $(3x^2 + x - 9) - (9x^2 + 5x - 2)$, $(8x^2 - x - 6) - (14x^2 + 3x + 1)$

17. $(80 - 9s) - (42 - 8s) = 38 - s$

18. e.g., John earned \$48 a week for w weeks, but lost \$2. Evans only earned \$18 a week for w weeks, but had an extra \$10. After w weeks, how much more did John have than Evans?

19.

$8x^2 - 5x + 6$	$x^2 - 6x + 27$	$6x^2 - x + 12$
$3x^2 + 21$	$5x^2 - 4x + 15$	$7x^2 - 8x + 9$
$4x^2 - 7x + 18$	$9x^2 - 2x + 3$	$2x^2 - 3x + 24$

20. e.g., If you start with $2x^2 + x + 8$ and want to subtract $3x^2$, there are only 2 x^2s to take away. You would have to use the zero principle to add x^2 and $-x^2$ and Thomas forgot to say that.

21. a) yes b) yes c) no

22. a) e.g., $(5p^2 + 2p - 4) - (3p^2 - p - 4)$
b) e.g., $(5p^2 + 2p - 4) - (6p^2 + 2p - 4)$

Lesson 6.6, pages 312–313

1. e.g., $2x^2 - 5$, $-x^2 - 8$, $x^2 - 6$

2. The possible polynomials are $3x^2 - 4x - 2$ and $-4x^2 + 3x - 2$. The sum is $-x^2 - x - 4$.

3. e.g., $6x$, $5x + 1$, $4x + 2$, $3x + 3$, $-4x + 2$, $x^2 + 4x + 1$

4. e.g., $-5x^2 - 3x$, $-5x^2 - 2x + 1$, $-5x^2 - x + 2$, $-3x^2 - 3x + 2$, $-4x^2 - 2x + 2$, $-4x^2 - 3x + 1$

5. e.g., $3x^2$, $2x^2 - x$, $2x^2 - 1$, $-2x^2 - x$

6. e.g., $-2x^2 + 2x + 3$, $-2x^2 + 3x + 2$, $-2x^2 + 2y + 3$, $-2x^2 + 3y + 2$, $-2x^2 + 2xy + 3$

7. e.g.,

length	$x + 14$	14	$3x$	$x + 7$
width	x	$2x$	$14 - x$	$x + 7$

8. e.g.,

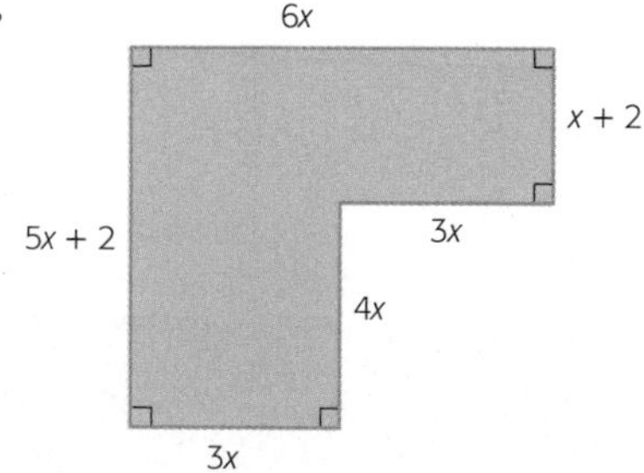

9. e.g., To make sure you don't miss any possibilities, it would make sense to start with using only one kind of tile four times, then you could use each type of tile three times and make a list of what other tile you could combine it with and continue this way. By using an organized list, you are less likely to leave something out.

10. e.g.,
0 tiles $(x^2 + 2x + 1) + (-x^2 - 2x - 1)$
2 tiles $(x^2 + 2x + 1) + (-x^2 - x - 2)$
4 tiles $(x^2 + 3) + (2x - 2)$
6 tiles $(x^2 + 2x - 1) + (2x^2 + 2)$
8 tiles $(x^2 + 2x + 1) + (2x^2 + 2)$

11. e.g.,
4 tiles $(x^2 + 2x + 1) - (3x^2 + 1)$
6 tiles $(x^2 + 2x - 1) - (2x^2 + 2)$
8 tiles $(x^2 + 2x + 1) - (-x^2 - 2x - 1)$

12. a) It could be 7, 5, 3, or 1 tiles.
b) e.g., The only way it would not be 7 tiles is if opposites are removed using the zero principle. If that happens, pairs of tiles disappear, so you could subtract 2, 4, or 6 from the total of 7 you would expect. You could not have fewer than 1 tile since you can't have a negative number of tiles and you could not have more than 7.

Lesson 6.7, pages 320–322

1. a) $4(3x^2 + 2)$ b) $6(2x - 4)$

2. $(-6x^2 + 15x - 9) \div 3$

3. a) $-20x^2$ b) $-20 + 12s$ c) $10y^2 - 8y$ d) $-4y$ e) $-2x^2 - 2x$ f) $4xy + 2y$

4. a) $3(x + 4)$ b) $2x(-x - 2)$ c) $4(-2x + 3)$ d) $x(3x - 1)$

5. a) $(16x^2 - 4x + 4) \div 4$ b) $(-15x^2 - 15x + 25) \div 5$

6. a) $-18y$ b) $12xy$ c) $30y^2$ d) $-5y$ e) $-5y$ f) $3y$

7. a) $6xy + 15$ b) $40x^2 - 16y + 16$ c) $6xy - 3x$ d) $4y^2 + 8x - 12$ e) $-2x^2 - 2x$ f) $-4x^2 - 6xy + 4$

8. a) $4x^2 - x + 2$ b) $5x + 1$ c) $x - 8$ d) $3x + 2$ e) $4x^2 - 9x + xy$ f) $-3x + 5y - 6$

9. e.g., You divide each term of the polynomial by the monomial and add them, so there are the same number of terms as quotients.

10. B

11. D

12. A

13. a) $15y + 5$ b) $-10x + 6$ c) $4x^2 + 2x$ d) $-6x^2 - 2x + 10$ e) $2t^2 - t + 4$ f) $-2s^2 + 5$ g) $5y + 2$ h) $4x^2 - 3x + 2$

14. a) e.g., because $16x$ and $2x$ are like terms
b) e.g., because $16x$ and 4 are not like terms

15. a) $10x + 15$ b) $15x^2 - 18x$ c) $4x^2 + 8x - 2$ d) 2

16. a) **A** and **D** b) e.g., $3(4x^2 - 8)$

17. a) $P = 14x - 4$, $A = 12x^2 - 8x$
b) $P = 12x + 6$, $A = 6x^2 + 9x$
c) $P = 18y + 12$, $A = 16y^2 + 24y$
d) $P = x + 27$, $A = 2x^2 + 12x + 16$
e) $P = 52$ cm, $A = 160$ cm²

18. a) e.g.,

s + 5
4

b) e.g.,

4
10 − 3m

19. Disagree. e.g., He divided the p^2 term correctly but forgot he had to divide the other two terms by 4 as well.

20. a) e.g., When you multiply by a constant you change the coefficient but not the variable. For example, $3(2x) = 6x$; the x doesn't change but the 2 does.
 b) e.g., When you multiply a constant by x, a term that was a constant becomes a variable to the first power. When you multiply an x by x, you end up with x^2, which is a higher power.

21. e.g., You have to multiply each part of the polynomial $3 - x$ by $5x$ and not just one part of it, so it should be $15x - 5x^2$. You can't combine those since they are not like terms.

Chapter Self-Test, page 324

1. a) e.g., $3j^2 + 2j - 5j - 3$ b) e.g., $-2m^2 - 5m + 6m$
 c) e.g., $3x^2 - 2x^2 + 5x + 2x + 3$

2. a) $P = w + w + 2w + 300 + 2w + 300 = 6w + 600$
 b) e.g., My goal is to exercise 180 min a week. For 3 days, I exercised m minutes. How many minutes are left for me to exercise that week?

3. a) $-2x^2 + 5x + 1$
 b) $-x^2 + x^2 - 3x + 2x - 3$ or $-x - 3$

4. a) $3s^2 - 3t + 1$ c) $5y^2 - 7xy - 2$
 b) $3x^2 - 3x - 4$ d) $7x^2 - 5y + 10$

5. a) $-28x^2$ d) $-3x$
 b) $-12k^2 + 24$ e) $6j^2 + 2j - 3$
 c) $-6t^2 + 10t$ f) $15r - 3$

6. e.g., A polynomial tells you how many of the x^2s, how many x's and how many 1's there are, so it only makes sense to count x^2s together, x's together, and constants together.

7. a) e.g., Start with $7x$.
 b) e.g., Add $-2x$. c) e.g., Subtract $-2x$.

8. a)

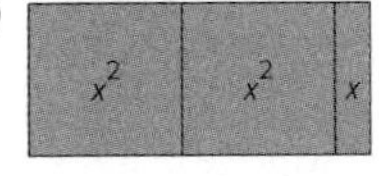

 b) e.g., This shows a rectangle with a width of x and a length of $2x + 1$. If you multiply these, you get the area and you can already see that the area is $2x^2 + x$.

Chapter Review, pages 327–328

1. a) The degree is 2, the coefficient of x is -4, the constant is 7, and the number of terms is 3.
 b) The degree is 1, the coefficient of x is -5, the constant is 8, and the number of terms is 2.
 c) The degree is 2, the coefficient of x is 0, the constant is -2, and the number of terms is 2.

2. $15w + 48$

3. a) b)

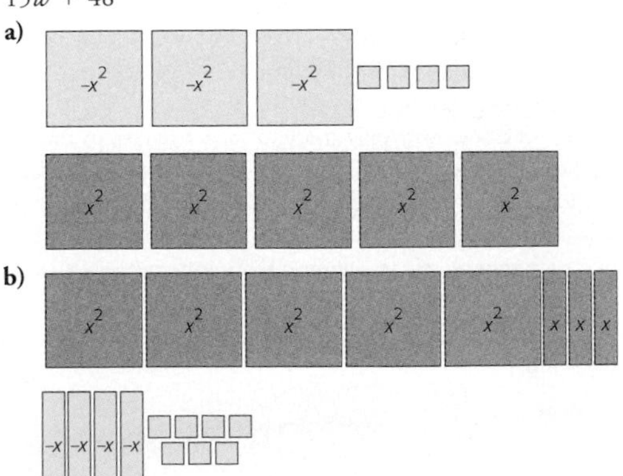

 c)

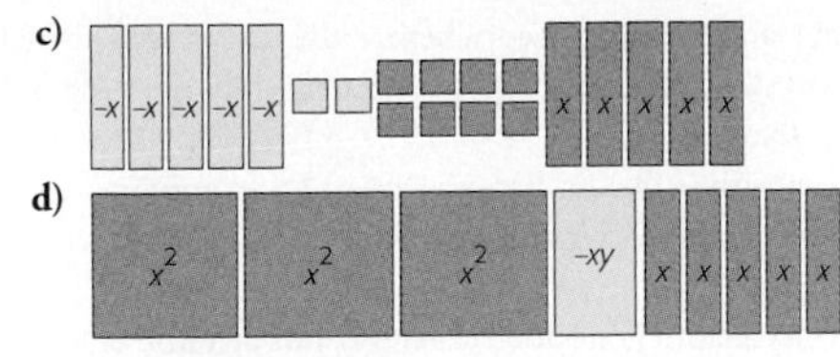

 d)

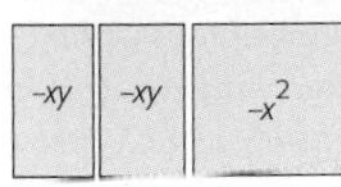

4. a) $2x^2 - 4$ c) 6
 b) $5x^2 - x - 7$ d) $2x^2 - 3xy + 5x$

5. a) $2x^2 + y^2 + 1$ b) $2x^2 - 3x + y + xy$

6. a) $-4t, 7t$ c) $-8t, 9t; 7, -3$
 b) $5, -8$ d) $5jk, -8jk$

7. a) $3s + 3t + 4t^2$ c) $t + 4t^2 + 4$
 b) $6j - 3$ d) $12j - 3jk - 3k$

8. D

9. e.g., $4r^2 + \pi r^2 + 4r + 4$

10. e.g., $(-5x^2 - 1) + (2x^2 - 4x + 2)$

11. a) will contain x^2 term c) will contain x^2 term
 b) will not contain x^2 term d) will contain x^2 term

12. $2x$ greater

13. not correct

14. e.g., $(5x^2 - 3x + 1) - (7x^2 - 5x - 5)$ or $(-4x^2 + 4x + 10) - (-2x^2 + 2x + 4)$

15. a) $-24y^2$ d) $2x^2 - x - 1$
 b) 8a e) $-8x^2 - 12x - 28$
 c) $-6x^2 + 12x$ f) $9x - 6$

16. not correct

17. e.g., $4(3x^2 - 2x), 4x(3x - 2), -4(-3x^2 + 2x), -4x(-3x + 2)$

18. e.g., Yes, if that monomial is 1.

Chapter 7

Lesson 7.1, pages 337–339

1. a) e.g., involves probabilities
 b) e.g., does not involve probability
 c) e.g., involves probabilities
 d) e.g., does not involve probability

2. a) e.g., involves probabilities
 b) e.g., involves probabilities
 c) e.g., does not involve probability
 d) e.g., involves probabilities

3. B

4. A

5. e.g., In the final round of *Jeopardy*, a player decides how much to wager based on his or her estimate of the probability their answer is right.

6. a) e.g., the probability of bike theft in the area
 b) e.g., the probability it will snow so much we won't be able to drive

7. a) e.g., the probability a patient will survive for a significant period of time with the transplant
 b) e.g., the probability each company will do well in the future
 c) e.g., the probability the plane will depart on time
 d) e.g., the probability a candidate wins a debate

8. a) e.g., In Canada: Type A 40%, Type B 11%, Type AB 4%, and Type O 45%.
 b) e.g., to decide how much of each blood type to have on hand for operations

9. a) e.g., If they are cheating, then whether the test catches them depends on the probability they are tested while the drug is still present in their bodies.
   b) e.g., False positives do not happen often, but sometimes do, which means a person who tests positive for a disease may not have the disease.
10. a) e.g., The city planners decided where to put a traffic light based on probabilities of accidents at particular intersections.
   b) e.g., If you buy a book from an online company, they email you about similar books because you are likely to be interested in buying those also.
   c) e.g., Each year, the flu vaccine is changed because the flu virus mutates. The World Heath Organization adjusts the contents of the vaccine to contain the strains most likely to occur the next year.
11. a) e.g., The farmer might see the horses are jumpy and say a storm is very likely.
   b) e.g., The farmer cannot be certain about whether there will be a storm.
12. a) e.g., involves probability b) e.g., involves probability
13. e.g., I would consider the percentage of the time the bus arrives early. If it is high, I would arrive early.
14. e.g., The engineers might look at the probability they would disrupt animal migration patterns if they put the road in a particular spot.
15. e.g., I decided the probability of getting a ride with my friend from a basketball game was high, so I didn't ask my mother to pick me up.
16. e.g., The probability of patients taking pills from the blister packs is higher than the probability of patients taking pills from the bottles.
17. e.g., In a study, patients were grouped to see who had high, medium, and low likelihood of appendicitis. In the high-likelihood group, there was a probability of 35% there was no appendicitis, so it was worth doing an ultrasound to avoid possibly unnecessary surgery.

Lesson 7.2, pages 346–347

1. e.g., The die is fair and is being rolled fairly.
2. a) yes b) e.g., Yes, assuming the spinner itself is fair.
3. e.g., No, as winter conditions might make the bus late.
4. e.g., Kate won about half the time, so the game is fair.
5. A
6. D
7. e.g., Each player is equally likely to win, which is not valid because skill is involved and it's unlikely all four players are equally skilled.
8. e.g., The order in which the head and tail appear does not matter.
9. e.g., The team match-ups and playing conditions in the next ten years will be like those in previous years.
10. e.g., The probability there is a lot of air traffic at the time I would be landing to make the connection.
11. a) e.g., A storm will follow the same pattern as similar storms from previous years.
   b) e.g., How likely it is it would start to snow before we arrive at our relatives.
12. e.g., City planners would use the probability of experiencing a blizzard during the next year.
13. e.g., no
14. e.g., Yes; even when you flip a coin, you are assuming you are flipping fairly and the coin is fair.
15. e.g., Her previous percentage of success in research that was funded.
16. a) e.g., $\frac{3}{4}$
   b) e.g., The prizes are all equally likely to be in any cereal box.

Lesson 7.3, pages 351–352

1. e.g., 4 out of 10 tails is more likely. There are only 10 ways to toss 9 heads out of 10, but there are many ways to toss 4 tails. I'm assuming that tails and heads are equally likely each toss.
2. e.g., the probability the artist's future recordings will be as successful as previous ones
3. e.g., Logan is only thinking about whole numbers and each number from 1 to 50 is equally likely to be chosen.
4. e.g., I could use a tree diagram, where each branch is either G or B. The outcome I want would be G, G, G, B. There would be 15 other outcomes, so the probability is $\frac{1}{16}$. I'm assuming that girls and boys are equally likely for every birth.
5. e.g., probability of snow; probability that road will be OK to drive if it does snow; probability that, if she leaves in the morning, she will make the presentation on time; probability of snow most important
6. e.g., The companies consider the age group of the driver and the probability of a member of that age group having an accident.
7. e.g., the probability that camping spots will be open; the probability that the weather will be stormy
8. e.g., She might check the safety records of the three airlines so she could estimate which airline is safer; she might check the on-time record of each airline to decide which is more likely to arrive on time
9. e.g., the probability that the batter will get a hit against the type of picture; the probability that the batter will get on base by walking; the probability that the batter will hit a sacrifice fly and drive in a run
10. e.g., The quarterback might consider the probability a play will get enough yards.
11. e.g., If you have the probability that the average Canadian will be mugged while out after dark, you may decide to go out after dark and not worry about it if you believe your neighbourhood is safe. The calculated probability may not apply.
12. e.g., agree
13. e.g., In some mathematical situations, I only need to communicate the answer I got. For probability, I have to understand the situation, figure out what assumptions to use, and state them. If I don't communicate clearly, other people might not agree with my solution.
14. e.g., If there is a high probability anyone will complete the first four tasks in the game on the first try, then completing those tasks should earn a low score.

Chapter Self-Test, page 355

1. a) e.g., involves probabilities
   b) e.g., involves probabilities
   c) e.g., involves probabilities
2. e.g., There might be probabilities involved in whether someone gets elected onto the student council. The likelihood they'll win is based on who else decides to run.
3. e.g., Boys and girls are equally likely to be born and my coin flips are fair. These assumptions are valid.
4. e.g., that tomorrow is a school day
5. e.g., The 70% does not apply more to some age groups than to other age groups or more to some subject areas than other subject areas.
6. e.g., Older people are more likely to die soon than younger people, so it is fair that older people pay more for the same insurance; smokers are more likely to die soon than non-smokers, so smokers should pay more.
7. e.g., the probability of storms or high waves; the probability of a steady wind

Chapter Review, pages 357–358

1. a) e.g., the probability the audience likes the performer's music
   b) e.g., the probability the battery is dead
   c) e.g., the probability that you don't sleep well
2. a) e.g., A survey of 50 000 people aged 12–17 was conducted in many countries around the world. 74% of respondents said they think global warming is a big problem. So, my estimate is 74%.
   b) e.g., I assumed the entire group of 12- to 17-year-olds is representative of how 15-year-olds feel.
3. e.g., The patient might ask about the probability of a bad reaction if she chooses a general anesthetic.
4. a) e.g., I rolled two dice 20 times and the difference was 1 six times, so the experimental probability was $\frac{6}{20}$, or $\frac{3}{10}$.
   b) e.g., The dice were fair, I rolled fairly, and 20 times is enough times to estimate the theoretical probability.
5. a) e.g., 100%
   b) e.g., The cafeteria will not change its pattern.
6. a) $\frac{1}{3}$
   b) e.g., The green section is $\frac{1}{3}$ of the whole spinner.
7. a) e.g., 70%
   b) e.g., The relative ability of the teams has not changed.
8. e.g., The player is consistent and is just as likely to get a hit one time as another time; these assumptions might not be valid.
9. a) e.g., Tomasz could ask everyone he knows to keep track of whether they win a prize or not each time they open a container of milk.
   b) e.g., He would be assuming that the containers with prizes are distributed randomly in his area and over the time he will measure.
10. e.g., Migraine headaches are very painful, so the patient might decide the 30% chance of success is worth the 5% chance of serious side effects.
11. a) e.g., The number of days with at least one scheduled event is decreasing, so the probability the number of days suddenly goes up is not very high.
    b) e.g., Lili might decide there will actually be lots more days with at least one scheduled event in future months, but they just have not been booked yet. So, the probability is not as low as it appears.

Cumulative Review: Chapters 4–7, pages 360–361

1. C
2. D
3. B
4. A
5. C
6. B
7. B
8. C
9. A
10. D
11. A
12. D
13. C
14. D
15. C
16. C

Chapter 8

Lesson 8.1, pages 370–372

1. a) b)

2. fewer than 6: D, E, F; others: A, B, C, G
3. fewer than 6: A; others: B and C
4. C
5. B
6. D
7.

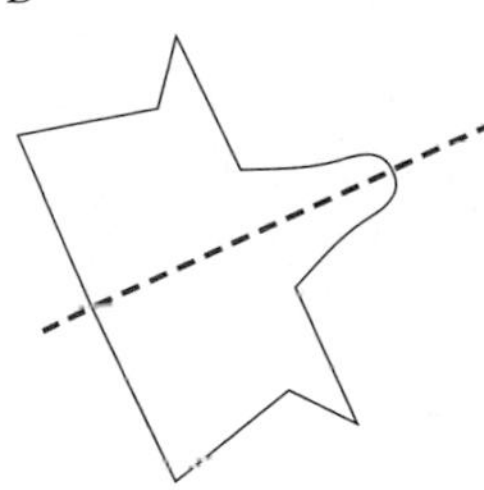

8. It is a square.
9. It must be isosceles.

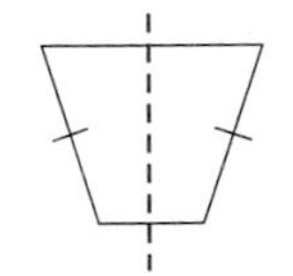

10. no
11. e.g.,

12. a) e.g.,

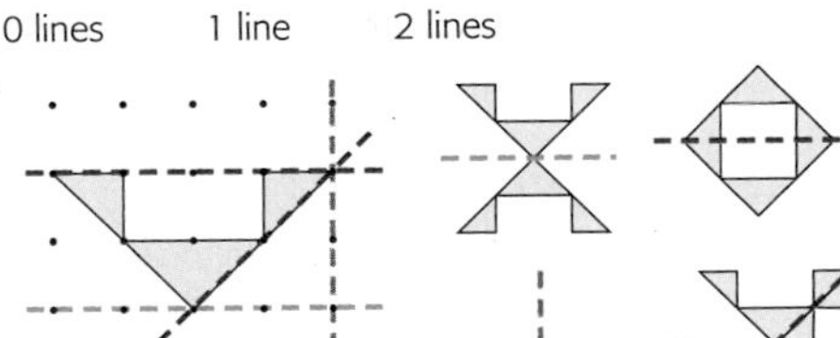

b) e.g.,

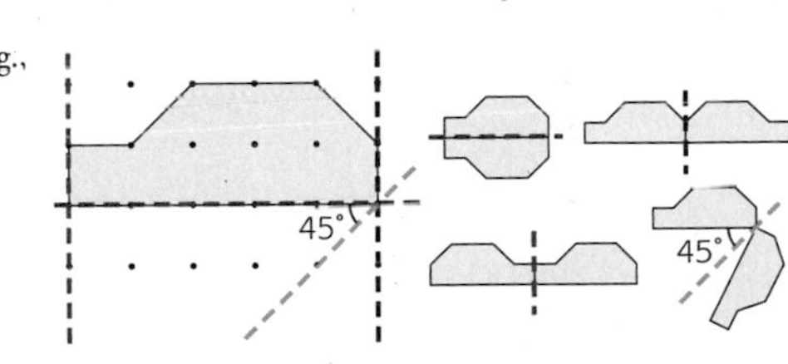

13. The number of lines of symmetry in a regular polygon and the number of sides it has are the same.
14. e.g.,

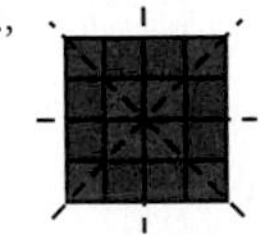

15. If a shape does not have at least four sides, it is a triangle. There are only three kinds of triangles: scalene, isosceles, and equilateral. Scalene triangles have no lines of symmetry, isosceles triangles have one line of symmetry, and equilateral triangles have 3 lines of symmetry. So if a shape has two lines of symmetry, it can't be a triangle.

Answers

16. e.g., **a)**, **b)**

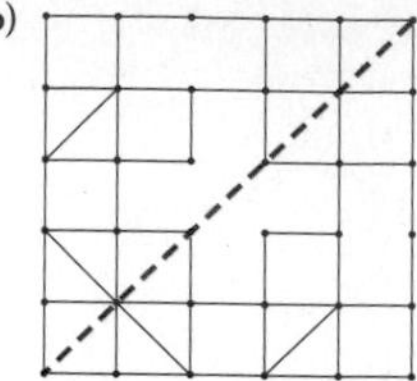

17. When a figure is reflected across a line, the combined figure has a line of symmetry, which is the same line as the line of reflection. e.g., There is a diagonal line of symmetry for a square, since you can reflect the upper half onto the lower half.

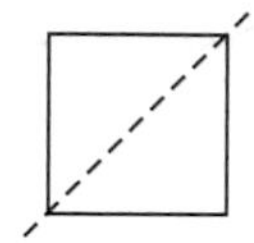

18. e.g.,

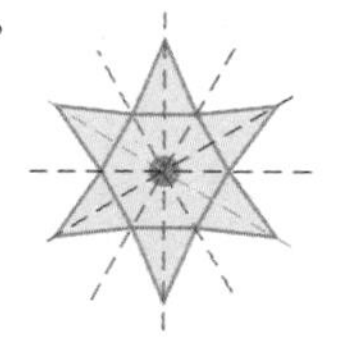

19. e.g.,

20. **a)**

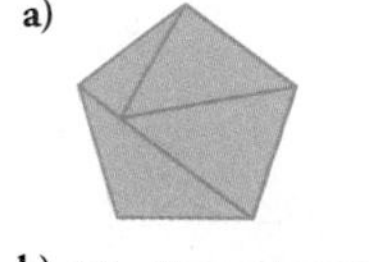

b) e.g.,

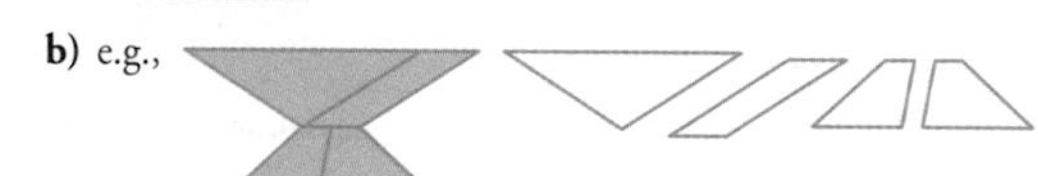

Lesson 8.2, pages 377–381

1. **a)** 4, 4, 90° **b)** 6, 6, 60° **c)** 1, 1, 360°

2. They are both correct.

3. A

4. B

5. **a)** 8, 8, 45° **b)** 2, 2, 180° **c)** 5, 5, 72°

6. Yes; 180° and 2

7. **a)** 4 **b)** 1 **c)** 2

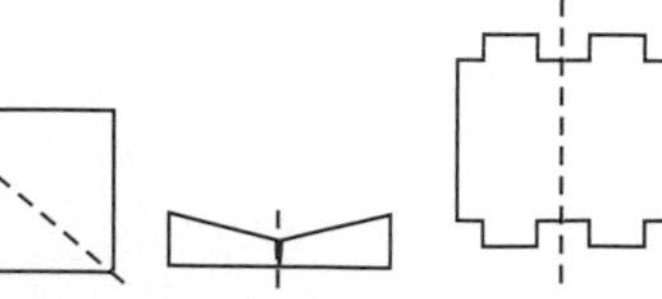

8. **a)** C, G, and I do not have line symmetry but have rotation symmetry.
b) A: 2; B: 1; C: 2; D: 5; E: 9; F: 4; G: 3; H: 1; I: 3

9. They have the same order of rotation symmetry.

10. **a)** A: 3, 120°; B: 4, 90°; C: 5, 72°; D: 6, 60°; E: 7, 52°; F: 8, 45°; G: 9, 40°
b) The number of sides in a regular polygon is equal to its order of rotation symmetry.

11. B, C, and E; also D and F

12. **a)** order 10 **b)** order 12

13. yes

14. **a)** no
b) The isosceles triangle and the irregular pentagon do not have rotation symmetry because they can only complete one turn to return to the original shape. The parallelogram has rotation symmetry.

15. It has rotation symmetry of order 4. I found out by tracing it and turning it to fit in its outline.

16. e.g.,

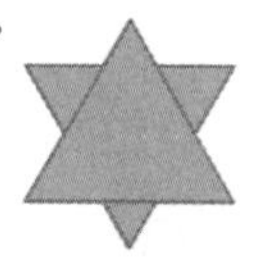

17. **a)** e.g., hubcap
b) e.g.,

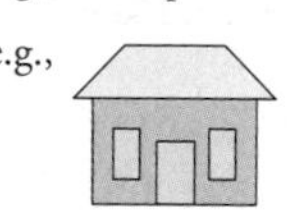

c) e.g.,

18. The shape is a circle. There are infinitely many ways it can fit into its own outline. That's what symmetry of order "infinity" means.

19. e.g., It is like line symmetry since polygons with rotation symmetry tend to have some equal sides, just like shapes with line symmetry. It is different because it is about turning rather than flipping.

20. The shape is an equilateral triangle.

Mid-Chapter Review, pages 384–385

1. more than one line of symmetry: A; other: B, C

2. e.g., a square and an irregular hexagon

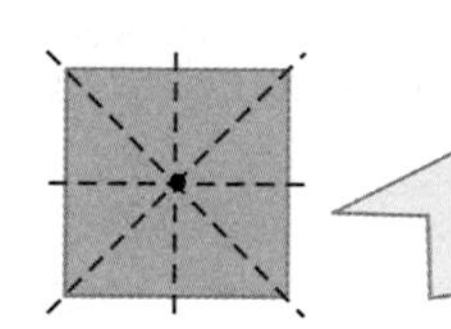

3. **a)** **b)**

4. **a)** 6, 60° **b)** fold in half, and in half again

5. agree

6. e.g., S N

7. e.g.,

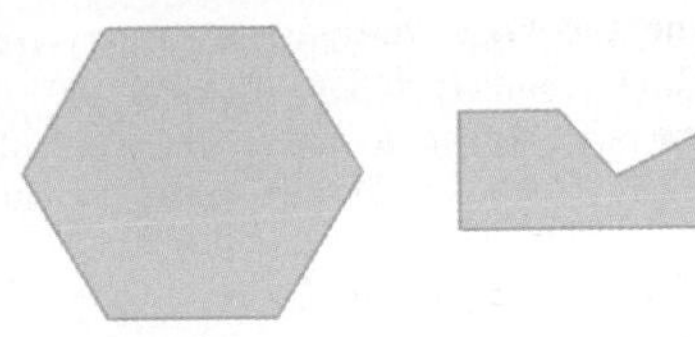

Lesson 8.4, pages 392–394

1. a), b)

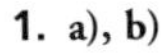

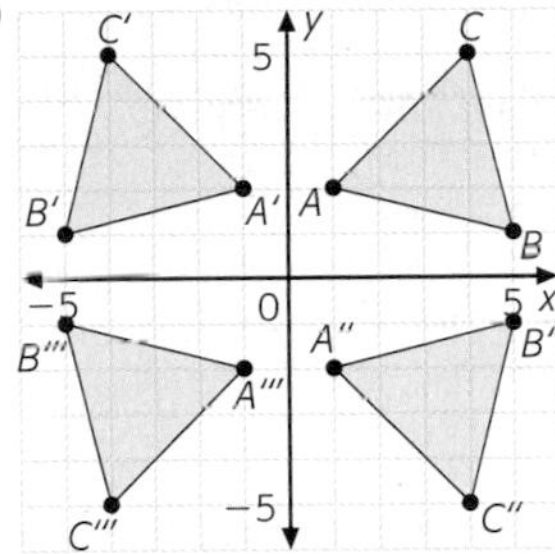

c) $A'(-1, 2)$, $B'(-5, 1)$, $C'(-4, 5)$, $A''(1, -2)$, $B''(5, -1)$, $C''(4, -5)$, $A'''(-1, -2)$, $B'''(-5, -1)$, $C'''(-4, -5)$

d) line symmetry and rotation symmetry of order 2

2. a) e.g., reflection across the x-axis; $A'(1, -3)$, $B'(5, -4)$, $C'(6, -2)$, $D'(5, -1)$, $E'(1, -1)$

b) e.g., rotation 180° about vertex E; $A'(1, -1)$, $B'(-3, -2)$, $C'(-4, 0)$, $D'(-3, 1)$, $E'(1, 1)$.

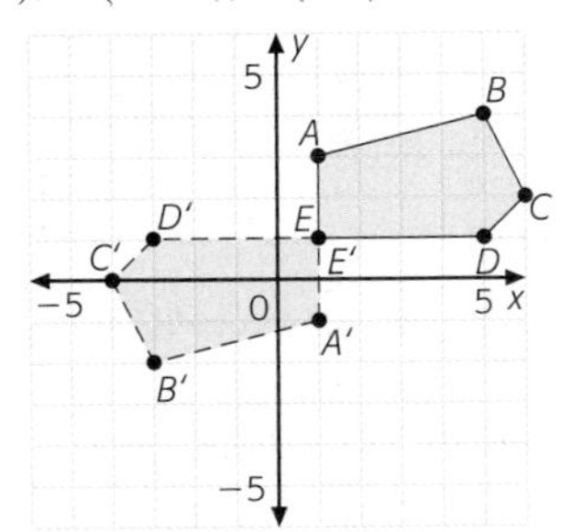

c) $A'(0, 2)$, $B'(4, 3)$, $C'(5, 1)$, $D'(4, 0)$, and $E'(0, 0)$; no

3. a) rotation symmetry of order 2 about the origin

b) rotation, 180° about the origin

4. agree

5. a) B **b)** A

6. B

7. a) e.g., translation (R4): $A'(1, 2)$, $B'(3, 3)$, $C'(5, 2)$, $D'(3, 1)$; translation (R4, D4): $A''(1, -2)$, $B''(3, -1)$, $C''(5, -2)$, $D''(3, -3)$; translation (D4): $A'''(-3, -2)$, $B'''(-1, -1)$, $C'''(1, -2)$, $D'''(-1, -3)$; two lines of reflection; rotation symmetry of order 2 around the point $(1, 0)$

b) e.g., rotation cw by 90°, 180°, 270° about $(1, 2)$: $A'(1, 6)$, $B'(2, 4)$, $C'(1, 2)$, $D'(0, 4)$; $A''(5, 2)$, $B''(3, 1)$, $C''(1, 2)$, $D''(3, 3)$; $A'''(1, -2)$, $B'''(0, 0)$, $C'''(1, 2)$, $D'''(2, 0)$; four lines of symmetry; rotation symmetry of order 4 around C.

8. e.g., **a)**

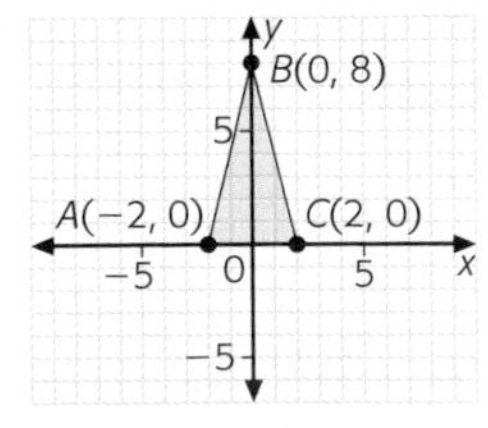

b) Reflect across the line of symmetry, the y-axis.

c) Reflect across the the x-axis. The new line of symmetry is the x-axis.

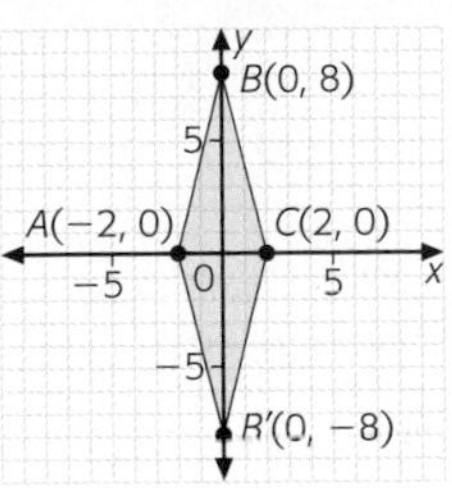

d) Rotate 180° about A.

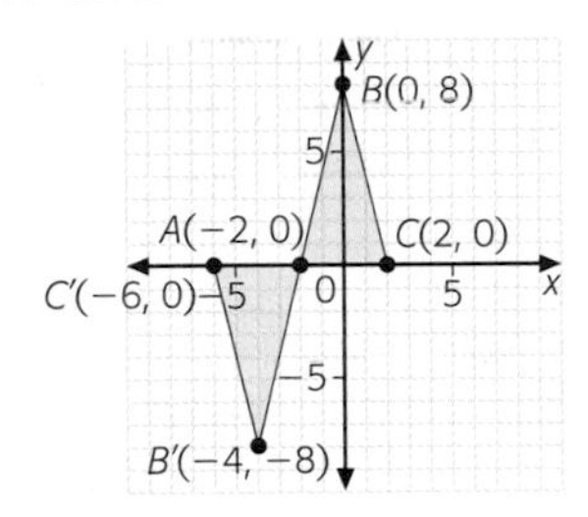

e) Rotate it 180° about $(0, 0)$.

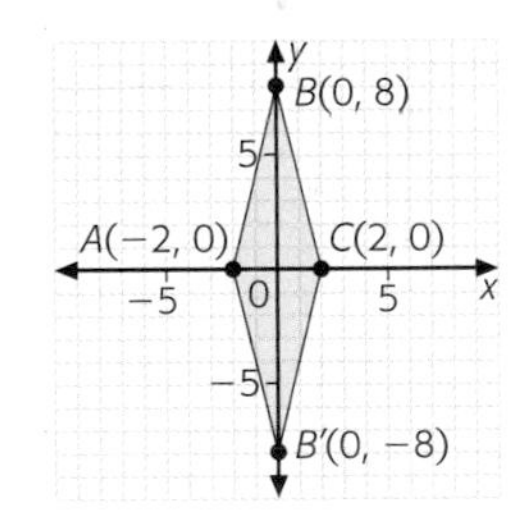

9.

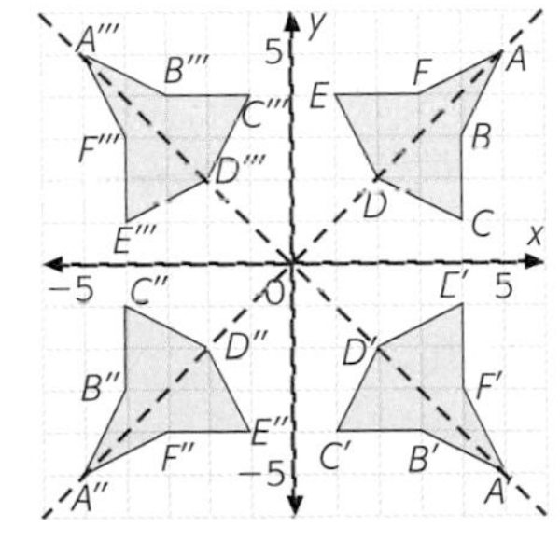

10. e.g., The left half of any rectangle can always be reflected to the right to create the whole shape.

11. e.g.,

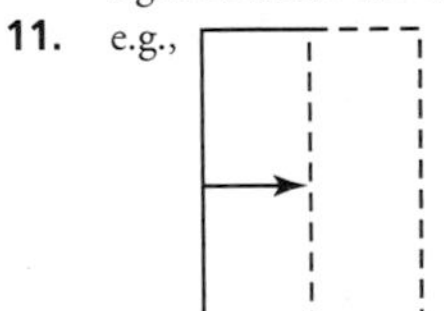

12. a) e.g., a reflection **b)** e.g., yes, line symmetry

13. (a, b) becomes $(-b, a)$.

Answers

Lesson 8.5, pages 400–401

1. $(6, -2), (4, -4), (0, -4), (-2, -2)$
2. 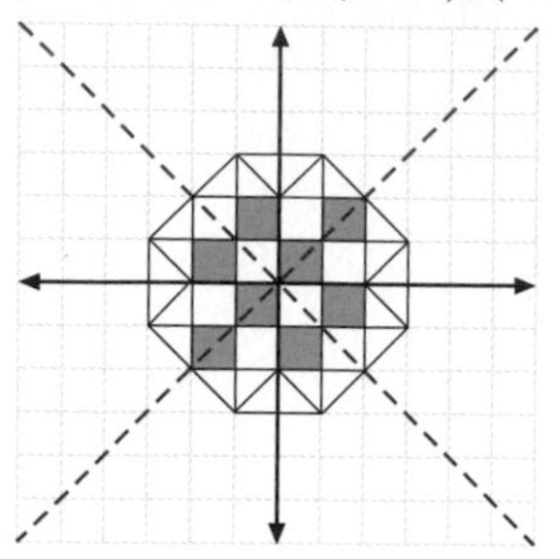
3. e.g., **a)** & **b)**

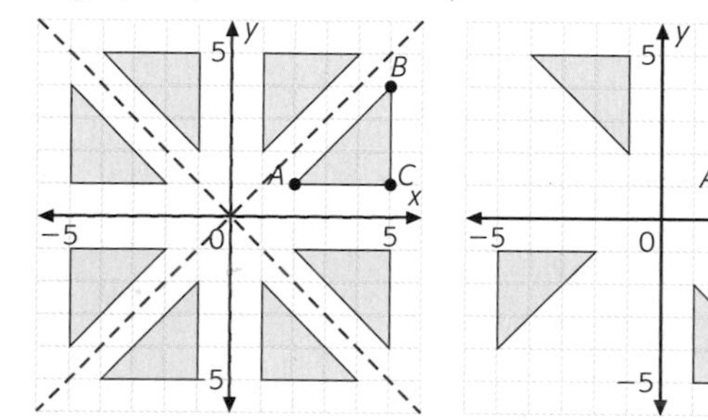

4. 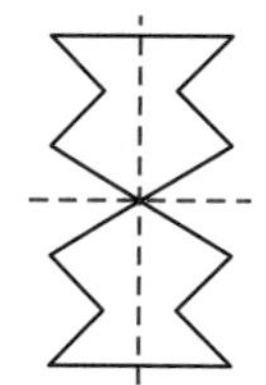
5. **a)** e.g.,

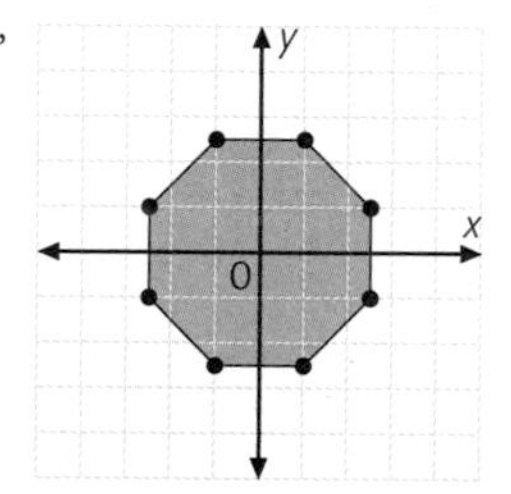

b) e.g., Reflect octagon across one of its lines of symmetry.

6. 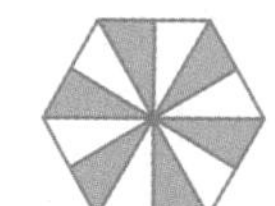
7. 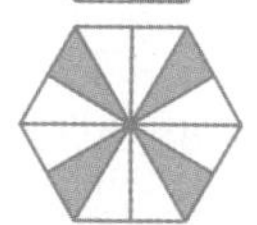
8. **a)**

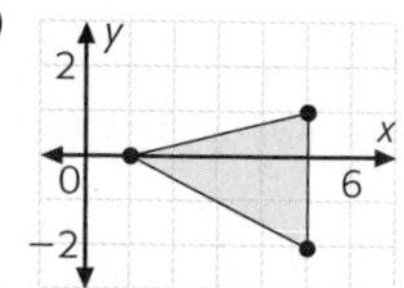

b) e.g., Reflect across $x = 5$: quadrilateral has line of symmetry at $x = 5$. Reflect across x-axis: triangle has line of symmetry at x-axis. Reflect across $x = 3$: resulting shape has 12 sides and line of symmetry at $x = 3$.

c) e.g., Rotate 90°, 180°, and 270° ccw about $(1, 0)$; resulting shape has rotation symmetry of order 4. Rotate 180° about $(5, -2)$; resulting shape has rotation symmetry of order 2.

9. e.g.,

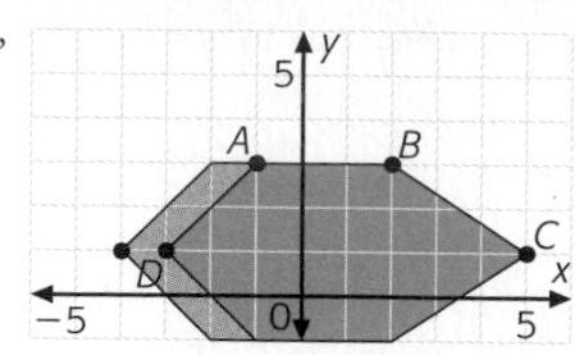

10. e.g., A butterfly shape is translated twice. The combined shape is reflected once. The resulting design has order of rotation symmetry 2 and two lines of symmetry. Draw what it might look like.

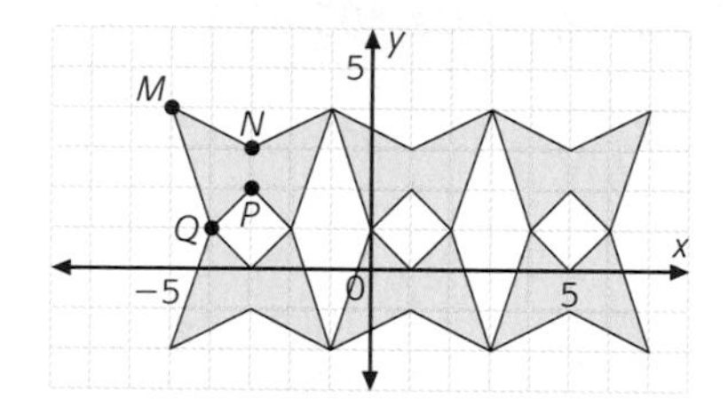

11. e.g.,

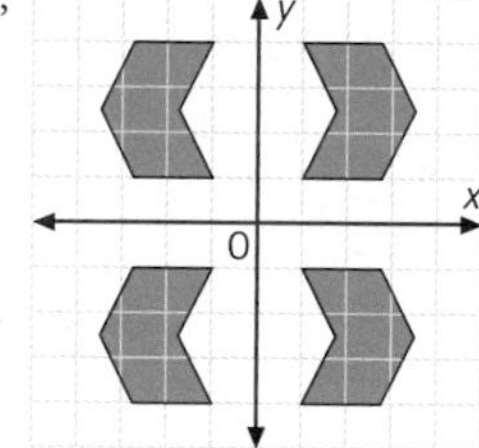

Chapter Self-Test, pages 402–403

1. Tiles 1 and 3 have four lines of symmetry; tile 2 has 14 lines of symmetry.
2.
3. **a)** none **b)** 3, 120° **c)** 5, 72°
4. A, B, D
5. **a)** rotation symmetry of order 4, 90°
   b) rotation symmetry of order 2, 180°
   c) line symmetry, rotation symmetry of order 4, 90°
6. Milos is right.
7. **a)** e.g.,

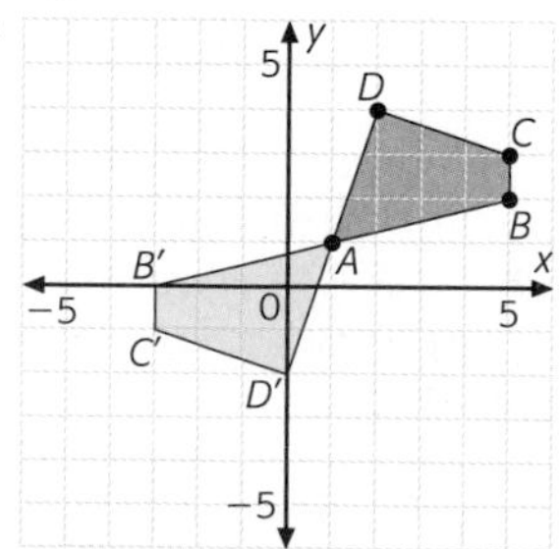

b) $A'(1, 1), B'(-3, 0), C'(-3, -1), D'(0, -2)$

8. **a)**

5 y
D
C
B
A
x
−5
0 A″
5
B″
C″
D″
−5

b) $A'(1, -1), B'(5, -2), C'(5, -3), D'(2, -4)$

Chapter Review, pages 405–406

1. **a)** & **b)**

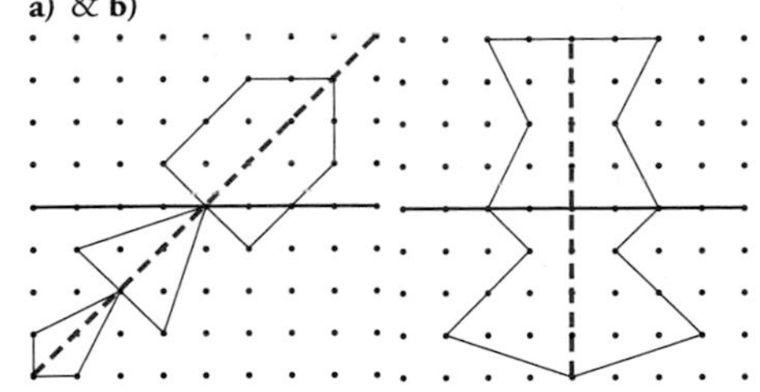

2. **a)** 5, 72° **b)** 5, 72° **c)** none **d)** 6, 60°

3. **a)** line symmetry **b)** line symmetry, rotation symmetry of order 2

4. **a)**

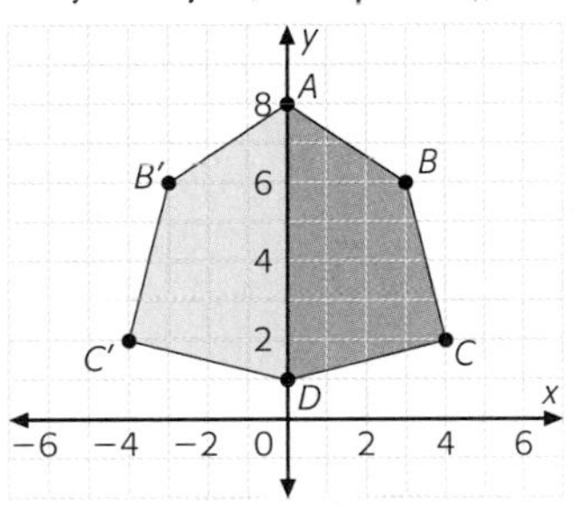

b) $A'(0, 8), B'(-3, 6), C'(-4, 2), D'(0, 1)$
c) line symmetry

5. **a)**

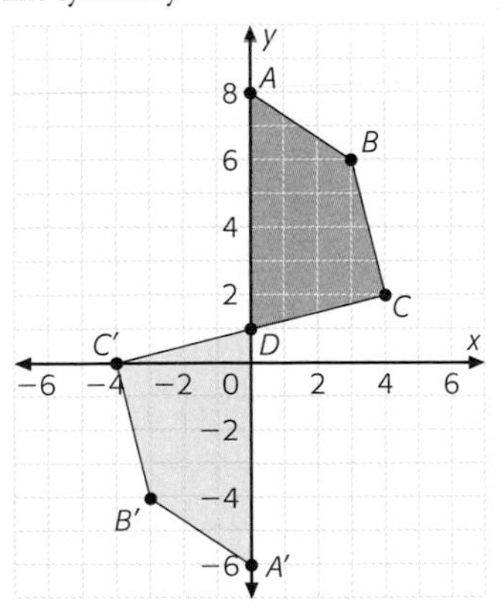

b) $A'(0, -6), B'(-3, -4), C'(-4, 0), D'(0, 1)$
c) rotation symmetry of order 2

6. **a)**

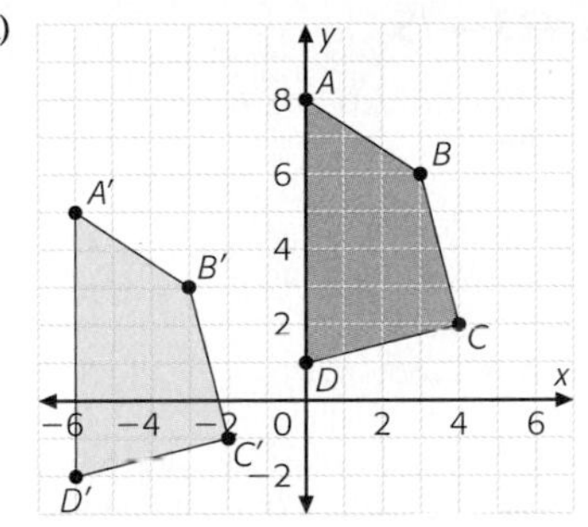

b) $A'(-6, 5), B'(-3, 3), C'(-2, -1), D'(-6, -2)$
c) The original shape did not have symmetry, and it was not rotated or reflected, so the new shape cannot have symmetry.

7. e.g.,

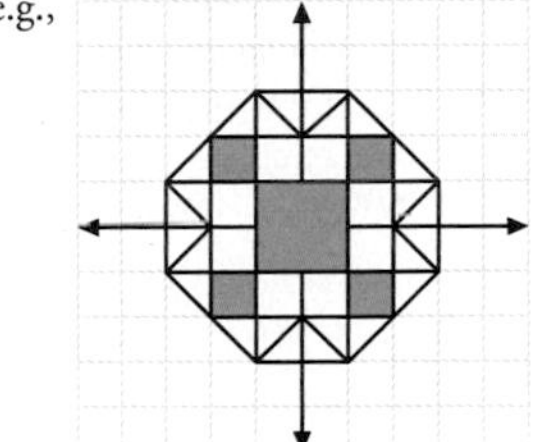

8. **a)** has line symmetry; does not have rotation symmetry
b) line and rotation symmetry, order 6, 60°

9. **a)** A, B **b)** B, C

Chapter 9

Lesson 9.2, pages 417–419

1. **a)** 90° **b)** 60° **c)** 45°

2. **a)** 57.5° **b)** 90° **c)** 105°

3. **a)** 76° **b)** 137°

4. A

5. D

6. e.g., chord LM (straight line), arc LM (curved line), semicircle KM, central angle $\angle LOM$

7. **a)** A central angle must have its vertex at the centre of a circle.
b) An inscribed angle must be formed by two chords.
c) The vertex of an inscribed angle must lie on the circle.
d) All four vertices of an inscribed quadrilateral must lie on the circle.

8. **a)** 120°
b) e.g., For a regular nonagon, the interior angles are all 140°.

9. Draw a diameter through the centre of a circle. Then inscribe an angle in one of the resulting semicircles. Since the central angle formed by a diameter is 180°, the inscribed angle will be 90°.

10. 45°

11. **a)** $\angle BOC = \angle DOE = 80°, \angle BOE = 134°$
b) $\angle BAC = \angle DAE = 40°, \angle CAD = 33°,$
$\angle BAD = \angle EAC = 73°, \angle BAE = 113°$

12. 40°

13. $\angle HFE = 40°, \angle PEF = 40°, \angle FPE = 100°, \angle EPH = 80°,$
$\angle PEH = 50°, \angle PHE = 50°, \angle FGE = 130°,$
$\angle GFE = 25°, \angle GEF = 25°$

14. $\angle APB = 140°$

Answers

Lesson 9.3, pages 423–425

1. **a)** $\angle W = 55°$, $\angle Y = 18°$ **b)** $\angle G = \angle H = \angle K = 110°$
c) $\angle A = 80°$, $\angle D = 70°$
2. **a)** $\angle Q = 80°$, $\angle S = 80°$
b) $\angle 1 = 40°$, $\angle 2 = 100°$, $\angle K = \angle 3 = \angle 4 = 60°$, $\angle 5 = 115°$
c) $\angle A = \angle B = \angle C = \angle E = \angle F = 90°$
3. $\angle A = \angle B = \angle D = 51°$, $\angle E = 129°$
4. **a)** $\angle Q = \angle R$ **b)** $\angle N = \angle M = \angle L$
5. B
6. e.g., Draw two diameters. Then draw inscribed angles by joining the endpoints of the diameters. All angles will be 90°, because they are all inscribed in a semicircle. Since all four angles are 90°, the quadrilateral is a rectangle.
7. **a)** $\angle WYX = 30°$, $\angle WXY = 120°$, $\angle VZW = \angle VWZ = 40°$, $\angle ZYW = 80°$, $\angle WZY = 60°$, $\angle YWZ = 40°$
b) $\angle ACB = 35°$, $\angle BDC = 25°$, $\angle BKC = 80°$, $\angle DKA = 80°$, $\angle BKA = 100°$, $\angle CBK = 65°$, $\angle DAC = 65°$, $\angle ABK = 55°$, $\angle ACD = 55°$
8. **a)** e.g., $\angle P = 107°$, $\angle Q = 76°$, $\angle R = 73°$, $\angle S = 104°$

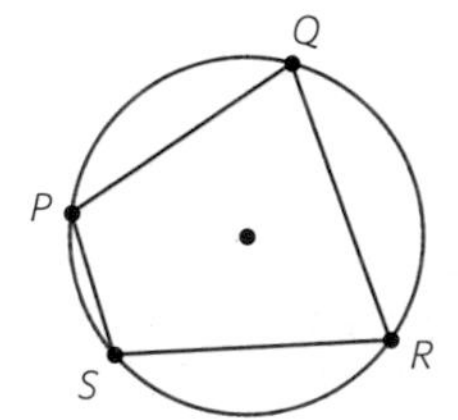

b) 180° **c)** 180°
d) e.g., Opposite angles in a quadrilateral inscribed in a circle are supplementary.
e) e.g., One central angle $= 2\angle P$ and the other central angle $= 2\angle R$. The two central angles add up to 360°, so $2\angle P + 2\angle R = 360°$. This means that $\angle P + \angle R = 180°$.
9. e.g., In a circle with centre *O* and point *P* on its circumference, minor arc *BC* makes an inscribed angle of 36° at *P*, minor arc *AB* makes an inscribed angle of 15° at *P*, and minor arc *CD* makes an inscribed angle of 22° at *P*. What angle does arc *AD* subtend at *O*? (146°)
10. no
11. e.g., Inscribed angles subtended by the same arc have the same measure, so I can draw more inscribed angles with endpoints *D* and *F*, and I know they will measure 80°.
12. yes
13. **a)** $\angle YAP = \angle PXB$, $\angle AYP = \angle XBP$, $\angle APY = \angle XPB$
b) They are similar.
c) e.g., Since $\Delta APY \sim \Delta XPB$, $\frac{PA}{PX} = \frac{PY}{PB}$. If you multiply both sides by *PX* and then by *PB*, you get $(PB)(PA) = (PX)(PY)$.
14. $\angle RPT = 72°$, $\angle PTQ = 35°$, $\angle RST = 108°$, $\angle QTS = 60°$, $\angle MRS = 48°$, $\angle PRM = 37°$

Lesson 9.4, pages 430–431

1. $\angle CRT = \angle CRP = 90°$
2. e.g., Use a string to form two chords on the sandbox. Mark the centre of each string. Using a carpenter's square, mark a chalk line perpendicular to each string. The centre of the sandbox will be where the two chalk lines cross.
3. B
4. D
5. **a)** Yes, the perpendicular bisector of the shorter chord intersects the diameter at its midpoint, or the centre of the circle.
b) e.g., Their intersection would be the centre.
6. **b)** The chords are the same length.
c) e.g., Chords equidistant from the centre of the circle are the same length.
d) e.g., I drew a chord perpendicular to the radius at point *P*. I imagined a mirror placed through the centre of the circle. The reflection of the chord I drew has to be the same distance from the centre as the original, since it is a reflection, and it must be the same size as well. Then, the conjecture works for any *P* and *Q*.
7. No, they are not equidistant.
8. less
9. No. To locate the centre of a circle using chords, the perpendicular lines from the chords pass through their midpoints.
10. The longest chord will be the diameter.
11. No. If you draw two chords using the three points, the perpendicular bisectors of those chords only intersect at one point, so there is only one possible circle.
12. e.g., Since *AC* is shorter than *BC*, chord *LM* is longer than chord *NO*, because the chord closer to the centre of the circle is the longer chord. $\angle CAL = \angle CAM = \angle CBO = \angle CBN = 90°$
13. no
14. **a)** & **b)** *PR* is a diameter.

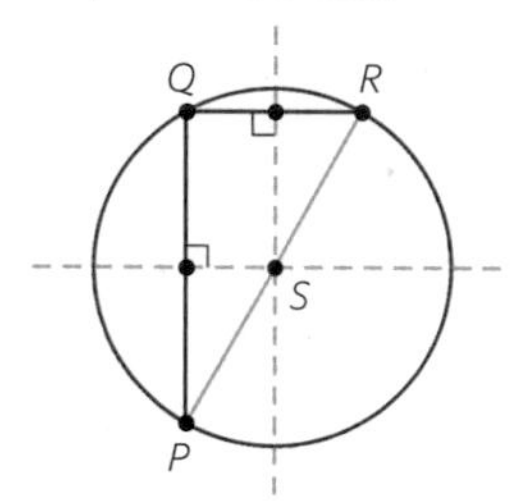

c) rectangle

Mid-Chapter Review, page 433

1. **a)** $\angle R = 65°$ **c)** $\angle YCZ = 120°$, $\angle CYZ = 30°$
b) $\angle D = 105°$ **d)** $\angle ACB = 132°$, $\angle D = 114°$
2. 150°
3. **a)** $\angle B = 90°$
b) $\angle E = 70°$, $\angle C = 140°$
4. $\angle DCE = 112°$
5. no, not always
6. $\angle T = \angle R = \angle S = \angle U = 53°$, $\angle P = 127°$
7. e.g., Trace the arc and put three points on its edge. Then draw two chords connecting the points, and construct the perpendicular bisectors of both chords. The intersection of the two perpendicular bisectors is the centre of the circle. Use a compass to draw a circle with this centre and a radius equal to the distance from it to the edge of the arc.

Lesson 9.5, pages 438–440

1. **a)** $x = 5$ cm **b)** $y = 6$ cm **c)** $AB = 12$ cm
2. yes
3. **a)** $PQ = 34$ cm **b)** $ST = 48$ m
4. C
5. B

6. D
7. Both equal 110°.
8. 16.0 cm
9. 9.5 cm
10. **a)** & **b)** only 1

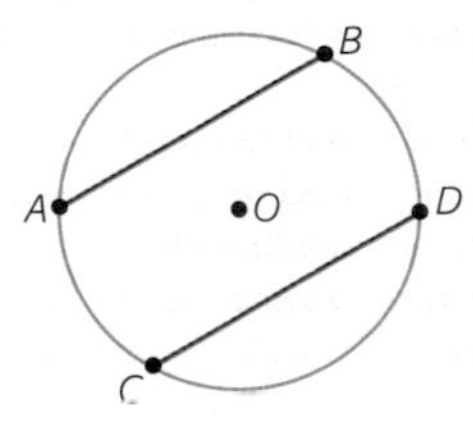

c) The distances are equal.

11. **a)** infinitely many
    b) e.g., Each chord is the same distance from the centre of the circle.
12. 16 m
13. 2.00 m, 1.50 m
14. **a)** The outer beams are chords of the circle.
    b) e.g., If the beams are the same length, then they will be the same distance from the centre.
    c) e.g., The circles all have the same centre.
15. **a)** *FG* **b)**

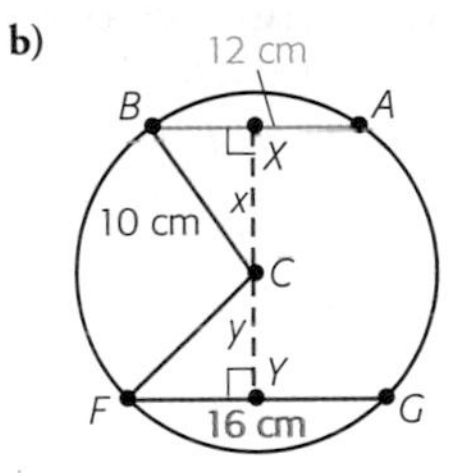

c) *AB*, 8 cm; *FG*, 6 cm

16. **a)** 20 cm **b)** 18 cm **c)** 73 cm^2
17. **a)** e.g., because they are all the same distance away from the centre of the Ferris wheel
    b) 4.3 m
18. **a)** 21.2 cm
    b) Yes; if the bowl is less than half full, the water's depth is 6.8 cm.
19. **a)** about 6 cm **b)** 2.12 cm

Lesson 9.6, pages 445–446

1. $AD = 3$ cm
2. A
3. A
4. B
5. **a)** & **b)**

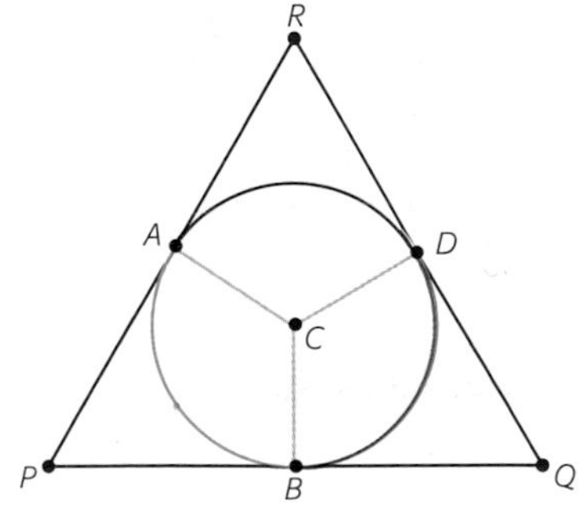

c) equilateral
d) The angles of the triangle are half as large as the central angles.

6. e.g., Extend the straight portions of the chain to meet at point *P*. $PR = PT$, because they start at the same point and are both tangent to the large circle. Similarly, $PQ = PS$. Then, $PR - PQ = PT - PS$, or $QR = ST$.

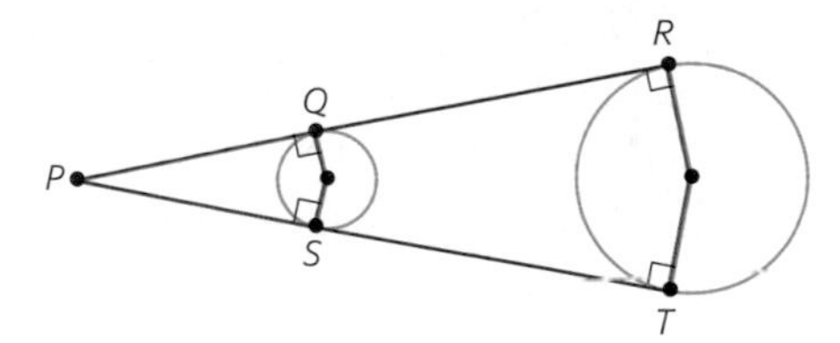

7. 0.5 m
8. yes
9. **a)**

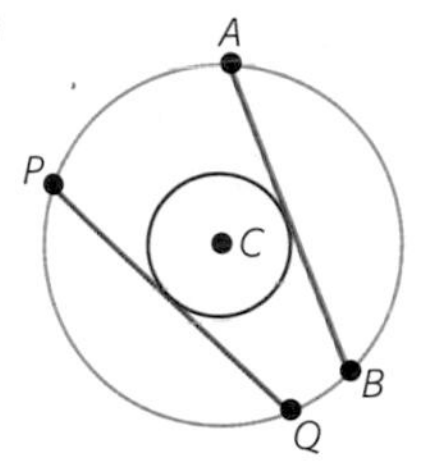

b) The chords are equidistant from the centre of the big circle, so they are the same length.
c) 5 cm

10. e.g., Draw five radii to divide the circle into five equal sections. Each central angle formed by two adjacent radii is 72°. Draw tangent lines to the endpoints of each radius. Mark the ten intersection points of the tangent lines. Draw the star by connecting all of these points.
11. 101 km
12. e.g., The higher you go, the farther away your point of tangency with Earth's surface is.
13. **a)** if the diameters are perpendicular
    b) if the diameters are not perpendicular
14. 45.2%

Lesson 9.7, pages 451–452

1. equilateral
2. They are the same length.
3. e.g., Draw chord *XY*, and measure this chord. Draw another chord the same length, beginning at *X*. Mark the other endpoint as *A*. Draw a chord the same length beginning at *A*. Mark the other endpoint as *B*. Arcs *XY*, *AX*, and *AB* will be the same length.
4. yes
5. **a)** $L = 4 \times 1.2 + 1.2\pi$ **b)** 8.6 m
6. *ABCD* and *PQRS*; supplementary opposite angles
7. e.g., If I look at different cases, and always get the same result, the result might be true in general.
8. e.g., There are actually circles.
9. Yes, they will be parallel for any two circles.

Chapter Self-Test, page 454

1. **a)** $\angle Q = 68°$, $\angle S = 112°$, $\angle ORS = 57°$
   b) $\angle BAE = 90°$, $\angle ABE = 60°$, $\angle BCE = 90°$, $\angle ADE = 60°$, $\angle ACE = 60°$, $\angle BCA = 30°$
2. **a)** $\angle W = \angle Y = 90°$, $\angle Z = 135°$ **b)** $XY = 3$ cm
3. about 147.3°
4. 38.4 cm
5. 8.9 cm

6. a) AB b)

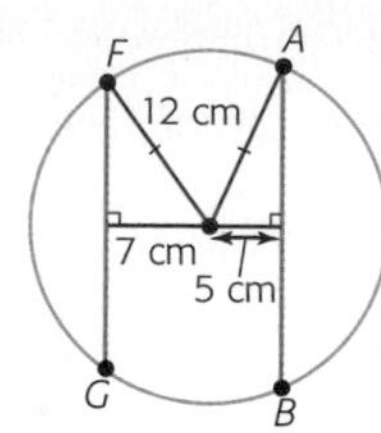

c) To the nearest centimetre, $AB = 22$ cm, $FG = 20$ cm.

7. about 89 cm

Chapter Review, pages 456–458

1. $\angle QCR = 110°$, $\angle CQR = 35°$
2. a) 90°
3. $\angle T = \angle U = \angle V = \angle W = 55°$
4. $HA = KB$, $FA = GB$, $DA = EB$, $HD = KE$, $FD = GE$, $HF = KG$
5. 13.5 cm
6. 9 cm
7. 56 cm
8. 5 cm
9. 39 cm
10. a) $ST = 20$ cm, $CP = 4$ cm, and $AQ = 6$ cm
    b) right triangle c) 4 cm
11. a) square b) kite
12. yes
13. e.g., eight vertical bars, two 179 cm, two 170 cm, two 150 cm, and two 113 cm
14. a) e.g., Canadian Broadcasting Corporation
    b) e.g., the property that all components are the same distance from the centre
    c) e.g., In this logo, I wanted the triangle-like shape at the top to have its two straight edges be the same length, so I made the edges tangent to the circle, because two tangents from the same external point are equal.

15. a) 265 cm b) 258 cm

Chapter 10

Lesson 10.1, pages 467–469

1. e.g., a) Do you play hockey?
    b) Which is your favourite music group or performer?
    c) How many times a week, on average, do you visit the library?
2. e.g., a) What animal(s) do you keep as pets: none, dogs and/or cats, other?
    b) Which toothpaste brand do you recommend?
    c) What is your preferred colour for jeans?
    d) Which type(s) of TV program do you watch regularly: sports, talk shows, drama, news, weather, other?
3. e.g., a) What activity did you spend most time on last summer: sports, travel, hiking or cycling, beach or lake activities, other?
    b) Are you in a French immersion program at school?
    c) What make and model of automobile(s) do you own?
4. a) no b) yes c) no d) yes e) no
5. a) yes
    b) e.g., What do you like most about school lunches?
6. e.g., a) Questions 1 and 2 are worded well. Question 3 is a little vague. The committee might ask for alternative ideas for the celebration, such as a dance.
    b) e.g., Question 3, "Do you think jackets, ties, and dresses should be required?"
    c) Question 1: if similar numbers of males and females are interested in a banquet; 2: if a banquet is wanted; 3: what type of banquet to hold; 4: what students can afford.
7. e.g., For question 5 survey: score 2; add "What do you like most about school lunches?" and "If the menu changed, would you choose to eat at the cafeteria more often?" Question 6 survey: score 2; add "Which type of celebration do you prefer: dance, banquet, other, none?"
8. e.g., a) "Are you physically active three or more times a week?"
    b) B. The graph for Survey B includes more detail.
    c) yes
9. e.g., Have you ever chosen not to fly for safety reasons?
10. e.g., a) no
    b) e.g., Provide people with a set of answers to choose from.
    c) e.g., How many times in a week do you engage in each activity: running, team sports, swimming, yoga, other?
    d) e.g., a questionnaire

Lesson 10.2, pages 473–476

1. e.g., a) Delete "that has been used by the hometown teams since 1920."
    b) Delete the first sentence.
2. e.g., a) experiment/observation c) experiment/observation
    b) questionnaire
3. a) yes
    b) e.g., Do you prefer appliances finished in stainless steel, white, or other?
4. a) questionnaire c) experiment/observation
    b) interview or questionnaire
5. e.g., The information gathered could be biased and therefore unfair.
6. e.g., a) biased toward some interest in music; confuses personal feelings with objective judgment
    b) Change the question to "Do you think music courses are A) very important B) important C) unimportant D) very unimportant?"
7. e.g., The survey was anonymous, so students may have included information they did not want their teacher to know.
8. e.g., a) yes b) no c) yes, no d) yes
    e) Rewrite B, "Do you think a student can have an after-school job and still maintain good grades?"
9. e.g., Survey II: replace A with Survey I version; rewrite B as "Do you think a student can have an after-school job and still maintain good grades?"
10. Biased answers or dishonest answers will not give accurate data.
11. e.g., a) Which newspaper(s) do you read regularly, if any?
    b) Do you read a serious newspaper or a trashy tabloid?
    c) The question in b) was biased.

Lesson 10.3, pages 480–483

1. a) population b) sample
2. a) no b) no c) yes

3. a) population b) sample c) sample d) sample e) sample
4. no
5. a) sample b) population c) population
6. a) rural Canadian teens not represented
   b) women who do not read cooking magazines not represented
   c) students who do not use library or cafeteria not represented
   d) families in which no one stays home during the day not represented.
   e) bilingual children who attend English-language schools not represented
7. e.g., a) Check that the ratio of surveys to population was the same for each region.
   b) no
   c) Conduct the survey by interview, and select people of each age group to interview.
8. a) e.g., census
   b) It should contain the same proportion of students as in the grade levels.
9. a) i and ii are biased; iii is not.
   b) e.g., i: all three; ii: none of them; iii: time of day
10. e.g., a) Give the survey to people who do not shop at the store.
   b) Survey all students.
   c) Sample oranges from more than one crate.
   d) Survey a greater surface area.
11. e.g., a) A sample should include all subgroups of a population in the same proportions as the population.
   b) when the population is not too large or if it is important to get a response from everyone in the population
12. e.g., How many Canadians live in rural areas? (6 385 551 or 22.1%)

Lesson 10.4, pages 488–489

1. a) e.g., How many dentists were surveyed? How was the sample selected? What was the exact question? What exact data were collected, and did they justify the conclusion?
   b) no
2. a) Advantages: bar and circle graphs show most popular choice clearly; table tells exactly how many of each mode of transport chosen. Disadvantages: bar graph and table do not show data as proportions; circle graph does not show quantities.
   b) e.g., circle graph
   c) e.g., yes
3. e.g., a) Ten cats were given bowls of Katto only, and one did not eat it.
   b) Ten cats, chosen at random, were given a choice between Katto and an unpleasant food.
   c) Ten cats, chosen at random, were given a choice between Katto and their regular brand.
4. e.g., no
5. a) accept b) reject c) reject d) accept
6. Each detail is needed to help readers decide whether the sample was fair.

Chapter Self-Test, pages 491–492

1. e.g., a) How much candy does each person in your family eat each day: A) 0 g B) 1–100 g C) 101–200 g D) more than 200 g?
   b) Do you think people should have the right to smoke A) anywhere? B) on private property? C) nowhere?
   c) How old are you?
   d) Will you require help to pay your school fees? (Yes/No)
2. e.g., How old are you?
   Do you have access to an ATV?
   Do you wear a helmet when you drive an ATV?
   How often do you operate an ATV?
   A. never **B.** occasionally **C.** frequently.
3. e.g., a) Choose a total of 100 boxes from different shipments, and count each colour.
   b) Have people respond to the question in an online school newsletter.
   c) Ask a random sample of the general public.
   d) Cut one orange from each case.
4. a) population b) sample c) sample
5. a) yes b) e.g., Call phone numbers at random.
6. e.g., a description of her sample showing it is representative, and a bar graph of average incomes for women grouped into classes by height
7. e.g., a) 2, 4 b) 1, 5, 6, 3; omit 2 and 4
   c) yes
8. e.g., Criterion (1): 3, good; Criterion (2) 2, acceptable.

Chapter Review, pages 494–496

1. e.g., a) Question 1 would take respondents some time to answer, and may be too complex to analyze easily; question 4 is difficult to answer if you don't know how much equipment rental will likely be; question 5 will not generate data on how much to charge for a fee.
   b) Respondents might not answer question 2 if they can't think of other activities.
   c) Start with question 3; reverse order of questions 4 and 5.
   d) Remove question 4, since there is not enough information for many respondents to answer it.
2. a) Do you support providing a separate cafeteria for staff at this school (Yes/No)?
   b) For each reasonable route, how long will it take me to get to school?
   c) Which party foods do you like (answer Y/N for each one): chips and dip? pizza? pasta salad? brownies?
3. a) Survey all the staff.
   b) Experiment by trying each route.
   c) Survey a sample of the attendees.
4. e.g., a) First sentence influences respondents to say yes.
   b) Respondents will likely answer yes to appear to be following the law.
5. e.g., a) does not give an idea of how many are opposed to the restrictions
   b) biased sample
6. a) Given opinions introduce bias. e.g., Do you believe smoking is or is not bad for your health?
   b) "Reckless" introduces bias. e.g., Should people who are injured during an activity and rescued by emergency services pay a charge according to the danger of the activity?
   c) "Cause danger" introduces bias. e.g., Should roller-bladers be allowed to use walking paths?
7. a) questionnaire c) experiment/observation
   b) experiment/observation
8. e.g., population: b, f, g; sample: a, c, d, e
9. a) e.g., If the population is large, it would be better to survey a sample.

b) e.g., A sample that best represents the school's population should have the same percentage of students in each grade as the whole school does.

10. e.g., a) You would destroy all automobiles if you tested the population.

b) It would take too much time and too many resources to measure the height of every Canadian.

c) All the jets are built in the same way, so any one of them should be a good indication of the noise level of others.

d) Testing may be destructive, so only a few suits should be tested.

e) It would be impossible to identify every tree in a large forest.

11. e.g., people who might be enticed by the free gift

12. a) The data are not organized.

b) Bar graph B

c) Bar graph A: most common pulse rate is in range 70–89; Bar graph B: in range 70–79

d) about 250

e) The group of 1000 is similar to the original group of 40.

Cumulative Review: Chapters 8–10, pages 498–499

1. D
2. A
3. A
4. B
5. B
6. C
7. D
8. B
9. C
10. A
11. C
12. D
13. A
14. C
15. D
16. C

Index

S

T

W

Z

Credits

This page constitutes an extension of the copyright page. We have made every effort to trace the ownership of all copyrighted material and to secure permission from copyright holders. In the event of any question arising from the use of any material, we will be pleased to make any necessary corrections in future printings. Thanks are due to the following artists, authors, publishers, and agents for permission to use the material indicated.

Cover Jurgen Ziewe/Shutterstock

Table of Contents page vi: Dave Starrett; page vii: Terrance Klassen/Alamy; page viii: Michael Jenner/Alamy; page ix: Gunter Marx/Alamy

Chapter 1 Opener: Stephen Van Horn/Shutterstock; page 6: top, Travel Ink/Getty Images; bottom, NASA; page 14: Galen Rowell/Peter Arnold Inc.; page 18: Martyn F. Chillmaid/Science Photo Library; page 20: Gregory Donald Horler/Shutterstock; page 21: Jan Kranendonk/Shutterstock; page 22: ©Olaf Kowalzik/Alamy; page 25: Samuel Acosta/Shutterstock; page 26: Frank Boellmann/Shutterstock; page 30: Koji Watanbe/Getty Images; page 33: Radius Images/Alamy; page 34: Jim Lane/Alamy; page 35: Laurence Gough/Shutterstock; page 36: Damir Karan/Shutterstock; page 41: ©image100/CORBIS; page 43: Photofusion Picture Library/Alamy.

Chapter 2 Opener: Dave Starrett; page 52: Christine Glade/istock; page 57: Sebastian Kaulitzki/Shutterstock; page 58: Isabelle Limbach/istock; page 82: ©Dorling Kindersley; page 84: Andre Jenny/Alamy; page 90: top, VStock/Alamy; bottom, Chuck Franklin/Alamy.

Chapter 3 Opener: Richard I'Anson/Getty Images; page 100: Robert Cocquyt/iStockphoto; page 116: Courtesy STScI & NASA; page 117: top left, ©Nir Elias/Reuters/Corbis; top right, Associated Press; bottom, Helder Almeida/iStockphoto; page 120: Rick Becker-Leckrone/Shutterstock; page 121: Media Minds/Alamy; page 128: photos.com; page 131: Bonnie Watton/Shutterstock; page 135: top, Bjorn Andren/Getty Images; bottom, Canadian Press Images; page 136: Mike Booth/Alamy; page 143: ©Bob Krist/Corbis.

Chapter 4 Opener: Terrance Klassen/Alamy; page 172: NASA; page 180: Ullamaija Hanninen/Getty Images; page 183: left, Raul Gonzalez Perez/Photo Researchers, Inc.; right, Peter Quigley/The University of Adelaide; page 195: top, ©Juniors Bildarchiv/Alamy; bottom, David Askham/Alamy.

Chapter 5 Opener: Guillen Photography/UW/USA/Florida/Alamy; page 198: Richard Lam/CP Images; page 206: Chris Hill/Shutterstock; page 212: Christopher Ewing/Shutterstock; page 215: sonya etchison/Shutterstock; page 225: OlgaLis/Shutterstock; page 226: Getty Images; page 230: danilo ducak/Shutterstock; page 249: top, David Eastley/Alamy; bottom, David Croft/Shutterstock; page 250: ©Wolfgang Kaehler/Corbis; page 258: Time & Life Pictures/Getty Images; page 263: Image Source Black/Alamy; page 265: Chuck Stoody/CP Images; page 268: Alexandru/Shutterstock; page 270: Volodymyr Kyrylyuk/Shutterstock; page 271: ©Jonathan Nourok/PhotoEdit.

Chapter 6 Opener: JUPITER IMAGES/Brand X/Alamy.

Chapter 7 Opener: Courtesy Baseball Canada; page 333: left, Steve Skjold/Alamy: right, Michael D Brown/Shutterstock; page 334: ©Dennis MacDonald/Alamy; page 337: top, Paul Bradforth/Alamy; bottom, JUPITERIMAGES/Brand X/Alamy; page 338: David Lewis/iStockphoto; page 339: Rannev/Shutterstock; page 340: Kiyoko Gotanda/Alamy; page 343: STILLFX/Shutterstock; page 345: Yellow Dog Productions/Getty Images; page 347: ©All Canada Photos/Alamy; page 348: Stefanie Angele/Shutterstock; page 349: Andrew Rubtsov/Alamy; page 350: iStockphoto; page 351: Image Source/Getty Images; page 352: Chris Rabior/Alamy; page 355: Harris Shiffman/Shutterstock; page 357: Paul Bradbury/Getty Images; page 359: jkitan/Shutterstock.

Chapter 8 Opener: Michael Jenner/Alamy; page 374: Harris Shiffman/Shutterstock; page 378: top left, Roman Pavlick/Shutterstock; top right, John Livingston, www.pathgallery.com; bottom left to right, Petr Svarc/Alamy; image broker/Alamy; Humberto Olarte Cupos/Alamy; page 382: left to right, Bryan & Cherry Alexander Photography/Alamy; JUPITER IMAGES/ABLESTOCK/Alamy; J Marshall-Tribaleye Images/Alamy; page 383: all, Patricia Fatta/Shutterstock; page 384: left, Ranneve/Shutterstock; middle & right, JUPITER IMAGES/ABLESTOCK/Alamy; page 385: Chan Pak Kei/iStockphoto; page 402: left to right, MELBA PHOTO AGENCY/Alamy; Mark Lavin/Alamy; Laurelie/Shutterstock; page 405: top left to right, Ramzi Hachicho/Shutterstock; Zastol'skiy Victor Leonidovich/Shutterstock; Westend61/Alamy; iStockphoto; bottom left, canadabrian/Alamy; bottom right, De Agostini Picture Library/Getty Images.

Chapter 9 Opener: Gunter Marx/Alamy; page 437: Eddie Gerald/Alamy; page 438: Westend61/Alamy; page 440: top to bottom, Peter Chigmaroff/Alamy; Astrid Lenz/Shutterstock; nolie/Shutterstock; page 445: Slavoljub Pantelic/iStockphoto; page 446: Images Etc Ltd./Alamy; page 447: Fred Espenak/Photo Researchers, Inc.; page 448: Brian Wiehn/iStockphoto; page 452: Courtesy Vincent Hale/Scoutcraft; page 458: Manor Photography/Alamy; page 459: ©Andrew Stevens/Alamy.

Chapter 10 Opener: Geostock/Getty Images; page 463: Carlos E. Santa Maria/Shutterstock; page 464: Chloe Johnson/Alamy; page 467: PhotoSpin, Inc./Alamy; page 468: JupiterImages/Comstock Images/Alamy; page 470: ©Mike Dobel/Alamy; page 474: top, Katrina Leigh/Shutterstock; bottom, Image Source/Getty Images; page 478: Ian Watt/Alamy; page 481: ©Chuck Savage/CORBIS; page 482: Don Mason/Getty Images; page 483: NASA oly; page 487: Corbis/FirstLight; page 489: Enigma/Alamy; page 490: ©2006 SASI Group (University of Sheffield) and Mark Newman (University of Michigan); page 491: top, tom carter/Alamy; bottom, Arco Images GmbH/Alamy; page 495: top, Lori Adamski Peek/Getty Images; bottom, archivberlin Fotoagentur GmbH/Alamy; page 497: Richard G. Bingham II/Alamy.

All additional photos by Dave Starrett.